COMPLETE SOLUTIONS MANUAL FOR ZILL'S

A FIRST COURSE IN DIFFERENTIAL EQUATIONS

THE CLASSIC FIFTH EDITION

WARREN S. WRIGHT
Loyola Marymount University

CAROL D. WRIGHT

BROOKS/COLE

™

THOMSON LEARNING

Australia • Canada • Mexico • Singapore • Spain • United Kingdom • United States

BROOKS/COLE

THOMSON LEARNING

Cover Design: *Roy R. Neuhaus*
Cover Photo: *The Stock Market/M. Mastrorillo*

For more information about this or any other Brooks/Cole product, contact:
BROOKS/COLE
511 Forest Lodge Road
Pacific Grove, CA 93950 USA
www.brookscole.com
1-800-423-0563 (Thomson Learning Academic Resource Center)

Printed in Canada

5   4   3   2   1

ISBN 0-534-38279-7

Table of Contents

1 Introduction to Differential Equations

1. Second-order; linear.

2. Third-order; nonlinear because of $(dy/dx)^4$.

3. First-order; nonlinear because of yy'.

4. First-order; linear.

5. Fourth-order; linear.

6. Second-order; nonlinear because of $\sin y$.

7. Second-order; nonlinear because of $\left(d^2y/dx^2\right)^2$.

8. Second-order; nonlinear because of $1/r^2$.

9. Third-order; linear.

10. First-order; nonlinear because of y^2.

11. From $y = e^{-x/2}$ we obtain $y' = -\frac{1}{2}e^{-x/2}$. Then $2y' + y = -e^{-x/2} + e^{-x/2} = 0$.

12. From $y = 8$ we obtain $y' = 0$, so that $y' + 4y = 0 + 4(8) = 32$.

13. From $y = e^{3x} + 10e^{2x}$ we obtain $dy/dx = 3e^{3x} + 20e^{2x}$. Then

$$\frac{dy}{dx} - 2y = \left(3e^{3x} + 20e^{2x}\right) - 2\left(e^{3x} + 10e^{2x}\right) = e^{3x}.$$

14. From $y = \dfrac{6}{5} - \dfrac{6}{5}e^{-20t}$ we obtain $dy/dt = 24e^{-20t}$, so that

$$\frac{dy}{dt} + 20y = 24e^{-20t} + 20\left(\frac{6}{5} - \frac{6}{5}e^{-20t}\right) = 24.$$

15. From $y = 5\tan 5x$ we obtain $y' = 25\sec^2 5x$. Then

$$y' = 25\sec^2 5x = 25\left(1 + \tan^2 5x\right) = 25 + (5\tan 5x)^2 = 25 + y^2.$$

16. From $y = \left(\sqrt{x} + c_1\right)^2$ we obtain $y' = 2\left(\sqrt{x} + c_1\right)/2\sqrt{x}$, so that

$$y' = \frac{\sqrt{x} + c_1}{\sqrt{x}} = \sqrt{\frac{\left(\sqrt{x} + c_1\right)^2}{x}} = \sqrt{\frac{y}{x}}.$$

17. From $y = \dfrac{1}{2}\sin x - \dfrac{1}{2}\cos x + 10e^{-x}$ we obtain $y' = \dfrac{1}{2}\cos x + \dfrac{1}{2}\sin x - 10e^{-x}$. Then

$$y' + y = \left(\frac{1}{2}\cos x + \frac{1}{2}\sin x - 10e^{-x}\right) + \left(\frac{1}{2}\sin x - \frac{1}{2}\cos x + 10e^{-x}\right) = \sin x.$$

1

18. First write the differential equation in the form $2xy + \left(x^2 + 2y\right) y' = 0$. Implicitly differentiating $x^2 y + y^2 = c_1$ we obtain $2xy + \left(x^2 + 2y\right) y' = 0$.

19. First write the differential equation in the form $y' = -2y/x$. From $y = -1/x^2$ we obtain $y' = 2x^{-3}$, so that $-2y/x = 2x^{-3} = y'$.

20. From $y = x + 1$ we obtain $y' = 1$, so that $(y')^3 + xy' = 1 + x = y$.

21. Implicitly differentiating $y^2 = c_1\left(x + \frac{1}{4}c_1\right)$ we obtain $y' = c_1/2y$. Then

$$2xy' + y(y')^2 = \frac{c_1 x}{y} + \frac{c_1^2}{4y} = \frac{y^2}{y} = y.$$

22. Writing $y = x|x|$ as $y = \begin{cases} x^2, & \text{if } x \geq 0 \\ -x^2, & \text{if } x < 0 \end{cases}$ we see that $|y| = x^2$, $-\infty < x < \infty$, and

$\sqrt{|y|} = \begin{cases} x, & \text{if } x \geq 0 \\ -x, & \text{if } x < 0 \end{cases}$. Since $y' = \begin{cases} 2x, & \text{if } x \geq 0 \\ -2x, & \text{if } x < 0, \end{cases}$ it is apparent that $y' = 2\sqrt{|y|}$.

23. From $y = x \ln x$ we obtain $y' = 1 + \ln x$. Then $y' - \frac{1}{x}y = 1$.

24. Differentiating $P = ac_1 e^{at}/\left(1 + bc_1 e^{at}\right)$ we obtain

$$\frac{dP}{dt} = \frac{\left(1 + bc_1 e^{at}\right) a^2 c_1 e^{at} - ac_1 e^{at} \cdot abc_1 e^{at}}{\left(1 + bc_1 e^{at}\right)^2}$$

$$= \frac{ac_1 e^{at}}{1 + bc_1 e^{at}} \cdot \frac{\left[a\left(1 + bc_1 e^{at}\right) - abc_1 e^{at}\right]}{1 + bc_1 e^{at}} = P(a - bP).$$

25. Implicitly differentiating $\ln \frac{2-x}{1-x} = \ln(2-x) - \ln(1-x) = t$ we obtain $\frac{-1}{2-x} \cdot \frac{dX}{dt} - \frac{-1}{1-x} \cdot \frac{dX}{dt} = 1$.

Then $\frac{dX}{dt} = (2 - X)(1 - x)$.

26. Differentiating $y = e^{-x^2} \int_0^x e^{t^2}\, dt + c_1 e^{-x^2}$ we obtain

$$y' = e^{-x^2} e^{x^2} - 2xe^{-x^2} \int_0^x e^{t^2}\, dt - 2c_1 xe^{-x^2} = 1 - 2xe^{-x^2} \int_0^x e^{t^2}\, dt - 2c_1 xe^{-x^2}.$$

Substituting into the differential equation, we have

$$y' + 2xy = 1 - 2xe^{-x^2} \int_0^x e^{t^2}\, dt - 2c_1 xe^{-x^2} + 2xe^{-x^2} \int_0^x e^{t^2}\, dt + 2c_1 xe^{-x^2} = 1.$$

27. First write the differential equation in the form $y' = \frac{-x^2 - y^2}{x^2 - xy}$. Then $c_1(x + y)^2 = xe^{y/x}$ implies

$c_1 = \frac{xe^{y/x}}{(x+y)^2}$ and implicit differentiation gives $2c_1(x + y)(1 + y') = xe^{y/x}\frac{xy' - y}{x^2} + e^{y/x}$. Solving for y' we obtain

$$y' = \frac{e^{y/x} - \frac{y}{x}e^{y/x} - 2c_1(x+y)}{2c_1(x+y) - e^{y/x}} = \frac{1 - \frac{y}{x} - \frac{2x}{x+y}}{\frac{2x}{x+y} - 1} = \frac{-x^2 - y^2}{x^2 - xy}.$$

28. From $y = c_1 e^{3x} + c_2 e^{-4x}$ we obtain $y' = 3c_1 e^{3x} - 4c_2 e^{-4x}$ and $y'' = 9c_1 e^{3x} + 16c_2 e^{-4x}$, so that $y'' + y' - 12y = 0$.

29. From $y = e^{3x} \cos 2x$ we obtain $y' = 3e^{3x} \cos 2x - 2e^{3x} \sin 2x$ and $y'' = 5e^{3x} \cos 2x - 12e^{3x} \sin 2x$, so that $y'' - 6y' + 13y = 0$.

30. From $y = e^{2x} + xe^{2x}$ we obtain $\dfrac{dy}{dx} = 3e^{2x} + 2xe^{3x}$ and $\dfrac{d^2y}{dx^2} = 8e^{2x} + 4xe^{2x}$ so that $\dfrac{d^2y}{dx^2} - 4\dfrac{dy}{dx} + 4y = 0$.

31. From $y = \cosh x + \sinh x$ we obtain $y' = \sinh x + \cosh x$ and $y'' = \cosh x + \sinh x = y$.

32. From $y = c_1 \cos 5x$ we obtain $y' = -5c_1 \sin 5x$ and $y'' = -25c_1 \cos 5x$, so that $y'' + 25y = 0$.

33. From $y = \ln|x + c_1| + c_2$ we obtain $y' = \dfrac{1}{x + c_1}$ and $y'' = \dfrac{-1}{(x + c_1)^2}$, so that $y'' + (y')^2 = 0$.

34. From $y = -\cos x \ln(\sec x + \tan x)$ we obtain $y' = -1 + \sin x \ln(\sec x + \tan x)$ and $y'' = \tan x + \cos x \ln(\sec x + \tan x)$. Then $y'' + y = \tan x$.

35. From $y = c_1 + c_2 x^{-1}$ we obtain $y' = -c_2 x^{-2}$ and $y'' = 2c_2 x^{-3}$, so that $x\dfrac{d^2y}{dx^2} + 2\dfrac{dy}{dx} = 0$.

36. From $y = x \cos(\ln x)$ we obtain $y' = -\sin(\ln x) + \cos(\ln x)$ and $y'' = \dfrac{-1}{x}\cos(\ln x) - \dfrac{1}{x}\sin(\ln x)$, so that $x^2 y'' - xy' + 2y = 0$.

37. From $y = x^2 + x^2 \ln x$ we obtain $y' = 3x + 2x \ln x$ and $y'' = 5 + 2\ln x$ so that $x^2 y'' - 3xy' + 4y = 0$.

38. From $y = c_1 \sin 3x + c_2 \cos 3x + 4e^x$ we obtain $y' = 3c_1 \cos 3x - 3c_2 \sin 3x + 4e^x$, $y'' = -9c_1 \sin 3x - 9c_2 \cos 3x + 4e^x$, and $y''' = -27c_1 \cos 3x + 27c_2 \sin 3x + 4e^x$, so that $y''' - y'' + 9y' - 9y = 0$.

39. From $y = x^2 e^x$ we obtain $y' = x^2 e^x + 2xe^x$, $y'' = x^2 e^x + 4xe^x 2e^x$, and $y''' = x^2 e^x + 6xe^x + 6e^x$, so that $y''' - 3y'' + 3y' - y = 0$.

40. From $y = c_1 x \ln x + 4x^2$ we obtain $y' = c_1 + c_1 \ln x + 8x$, $y'' = c_1 x^{-1} + 8$, and $y''' = -c_1 x^{-2}$, so that $x^3 \dfrac{d^3y}{dx^3} + 2x^2 \dfrac{d^2y}{dx^2} - x\dfrac{dy}{dx} + y = 12x^2$.

41. From $y = \begin{cases} -x^2, & x < 0 \\ x^2, & x \geq 0 \end{cases}$ we obtain $y' = \begin{cases} -2x, & x < 0 \\ 2x, & x \geq 0 \end{cases}$ so that $xy' - 2y = 0$.

42. From $y = \begin{cases} 0, & x < 0 \\ x^3, & x \geq 0 \end{cases}$ we obtain $y' = \begin{cases} 0, & x < 0 \\ 3x^2, & x \geq 0 \end{cases}$ so that $(y')^2 = \begin{cases} 0, & x < 0 \\ 9x^4, & x \geq 0. \end{cases}$

43. From $y = cx + c^2$ we obtain $y' = c$ so that $xy' + (y')^2 = cx + c^2 = y$. From $y = kx^2$ we obtain $y' = 2kx$ so that $xy' + (y')^2 = y$ implies that $x^2k(1 + 4k) = 0$. Then $k = -1/4$ produces a singular solution.

44. From $y = cx + \sqrt{1 + c^2}$ we obtain $y' = c$ so that $xy' + \sqrt{1 + (y')^2} = y$. From $x^2 + y^2 = 1$ we obtain $y' = -x/y$. Then for $y \neq 0$, $xy' + \sqrt{1 + (y')^2} = \dfrac{-x^2}{y} + \dfrac{1}{\sqrt{y^2}} = \dfrac{y^2}{y} = y$. The condition $-1 < x < 1$ is implied by $x^2 + y^2 = 1$ together with $y \neq 0$.

45. By inspection, $y = -1$ is a singular solution. Note that this is the "solution" obtained by computing the limit as c approaches infinity of the one-parameter family of solutions.

46. The function $y = \begin{cases} \sqrt{4 - x^2}, & -2 < x < 0 \\ -\sqrt{4 - x^2}, & 0 \leq x < 2 \end{cases}$ is not continuous at $x = 0$ (the left hand limit is 2 and the right hand limit is -2,) and hence y' does not exist at $x = 0$.

47. From $y = e^{mx}$ we obtain $y' = me^{mx}$ and $y'' = m^2 e^{mx}$. Then $y'' - 5y' + 6y = 0$ implies

$$m^2 e^{mx} - 5me^{mx} + 6e^{mx} = (m - 2)(m - 3)e^{mx} = 0.$$

Since $e^{mx} > 0$ for all x, $m = 2$ and $m = 3$. Thus $y = e^{2x}$ and $y = e^{3x}$ are solutions.

48. From $y = e^{mx}$ we obtain $y' = me^{mx}$ and $y'' = m^2 e^{mx}$. Then $y'' + 10y' + 25y = 0$ implies

$$m^2 e^{mx} + 10me^{mx} + 25e^{mx} = (m + 5)^2 e^{mx} = 0.$$

Since $e^{mx} > 0$ for all x, $m = 5$. Thus, $y = e^{5x}$ is a solution.

49. Using $y' = mx^{m-1}$ and $y'' = m(m-1)x^{m-2}$ and substituting into the differential equation we obtain $m(m - 1)x^m - x^m = \left(m^2 - m - 1\right)x^m = 0$. Solving $m^2 - m - 1 = 0$ we obtain $m = \left(1 \pm \sqrt{5}\right)/2$. Thus, two solutions of the differential equation on the interval $0 < x < \infty$ are $y = x^{(1+\sqrt{5})/2}$ and $y = x^{(1-\sqrt{5})/2}$.

50. Using $y' = mx^{m-1}$ and $y'' = m(m-1)x^{m-2}$ and substituting into the differential equation we obtain $x^2 y'' + 6xy' + 4y = [m(m - 1) + 6m + 4]x^m$. The right side will be zero provided m satisfies

$$m(m - 1) + 6m + 4 = m^2 + 5m + 4 = (m + 4)(m + 1) = 0.$$

Thus, $m = -4, -1$ and two solutions of the differential equation on the interval $0 < x < \infty$ are $y = x^{-4}$ and $y = x^{-1}$.

51. It is easily shown that $y_1 = x^2$ and $y_2 = x^3$ are solutions. If $y_3 = c_1 y_1 + c_2 y_2 = c_1 x^2 + c_2 x^3$ then $y_3' = 2c_1 x + 3c_2 x^2$ and $y_3'' = 2c_1 + 6c_2 x$ so that $x^2 y_3'' - 4xy_3' + 6y_3 = 0$. Hence $c_1 y_1$, $c_2 y_2$, and $y_1 + y_2$ are solutions.

52. It is easily shown that $y_1 = x^2$ and $y_2 = x^3$ are solutions. If $y = c_1 y_1 = 2c_1 x + 2c_1$ then $y' = 2c_1$ so

that $xy' + \dfrac{(y')^2}{2} = 2c_1 x + 2c_1^2 \neq y$ for $c_1 \neq 0$ and $c_1 \neq 1$. If $y = c_2 y_2 = (-c_2/2)x^2$ then $y' = -c_2 x$

so that $xy' + \dfrac{(y')^2}{2} = \dfrac{-c_2^2}{2} x^2 \neq y$ for $c_2 \neq 0$ and $c_2 \neq 1$. If $y = y_1 + y_2 = -x^2/2 + 2x + 2$ then

$y' = -x + 2$ so that $xy' + \dfrac{(y')^2}{2} = \dfrac{-x^2}{2} + 2 \neq y$. Thus, none of $c_1 y_1$, $c_2 y_2$, and $y_1 + y_2$ are solutions.

53. (a) $y = 0$ **(b)** no real solution   **(c)** $y = 1$ or $y = -1$

Exercises 1.2

1. The sum of the forces acting on the body is $mg - kv$ where k is a constant of proportionality, and the minus sign indicates that the resistance acts in a direction opposite to the motion. From Newton's second law we have $mg - kv = m\dfrac{dv}{dt}$ or $\dfrac{dv}{dt} + \dfrac{k}{m}v = g$.

2. From Newton's second law we obtain $m\dfrac{dv}{dt} = -kv^2 + mg$.

3. (a) From $g = k/R^2$ we find $k = gR^2$.

     (b) Using $a = \dfrac{d^2 r}{dt^2}$ and part (a) we obtain $\dfrac{d^2 r}{dt^2} = a = \dfrac{k}{r^2} = \dfrac{gR^2}{r^2}$ or $\dfrac{d^2 r}{dt^2} - \dfrac{gR^2}{r^2} = 0$.

     (c) Part (b) becomes $\dfrac{dv}{dr}\dfrac{dr}{dt} - \dfrac{gR^2}{r^2} = 0$ or $v\dfrac{dv}{dr} - \dfrac{gR^2}{r^2} = 0$.

4. (a) The sum of the forces acting on the satellite is $ma - kv$, so by Newton's second law,

     $ma - kv = m\dfrac{d^2 r}{dt^2}$. From Problem 3, $a = \dfrac{gR^2}{r^2}$. Thus, using $v = \dfrac{dr}{dt}$, $m\dfrac{gR^2}{r^2} - kv = m\dfrac{d^2 r}{dt^2}$ or

     $\dfrac{d^2 r}{dt^2} + \dfrac{k}{m}\dfrac{dr}{dt} = \dfrac{gR^2}{r^2}$.

     (b) Letting $R = r$ and $\dfrac{dr}{dt} = v$, the equation is part (b) becomes $\dfrac{dv}{dt} + \dfrac{k}{m}v = g$, which is the

     equation is Problem 1.

5. Since $i = \dfrac{dq}{dt}$ and $L\dfrac{d^2 q}{dt^2} + R\dfrac{dq}{dt} = E(t)$ we obtain $L\dfrac{di}{dt} + Ri = E(t)$.

6. By Kirchoff's second law we obtain $R\dfrac{dq}{dt} + \dfrac{1}{C}q = E(t)$.

7. The differential equation is $\dfrac{dh}{dt} = -\dfrac{0.6A_0}{A_w}\sqrt{2gh}$. Using $A_0 = \pi\left(\dfrac{2}{12}\right)^2 = \dfrac{\pi}{36}$, $A_w = 10^2 = 100$, and $g = 32$ this becomes

$$\dfrac{dh}{dt} = -\dfrac{0.6\pi/36}{100}\sqrt{64h} = -\dfrac{8\pi\sqrt{h}}{6000} = -\dfrac{\pi}{750}\sqrt{h}.$$

Exercises 1.2

8. The differential equation is $\dfrac{dh}{dt} = -\dfrac{0.6A_0}{A_w}\sqrt{2gh}$. Using $A_0 = \pi\left(\dfrac{1}{24}\right)^2 = \dfrac{\pi}{576}$, $A_w = \pi(2)^2 = 4\pi$, and $g = 32$ this becomes

$$\frac{dh}{dt} = -\frac{0.6\pi/576}{4\pi}\sqrt{64h} = -\frac{0.6(8)}{4(576)}\sqrt{h} = -\frac{1}{480}\sqrt{h}.$$

9. The differential equation is $\dfrac{dh}{dt} = -\dfrac{0.6A_0}{A_w}\sqrt{2gh}$. We have $A_0 = \pi\left(\dfrac{1}{12}\right)^2 = \dfrac{\pi}{144}$
and $g = 32$. To find A_w we solve $x^2 + (5-h)^2 = 25$ where x represents the
radius of the circular area of the surface of the water whose depth is h. From
$x = \sqrt{10h - h^2}$ we obtain $A_w = \pi(10h - h^2)$. Thus

$$\frac{dh}{dt} = -\frac{0.6\pi/144}{\pi(10h - h^2)}\sqrt{64h} = -\frac{1}{30h(10-h)}\sqrt{h} = -\frac{1}{30\sqrt{h}\,(10-h)}.$$

10. The differential equation is $A'(t) = kA(t)$ where $k > 0$.

11. The differential equation is $x'(t) = r - kx(t)$ where $k > 0$.

12. Equating Newton's law with the net forces in the x- and y-directions gives $m\dfrac{d^2x}{dt^2} = 0$ and
$m\dfrac{d^2y}{dt^2} = -mg$, respectively.

13. From Newton's second law in the x-direction we have

$$m\frac{d^2x}{dt^2} = -k\cos\theta = -k\frac{1}{v}\frac{dx}{dt} = -|c|\frac{dx}{dt}.$$

In the y-direction we have

$$m\frac{d^2y}{dt^2} = -mg - k\sin\theta = -mg - k\frac{1}{v}\frac{dy}{dt} = -mg - |c|\frac{dy}{dt}.$$

14. The differential equation is $x'(t) = k(\alpha - x)(\beta - x)$ where α and β are the given amounts of chemicals
A and B, respectively, and $k > 0$.

15. To better understand the problem extend the line L down to the x-axis. Then we
see from the figure that $\phi = 2\theta$, $\tan\phi = \dfrac{x}{y}$, and $\dfrac{dy}{dx} = \tan\left(\dfrac{\pi}{2} - \theta\right) = \cot\theta$. Now

$$\tan\phi = \tan 2\theta = \frac{2\tan\theta}{1 - \tan^2\theta} = \frac{x}{y}, \text{ so } \frac{x}{y} = \frac{2(dx/dy)}{1 - (dx/dy)^2} \text{ and } x\left(\frac{dx}{dy}\right)^2 + 2y\left(\frac{dx}{dy}\right) = x.$$

16. We have from Archimedes' principle

upward force of water on barrel = weight of water displaced

$$= (62.4) \times (\text{volume of water displaced})$$

$$= (62.4)\pi(s/2)^2 y = 15.6\pi s^2 y.$$

It then follows from Newton's second law that $\dfrac{w}{g}\dfrac{d^2y}{dt^2} = -15.6\pi s^2 y$ or $\dfrac{d^2y}{dt^2} + \dfrac{15.6\pi s^2 g}{w} y = 0$, where $g = 32$ and w is the weight of the barrel in pounds.

17. By combining Newton's second law of motion with his law of gravitation, we obtain
$$m\frac{d^2y}{dt^2} = -k_1\frac{mM}{y^2},$$ where M is the mass of the earth and k_1 is a constant of proportionality.

Dividing by m gives $\dfrac{d^2y}{dt^2} = -\dfrac{k}{y^2}$, where $k = k_1 M$. The constant k is gR^2, where R is the radius of the earth. This follows from the fact that on the surface of the earth $y = R$ so that $k_1\dfrac{mM}{R^2} = mg$, $k_1 M = gR^2$, or $k = gR^2$. If $t = 0$ is the time at which burnout occurs, then $y(0) = R + y_B$, where y_B is the distance from the earth's surface to the rocket at the time of burnout, and $y'(0) = V_B$ is the corresponding velocity at that time.

18. Substituting into the differential equation we obtain $-(m_0 - at)g = (m_0 - at)\dfrac{dv}{dt} + b(-a)$ or
$$(m_0 - at)\frac{dv}{dt} = ab - m_0 g + agt.$$

19. By the Pythagorean Theorem the slope of the tangent line is $y' = \dfrac{-y}{\sqrt{s^2 - y^2}}$.

20. (a) We have $M_r = \dfrac{4}{3}\delta r^3$ and $M = \dfrac{4}{3}\delta R^3$. Then $M_r = r^3\dfrac{M}{R^3}$ and

$$F = -k\frac{M_r m}{r^2} = -k\frac{r^3 Mm/R^3}{r^2} = -k\frac{mM}{R^3} r.$$

(b) From $F = ma = m\dfrac{d^2r}{dt^2}$ and part **(a)** we have $m\dfrac{d^2r}{dt^2} = -k\dfrac{mM}{R^3} r$ or $\dfrac{d^2r}{dt^2} = -\dfrac{kM}{R^3} r = -w^2 r$ where $w^2 = k\dfrac{M}{R^3}$.

21. The differential equation is $\dfrac{dA}{dt} = k(M - A)$.

22. The differential equation is $\dfrac{dA}{dt} = k_1(M - A) - k_2 A$.

Chapter 1 Review Exercises

1. First-order; ordinary; nonlinear because of y^2.

2. Third-order; ordinary; nonlinear because of $\sin xy$.

3. Second-order; partial.

4. Second-order; ordinary; linear.

5. From $y = x + \tan x$ we obtain $y' = 1 + \sec^2 x$, and $y'' = 2\sec^2 x \tan x$. Using $1 + \tan^2 x = \sec^2 x$ we have $y' + 2xy = 2 + x^2 + y^2$.

6. From $y = c_1 \cos(\ln x) + c_2 \sin(\ln x)$ we obtain $y' = \dfrac{1}{x}[c_2 \cos(\ln x) - c_1 \sin(\ln x)]$ and

$$y'' = \frac{-1}{x^2}[c_1 \cos(\ln x) + c_2 \sin(\ln x) + c_2 \cos(\ln x) - c_1 \sin(\ln x)]$$

so that $x^2 y'' + xy' + y = 0$.

7. From $y = c_1 e^x + c_2 e^{-x} + c_3 e^{2x} + 3$ we obtain $y' = c_1 e^x - c_2 e^{-x} + 2c_3 e^{2x}$, $y'' = c_1 e^x + c_2 e^{-x} + 4c_3 e^{2x}$, and $y''' = c_1 e^x - c_2 e^{-x} + 8c_3 e^{2x}$ so that $y''' - 2y'' - y' + 2y = 6$.

8. From $y = \sin 2x + \cosh 2x$ we obtain $y^{(4)} = 16\sin 2x + 16\cosh 2x$ so that $y^{(4)} - 16y = 0$.

9. $y = x^2$

10. $y = e^{5x}$

11. $y = \frac{1}{2}x^2$

12. $y = 2$

13. $y = e^x$, $y = 0$

14. $y = \sqrt{x}$

15. $y = \sin x$, $y = \cos x$, $y = 0$

16. $y = e^x$

17. For all values of y, $y^2 - 2y \geq -1$. Avoiding left– and right–hand derivatives, we then must have $x^2 - x - 1 > -1$. That is, $x < 0$ or $x > 1$.

18. If $|x| < 2$ and $|y| > 2$, then $(dy/dx)^2 < 0$ and the differential equation has no real solutions. This is also true for $|x| > 2$ and $|y| < 2$.

19. The differential equation is $\dfrac{dh}{dt} = -\dfrac{A_0}{A_w}\sqrt{2gh}$. We have $A_0 = \dfrac{1}{4}$. To find A_w we note that the radius r corresponding to A_w satisfies $\dfrac{r}{h} = \dfrac{8}{20}$. Thus $r = \dfrac{2h}{5}$ and $A_w = \dfrac{4\pi h^2}{25}$. Then

$$\frac{dh}{dt} = -\frac{1/4}{4\pi h^2/25}\sqrt{2gh} = -\frac{25\sqrt{2gh}}{16\pi h^{3/2}}.$$

20. From Newton's second law we obtain $m\dfrac{dv}{dt} = \dfrac{1}{2}mg - \mu\dfrac{\sqrt{3}}{2}mg$ or $\dfrac{dv}{dt} = 16\left(1 - \sqrt{3}\,\mu\right)$.

2 First-Order Differential Equations

Exercises 2.1

1. For $f(x,y) = y^{2/3}$ we have $\dfrac{\partial f}{\partial y} = \dfrac{2}{3}y^{-1/3}$. Thus the differential equation will have a unique solution in any rectangular region of the plane where $y \neq 0$.

2. For $f(x,y) = \sqrt{xy}$ we have $\dfrac{\partial f}{\partial y} = \dfrac{1}{2}\sqrt{\dfrac{x}{y}}$. Thus the differential equation will have a unique solution in any region where $x > 0$ and $y > 0$ or where $x < 0$ and $y < 0$.

3. For $f(x,y) = \dfrac{y}{x}$ we have $\dfrac{\partial f}{\partial y} = \dfrac{1}{x}$. Thus the differential equation will have a unique solution in any region where $x \neq 0$.

4. For $f(x,y) = x + y$ we have $\dfrac{\partial f}{\partial y} = 1$. Thus the differential equation will have a unique solution in the entire plane.

5. For $f(x,y) = \dfrac{x^2}{4 - y^2}$ we have $\dfrac{\partial f}{\partial y} = \dfrac{2x^2 y}{(4 - y^2)^2}$. Thus the differential equation will have a unique solution in any region where $y < -2$, $-2 < y < 2$, or $y > 2$.

6. For $f(x,y) = \dfrac{x^2}{1 + y^3}$ we have $\dfrac{\partial f}{\partial y} = \dfrac{-3x^2 y^2}{(1 + y^3)^2}$. Thus the differential equation will have a unique solution in any region where $y \neq -1$.

7. For $f(x,y) = \dfrac{y^2}{x^2 + y^2}$ we have $\dfrac{\partial f}{\partial y} = \dfrac{2x^2 y}{(x^2 + y^2)^2}$. Thus the differential equation will have a unique solution in any region not containing $(0,0)$.

8. For $f(x,y) = \dfrac{y + x}{y - x}$ we have $\dfrac{\partial f}{\partial y} = \dfrac{-2x}{(y - x)^2}$. Thus the differential equation will have a unique solution in any region where $y < x$ or where $y > x$.

9. For $f(x,y) = x^3 \cos y$ we have $\dfrac{\partial f}{\partial y} = -x^3 \sin y$. Thus the differential equation will have a unique solution in the entire plane.

10. For $f(x,y) = (x - 1)e^{y/(x-1)}$ we have $\dfrac{\partial f}{\partial y} = e^{y/(x-1)}$. Thus the differential equation will have a unique solution in any region where $x \neq 1$.

11. Two solutions are $y = 0$ and $y = x^3$.

12. Two solutions are $y = 0$ and $y = x^2$. (Also, any constant multiple of x^2 is a solution.)

13. The solution is $y = 0$, which is unique by Theorem 2.1.

9

14. A function satisfying the differential equation and the initial condition is $y = 1$. Although $f(x, y) = |y - 1|$ is continuous, $\partial f / \partial y$ is not continuous at $y = 1$, so Theorem 2.1 does not apply.

15. For $y = cx$ we have $y' = c$, from which we see that $y = cx$ is a solution of $xy' = y$ for all values of c. All of these solutions satisfy the initial condition $y(0) = 0$. The piecewise defined function is not a solution since it is not differentiable at $x = 0$.

16. (a) Since $1 + y^2$ and its partial derivative with respect to y are continuous everywhere in the plane, the differential equation has a unique solution through every point in the plane.

(b) Since $\dfrac{d}{dx}(\tan x) = \sec^2 x = 1 + \tan^2 x$ and $\tan 0 = 0$, $y = \tan x$ satisfies the differential equation and the initial condition.

(c) Since $-2 < \pi/2 < 2$ and $\tan x$ is undefined for $x = \pi/2$, $y = \tan x$ is not a solution on the interval $-2 < x < 2$.

(d) Since $\tan x$ is differentiable and continuous on $-1 < x < 1$, $y = \tan x$ is a solution of the initial value problem on the interval $-1 < x < 1$.

For Problems 17–20 we identify $f(x, y) = \sqrt{y^2 - 9}$ and $\partial f / \partial y = y^2/\sqrt{y^2 - 9}$. We further note that $f(x, y)$ is discontinuous for $|y| < 3$ and that $\partial f / \partial y$ is discontinuous for $|y| < 3$. We then apply Theorem 2.1.

17. The differential equation has a unique solution at $(1, 4)$.

18. The differential equation is not guaranteed to have a unique solution at $(5, 3)$.

19. The differential equation is not guaranteed to have a unique solution at $(2, -3)$.

20. The differential equation is not guaranteed to have a unique solution at $(-1, 1)$.

——————— Exercises 2.2 ———————

In many of the following problems we will encounter an expression of the form $\ln |g(y)| = f(x) + c$. To solve for $g(y)$ we exponentiate both sides of the equation. This yields $|g(y)| = e^{f(x)+c} = e^c e^{f(x)}$ which implies $g(y) = \pm e^c e^{f(x)}$. Letting $c_1 = \pm e^c$ we obtain $g(y) = c_1 e^{f(x)}$.

1. From $dy = \sin 5x \, dx$ we obtain $y = -\dfrac{1}{5} \cos 5x + c$.

2. From $dy = (x + 1)^2 \, dx$ we obtain $y = \dfrac{1}{3}(x + 1)^3 + c$.

3. From $dy = -e^{-3x} \, dx$ we obtain $y = \dfrac{1}{3} e^{-3x} + c$.

4. From $dy = \dfrac{1}{x^2}\,dx$ we obtain $y = \dfrac{-1}{x} + c$.

5. From $dy = \dfrac{x+6}{x+1}\,dx = \left(1 + \dfrac{5}{x+1}\right)dx$ we obtain $y = x + 5\ln|x+1| + c$.

6. From $dy = 2xe^{-x}dx$ we obtain $y = -2xe^{-x} + 2e^{-x} + c$.

7. From $\dfrac{1}{y}\,dy = \dfrac{4}{x}\,dx$ we obtain $\ln|y| = 4\ln|x| + c$ or $y = c_1 x^4$.

8. From $\dfrac{1}{y}\,dy = -2x\,dx$ we obtain $\ln|y| = -x^2 + c$ or $y = c_1 e^{-x^2}$.

9. From $\dfrac{1}{y^3}\,dy = \dfrac{1}{x^2}\,dx$ we obtain $y^{-2} = \dfrac{2}{x} + c$.

10. From $\dfrac{1}{y+1}\,dy = \dfrac{1}{x}\,dx$ we obtain $\ln|y+1| = \ln|x| + c$ or $y + 1 = c_1 x$.

11. From $y^2\,dy = \left(\dfrac{1}{x^2} + \dfrac{1}{x}\right)dx$ we obtain $\dfrac{1}{3}y^3 = \dfrac{-1}{x} + \ln|x| + c$ or $xy^3 = -3 + 3x\ln|x| + c_1 x$.

12. From $\left(\dfrac{1}{y} + 2y\right)dy = \sin x\,dx$ we obtain $\ln|y| + y^2 = -\cos x + c$.

13. From $e^{-2y}dy = e^{3x}dx$ we obtain $3e^{-2y} + 2e^{3x} = c$.

14. From $ye^y dy = \left(e^{-x} + e^{-3x}\right)dx$ we obtain $ye^y - e^y + e^{-x} + \dfrac{1}{3}e^{-3x} = c$.

15. From $\dfrac{y}{2+y^2}\,dy = \dfrac{x}{4+x^2}\,dx$ we obtain $\ln|2+y^2| = \ln|4+x^2| + c$ or $2 + y^2 = c_1\left(4 + x^2\right)$.

16. From $\left(\dfrac{1}{y^2} + 1\right)dy = \dfrac{1}{1+x^2}\,dx$ we obtain $\dfrac{-1}{y} + y = \tan^{-1} x + c$.

17. From $2y\,dy = \dfrac{x}{x+1}\,dx$ we obtain $y^2 = x - \ln|x+1| + c$.

18. From $\dfrac{y^2}{y+1}\,dy = \dfrac{1}{x^2}\,dx$ we obtain $\dfrac{1}{2}y^2 - y + \ln|y+1| = -\dfrac{1}{x} + c$ or $\dfrac{1}{2}y^2 - y + \ln|y+1| = -\dfrac{1}{x} + c_1$.

19. From $\left(y + 2 + \dfrac{1}{y}\right)dy = x^2\ln x\,dx$ we obtain $\dfrac{y^2}{2} + 2y + \ln|y| = \dfrac{x^3}{3}\ln|x| - \dfrac{1}{9}x^3 + c$.

20. From $\dfrac{1}{(2y+3)^2}\,dy = \dfrac{1}{(4x+5)^2}\,dx$ we obtain $\dfrac{2}{2y+3} = \dfrac{1}{4x+5} + c$.

21. From $\dfrac{1}{S}\,dS = k\,dr$ we obtain $S = ce^{kr}$.

22. From $\dfrac{1}{Q-70}\,dQ = k\,dt$ we obtain $\ln|Q - 70| = kt + c$ or $Q - 70 = c_1 e^{kt}$.

23. From $\dfrac{1}{P-P^2}\,dP = \left(\dfrac{1}{P} + \dfrac{1}{1-P}\right)dP = dt$ we obtain $\ln|P| - \ln|1-P| = t + c$ so that $\ln\dfrac{P}{1-P} = t + c$

or $\dfrac{P}{1-P} = c_1 e^t$. Solving for P we have $P = \dfrac{c_1 e^t}{1 + c_1 e^t}$.

24. From $\dfrac{1}{N}\,dN = \left(te^{t+2} - 1\right)dt$ we obtain $\ln|N| = te^{t+2} - e^{t+2} - t + c.$

25. From $\dfrac{1}{\csc y}\,dy = -\dfrac{1}{\sec^2 x}\,dx$ or $\sin y\,dy = -\cos^2 x\,dx = -\dfrac{1}{2}(1 + \cos 2x)\,dx$ we obtain

$-\cos y = -\dfrac{1}{2}x - \dfrac{1}{4}\sin 2x + c$ or $4\cos y = 2x + \sin 2x + c_1.$

26. From $2y\,dy = -\dfrac{\sin 3x}{\cos^3 3x}\,dx = -\tan 3x \sec^2 3x\,dx$ we obtain $y^2 = -\dfrac{1}{6}\sec^2 3x + c.$

27. From $\dfrac{e^{2y} - y}{e^y}\,dy = -\dfrac{\sin 2x}{\cos x}\,dx = -\dfrac{2\sin x \cos x}{\cos x}\,dx$ or $\left(e^y - ye^{-y}\right)dy = -2\sin x\,dx$ we obtain

$e^y + ye^{-y} + e^{-y} = 2\cos x + c.$

28. From $\tan y\,dy = x\cos x\,dx$ we obtain $\ln|\sec y| = x\sin x + \cos x + c.$

29. From $\dfrac{e^y}{(e^y + 1)^2}\,dy = \dfrac{-e^x}{(e^x + 1)^3}\,dx$ we obtain $-(e^y + 1)^{-1} = \dfrac{1}{2}(e^x + 1)^{-2} + c.$

30. From $\dfrac{y}{(1 + y^2)^{1/2}}\,dy = \dfrac{x}{(1 + x^2)^{1/2}}\,dx$ we obtain $\left(1 + y^2\right)^{1/2} = \left(1 + x^2\right)^{1/2} + c.$

31. From $\dfrac{y}{(y + 1)^2}\,dy = \dfrac{1}{1 - x^2}\,dx$ or $\left(\dfrac{1}{y + 1} - \dfrac{1}{(y + 1)^2}\right)dy = \left(\dfrac{1/2}{1 + x} + \dfrac{1/2}{1 - x}\right)dx$ we obtain

$$\ln|y + 1| + \dfrac{1}{y + 1} = \dfrac{1}{2}\ln|1 + x| - \dfrac{1}{2}\ln|1 - x| + c.$$

32. From $2y\,dy = (2x + 1)\,dx$ we obtain $y^2 = x^2 + x + c.$

33. From $\dfrac{y - 2}{y + 3}\,dy = \dfrac{x - 1}{x + 4}\,dx$ or $\left(1 - \dfrac{5}{y - 3}\right)dy = \left(1 - \dfrac{5}{x + 4}\right)dx$ we obtain

$$y - 5\ln|y - 3| = x - 5\ln|x + 4| + c \quad\text{or}\quad \left(\dfrac{x + 4}{y - 3}\right)^5 = c_1 e^{x - y}.$$

34. From $\dfrac{y + 1}{y - 1}\,dy = \dfrac{x + 2}{x - 3}\,dx$ or $\left(1 + \dfrac{2}{y - 1}\right)dy = \left(1 + \dfrac{5}{x - 3}\right)dx$ we obtain

$$y + 2\ln|y - 1| = x + 5\ln|x - 3| + c \quad\text{or}\quad \dfrac{(y - 1)^2}{(x - 3)^5} = c_1 e^{x - y}.$$

35. From $\dfrac{1}{(2\cos^2 y - 1) - \cos^2 y}\,dy = \sin x\,dx$ or $\dfrac{1}{\cos^2 y - 1}\,dy = -\csc^2 y\,dy = \sin x\,dx$ we obtain

$\cot y = -\cos x + c.$

36. From $\sec y\,\dfrac{dy}{dx} + \sin x\cos y - \cos x\sin y = \sin x\cos y + \cos x\sin y$ we find $\sec y\,dy = 2\sin y\cos x\,dx$ or

$\dfrac{1}{2\sin y\cos y}\,dy = \csc 2y\,dy = \cos x\,dx.$ Then $\dfrac{1}{2}\ln|\csc 2y - \cot 2y| = \sin x + c.$

37. From $x \, dx = \dfrac{1}{\sqrt{1-y^2}} \, dy$ we obtain $\dfrac{1}{2}x^2 = \sin^{-1} y + c$ or $y = \sin\left(\dfrac{x^2}{2} + c_1\right)$.

38. From $\dfrac{y}{\sqrt{4+y^2}} \, dy = \dfrac{1}{\sqrt{4-x^2}} \, dx$ we obtain $\sqrt{4+y^2} = \sin^{-1}\dfrac{x}{2} + c$.

39. From $\dfrac{1}{y^2} \, dy = \dfrac{1}{e^x + e^{-x}} \, dx = \dfrac{e^x}{(e^x)^2 + 1} \, dx$ we obtain $-\dfrac{1}{y} = \tan^{-1} e^x + c$.

40. To integrate $dx/(x + \sqrt{x})$ make the substitution $u^2 = x$. Then $2u \, du = dx$ and

$$\int \frac{dx}{x + \sqrt{x}} = \int \frac{2u \, du}{u^2 + u} = \int \frac{2 \, du}{u + 1} = 2\ln|u + 1| + c = 2\ln\left(\sqrt{x} + 1\right) + c.$$

Thus, from $\dfrac{1}{y + \sqrt{y}} \, dy = \dfrac{1}{x + \sqrt{x}} \, dx$ we obtain $2\ln\left(\sqrt{y} + 1\right) = 2\ln\left(\sqrt{x} + 1\right) + c$ or

$\sqrt{y} + 1 = c_1\left(\sqrt{x} + 1\right)$.

41. From $\dfrac{\sin x}{1 + \cos x} \, dx = \dfrac{1}{e^{-y} + 1} \, dy = \dfrac{e^y}{1 + e^y} \, dy$ we obtain $-\ln(1 + \cos x) = \ln(1 + e^y) + c$ or

$(1 + e^y)(1 + \cos x) = c_1$. Using $y(0) = 0$ we find $c_1 = 4$. The solution of the initial-value problem

is $(1 + e^y)(1 + \cos x) = 4$.

42. From $\dfrac{1}{1 + (2y)^2} \, dy = \dfrac{-x}{1 + (x^2)^2} \, dx$ we obtain

$$\frac{1}{2} \tan^{-1} 2y = -\frac{1}{2} \tan^{-1} x^2 + c \quad \text{or} \quad \tan^{-1} 2y + \tan^{-1} x^2 = c_1.$$

Using $y(1) = 0$ we find $c_1 = \pi/4$. The solution of the initial-value problem is

$$\tan^{-1} 2y + \tan^{-1} x^2 = \frac{\pi}{4}.$$

43. From $\dfrac{y}{\sqrt{y^2 + 1}} \, dy = 4x \, dx$ we obtain $\sqrt{y^2 + 1} = 2x^2 + c$. Using $y(0) = 1$ we find $c = \sqrt{2}$. The

solution of the initial-value problem is $\sqrt{y^2 + 1} = 2x^2 + \sqrt{2}$.

44. From $\dfrac{1}{y} \, dy = (1 - t) \, dt$ we obtain $\ln|y| = t - \dfrac{1}{2}t^2 + c$ or $y = c_1 e^{t - t^2/2}$. Using $y(1) = 3$ we find

$c = 3e^{-1/2}$. The solution of the initial-value problem is $y = 3e^{t - t^2/2 - 1/2} = 3e^{-(t-1)^2/2}$.

45. From $\dfrac{1}{x^2 + 1} \, dx = 4 \, dy$ we obtain $\tan^{-1} x = 4y + c$. Using $x(\pi/4) = 1$ we find $c = -3\pi/4$. The

solution of the initial-value problem is $\tan^{-1} x = 4y - \dfrac{3\pi}{4}$ or $x = \tan\left(4y - \dfrac{3\pi}{4}\right)$.

46. From $\dfrac{1}{y^2 - 1} \, dy = \dfrac{1}{x^2 - 1} \, dx$ or $\dfrac{1}{2}\left(\dfrac{1}{y-1} - \dfrac{1}{y+1}\right) dy = \dfrac{1}{2}\left(\dfrac{1}{x-1} - \dfrac{1}{x+1}\right) dx$ we obtain

$\ln|y-1| - \ln|y+1| = \ln|x-1| - \ln|x+1| + c$ or $\dfrac{y-1}{y+1} = \dfrac{x-1}{x+1} + c$. Using $y(2) = 2$ we find $c = 0$.

The solution of the initial-value problem is $\dfrac{y-1}{y+1} = \dfrac{x-1}{x+1}$ or $y = x$.

47. From $\dfrac{1}{y}\,dy = \dfrac{1-x}{x^2}\,dx = \left(\dfrac{1}{x^2} - \dfrac{1}{x}\right)dx$ we obtain $\ln|y| = -\dfrac{1}{x} - \ln|x| = c$ or $xy = c_1 e^{-1/x}$. Using $y(-1) = -1$ we find $c_1 = e^{-1}$. The solution of the initial-value problem is $xy = e^{-1-1/x}$.

48. From $\dfrac{1}{1-2y}\,dy = dx$ we obtain $-\dfrac{1}{2}\ln|1-2y| = x + c$ or $1 - 2y = c_1 e^{-2x}$. Using $y(0) = 5/2$ we find $c_1 = -4$. The solution of the initial-value problem is $1 - 2y = -4e^{-2x}$ or $y = 2e^{-2x} + \dfrac{1}{2}$.

49. From $\left(\dfrac{-1/6}{y+3} + \dfrac{1/6}{y-3}\right)dy = dx$ we obtain $\dfrac{y-3}{y+3} = ce^{6x}$.

    (a) If $y(0) = 0$ then $y = 3\,\dfrac{1 - e^{6x}}{1 + e^{6x}}$.

    (b) If $y(0) = 3$ then $y = 3$.

    (c) If $y(1/3) = 1$ then $y = 3\,\dfrac{2 - e^{6x-2}}{2 + e^{6x-2}}$.

50. From $\left(\dfrac{1}{y-1} + \dfrac{-1}{y}\right)dy = \dfrac{1}{x}\,dx$ we obtain $\ln|y-1| - \ln|y| = \ln|x| + c$ or $y = \dfrac{1}{1 - c_1 x}$. Another solution is $y = 0$.

    (a) If $y(0) = 1$ then $y = 1$.

    (b) If $y(0) = 0$ then $y = 0$.

    (c) If $y(1/2) = 1/2$ then $y = \dfrac{1}{1 + 2x}$.

51. By inspection a singular solution is $y = 1$.

52. By inspection a singular solution is $y = 0$.

53. The singular solution $y = 1$ satisfies the initial-value problem.

54. Separating variables we obtain $\dfrac{dy}{(y-1)^2} = dx$. Then $-\dfrac{1}{y-1} = x + c$ and $y = \dfrac{x+c-1}{x+c}$. Setting $x = 0$ and $y = 1.01$ we obtain $c = -100$. The solution is $y = \dfrac{x - 101}{x - 100}$.

55. Separating variables we obtain $\dfrac{dy}{(y-1)^2 + 0.01} = dx$. Then $10\tan^{-1} 10(y-1) = x + c$ and $y = 1 + \dfrac{1}{10}\tan\dfrac{x+c}{10}$. Setting $x = 0$ and $y = 1$ we obtain $c = 0$. The solution is $y = 1 + \dfrac{1}{10}\tan\dfrac{x}{10}$.

56. Separating variables we obtain $\dfrac{dy}{(y-1)^2 - 0.01} = dx$. Then $5\ln\left|\dfrac{10y-11}{10y-9}\right| = x + c$. Setting $x = 0$

and $y = 1$ we obtain $c = 5\ln 1 = 0$. The solution is $5\ln\left|\dfrac{10y-11}{10y-9}\right| = x$.

57. Let $u = x + y + 1$ so that $du/dx = 1 + dy/x$. Then $\dfrac{du}{dx} - 1 = u^2$ or $\dfrac{1}{1+u^2}du = dx$. Thus $\tan^{-1}u = x + c$ or $u = \tan(x+c)$, and $x + y + 1 = \tan(x+c)$ or $y = \tan(x+c) - x - 1$.

58. Let $u = x + y$ so that $du/dx = 1 + dy/dx$. Then $\dfrac{du}{dx} - 1 = \dfrac{1-u}{u}$ or $u\,du = dx$. Thus $\dfrac{1}{2}u^2 = x + c$ or $u^2 = 2x + c_1$, and $(x+y)^2 = 2x + c_1$.

59. Let $u = x + y$ so that $du/dx = 1 + dy/dx$. Then $\dfrac{du}{dx} - 1 = \tan^2 u$ or $\cos^2 u\,du = dx$. Thus $\dfrac{1}{2}u + \dfrac{1}{4}\sin 2u = x + c$ or $2u + \sin 2u = 4x + c_1$, and $2(x+y) + \sin 2(x+y) = 4x + c_1$ or $2y + \sin 2(x+y) = 2x + c_1$.

60. Let $u = x + y$ so that $du/dx = 1 + dy/dx$. Then $\dfrac{du}{dx} - 1 = \sin u$ or $\dfrac{1}{1+\sin u}du = dx$. Multiplying by $(1-\sin u)/(1-\sin u)$ we have $\dfrac{1-\sin u}{\cos^2 u}du = dx$ or $\left(\sec^2 u - \tan u\sec u\right)du = dx$. Thus $\tan u - \sec u = x + c$ or $\tan(x+y) - \sec(x+y) = x + c$.

61. Let $u = y - 2x + 3$ so that $du/dx = dy/dx - 2$. Then $\dfrac{du}{dx} + 2 = 2 + \sqrt{u}$ or $\dfrac{1}{\sqrt{u}}du = dx$. Thus $2\sqrt{u} = x + c$ and $2\sqrt{y-2x+3} = x + c$.

62. Let $u = y - x + 5$ so that $du/dx = dy/dx - 1$. Then $\dfrac{du}{dx} + 1 = 1 + e^u$ or $e^{-u}du = dx$. Thus $-e^{-u} = x + c$ and $-e^{y-x+5} = x + c$.

Exercises 2.3

1. Since $f(tx, ty) = (tx)^3 + 2(tx)(ty)^2 - \dfrac{(ty)^4}{tx} = t^3 f(x,y)$, the function is homogeneous of degree 3.

2. Since $f(tx, ty) = \sqrt{tx + ty}\,(4tx + 3ty) = t^{3/2}f(x,y)$, the function is homogeneous of degree 3/2.

3. Since $f(tx, ty) = \dfrac{(tx)^3(ty) - (tx)^2(ty)^2}{(tx + 8ty)^2} = t^2 f(x,y)$, the function is homogeneous of degree 2.

4. Since $f(tx, ty) = \dfrac{tx}{(ty)^2 + \sqrt{(tx)^4 + (ty)^4}} = \dfrac{1}{t}f(x,y)$, the function is homogeneous of degree -1.

5. Since $f(tx, ty) = \cos\dfrac{(tx)^2}{x+y} \ne t^n\cos\dfrac{x^2}{x+y}$ for any n, the function is not homogeneous.

6. Since $f(tx, ty) = \sin\dfrac{x}{x+y} = f(x,y)$, the function is homogeneous of degree 0.

7. Since $f(tx, ty) \ln t^2 + \ln x^2 - 2(\ln t + \ln y) = f(x, y)$, the function is homogeneous of degree 0.

8. Since $f(tx, ty) = \dfrac{3 \ln tx}{3 \ln ty} \neq t^n \dfrac{\ln x}{\ln y}$ for any n, the function is not homogeneous.

9. Since $f(tx, ty) = \left(\dfrac{1}{tx} + \dfrac{1}{ty}\right)^2 = \dfrac{1}{t^2} f(x, y)$, the function is homogeneous of degree -2.

10. Since $f(tx, ty) = (tx + ty + 1)^2 \neq t^n (x + y + 1)^2$ for any n, the function is not homogeneous.

11. Letting $y = ux$ we have

$$(x - ux)\, dx + x(u\, dx + x\, du) = 0$$

$$dx + x\, du = 0$$

$$\frac{dx}{x} + du = 0$$

$$\ln|x| + u = c$$

$$x \ln|x| + y = cx.$$

12. Letting $y = ux$ we have

$$(x + ux)\, dx + x(u\, dx + x\, du) = 0$$

$$(1 + 2u)\, dx + x\, du = 0$$

$$\frac{dx}{x} + \frac{du}{1 + 2u} = 0$$

$$\ln|x| + \frac{1}{2} \ln|1 + 2u| = c$$

$$x^2 \left(1 + 2\frac{y}{x}\right) = c_1$$

$$x^2 + 2xy = c_1.$$

13. Letting $x = vy$ we have

$$vy(v\, dy + y\, dv) + (y - 2vy)\, dy = 0$$

$$vy\, dv + \left(v^2 - 2v + 1\right) dy = 0$$

$$\frac{v\, dv}{(v - 1)^2} + \frac{dy}{y} = 0$$

$$\ln|v - 1| - \frac{1}{v - 1} + \ln|y| = c$$

$$\ln\left|\frac{x}{y} - 1\right| - \frac{1}{x/y - 1} + \ln y = c$$

$$(x - y)\ln|x - y| - y = c(x - y).$$

14. Letting $x = vy$ we have

$$y(v\,dy + y\,dv) - 2(vy + y)\,dy = 0$$

$$y\,dv - (v + 2)\,dy = 0$$

$$\frac{dv}{v + 2} - \frac{dy}{y} = 0$$

$$\ln|v + 2| - \ln|y| = c$$

$$\ln\left|\frac{x}{y} + 2\right| - \ln|y| = c$$

$$x + 2y = c_1 y^2.$$

15. Letting $y = ux$ we have

$$\left(u^2 x^2 + ux^2\right)dx - x^2(u\,dx + x\,du) = 0$$

$$u^2\,dx - x\,du = 0$$

$$\frac{dx}{x} - \frac{du}{u^2} = 0$$

$$\ln|x| + \frac{1}{u} = c$$

$$\ln|x| + \frac{x}{y} = c$$

$$y\ln|x| + x = cy.$$

16. Letting $y = ux$ we have

$$\left(u^2 x^2 + ux^2\right)dx + x^2(u\,dx + x\,du) = 0$$

$$\left(u^2 + 2u\right)dx + x\,du = 0$$

$$\frac{dx}{x} + \frac{du}{u(u + 2)} = 0$$

$$\ln|x| + \frac{1}{2}\ln|u| - \frac{1}{2}\ln|u + 2| = c$$

17

$$\frac{x^2 u}{u+2} = c_1$$

$$x^2 \frac{y}{x} = c_1 \left(\frac{y}{x} + 2 \right)$$

$$x^2 y = c_1 (y + 2x).$$

17. Letting $y = ux$ we have

$$(ux - x)\,dx - (ux + x)(u\,dx + x\,du) = 0$$

$$\left(u^2 + 1\right) dx + x(u+1)\,du = 0$$

$$\frac{dx}{x} + \frac{u+1}{u^2+1}\,du = 0$$

$$\ln|x| + \frac{1}{2}\ln\left(u^2 + 1\right) + \tan^{-1} u = c$$

$$\ln x^2 \left(\frac{y^2}{x^2} + 1 \right) + 2\tan^{-1}\frac{y}{x} = c_1$$

$$\ln\left(x^2 + y^2\right) + 2\tan^{-1}\frac{y}{x} = c_1.$$

18. Letting $y = ux$ we have

$$(x + 3ux)\,dx - (3x + ux)(u\,dx + x\,du) = 0$$

$$\left(u^2 - 1\right) dx + x(u+3)\,du = 0$$

$$\frac{dx}{x} + \frac{u+3}{(u-1)(u+1)}\,du = 0$$

$$\ln|x| + 2\ln|u-1| - \ln|u+1| = c$$

$$\frac{x(u-1)^2}{u+1} = c_1$$

$$x\left(\frac{y}{x} - 1\right)^2 = c_1 \left(\frac{y}{x} + 1\right)$$

$$(y - x)^2 = c_1(y + x).$$

18

19. Letting $y = ux$ we have

$$-ux\,dx + (x + \sqrt{u}\,x)(u\,dx + x\,du) = 0$$

$$(x + x\sqrt{u})\,du + u^{3/2}\,dx = 0$$

$$\left(u^{-3/2} + \frac{1}{u}\right)du + \frac{dx}{x} = 0$$

$$-2u^{-1/2} + \ln|u| + \ln|x| = c$$

$$\ln|y/x| + \ln|x| = 2\sqrt{x/y} + c$$

$$y(\ln|y| - c)^2 = 4x.$$

20. Letting $y = ux$ we have

$$\left(ux + \sqrt{x^2 + u^2x^2}\right)dx - x(u\,dx + x\,du) = 0$$

$$x\sqrt{1 + u^2}\,dx - x^2\,du = 0$$

$$\frac{dx}{x} - \frac{du}{\sqrt{1 + u^2}} = 0$$

$$\ln|x| - \ln\left|u + \sqrt{1 + u^2}\right| = c$$

$$u + \sqrt{1 + u^2} = c_1 x$$

$$y + \sqrt{y^2 + x^2} = c_1 x^2.$$

21. Letting $x = vy$ we have

$$2v^2y^3(v\,dy + y\,dv) - \left(3v^3y^3 + y^3\right)dy = 0$$

$$2v^2y\,dv - \left(v^3 + 1\right)dy = 0$$

$$\frac{2v^2}{v^3 + 1}\,dv - \frac{dy}{y} = 0$$

$$\frac{2}{3}\ln\left|v^3 + 1\right| - \ln|y| = c$$

$$\left(v^3 + 1\right)^{2/3} = c_1 y$$

$$\left(\frac{x^3}{y^3} + 1\right)^2 = c_2 y^3$$

$$\left(x^3 + y^3\right)^2 = c_2 y^9.$$

22. Letting $y = ux$ we have

$$\left(x^4 + u^4 x^4\right) dx - 2x^3 ux(u\,dx + x\,du) = 0$$

$$\left(u^2 - 1\right)^2 dx - 2xu\,du = 0$$

$$\frac{dx}{x} - \frac{2u\,du}{\left(u^2 - 1\right)^2} = 0$$

$$\ln|x| + \frac{1}{u^2 - 1} = c$$

$$\left(y^2 - x^2\right)\ln|x| + x^2 = c\left(y^2 - x^2\right).$$

23. Letting $y = ux$ we have

$$\left(x^2 + u^2 x^2\right) dx - ux^2(u\,dx + x\,du) = 0$$

$$dx - ux\,du = 0$$

$$\frac{dx}{x} - u\,du = 0$$

$$\ln|x| - \frac{1}{2}u^2 = c$$

$$2\ln|x| - (y/x)^2 = c.$$

24. Letting $y = ux$ we have

$$\left(u^3 x^3 + x^3 + u^2 x^3\right) dx - u^2 x^3(u\,dx + x\,du) = 0$$

$$\left(1 + u^2\right) dx - u^2 x\,du = 0$$

$$\frac{dx}{x} - \frac{u^2}{u^2 + 1}\,du = 0$$

$$\ln|x| - u + \tan^{-1} u = c$$

$$\ln|x| - \frac{y}{x} + \tan^{-1}\frac{y}{x} = c.$$

20

25. Letting $x = vy$ we have

$$y(v\,dy + y\,dv) - \left(vy + 4ye^{-2v}\right)dy = 0$$

$$y\,dv - 4e^{-2v}\,dy = 0$$

$$e^{2v}\,dv - \frac{4\,dy}{y} = 0$$

$$\frac{1}{2}e^{2v} - 4\ln|y| = c$$

$$e^{2x/y} - 8\ln|y| = c_1.$$

26. Letting $y = ux$ we have

$$\left(x^2 e^{-u} + u^2 x^2\right)dx - ux^2(u\,dx + x\,du) = 0$$

$$e^{-u}\,dx - ux\,du = 0$$

$$\frac{dx}{x} - ue^u\,du = 0$$

$$\ln|x| - ue^u + e^u = c$$

$$x\ln|x| - (y - x)e^{y/x} = cx.$$

27. Letting $y = ux$ we have

$$(ux + x\cot u)\,dx - x(u\,dx + x\,du) = 0$$

$$\cot u\,dx - x\,du = 0$$

$$\frac{dx}{x} - \tan u\,du = 0$$

$$\ln|x| + \ln|\cos u| = c$$

$$x\cos\frac{y}{x} = c.$$

28. Letting $y = ux$ we have

$$ux\ln u\,dx - x(u\,dx + x\,du) = 0$$

$$(u\ln u - u)\,dx - x\,du = 0$$

$$\frac{dx}{x} - \frac{du}{u\ln u - u} = 0$$

21

$$\ln|x| - \ln|\ln u - 1| = c$$

$$\frac{x}{\ln u - 1} = c_1$$

$$x = c_1\left(\ln\frac{y}{x} - 1\right)$$

$$\ln y = c_2 x + \ln x + 1$$

$$y = xe^{1+c_2 x}.$$

29. Letting $y = ux$ we have

$$\left(x^2 + ux^2 - u^2 x^2\right)dx + ux^2(u\,dx + x\,du) = 0$$

$$(1 + u)\,dx + xu\,du = 0$$

$$\frac{dx}{x} + \frac{u\,du}{u + 1} = 0$$

$$\ln|x| + u - \ln|u + 1| = c$$

$$\frac{u + 1}{x} = c_1 e^u$$

$$\frac{y}{x} + 1 = c_1 x e^{y/x}$$

$$y = c_1 x^2 e^{y/x} - x.$$

30. Letting $y = ux$ we have

$$\left(x^2 + ux^2 + 3u^2 x^2\right)dx - \left(x^2 + 2ux^2\right)(u\,dx + x\,du) = 0$$

$$\left(1 + u^2\right)dx - x(1 + 2u)\,du = 0$$

$$\frac{dx}{x} - \frac{1 + 2u}{1 + u^2}\,du = 0$$

$$\ln|x| - \tan^{-1}u - \ln\left(1 + u^2\right) = c$$

$$\frac{x}{1 + u^2} = c_1 e^{\tan^{-1}u}$$

$$x^3 = \left(y^2 + x^2\right)c_1 e^{\tan^{-1}y/x}.$$

31. Letting $y = ux$ we have

$$\left(x^3 - u^3 x^3\right) dx + u^2 x^3 (u\, dx + x\, du) = 0$$

$$dx + u^2 x\, du = 0$$

$$\frac{dx}{x} + u^2\, du = 0$$

$$\ln|x| + \frac{1}{3} u^3 = c$$

$$3x^3 \ln|x| + y^3 = c_1 x^3.$$

Using $y(1) = 2$ we find $c_1 = 8$. The solution of the initial-value problem is $3x^3 \ln|x| + y^3 = 8x^3$.

32. Letting $y = ux$ we have

$$\left(x^2 + 2u^2 x^2\right) dx - ux^2 (u\, dx + x\, du) = 0$$

$$\left(1 + u^2\right) dx - ux\, du = 0$$

$$\frac{dx}{x} - \frac{u\, du}{1 + u^2} = 0$$

$$\ln|x| - \frac{1}{2} \ln\left(1 + u^2\right) = c$$

$$\frac{x^2}{1 + u^2} = c_1$$

$$x^4 = c_1 \left(y^2 + x^2\right).$$

Using $y(-1) = 1$ we find $c_1 = 1/2$. The solution of the initial-value problem is $2x^4 = y^2 + x^2$.

33. Letting $y = ux$ we have

$$\left(3ux^2 + u^2 x^2\right) dx - 2x^2 (u\, dx + x\, du) = 0$$

$$\left(u^2 + u\right) dx - 2x\, du = 0$$

$$\frac{dx}{x} - \frac{2\, du}{u(u + 1)} = 0$$

$$\ln|x| - 2\ln|u| + 2\ln|u + 1| = c$$

$$\frac{x(u + 1)^2}{u^2} = c_1$$

$$x \left(\frac{y}{x} + 1\right)^2 = c_1 \left(\frac{y}{x}\right)^2$$

$$x(y + x)^2 = c_1 y^2.$$

Using $y(1) = -2$ we find $c_1 = 1/4$. The solution of the initial-value problem is $4x(y+x)^2 = y^2$.

34. Letting $x = vy$ we have

$$vy^2(v\,dy + y\,dv) - \left(v^2y^2 + vy\sqrt{v^2y^2 + y^2}\,\right)dy = 0$$

$$y\,dv - \sqrt{v^2 + 1}\,dy = 0$$

$$\frac{dv}{\sqrt{v^2 + 1}} - \frac{dy}{y} = 0$$

$$\ln\left|v + \sqrt{v^2 + 1}\,\right| - \ln|y| = c$$

$$\frac{x}{y} + \sqrt{\frac{x^2}{y^2} + 1} = c_1 y$$

$$x + \sqrt{x^2 + y^2} = c_1 y^2.$$

Using $y(0) = 1$ we find $c_1 = 1$. The solution of the initial-value problem is $x + \sqrt{x^2 + y^2} = y^2$.

35. Letting $y = ux$ we have

$$(x + uxe^u)\,dx - xe^u(u\,dx + x\,du) = 0$$

$$dx - xe^u\,du = 0$$

$$\frac{dx}{x} - e^u\,du = 0$$

$$\ln|x| - e^u = c$$

$$\ln|x| - e^{y/x} = c.$$

Using $y(1) = 0$ we find $c = -1$. The solution of the initial-value problem is $\ln|x| = e^{y/x} - 1$.

36. Letting $x = vy$ we have

$$y(v\,dy + y\,dv) + (y\cos v - vy)\,dy = 0$$

$$y\,dv + \cos v\,dy = 0$$

$$\sec v\,dv + \frac{dy}{y} = 0$$

$$\ln|\sec v + \tan v| + \ln|y| = c$$

$$y\left(\sec\frac{x}{y} + \tan\frac{x}{y}\right) = c_1.$$

Using $y(0) = 2$ we find $c_1 = 2$. The solution of the initial-value problem is $y\left(\sec\dfrac{x}{y} + \tan\dfrac{x}{y}\right) = 2$.

37. Letting $y = ux$ we have

$$\left(u^2x^2 + 3ux^2\right)dx - \left(4x^2 + ux^2\right)(u\,dx + x\,du) = 0$$

$$-u\,dx - x(4 + u)\,du = 0$$

$$\frac{dx}{x} + \frac{4 + u}{u}\,du = 0$$

$$\ln|x| + 4\ln|u| + u = c$$

$$xu^4 = c_1 e^{-u}$$

$$y^4 = c_1 x^3 e^{-y/x}.$$

Using $y(1) = 1$ we find $c_1 = e$. The solution of the initial-value problem is $y^4 = x^3 e^{1-y/x}$.

38. Letting $y = ux$ we have

$$\left(u^3x^3 + 2ux^3\right)dx - 2x^3(u\,dx + x\,du) = 0$$

$$u^3\,dx - 2x\,du = 0$$

$$\frac{dx}{x} - \frac{2\,du}{u^3} = 0$$

$$\ln|x| + \frac{1}{u^2} = c$$

$$x = c_1 e^{-x^2/y^2}.$$

Using $y(1) = \sqrt{2}$ we find $c_1 = e^{1/2}$. The solution of the initial-value problem is $x = e^{-x^2/y^2 + 1/2}$.

39. Letting $y = ux$ we have

$$\left(x - ux - u^{3/2}x\right)dx + \left(x + \sqrt{u}\,x\right)(u\,dx + x\,du) = 0$$

$$dx + x\left(1 + \sqrt{u}\right)du = 0$$

$$\frac{dx}{x} + \left(1 + \sqrt{u}\right)du = 0$$

$$\ln x + u + \frac{2}{3}u^{3/2} = c$$

$$3x^{3/2}\ln x + 3x^{1/2}y + 2y^{3/2} = c_1 x^{3/2}.$$

25

Using $y(1) = 1$ we find $c_1 = 5$. The solution of the initial-value problem is

$$3x^{3/2} \ln x + 3x^{1/2}y + 2y^{3/2} = 5x^{3/2}.$$

(Note: Since the solution involves $\sqrt{x}$, $x \geq 0$ and we do not need an absolute value sign in $\ln x$.)

40. Letting $x = vy$ we have

$$y(v\, dy + y\, dv) + vy(\ln vy - \ln y - 1)\, dy = 0$$

$$y\, dv + v \ln v\, dy = 0$$

$$\frac{dv}{v \ln v} + \frac{dy}{y} = 0$$

$$\ln |\ln |v|| + \ln |y| = c$$

$$y \ln \left| \frac{x}{y} \right| = c_1.$$

Using $y(1) = e$ we find $c_1 = -e$. The solution of the initial-value problem is $y \ln \left| \dfrac{x}{y} \right| = -e$.

41. Letting $x = vy$ we have

$$y^2(v\, dy + y\, dv) + \left(v^2 y^2 + vy^2 + y^2\right) dy = 0$$

$$y\, dv + (v + 1)^2\, dy = 0$$

$$\frac{dv}{(v + 1)^2} + \frac{dy}{y} = 0$$

$$-\frac{1}{v + 1} + \ln |y| = c$$

$$-\frac{y}{x + y} + \ln |y| = c.$$

Using $y(0) = 1$ we find $c = -1$. The solution of the initial-value problem is

$$(x + y) \ln |y| = y - (x + y) \quad \text{or} \quad (x + y) \ln |y| = -x.$$

26

42. Letting $y = ux$ we have

$$\left(\sqrt{x} + \sqrt{ux}\right)^2 dx - x(u\,dx + x\,du) = 0$$

$$\left(1 + 2\sqrt{u}\right) dx - x\,du = 0$$

$$\frac{dx}{x} - \frac{du}{1 + 2\sqrt{u}} = 0$$

$$\ln|x| = \int \frac{du}{1 + 2\sqrt{u}} \qquad \boxed{u = t^2, \ du = 2t\,dt}$$

$$= \int \frac{2t}{1 + 2t}\,dt = t - \frac{1}{2}\ln|1 + 2t| + c$$

$$= \sqrt{\frac{y}{x}} - \frac{1}{2}\ln\left|1 + 2\sqrt{\frac{y}{x}}\right| + c$$

$$x^2\left(1 + 2\sqrt{\frac{y}{x}}\right) = c_1 e^{2\sqrt{y/x}}$$

$$x^{3/2}\left(\sqrt{x} + 2\sqrt{y}\right) = c_1 e^{2\sqrt{y/x}}.$$

Using $y(1) = 0$ we find $c_1 = 1$. The solution of the initial-value problem is

$$x^{3/2}\left(\sqrt{x} + 2\sqrt{y}\right) = e^{2\sqrt{y/x}}.$$

43. Letting $x = vy$ we have

$$\left(vy + \sqrt{y^2 - vy^2}\right) dy - y(v\,dy + y\,dv) = 0$$

$$\sqrt{1 - v}\,dy - y\,dv = 0$$

$$\frac{dy}{y} - \frac{dv}{\sqrt{1 - v}} = 0$$

$$\ln|y| + 2\sqrt{1 - v} = c$$

$$\ln|y| + 2\sqrt{1 - x/y} = c.$$

Using $y(1/2) = 1$ we find $c = \sqrt{2}$. The solution of the initial-value problem is

$$\ln|y| + 2\sqrt{1 - x/y} = \sqrt{2}.$$

44. Letting $y = ux$ we have

$$x(u\,dx + x\,du) - (ux + x\cosh u)\,dx = 0$$

$$x\,du - \cosh u\,dx = 0$$

$$\operatorname{sech} u\,du - \frac{dx}{x} = 0$$

$$\tan^{-1}(\sinh u) - \ln|x| = c$$

$$\tan^{-1}\left(\sinh\frac{y}{x}\right) - \ln|x| = c.$$

Using $y(1) = 0$ we find $c = 0$. The solution of the initial-value problem is $\tan^{-1}\left(\sinh\frac{y}{x}\right) = \ln|x|$.

45. From $x = vy$ we obtain $dx = v\,dy + y\,dv$ and the differential equation becomes

$$M(vy, y)(v\,dy + y\,dv) + N(vy, y)\,dy = 0.$$

Using $M(vy, y) = y^n M(v, 1)$ and $N(vy, y) = y^2 N(v, 1)$ and simplifying we have

$$y^n M(v, 1)(v\,dy + y\,dv) + y^n N(v, 1)\,dy = 0$$

$$[vM(v, 1) + N(v, 1)]\,dy + yM(v, 1)\,dv = 0$$

$$\frac{dy}{y} + \frac{M(v, 1)\,dv}{vM(v, 1) + N(v, 1)} = 0.$$

46. From $x = r\cos\theta$ and $y = r\sin\theta$ we obtain $dx = \cos\theta\,dr - r\sin\theta\,d\theta$ and $dy = \sin\theta\,dr + r\cos\theta\,d\theta$. Using

$$M(x, y) = M(r\cos\theta, r\sin\theta) = r^n M(\cos\theta, \sin\theta)$$

and

$$N(x, y) = N(r\cos\theta, r\sin\theta) = r^n N(\cos\theta, \sin\theta)$$

the differential equation becomes

$$r^n M(\cos\theta, \sin\theta)(\cos\theta\,dr - r\sin\theta\,d\theta) + r^n N(\cos\theta, \sin\theta)(\sin\theta\,dr + r\cos\theta\,d\theta) = 0.$$

Simplifying we have

$$[M(\cos\theta, \sin\theta)\cos\theta + N(\cos\theta, \sin\theta)\sin\theta]\,dr - [rM(\cos\theta, \sin\theta)\sin\theta - rN(\cos\theta, \sin\theta)\cos\theta]\cdot d\theta = 0$$

$$\frac{dr}{r} - \frac{M(\cos\theta, \sin\theta)\sin\theta - rN(\cos\theta, \sin\theta)\cos\theta}{M(\cos\theta, \sin\theta)\cos\theta + N(\cos\theta, \sin\theta)\sin\theta}\,d\theta = 0.$$

47. Using $M(x,y) = y^n M\left(\dfrac{x}{y}, 1\right)$ and $N(x,y) = y^n M\left(\dfrac{x}{y}, 1\right)$ we obtain

$$y^n M\left(\frac{x}{y}, 1\right) dx + y^n N\left(\frac{x}{y}, 1\right) dy = 0$$

$$M\left(\frac{x}{y}, 1\right) + N\left(\frac{x}{y}, 1\right)\frac{dy}{dx} = 0$$

or $\quad \dfrac{dy}{dx} = -\dfrac{M(x/y, 1)}{N(x/y, 1)} = G\left(\dfrac{x}{y}\right).$

48. If we let $u = y/x$, then by homogeneity $f(x,y) = x^n f\left(1, \dfrac{y}{x}\right) = x^n f(1, u)$. Using the chain rule for partial derivatives, we obtain

$$\frac{\partial f(x,y)}{\partial x} = x^n \frac{\partial f(1,u)}{\partial u}\frac{\partial u}{\partial x} + nx^{n-1}f(1,u) = x^n \frac{\partial f(1,u)}{\partial u}\left(-\frac{y}{x^2}\right) + nx^{n-1}f(1,u)$$

$$= -yx^{n-2}\frac{\partial f(1,u)}{\partial u} + nx^{n-1}f(1,u)$$

and

$$\frac{\partial f(x,y)}{\partial y} = x^n\frac{\partial f(1,u)}{\partial u}\frac{\partial u}{\partial y} = x^n\frac{\partial f(1,u)}{\partial u}\left(\frac{1}{x}\right) = x^{n-1}\frac{\partial f(1,u)}{\partial u}.$$

Then

$$x\frac{\partial f}{\partial x} + y\frac{\partial f}{\partial y} = -yx^{n-1}\frac{\partial f(1,u)}{\partial u} + nx^n f(1,u) + yx^{n-1}\frac{\partial f(1,u)}{\partial u}$$

$$= nx^n f(1,u) = nx^n f\left(1, \frac{y}{x}\right) = nf(x,y).$$

Exercises 2.4

1. Let $M = 2x - 1$ and $N = 3y + 7$ so that $M_y = 0 = N_x$. From $f_x = 2x - 1$ we obtain $f = x^2 - x + h(y)$, $h'(y) = 3y + 7$, and $h(y) = \dfrac{3}{2}y^2 + 7y$. The solution is $x^2 - x + \dfrac{3}{2}y^2 + 7y = c$.

2. Let $M = 2x + y$ and $N = -x - 6y$. Then $M_y = 1$ and $N_x = -1$, so the equation is not exact.

3. Let $M = 5x + 4y$ and $N = 4x - 8y^3$ so that $M_y = 4 = N_x$. From $f_x = 5x + 4y$ we obtain $f = \dfrac{5}{2}x^2 + 4xy + h(y)$, $h'(y) = -8y^3$, and $h(y) = -2y^4$. The solution is $\dfrac{5}{2}x^2 + 4xy - 2y^4 = c$.

4. Let $M = \sin y - y\sin x$ and $N = \cos x + x\cos y - y$ so that $M_y = \cos y - \sin x = N_x$. From $f_x = \sin y - y\sin x$ we obtain $f = x\sin y + y\cos x + h(y)$, $h'(y) = -y$, and $h(y) = \dfrac{1}{2}y^2$. The solution is $x\sin y + y\cos x - \dfrac{1}{2}y^2 = c$.

29

5. Let $M = 2y^2x - 3$ and $N = 2yx^2 + 4$ so that $M_y = 4xy = N_x$. From $f_x = 2y^2x - 3$ we obtain $f = x^2y^2 - 3x + h(y)$, $h'(y) = 4$, and $h(y) = 4y$. The solution is $x^2y^2 - 3x + 4y = c$.

6. Let $M = 4x^3 - 3y\sin 3x - y/x^2$ and $N = 2y - 1/x + \cos 3x$ so that $M_y = -3\sin 3x - 1/x^2$ and $N_x = 1/x^2 - 3\sin 3x$. The equation is not exact.

7. Let $M = x^2 - y^2$ and $N = x^2 - 2xy$ so that $M_y = -2y$ and $N_x = 2x - 2y$. The equation is not exact.

8. Let $M = 1 + \ln x + y/x$ and $N = -1 + \ln x$ so that $M_y = 1/x = N_x$. From $f_y = -1 + \ln x$ we obtain $f = -y + y\ln x + h(y)$, $h'(x) = 1 + \ln x$, and $h(y) = x\ln x$. The solution is $-y + y\ln x + x\ln x = c$.

9. Let $M = y^3 - y^2\sin x - x$ and $N = 3xy^2 + 2y\cos x$ so that $M_y = 3y^2 - 2y\sin x = N_x$. From $f_x = y^3 - y^2\sin x - x$ we obtain $f = xy^3 + y^2\cos x - \frac{1}{2}x^2 + h(y)$, $h'(y) = 0$, and $h(y) = 0$. The solution is $xy^3 + y^2\cos x - \frac{1}{2}x^2 = c$.

10. Let $M = x^3 + y^3$ and $N = 3xy^2$ so that $M_y = 3y^2 = N_x$. From $f_x = x^3 + y^3$ we obtain $f = \frac{1}{4}x^4 + xy^3 + h(y)$, $h'(y) = 0$, and $h(y) = 0$. The solution is $\frac{1}{4}x^4 + xy^3 = c$.

11. Let $M = y\ln y - e^{-xy}$ and $N = 1/y + x\ln y$ so that $M_y = 1 + \ln y + ye^{-xy}$ and $N_x = \ln y$. The equation is not exact.

12. Let $M = 2x/y$ and $N = -x^2/y^2$ so that $M_y = -2x/y^2 = N_x$. From $f_x = 2x/y$ we obtain $f = \frac{x^2}{y} + h(y)$, $h'(y) = 0$, and $h(y) = 0$. The solution is $x^2 = cy$.

13. Let $M = y - 6x^2 - 2xe^x$ and $N = x$ so that $M_y = 1 = N_x$. From $f_x = y - 6x^2 - 2xe^x$ we obtain $f = xy - 2x^3 - 2xe^x + 2e^x + h(y)$, $h'(y) = 0$, and $h(y) = 0$. The solution is $xy - 2x^3 - 2xe^x + 2e^x = c$.

14. Let $M = 3x^2y + e^y$ and $N = x^3 + xe^y - 2y$ so that $M_y = 3x^2 + e^y = N_x$. From $f_x = 3x^2y + e^y$ we obtain $f = x^3y + xe^y + h(y)$, $h'(y) = -2y$, and $h(y) = -y^2$. The solution is $x^3y + xe^y - y^2 = c$.

15. Let $M = 1 - 3/x + y$ and $N = 1 - 3/y + x$ so that $M_y = 1 = N_x$. From $f_x = 1 - 3/x + y$ we obtain $f = x - 3\ln|x| + xy + h(y)$, $h'(y) = 1 - \frac{3}{y}$, and $h(y) = y - 3\ln|y|$. The solution is $x + y + xy - 3\ln|xy| = c$.

16. Let $M = xy^2\sinh x + y^2\cosh x$ and $N = e^y + 2xy\cosh x$ so that $M_y = 2xy\sinh x + 2y\cosh x = N_x$. From $f_y = e^y + 2xy\cosh x$ we obtain $f = e^y + xy^2\cosh x + h(y)$, $h'(y) = 0$, and $h(y) = 0$. The solution is $e^y + xy^2\cosh x = c$.

17. Let $M = x^2y^3 - 1/\left(1 + 9x^2\right)$ and $N = x^3y^2$ so that $M_y = 3x^2y^2 = N_x$. From $f_x = x^2y^3 - 1/\left(1 + 9x^2\right)$ we obtain $f = \frac{1}{3}x^3y^3 - \frac{1}{3}\arctan(3x) + h(y)$, $h'(y) = 0$, and $h(y) = 0$. The solution is $x^3y^3 - \arctan(3x) = c$.

18. Let $M = -2y$ and $N = 5y - 2x$ so that $M_y = -2 = N_x$. From $f_x = -2y$ we obtain $f = -2xy + h(y)$, $h'(y) = 5y$, and $h(y) = \dfrac{5}{2}y^2$. The solution is $-2xy + \dfrac{5}{2}y^2 = c$.

19. Let $M = \tan x - \sin x \sin y$ and $N = \cos x \cos y$ so that $M_y = -\sin x \cos y = N_x$. From $f_x = \tan x - \sin x \sin y$ we obtain $f = \ln|\sec x| + \cos x \sin y + h(y)$, $h'(y) = 0$, and $h(y) = 0$. The solution is $\ln|\sec x| + \cos x \sin y = c$.

20. Let $M = 3x \cos 3x + \sin 3x - 3$ and $N = 2y + 5$ so that $M_y = 0 = N_x$. From $f_x = 3x \cos 3x + \sin 3x - 3$ we obtain $f = x \sin 3x - 3x + h(y)$, $h'(y) = 2y + 5$, and $h(y) = y^2 + 5y$. The solution is $x \sin 3x - 3x + y^2 + 5y = c$.

21. Let $M = 4x^3 + 4xy$ and $N = 2x^2 + 2y - 1$ so that $M_y = 4x = N_x$. From $f_x = 4x^3 + 4xy$ we obtain $f = x^4 + 2x^2 y + h(y)$, $h'(y) = 2y - 1$, and $h(y) = y^2 - y$. The solution is $x^4 + 2x^2 y + y^2 - y = c$.

22. Let $M = 2y \sin x \cos x - y + 2y^2 e^{xy^2}$ and $N = -x + \sin^2 x + 4xye^{xy^2}$ so that
$$M_y = 2 \sin x \cos x - 1 + 4xy^3 e^{xy^2} + 4ye^{xy^2} = N_x.$$
From $f_x = 2y \sin x \cos x - y + 2y^2 e^{xy^2}$ we obtain $f = y \sin^2 x - xy + 2e^{xy^2} + h(y)$, $h'(y) = 0$, and $h(y) = 0$. The solution is $y \sin^2 x - xy + 2e^{xy^2} = c$.

23. Let $M = 4x^3 y - 15x^2 - y$ and $N = x^4 + 3y^2 - x$ so that $M_y = 4x^3 - 1 = N_x$. From $f_x = 4x^3 y - 15x^2 - y$ we obtain $f = x^4 y - 5x^3 - xy + h(y)$, $h'(y) = 3y^2$, and $h(y) = y^3$. The solution is $x^4 y - 5x^3 - xy + y^3 = c$.

24. Let $M = 1/x + 1/x^2 - y/\left(x^2 + y^2\right)$ and $N = ye^y + x/\left(x^2 + y^2\right)$ so that $M_y = \left(y^2 - x^2\right)/\left(x^2 + y^2\right)^2 = N_x$. From $f_x = 1/x + 1/x^2 - y/\left(x^2 + y^2\right)$ we obtain
$$f = \ln|x| - \frac{1}{x} - \arctan\left(\frac{x}{y}\right) + h(y), \quad h'(y) = ye^y, \quad \text{and } h(y) = ye^y - e^y. \text{ The solution is}$$
$$\ln|x| - \frac{1}{x} - \arctan\left(\frac{x}{y}\right) + ye^y - e^y = c.$$

25. Let $M = x^2 + 2xy + y^2$ and $N = 2xy + x^2 - 1$ so that $M_y = 2(x + y) = N_x$. From $f_x = x^2 + 2xy + y^2$ we obtain $f = \dfrac{1}{3}x^3 + x^2 y + xy^2 + h(y)$, $h'(y) = -1$, and $h(y) = -y$. The general solution is $\dfrac{1}{3}x^3 + x^2 y + xy^2 - y = c$. If $y(1) = 1$ then $c = 4/3$ and the solution of the initial-value problem is $\dfrac{1}{3}x^3 + x^2 y + xy^2 - y = \dfrac{4}{3}$.

26. Let $M = e^x + y$ and $N = 2 + x + ye^y$ so that $M_y = 1 = N_x$. From $f_x = e^x + y$ we obtain $f = e^x + xy + h(y)$, $h'(y) = 2 + ye^y$, and $h(y) = 2y + ye^y - y$. The general solution is $e^x + xy + 2y + ye^y - e^y = c$. If $y(0) = 1$ then $c = 3$ and the solution of the initial-value problem is $e^x + xy + 2y + ye^y - e^y = 3$.

27. Let $M = 4y + 2x - 5$ and $N = 6y + 4x - 1$ so that $M_y = 4 = N_x$. From $f_x = 4y + 2x - 5$ we obtain $f = 4xy + x^2 - 5x + h(y)$, $h'(y) = 6y - 1$, and $h(y) = 3y^2 - y$. The general solution is $4xy + x^2 - 5x + 3y^2 - y = c$. If $y(-1) = 2$ then $c = 8$ and the solution of the initial-value problem is $4xy + x^2 - 5x + 3y^2 - y = 8$.

28. Let $M = x/2y^4$ and $N = (3y^2 - x^2)/y^5$ so that $M_y = -2x/y^5 = N_x$. From $f_x = x/2y^4$ we obtain
$$f = \frac{x^2}{4y^4} + h(y), \quad h'(y) = \frac{3}{y^3}, \quad \text{and } h(y) = -\frac{3}{2y^2}. \quad \text{The general solution is } \frac{x^2}{4y^4} - \frac{3}{2y^2} = c. \text{ If } y(1) = 1$$
then $c = -5/4$ and the solution of the initial-value problem is $\dfrac{x^2}{4y^4} - \dfrac{3}{2y^2} = -\dfrac{5}{4}$.

29. Let $M = y^2 \cos x - 3x^2 y - 2x$ and $N = 2y \sin x - x^3 + \ln y$ so that $M_y = 2y \cos x - 3x^2 = N_x$. From $f_x = y^2 \cos x - 3x^2 y - 2x$ we obtain $f = y^2 \sin x - x^3 y - x^2 + h(y)$, $h'(y) = \ln y$, and $h(y) = y \ln y - y$. The general solution is $y^2 \sin x - x^3 y - x^2 + y \ln y - y = c$. If $y(0) = e$ then $c = 0$ and the solution of the initial-value problem is $y^2 \sin x - x^3 y - x^2 + y \ln y - y = 0$.

30. Let $M = y^2 + y \sin x$ and $N = 2xy - \cos x - 1/(1 + y^2)$ so that $M_y = 2y + \sin x = N_x$. From $f_x = y^2 + y \sin x$ we obtain $f = xy^2 - y \cos x + h(y)$, $h'(y) = \dfrac{-1}{1 + y^2}$, and $h(y) = -\tan^{-1} y$. The general solution is $xy^2 - y \cos x - \tan^{-1} y = c$. If $y(0) = 1$ then $c = -1 - \pi/4$ and the solution of the initial-value problem is $xy^2 - y \cos x - \tan^{-1} y = -1 - \dfrac{\pi}{4}$.

31. Equating $M_y = 3y^2 + 4kxy^3$ and $N_x = 3y^2 + 40xy^3$ we obtain $k = 10$.

32. Equating $M_y = -xy \cos xy - \sin xy + 4ky^3$ and $N_x = -20y^3 - xy \cos xy - \sin xy$ we obtain $k = -5$.

33. Equating $M_y = 4xy + e^x$ and $N_x = 4xy + ke^x$ we obtain $k = 1$.

34. Equating $M_y = 18xy^2 - \sin y$ and $N_x = 2kxy^2 - \sin y$ we obtain $k = 9$.

35. Since $f_y = N(x, y) = xe^{xy} + 2xy + 1/x$ we obtain $f = e^{xy} + xy^2 + \dfrac{y}{x} + h(x)$ so that $f_x = ye^{xy} + y^2 - \dfrac{y}{x^2} + h'(x)$. Let $M(x, y) = ye^{xy} + y^2 - \dfrac{y}{x^2}$.

36. Since $f_x = M(x, y) = y^{1/2} x^{-1/2} + x (x^2 + y)^{-1}$ we obtain $f = 2y^{1/2} x^{1/2} + \dfrac{1}{2} \ln |x^2 + y| + h(x)$ so that $f_y = y^{-1/2} x^{1/2} + \dfrac{1}{2} (x^2 + y)^{-1} + h'(x)$. Let $N(x, y) = y^{-1/2} x^{1/2} + \dfrac{1}{2} (x^2 + y)^{-1}$.

37. Let $M = 6xy^3$ and $N = 4y^3 + 9x^2 y^2$ so that $M_y = 18xy^2 = N_x$. From $f_x = 6xy^3$ we obtain $f = 3x^2 y^3 + h(y)$, $h'(y) = 4y^3$, and $h(y) = y^4$. The solution of the differential equation is $3x^2 y^3 + y^4 = c$.

38. Let $M = -y/x^2$ and $N = 1/y + 1/x$ so that $M_y = -1/x^2 = N_x$. From $f_x = -y/x^2$ we obtain $f = \dfrac{y}{x} + h(y)$, $h'(y) = \dfrac{1}{y}$, and $h(y) = \ln y$. The solution of the differential equation is $\dfrac{y}{x} + \ln |y| = c$.

39. Let $M = -x^2y^2 \sin x + 2xy^2 \cos x$ and $N = 2x^2y \cos x$ so that $M_y = -2x^2y \sin x + 4xy \cos x = N_x$. From $f_y = 2x^2y \cos x$ we obtain $f = x^2y^2 \cos x + h(y)$, $h'(y) = 0$, and $h(y) = 0$. The solution of the differential equation is $x^2y^2 \cos x = c$.

40. Let $M = xye^x + y^2e^x + ye^x$ and $N = xe^x + 2ye^x$ so that $M_y = xe^x + 2ye^x + e^x = N_x$. From $f_y = xe^x + 2ye^x$ we obtain $f = xye^x + y^2e^x + h(x)$, $h'(y) = 0$, and $h(y) = 0$. The solution of the differential equation is $xye^x + y^2e^x = c$.

41. Let $M = 2xy^2 + 3x^2$ and $N = 2x^2y$ so that $M_y = 4xy = N_x$. From $f_x = 2xy^2 + 3x^2$ we obtain $f = x^2y^2 + x^3 + h(y)$, $h'(y) = 0$, and $h(y) = 0$. The solution of the differential equation is $x^2y^2 + x^3 = c$.

42. Let $M = \left(x^2 + 2xy - y^2\right) / \left(x^2 + 2xy + y^2\right)$ and $N = \left(y^2 + 2xy - x^2\right) / \left(y^2 + 2xy + x^2\right)$ so that $M_y = -4xy/(x+y)^3 = N_x$. From $f_x = \left(x^2 + 2xy + y^2 - 2y^2\right)/(x+y)^2$ we obtain

$$f = x + \frac{2y^2}{x+y} + h(y), \quad h'(y) = -1, \text{ and } h(y) = -y. \text{ The solution of the differential equation is}$$

$x^2 + y^2 = c(x+y)$.

43. Identifying $M = -g(x)$ and $N = h(y)$ we see that exactness follows from $M_y = 0 = N_x$.

──── Exercises 2.5 ────

1. For $y' - 5y = 0$ an integrating factor is $e^{-\int 5dx} = e^{-5x}$ so that $\dfrac{d}{dx}\left[e^{-5x}y\right] = 0$ and $y = ce^{5x}$ for $-\infty < x < \infty$.

2. For $y' + 2y = 0$ an integrating factor is $e^{\int 2dx} = e^{2x}$ so that $\dfrac{d}{dx}\left[e^{2x}y\right] = 0$ and $y = ce^{-2x}$ for $-\infty < x < \infty$.

3. For $y' + 4y = \dfrac{4}{3}$ an integrating factor is $e^{\int 4dx} = e^{4x}$ so that $\dfrac{d}{dx}\left[e^{4x}y\right] = \dfrac{4}{3}e^{4x}$ and $y = \dfrac{1}{3} + ce^{-4x}$ for $-\infty < x < \infty$.

4. For $y' + \dfrac{2}{x}y = 3/x$ an integrating factor is $e^{\int (2/x)dx} = x^2$ so that $\dfrac{d}{dx}\left[x^2y\right] = 3x$ and $y = \dfrac{3}{2} + cx^{-2}$ for $0 < x < \infty$.

5. For $y' + y = e^{3x}$ an integrating factor is $e^{\int dx} = e^x$ so that $\dfrac{d}{dx}[e^xy] = e^{4x}$ and $y = \dfrac{1}{4}e^{3x} + ce^{-x}$ for $-\infty < x < \infty$.

6. For $y' - y = e^x$ an integrating factor is $e^{-\int dx} = e^{-x}$ so that $\dfrac{d}{dx}\left[e^{-x}y\right] = 1$ and $y = xe^x + ce^x$ for $-\infty < x < \infty$.

7. For $y' + 3x^2y = x^2$ an integrating factor is $e^{\int 3x^2 dx} = e^{x^3}$ so that $\dfrac{d}{dx}\left[e^{x^3}y\right] = x^2e^{x^3}$ and $y = \dfrac{1}{3} + ce^{-x^3}$ for $-\infty < x < \infty$.

8. For $y' + 2xy = x^3$ an integrating factor is $e^{\int 2x\,dx} = e^{x^2}$ so that $\dfrac{d}{dx}\left[e^{x^2}y\right] = x^3 e^{x^2}$ and

   $y = \dfrac{1}{2}x^2 - \dfrac{1}{2} + ce^{-x^2}$ for $-\infty < x < \infty$.

9. For $y' + \dfrac{1}{x}y = \dfrac{1}{x^2}$ an integrating factor is $e^{\int(1/x)dx} = x$ so that $\dfrac{d}{dx}[xy] = \dfrac{1}{x}$ and $y = \dfrac{1}{x}\ln x + \dfrac{c}{x}$
   for $0 < x < \infty$.

10. For $y' - 2y = x^2 + 5$ an integrating factor is $e^{-\int 2dx} = e^{-2x}$ so that $\dfrac{d}{dx}\left[e^{-2x}y\right] = x^2 e^{-2x} + 5e^{-2x}$

    and $y = -\dfrac{1}{2}x^2 - \dfrac{1}{2}x - \dfrac{11}{4} + ce^{2x}$ for $-\infty < x < \infty$.

11. For $\dfrac{dx}{dy} + \dfrac{1}{2y}x = -2y$ an integrating factor is $e^{\int(1/2y)dy} = y^{1/2}$ so that $\dfrac{d}{dy}\left[y^{1/2}x\right] = -2y^{3/2}$ and

    $x = -\dfrac{4}{5}y^2 + cy^{-1/2}$ for $0 < y < \infty$.

12. For $\dfrac{dx}{dy} - x = y$ an integrating factor is $e^{-\int dy} = e^{-y}$ so that $\dfrac{d}{dy}\left[e^{-y}x\right] = ye^{-y}$ and $x = -y-1+ce^{y}$

    for $-\infty < y < \infty$.

13. For $y' + \dfrac{1}{x}y = \sin x$ an integrating factor is $e^{\int(1/x)dx} = x$ so that $\dfrac{d}{dx}[xy] = x\sin x$ and

    $y = \dfrac{\sin x}{x} - \cos x + \dfrac{c}{x}$ for $0 < x < \infty$.

14. For $y' + \dfrac{x}{1+x^2}y = -x$ an integrating factor is $e^{\int[x/(1+x^2)]dx} = \sqrt{1+x^2}$ so that

    $\dfrac{d}{dx}\left[\sqrt{1+x^2}\,y\right] = -x\sqrt{1+x^2}$ and $y = -\dfrac{1}{3}\left(1+x^2\right) + c\left(1+x^2\right)^{-1/2}$ for $-\infty < x < \infty$.

15. For $y' + \dfrac{e^x}{1+e^x}y = 0$ an integrating factor is $e^{\int[e^x/(1+e^x)]dx} = 1 + e^x$ so that $\dfrac{d}{dx}[1 + e^x y] = 0$ and

    $y = \dfrac{c}{1+e^x}$ for $-\infty < x < \infty$.

16. For $y' + \dfrac{3x^2}{x^3 - 1}y = 0$ an integrating factor is $e^{\int[3x^2/(x^3-1)]dx} = x^3 - 1$ so that $\dfrac{d}{dx}\left[\left(x^3 - 1\right)y\right] = 0$

    and $y = \dfrac{c}{x^3 - 1}$ for $1 < x < \infty$.

17. For $y' + (\tan x)y = \sec x$ an integrating factor is $e^{\int \tan x\,dx} = \sec x$ so that $\dfrac{d}{dx}[(\sec x)\,y] = \sec^2 x$ and
    $y = \sin x + c\cos x$ for $-\pi/2 < x < \pi/2$.

18. For $y' + (\cot x)y = 2\cos x$ an integrating factor is $e^{\int \cot x\,dx} = \sin x$ so that
    $\dfrac{d}{dx}[(\sin x)\,y] = 2\sin x\cos x$ and $y = \sin x + c\csc x$ for $0 < x < \pi$.

19. For $y' + \dfrac{4}{x}y = x^2 - 1$ an integrating factor is $e^{\int (4/x)dx} = x^4$ so that $\dfrac{d}{dx}\left[x^4 y\right] = x^6 - x^4$ and

$y = \dfrac{1}{7}x^3 - \dfrac{1}{5}x + cx^{-4}$ for $0 < x < \infty$.

20. For $y' - \dfrac{x}{(1+x)}y = x$ an integrating factor is $e^{-\int [x/(1+x)]dx} = (x+1)e^{-x}$ so that

$\dfrac{d}{dx}\left[(x+1)e^{-x}y\right] = x(x+1)e^{-x}$ and $y = -x - \dfrac{2x+3}{x+1} + \dfrac{ce^x}{x+1}$ for $-1 < x < \infty$

21. For $y' + \left(1 + \dfrac{2}{x}\right)y = \dfrac{e^x}{x^2}$ an integrating factor is $e^{\int [1+(2/x)]dx} = x^2 e^x$ so that $\dfrac{d}{dx}\left[x^2 e^x y\right] = e^{2x}$ and

$y = \dfrac{1}{2}\dfrac{e^x}{x^2} + \dfrac{ce^{-x}}{x^2}$ for $0 < x < \infty$.

22. For $y' + \left(1 + \dfrac{1}{x}\right)y = \dfrac{1}{x}e^{-x}\sin 2x$ an integrating factor is $e^{\int [1+(1/x)]dx} = xe^x$ so that

$\dfrac{d}{dx}\left[xe^x y\right] = \sin 2x$ and $xe^x y = -\dfrac{1}{2}\cos 2x + c$ for $0 < x < \infty$.

23. For $y' + (\cot x)y = \sec^2 x \csc x$ an integrating factor is $e^{\int \cot x dx} = \sin x$ so that $\dfrac{d}{dx}\left[(\sin x)\,y\right] = \sec^2 x$

and $y = \sec x + c\csc x$ for $0 < x < \pi/2$.

24. For $y' + \dfrac{2\sin x}{(1-\cos x)}y = \tan x(1 - \cos x)$ an integrating factor is $e^{\int [2\sin x/(1-\cos x)]dx} = (1 - \cos x)^2$

so that $\dfrac{d}{dx}\left[(1 - \cos x)^2 y\right] = \tan x - \sin x$ and $y(1 - \cos x)^2 = \ln|\sec x| + \cos x + c$ for $0 < x < \pi/2$.

25. For $\dfrac{dx}{dy} + \left(1 + \dfrac{2}{y}\right)x = e^y$ an integrating factor is $e^{\int [1+(2/y)]dy} = y^2 e^y$ so that $\dfrac{d}{dy}\left[y^2 e^y x\right] = y^2 e^{2y}$

and $x = \dfrac{1}{2}e^y - \dfrac{1}{2}\dfrac{e^y}{y} + \dfrac{1}{4}\dfrac{e^y}{y^2} + \dfrac{ce^{-y}}{y^2}$ for $0 < y < \infty$.

26. For $y' - \dfrac{3}{x}y = \dfrac{x^4}{x+1}$ an integrating factor is $e^{-\int (3/x)dx} = x^{-3}$ so that $\dfrac{d}{dx}\left[x^{-3}y\right] = \dfrac{x}{x+1}$ and

$y = x^4 - x^3 \ln|x + 1| + cx^3$ for $-1 < x < \infty$.

27. For $y' + \left(3 + \dfrac{1}{x}\right)y = \dfrac{e^{-3x}}{x}$ an integrating factor is $e^{\int [3+(1/x)]dx} = xe^{3x}$ so that $\dfrac{d}{dx}\left[xe^{3x}y\right] = 1$ and

$y = e^{-3x} + \dfrac{ce^{-3x}}{x}$ for $0 < x < \infty$.

28. For $y' + \dfrac{x+2}{x+1}y = \dfrac{2xe^{-x}}{x+1}$ an integrating factor is $e^{\int [(x+2)/(x+1)]dx} = (x+1)e^x$ so that

$\dfrac{d}{dx}\left[(x+1)e^x y\right] = 2x$ and $(x+1)e^x y = x^2 + c$ for $-1 < x < \infty$.

29. For $\dfrac{dx}{dy} - \dfrac{4}{y}x = 4y^5$ an integrating factor is $e^{-\int (4/y)dy} = y^{-4}$ so that $\dfrac{d}{dy}\left[y^{-4}x\right] = 4y$ and

$x = 2y^6 + cy^4$ for $0 < y < \infty$.

30. For $y' + \dfrac{2}{x}y = \dfrac{1}{x}(e^x + \ln x)$ an integrating factor is $e^{\int (2/x)dx} = x^2$ so that $\dfrac{d}{dx}\left[x^2 y\right] = xe^x + x\ln x$

and $x^2 y = xe^x - e^x + \dfrac{x^2}{2}\ln x - \dfrac{1}{4}x^2 + c$ for $0 < x < \infty$.

31. For $y' + y = \dfrac{1 - e^{-2x}}{e^x + e^{-x}}$ an integrating factor is $e^{\int dx} = e^x$ so that $\dfrac{d}{dx}\left[e^x y\right] = \dfrac{e^x - e^{-x}}{e^x + e^{-x}}$ and

$y = e^{-x}\ln(e^x + e^{-x}) + ce^{-x}$ for $-\infty < x < \infty$.

32. For $y' - y = \sinh x$ an integrating factor is $e^{-\int dx} = e^{-x}$ so that $\dfrac{d}{dx}\left[e^{-x}y\right] = \dfrac{1}{2}\left(1 - e^{-2x}\right)$ and

$y = \dfrac{1}{2}xe^x + \dfrac{1}{4}e^{-x} + ce^x$ for $-\infty < x < \infty$.

33. For $\dfrac{dx}{dy} + \left(2y + \dfrac{1}{y}\right)x = 2$ an integrating factor is $e^{\int [2y + (1/y)]dy} = ye^{y^2}$ so that $\dfrac{d}{dy}\left[ye^{y^2}x\right] = 2ye^{y^2}$

and $x = \dfrac{1}{y} + \dfrac{1}{y}ce^{-y^2}$ for $0 < y < \infty$.

34. For $\dfrac{dx}{dy} + \dfrac{2}{y}x = e^y$ an integrating factor is $e^{\int (2/y)dy} = y^2$ so that $\dfrac{d}{dy}\left[y^2 x\right] = y^2 e^y$ and

$x = e^y - \dfrac{2}{y}e^y + \dfrac{2}{y^2} + \dfrac{c}{y^2}$ for $0 < y < \infty$.

35. For $\dfrac{dr}{d\theta} + r\sec\theta = \cos\theta$ an integrating factor is $e^{\int \sec\theta\, d\theta} = \sec\theta + \tan\theta$ so that

$\dfrac{d}{d\theta}[r(\sec\theta + \tan\theta)] = 1 + \sin\theta$ and $r(\sec\theta + \tan\theta) = \theta - \cos\theta + c$ for $-\pi/2 < \theta < \pi/2$.

36. For $\dfrac{dP}{dt} + (2t - 1)P = 4t - 2$ an integrating factor is $e^{\int (2t-1)\,dt} = e^{t^2 - t}$ so that

$\dfrac{d}{dt}\left[Pe^{t^2 - t}\right] = (4t - 2)e^{t^2 - t}$ and $P = 2 + ce^{t - t^2}$ for $-\infty < t < \infty$.

37. For $y' + \dfrac{4}{x + 2}y = \dfrac{5}{(x + 2)^2}$ an integrating factor is $e^{\int [4/(x+2)]dx} = (x + 2)^4$ so that

$\dfrac{d}{dx}\left[(x + 2)^4 y\right] = 5(x + 2)^2$ and $y = \dfrac{5}{3}(x + 2)^{-1} + c(x + 2)^{-4}$ for $-2 < x < \infty$.

38. For $y' + \dfrac{2}{x^2 - 1}y = \dfrac{x + 1}{x - 1}$ an integrating factor is $e^{\int [2/(x^2 - 1)]dx} = \dfrac{x - 1}{x + 1}$ so that $\dfrac{d}{dx}\left[\dfrac{x - 1}{x + 1}y\right] = 1$
and $(x - 1)y = x(x + 1) + c(x + 1)$ for $-1 < x < 1$.

39. For $y' + (\cosh x)y = 10\cosh x$ an integrating factor is $e^{\int \cosh x\,dx} = e^{\sinh x}$ so that

$\dfrac{d}{dx}\left[e^{\sinh x}y\right] = 10(\cosh x)e^{\sinh x}$ and $y = 10 + ce^{-\sinh x}$ for $-\infty < x < \infty$.

40. For $\dfrac{dx}{dy} + 2x = 3e^y$ an integrating factor is $e^{\int 2dy} = e^{2y}$ so that $\dfrac{d}{dy}\left[e^{2y}x\right] = 3e^{3y}$ and $x = e^y + ce^{-2y}$

for $-\infty < y < \infty$.

41. For $y' + 5y = 20$ an integrating factor is $e^{\int 5dx} = e^{5x}$ so that $\dfrac{d}{dx}\left[e^{5x}y\right] = 20e^{5x}$ and $y = 4 + ce^{-5x}$

for $-\infty < x < \infty$. If $y(0) = 2$ then $c = -2$ and $y = 4 - 2e^{-5x}$.

42. For $y' - 2y = x\left(e^{3x} - e^{2x}\right)$ an integrating factor is $e^{-\int 2dx} = e^{-2x}$ so that $\dfrac{d}{dx}\left[e^{-2x}y\right] = xe^x - x$

and $y = xe^{3x} - e^{3x} - \frac{1}{2}x^2e^{2x} + ce^{2x}$ for $-\infty < x < \infty$. If $y(0) = 2$ then $c = 3$ and

$y = xe^{3x} - e^{3x} - \dfrac{1}{2}x^2e^{2x} + 3e^{2x}$.

43. For $\dfrac{di}{dt} + \dfrac{R}{L}i = \dfrac{E}{L}$ an integrating factor is $e^{\int (R/L)\,dt} = e^{Rt/L}$ so that $\dfrac{d}{dt}\left[ie^{Rt/L}\right] = \dfrac{E}{L}e^{Rt/L}$ and

$i = \dfrac{E}{R} + ce^{-Rt/L}$ for $-\infty < t < \infty$. If $i(0) = i_0$ then $c = i_0 - E/R$ and $i = \dfrac{E}{R} + \left(i_0 - \dfrac{E}{R}\right)e^{-Rt/L}$.

44. For $\dfrac{dx}{dy} - \dfrac{1}{y}x = 2y$ an integrating factor is $e^{-\int (1/y)dy} = \dfrac{1}{y}$ so that $\dfrac{d}{dy}\left[\dfrac{1}{y}x\right] = 2$ and $x = 2y^2 + cy$

for $0 < y < \infty$. If $y(1) = 5$ then $c = -49/5$ and $x = 2y^2 - \dfrac{49}{5}y$.

45. For $y' + (\tan x)y = \cos^2 x$ an integrating factor is $e^{\int \tan x dx} = \sec x$ so that $\dfrac{d}{dx}\left[(\sec x)\,y\right] = \cos x$ and

$y = \sin x \cos x + c \cos x$ for $-\pi/2 < x < \pi/2$. If $y(0) = -1$ then $c = -1$ and $y = \sin x \cos x - \cos x$.

46. For $\dfrac{dQ}{dx} - 5x^4 Q = 0$ an integrating factor is $e^{-\int 5x^4\,dx} = e^{-x^5}$ so that $\dfrac{d}{dx}\left[e^{-x^5}Q\right] = 0$ and $Q = ce^{x^5}$

for $-\infty < x < \infty$. If $Q(0) = -7$ then $c = -7$ and $Q = -7e^{x^5}$.

47. For $\dfrac{dT}{dt} - kT = -50k$ an integrating factor is $e^{\int (-k)\,dt} = e^{-kt}$ so that $\dfrac{d}{dt}\left[Te^{-kt}\right] = -50ke^{-kt}$ and

$T = 50 + ce^{kt}$ for $-\infty < t < \infty$. If $T(0) = 150$ then $c = 150$ and $T = 50 + 150e^{kt}$.

48. For $y' + \left(1 + \dfrac{2}{x}\right)y = \dfrac{2}{x}e^{-x}$ an integrating factor is $e^{\int (1+2/x)dx} = x^2 e^x$ so that $\dfrac{d}{dx}\left[x^2e^xy\right] = 2x$

and $y = e^{-x} + \dfrac{c}{x^2}e^{-x}$ for $0 < x < \infty$. If $y(1) = 0$ then $c = -1$ and $y = e^{-x} - \dfrac{1}{x^2}e^{-x}$.

49. For $y' + \dfrac{1}{x+1}y = \dfrac{\ln x}{x+1}$ an integrating factor is $e^{\int [1/(x+1)]dx} = x + 1$ so that $\dfrac{d}{dx}\left[(x+1)\,y\right] = \ln x$

and $y = \dfrac{x}{x+1}\ln x - \dfrac{x}{x+1} + \dfrac{c}{x+1}$ for $0 < x < \infty$. If $y(1) = 10$ then $c = 21$ and

$y = \dfrac{x}{x+1}\ln x - \dfrac{x}{x+1} + \dfrac{21}{x+1}$.

50. For $y' + \dfrac{1}{x}y = \dfrac{1}{x}e^x$ an integrating factor is $e^{\int (1/x)dx} = x$ so that $\dfrac{d}{dx}\left[xy\right] = e^x$ and $y = \dfrac{1}{x}e^x + \dfrac{c}{x}$

for $0 < x < \infty$. If $y(1) = 2$ then $c = 2 - e$ and $y = \dfrac{1}{x}e^x + \dfrac{2-e}{x}$.

51. For $y' + \dfrac{2}{x(x-2)}y = 0$ an integrating factor is $e^{\int [2/x(x-2)]dx} = \dfrac{x-2}{x}$ so that $\dfrac{d}{dx}\left[\dfrac{x-2}{x}y\right] = 0$ and

$(x-2)y = cx$ for $2 < x < \infty$. If $y(3) = 6$ then $c = 2$ and $y = \dfrac{2x}{x-2}$.

52. For $y' + (\cot x)y = 0$ an integrating factor is $e^{\int \cot x\, dx} = \sin x$ so that $\dfrac{d}{dx}[(\sin x)\,y] = 0$ and

$y = c \csc x$ for $-\pi < x < 0$. If $y(-\pi/2) = 1$ then $c = -1$ and $y = -\csc x$.

53. For $\dfrac{dx}{dy} + \dfrac{1}{y}x = 1$ an integrating factor is $e^{\int(1/y)dy} = y$ so that $\dfrac{d}{dy}[yx] = y$ and $x = \dfrac{1}{2}y + \dfrac{c}{y}$ for

$0 < y < \infty$. If $y(5) = 2$ then $c = 8$ and $x = \dfrac{1}{2}y + \dfrac{8}{y}$.

54. For $y' + \left(\sec^2 x\right)y = \sec^2 x$ an integrating factor is $e^{\int (\sec^2 x)dx} = e^{\tan x}$ so that

$\dfrac{d}{dx}\left[e^{\tan x}y\right] = \sec^2 x\, e^{\tan x}$ and $y = 1 + ce^{-\tan x}$ for $-\pi/2 < x < \pi/2$. If $y(0) = -3$ then $c = -4$ and

$y = 1 - 4e^{-\tan x}$.

55. For $y' + 2y = f(x)$ an integrating factor is e^{2x} so that

$$ye^{2x} = \begin{cases} \frac{1}{2}e^{2x} + c_1, & 0 \le x \le 3; \\ c_2, & x > 3. \end{cases}$$

If $y(0) = 0$ then $c_1 = -1/2$ and for continuity we must have $c_2 = \frac{1}{2}e^6 - \frac{1}{2}$ so that

$$y = \begin{cases} \frac{1}{2}\left(1 - e^{-2x}\right), & 0 \le x \le 3; \\ \frac{1}{2}\left(e^6 - 1\right)e^{-2x}, & x > 3. \end{cases}$$

56. For $y' + y = f(x)$ an integrating factor is e^x so that

$$ye^x = \begin{cases} e^x + c_1, & 0 \le x \le 1; \\ -e^x + c_2, & x > 1. \end{cases}$$

If $y(0) = 1$ then $c_1 = 0$ and for continuity we must have $c_2 = 2e$ so that

$$y = \begin{cases} 1, & 0 \le x \le 1; \\ 2e^{1-x} - 1, & x > 1. \end{cases}$$

57. For $y' + 2xy = f(x)$ an integrating factor is e^{x^2} so that

$$ye^{x^2} = \begin{cases} \frac{1}{2}e^{x^2} + c_1, & 0 \le x < 1; \\ c_2, & x \ge 1. \end{cases}$$

38

If $y(0) = 2$ then $c_1 = 3/2$ and for continuity we must have $c_2 = \dfrac{1}{2}e + \dfrac{3}{2}$ so that

$$y = \begin{cases} \frac{1}{2} + \frac{3}{2}e^{-x^2}, & 0 \le x < 1; \\ \left(\frac{1}{2}e + \frac{3}{2}\right)e^{-x^2}, & x \ge 1. \end{cases}$$

58. For
$$y' + \frac{2x}{1+x^2}y = \begin{cases} \frac{x}{1+x^2}, & 0 \le x < 1; \\ \frac{-x}{1+x^2}, & x \ge 1 \end{cases}$$

an integrating factor is $1 + x^2$ so that

$$\left(1 + x^2\right)y = \begin{cases} \frac{1}{2}x^2 + c_1, & 0 \le x < 1; \\ -\frac{1}{2}x^2 + c_2, & x \ge 1. \end{cases}$$

If $y(0) = 0$ then $c_1 = 0$ and for continuity we must have $c_2 = 1$ so that

$$y = \begin{cases} \frac{1}{2} - \frac{1}{2(1+x^2)}, & 0 \le x < 1; \\ \frac{3}{2(1+x^2)} - \frac{1}{2}, & x \ge 1. \end{cases}$$

—————— **Exercises 2.6** ——————

1. From $y' + \dfrac{1}{x}y = \dfrac{1}{x}y^{-2}$ and $w = y^3$ we obtain $\dfrac{dw}{dx} + \dfrac{3}{x}w = \dfrac{3}{x}$. An integrating factor is x^3 so that $x^3 w = x^3 + c$ or $y^3 = 1 + cx^{-3}$.

2. From $y' - y = e^x y^2$ and $w = y^{-1}$ we obtain $\dfrac{dw}{dx} + w = -e^x$. An integrating factor is e^x so that $e^x w = -\dfrac{1}{2}e^{2x} + c$ or $y^{-1} = -\dfrac{1}{2}e^x + ce^{-x}$.

3. From $y' + y = xy^4$ and $w = y^{-3}$ we obtain $\dfrac{dw}{dx} - 3w = -3x$. An integrating factor is e^{-3x} so that $e^{-3x} = xe^{-3x} + \dfrac{1}{3}e^{-3x} + c$ or $y^{-3} = x + \dfrac{1}{3} + ce^{3x}$.

4. From $y' - \left(1 + \dfrac{1}{x}\right)y = y^2$ and $w = y^{-1}$ we obtain $\dfrac{dw}{dx} + \left(1 + \dfrac{1}{x}\right)w = -1$. An integrating factor is xe^x so that $xe^x w = -xe^x + e^x + c$ or $y^{-1} = -1 + \dfrac{1}{x} + \dfrac{c}{x}e^{-x}$.

5. From $y' - \dfrac{1}{x}y = -\dfrac{1}{x^2}y^2$ and $w = y^{-1}$ we obtain $\dfrac{dw}{dx} + \dfrac{1}{x}w = \dfrac{1}{x^2}$. An integrating factor is x so that $xw = \ln x + c$ or $y^{-1} = \dfrac{1}{x}\ln x + \dfrac{c}{x}$.

6. From $y' + \dfrac{2}{3(1+x^2)}y = \dfrac{2x}{3(1+x^2)}y^4$ and $w = y^{-3}$ we obtain $\dfrac{dw}{dx} - \dfrac{2x}{1+x^2}w = \dfrac{-2x}{1+x^2}$. An integrating factor is $\dfrac{1}{1+x^2}$ so that $\dfrac{w}{1+x^2} = \dfrac{1}{1+x^2} + c$ or $y^{-3} = 1 + c\left(1+x^2\right)$.

7. From $y' - \dfrac{2}{x}y = \dfrac{3}{x^2}y^4$ and $w = y^{-3}$ we obtain $\dfrac{dw}{dx} + \dfrac{6}{x}w = -\dfrac{9}{x^2}$. An integrating factor is x^6 so that $x^6 w = -\dfrac{9}{5}x^5 + c$ or $y^{-3} = -\dfrac{9}{5}x^{-1} + cx^{-6}$. If $y(1) = \dfrac{1}{2}$ then $c = \dfrac{49}{5}$ and $y^{-3} = -\dfrac{9}{5}x^{-1} + \dfrac{49}{5}x^{-6}$.

8. From $y' + y = y^{-1/2}$ and $w = y^{3/2}$ we obtain $\dfrac{dw}{dx} + \dfrac{3}{2}w = \dfrac{3}{2}$. An integrating factor is $e^{3x/2}$ so that $e^{3x/2}w = e^{3x/2} + c$ or $y^{3/2} = 1 + ce^{-3x/2}$. If $y(0) = 4$ then $c = 7$ and $y^{3/2} = 1 + 7e^{-3x/2}$.

9. From $\dfrac{dx}{dy} - yx = y^3 x^2$ and $w = x^{-1}$ we obtain $\dfrac{dw}{dy} + yx = -y^3$. An integrating factor is $e^{y^2/2}$ so that $e^{y^2/2}w = -ye^{y^2/2} + 2e^{y^2/2} + c$ or $x^{-1} = 2 - y^2 + ce^{-y^2/2}$. If $y(1) = 0$ then $c = -1$ and $x^{-1} = 2 - y^2 - e^{-y^2/2}$.

10. From $y' - \dfrac{1}{2x}y = -\dfrac{x}{2}y^{-2}$ and $w = y^3$ we obtain $\dfrac{dw}{dx} - \dfrac{3}{2x}w = -\dfrac{3}{2}x$. An integrating factor is $x^{-3/2}$ so that $x^{-3/2}w = -3x^{1/2} + c$ or $y^3 = -3x^2 + cx^{3/2}$. If $y(1) = 1$ then $c = 4$ and $y^3 = -3x^2 + 4x^{3/2}$.

11. Identify $P(x) = -2$, $Q(x) = -1$, and $R(x) = 1$. Then $\dfrac{dw}{dx} + (-1+4)w = -1$. An integrating factor is e^{3x} so that $e^{3x}w = -\dfrac{1}{3}e^{3x} + c$ or $u = \dfrac{1}{ce^{-3x} - 1/3}$. Thus, $y = 2 + u$.

12. Identify $P(x) = 1 - x$, $Q(x) = -1$, and $R(x) = x$. Then $\dfrac{dw}{dx} + (-1 + 2x)w = -x$. An integrating factor is $e^{x^2 - x}$ so that $e^{x^2-x}w = -\int xe^{x^2-x}dx + c$ or $u = \dfrac{-e^{x^2-x}}{\int xe^{x^2-x}dx + c}$. Thus, $y = 1 + u$.

13. Identify $P(x) = -4/x^2$, $Q(x) = -1/x$, and $R(x) = 1$. Then $\dfrac{dw}{dx} + \left(-\dfrac{1}{x} + \dfrac{4}{x}\right)w = -1$. An integrating factor is x^3 so that $x^3 w = -\dfrac{1}{4}x^4 + c$ or $u = \left[-\dfrac{1}{4}x + cx^{-3}\right]^{-1}$. Thus, $y = \dfrac{2}{x} + u$.

14. Identify $P(x) = 2x^2$, $Q(x) = 1/x$, and $R(x) = -2$. Then $\dfrac{dw}{dx} + \left(\dfrac{1}{x} - 4x\right)w = 2$. An integrating factor is xe^{-2x^2} so that $xe^{-2x^2}w = -\dfrac{1}{2}e^{-2x^2} + c$ or $u = \left[-\dfrac{1}{2x} + \dfrac{c}{x}e^{2x^2}\right]^{-1}$. Thus, $y = x + u$.

15. Identify $P(x) = e^{2x}$, $Q(x) = 1 + 2e^x$, and $R(x) = 1$. Then $\dfrac{dw}{dx} + (1 + 2e^x - 2e^x)w = -1$. An integrating factor is e^x so that $e^x w = -e^x + c$ or $u = \dfrac{1}{ce^{-x} - 1}$. Thus, $y = -e^x + u$.

16. Identify $P(x) = \sec^2 x$, $Q(x) = -\tan x$, and $R(x) = 1$. Then $\dfrac{dw}{dx} + (-\tan x + 2\tan x)w = -1$. An integrating factor is $\sec x$ so that

$$w \sec x = -\ln|\sec x + \tan x| + c \quad \text{or} \quad u = [-\cos x \ln|\sec x + \tan x| + c \cos x]^{-1}.$$

Thus, $y = \tan x + u$.

17. Identify $P(x) = 6$, $Q(x) = 5$, $R(x) = 1$, and $y_1 = -2$. An integrating factor for $\dfrac{dw}{dx} + (5-4)w = -1$

is e^x so that $e^x w = -e^x + c$ or $u = \dfrac{1}{ce^{-x} - 1}$. Thus, $y = -2 + u$.

18. Identify $P(x) = 9$, $Q(x) = 6$, $R(x) = 1$, and $y_1 = -3$. An integrating factor for $\dfrac{dw}{dx} + (6-6)w = -1$

is 1 so that $w = -x + c$ or $u = \dfrac{1}{-x+c}$. Thus, $y = -3 + u$.

19. Let $y = xy' + f(y')$ where $f(t) = 1 - \ln t$. A family of solutions is $y = cx + 1 - \ln c$. The singular
solution is given by $x = t^{-1}$ and $y = 2 - \ln t$ or $y = 2 + \ln x$.

20. Let $y = xy' + f(y')$ where $f(t) = t^{-2}$. A family of solutions is $y = cx + c^{-2}$. The singular solution
is given by $x = 2t^{-3}$ and $y = 3t^{-2}$ or $4y^3 = 27x^2$.

21. Let $y = xy' + f(y')$ where $f(t) = -t^3$. A family of solutions is $y = cx - c^3$. The singular solution
is given by $x = 3t^2$ and $y = 2t^3$ or $27y^2 = 4x^3$.

22. Let $y = xy' + f(y')$ where $f(t) = 4t + t^2$. A family of solutions is $y = cx + 4c + c^2$. The singular
solution is given by $x = -4 - 2t$ and $y = -t^2$ or $y = -\dfrac{1}{4}(x+4)^2$.

23. Let $y = xy' + f(y')$ where $f(t) = -e^t$. A family of solutions is $y = cx - e^c$. The singular solution
is given by $x = e^t$ and $y = -e^t + te^t$ or $y = x \ln x - x$.

24. Let $y = xy' + f(y')$ where $f(t) = \ln t$. A family of solutions is $y = cx + \ln c$. The singular solution
is given by $x = -\dfrac{1}{t}$ and $y = \ln t - 1$ or $y = \ln\left(-\dfrac{1}{x}\right) - 1$.

25. Assume that y_1 is a solution of $\dfrac{dy}{dx} = P(x) + Q(x)y + R(x)y^2$ and u is a solution of

$$\frac{du}{dx} - [Q(x) + 2y_1 R(x)]\, u = R(x)u^2.$$

If $y = y_1 + u$ then

$$P(x) + Q(x)(y_1 + u) + R(x)(y_1 + u)^2$$

$$= \left[P(x) + Q(x)y_1 + R(x)y_1^2\right] + \left[Q(x)u + 2y_1 R(x)u + R(x)u^2\right]$$

$$= \frac{dy_1}{dx} + \frac{du}{dx} = \frac{dy}{dx}.$$

26. Assume that $\dfrac{du}{dx} - (Q + 2y_1 R)u = Ru^2$ and let $w = u^{-1}$ so that $\dfrac{dw}{dx} = -u^{-2}\dfrac{du}{dx}$. Multiply the given differential equation by $-u^2$ obtaining $\dfrac{dw}{dx} + (Q + 2y_1 R)w = -R$.

27. If $y' + y^2 - Q(x)y - P(x) = 0$ and $y = \dfrac{w'}{w}$ then $\dfrac{dy}{dx} = \dfrac{ww'' - w'w'}{w^2}$ and $w'' - Q(x)w' - P(x)w = 0$.

28. **(a)** Assume that $F = F(t, s)$ and $F(y - cx, c) = 0$. Then, by the chain rule,

$[F_t(y - cx, c)] (y' - c) = 0$. Assuming $F_t \neq 0$ we have $y' = c$ and

$F(y - xy', y') = F(y - cy, c) = 0$.

   (b) Write the differential equation in the form $(y - xy')^3 + (y')^2 + 5 = 0$. By **(a)** a family of solutions is $(y - cx)^3 + c^2 + 5 = 0$.

29. If $y = cx + f(c)$ then $y' = c$ and substituting into the differential equation $y = xy' + f(y')$ we obtain the identity $cx + f(c) = y = xy' + f(y') = xc + f(c)$.

30. From $x = -f'(t)$ and $y = f(t) - tf'(t)$ we obtain $\dfrac{dy}{dx} = \dfrac{dy/dt}{dx/dt} = \dfrac{-tf''(t)}{-f''(t)} = t$ for $f''(t) \neq 0$.

Substituting into $y = xy' + f(y')$ we find $f(t) - tf'(t) = xt + f(t)$. Since $x = -f'(t)$, this becomes $f(t) - tf'(t) = -tf'(t) + f(t)$, which is an identity. Thus, the parametric equations form a solution of $y = xy' + f(y')$.

Exercises 2.7

1. Let $u = e^{2y}$. Then $\dfrac{du}{dy} = 2e^{2y}\dfrac{dy}{dx}$ and the equation becomes $\dfrac{du}{dx} + \dfrac{2}{x}u = \dfrac{2\ln x}{x^2}$. This equation is linear with integrating factor x^2. Thus $\dfrac{d}{dx}\left[x^2 u\right] = 2\ln x$ and

$$x^2 u = 2x\ln x - 2x + c \quad \text{or} \quad x^2 e^{2y} = 2x\ln x - 2x + c.$$

2. Let $u = \ln y$. Then $\dfrac{du}{dx} = \dfrac{1}{y}\dfrac{dy}{dx}$ and the equation becomes $\dfrac{du}{dx} + u = e^x$. This equation is linear with integrating factor e^x. Thus $\dfrac{d}{dx}\left[e^x u\right] = e^{2x}$ and

$$u = \frac{1}{2}e^x + ce^{-x} \quad \text{or} \quad \ln y = \frac{1}{2}e^x + ce^{-x}.$$

3. Let $u = ye^x$. Then $y = ue^{-x}$ and $dy = -ue^{-x}\,dx + e^{-x}\,du$, and the equation becomes

$$ue^{-x}dx + (1 + u)(-ue^{-x}dx + e^{-x}du) = 0 \quad \text{or} \quad (1 + u)\,du = u^2 dx.$$

Separating variables and integrating we find

$$-\frac{1}{u} + \ln|u| = x + c \implies -\frac{1}{ye^x} + \ln|y| + x = x + c \implies y\ln|y| = e^{-x} + cy.$$

4. Let $u = \dfrac{x}{y}$ so that $x = uy$ and $dx = u\,dy + y\,du$. The equation becomes

$$(2 + e^{-u})(u\,dy + y\,du) + 2(1 - u)\,dy = 0 \quad \text{or} \quad \frac{2 + e^{-u}}{2 + ue^{-u}}\,du + \frac{dy}{y} = 0.$$

Writing this in form $\dfrac{2e^u + 1}{2e^u + u}\,du + \dfrac{dy}{y} = 0$ and integrating we find

$$\ln|2e^u + u| + \ln|y| = c \implies y(2e^u + u) = c_1 \implies y\left(2e^{x/y} + \frac{x}{y}\right) = c \implies 2ye^{x/y} + x = c.$$

5. Let $u = \dfrac{y}{x^4}$ so that $y = ux^4$ and $dy = 4ux^3\,dx + x^4\,du$. The equation becomes

$$4ux^3 + x^4\frac{du}{dx} - 4x^3u = 2x^5e^u \quad \text{or} \quad e^{-u}\,du = 2x\,dx.$$

Integrating we find $-e^{-u} = x^2 + c$ or $-e^{-y/x^4} = x^2 + c$.

6. Let $u = x + y$ so that $\dfrac{du}{dx} = 1 + \dfrac{dy}{dx}$. The equation becomes

$$\left(\frac{du}{dx} - 1\right) + u + 1 = u^2e^{3x} \quad \text{or} \quad \frac{du}{dx} + u = u^2e^{3x}.$$

This is a Bernoulli equation and we use the substitution $w = u^{-1}$ to obtain $\dfrac{dw}{dx} - w = e^{-3x}$. An integrating factor is e^{-x}, so

$$\frac{d}{dx}[e^{-x}w] = e^{-2x} \implies w = -\frac{1}{2}e^{3x} + ce^x \implies u = \frac{1}{-\frac{1}{2}e^{3x} + ce^x} \implies y = \frac{2}{-e^{3x} + c_1e^x} - x.$$

7. Let $u = y^2$ so that $\dfrac{du}{dx} = 2yy'$. The equation becomes $\dfrac{du}{dx} + u = -x^2 - x$. An integrating factor is e^x, so

$$\frac{d}{dx}[e^xu] = -\left(x^2 + x\right)e^x \implies e^xu = -\left(x^2e^x - xe^x + e^x\right) + c \implies y^2 = -x^2 + x - 1 + ce^{-x}.$$

8. Let $u = y + 1$ so that $\dfrac{du}{dx} = \dfrac{dy}{dx}$. The equation becomes

$$\frac{du}{dx} = u - 1 + xu^2 + 1 \quad \text{or} \quad \frac{du}{dx} - u = xu^2.$$

This is a Bernoulli equation and we use the substitution $w = u^{-1}$ to obtain $\dfrac{dw}{dx} + w = -x$. An integrating factor is e^x, so

$$\frac{d}{dx}[e^x w] = -xe^x \implies w = -x+1+ce^{-x} \implies u = (1-x+ce^{-x})^{-1} \implies y = (1-x+ce^{-x})^{-1} - 1.$$

9. Let $u = \ln(\tan y)$ so that $\dfrac{du}{dx} = \dfrac{\sec^2 y}{\tan y}\dfrac{dy}{dx} = 2\csc 2y\,\dfrac{dy}{dx}$. The equation becomes $x\,\dfrac{du}{dx} = 2x - u$ or

$\dfrac{du}{dx} + \dfrac{1}{x}u = 2$. An integrating factor is x, so

$$\frac{d}{dx}[xu] = 2x \implies u = x + \frac{c}{x} \implies \ln(\tan y) = x + \frac{c}{x}.$$

10. Let $u = x^2 y$ so that $\dfrac{du}{dx} = x^2\dfrac{dy}{dx} + 2xy$. The equation becomes $\dfrac{du}{dx} = u^2 + 1$. Separating variables and integrating we have

$$\frac{du}{u^2+1} = dx \implies \tan^{-1} u = x + c \implies \tan^{-1} x^2 y = x + c.$$

11. Let $u = x^3 y^3$ so that $\dfrac{du}{dx} = 3x^3 y^2\dfrac{dy}{dx} + 3x^2 y^3$. The equation becomes $\dfrac{1}{3}x\,\dfrac{du}{dx} = 2x^3 - 3$. Separating variables and integrating we have

$$du = 6x^2 - \frac{9}{x} \implies u = 2x^3 - 9\ln|x| + c \implies x^3 y^2 = 2x^3 - 9\ln|x| + c.$$

12. Let $u = e^y$ so that $u' = e^y y'$. The equation becomes $xu' - 2u = x^2$ or $u' - \dfrac{2}{x}u = x$. An integrating factor is x^{-2}, so

$$\frac{d}{dx}\left[x^{-2}u\right] = \frac{1}{x} \implies u = x^2\ln|x| + cx^2 \implies e^y = x^2\ln|x| + cx^2.$$

13. Let $u = x + y$ so that $u' = 1 + y'$. The equation becomes $u' = e^{-u}\sin x$. Separating variables and integrating we have

$$e^u\,du = \sin x\,dx \implies e^u = -\cos x + c \implies e^{x+y} = -\cos x + c.$$

14. Let $u = \sin y \cosh x$ so that $du = \sin y \sinh x\,dx + \cos y \cosh x\,dy$. The equation becomes $du = 0$. The solution is $u = c$ or $\sin y \cosh x = c$.

15. Let $u = y^2\ln x$ so that $\dfrac{du}{dy} = \dfrac{y^2}{x}\dfrac{dx}{dy} + 2y\ln x$ or $\dfrac{x}{y}\dfrac{du}{dy} = y\dfrac{dy}{dx} + 2x\ln x$. The equation becomes

$\dfrac{x}{y}\dfrac{du}{dy} = xe^y$ or $\dfrac{1}{y}\dfrac{du}{dy} = e^y$. Separating variables we have

$$du = ye^y \implies u = ye^y - e^y + c \implies y^2\ln x = ye^y - e^y + c.$$

16. Let $u = -\cos y$ so that $\dfrac{du}{dx} = \sin y \, \dfrac{dy}{dx}$. The equation becomes $x\dfrac{du}{dx} - u = -x^2 e^x$ or $\dfrac{du}{dx} - \dfrac{1}{x}u = -xe^x$.

An integrating factor is $1/x$, so

$$\frac{d}{dx}\left[\frac{1}{x}u\right] = -e^x \implies u = -xe^x + cx \implies \cos y = xe^x - cx.$$

17. Let $u = y'$ so that $u' = y''$. The equation becomes $u' = -u - 1$ which is separable. Thus

$$\frac{du}{u^2 + 1} = -dx \implies \tan^{-1} u = -x + c_1 \implies y' = \tan(c_1 - x) \implies y = \ln|\cos(c_1 - x)| + c_2.$$

18. Let $u = y'$ so that $u' = y''$. The equation becomes $u' - \dfrac{1}{x}u = u^2$, which is Bernoulli. Using the

substitution $w = u^{-1}$ we obtain $\dfrac{dw}{dx} + \dfrac{1}{x}w = -1$. An integrating factor is x, so

$$\frac{d}{dx}[xw] = -x \implies w = -\frac{1}{2}x + \frac{1}{x}c \implies \frac{1}{u} = \frac{c_1 - x^2}{2x} \implies u = \frac{2x}{c_1 - x^2} \implies y = -\ln\left|c_1 - x^2\right| + c_2.$$

19. Let $u = y'$ so that $u' = y''$. The equation becomes $u' - \dfrac{1}{x}u = \dfrac{1}{x}u^3$, which is Bernoulli. Using

$w = u^{-2}$ we obtain $\dfrac{dw}{dx} + \dfrac{2}{x}w = -\dfrac{2}{x}$. An integrating factor is x^2, so

$$\frac{d}{dx}\left[x^2 w\right] = -2x \implies w = -1 + \frac{c_1}{x^2} \implies \frac{1}{u^2} = \frac{c_1 - x^2}{x^2} \implies u = \frac{|x|}{\sqrt{c_1 - x^2}}$$

$$\implies y = \pm\sqrt{c_1 - x^2} + c_2.$$

20. Let $u = y'$ so that $u' = y''$. The equation becomes $x^2 u' + u^2 = 0$. Separating variables we obtain

$$\frac{du}{u^2} = -\frac{dx}{x^2} \implies -\frac{1}{u} = \frac{1}{x} + c_1 = \frac{c_1 x + 1}{x} \implies u = -\frac{1}{c_1}\left(\frac{x}{x + 1/c_1}\right) = \frac{1}{c_1}\left(\frac{1}{c_1 x + 1} - 1\right)$$

$$\implies y = \frac{1}{c_1^2}\ln|c_1 x + 1| - \frac{1}{c_1}x + c_2.$$

21. Let $u = y'$ so that $u' = y''$. The equation becomes $u = xu' + (u')^3 + 1$. This is a Clairaut equation

with $f(t) = 1 + t^3$. A family of solutions is $u = c_1 x + \left(1 + c_1^3\right)$, $y = \dfrac{1}{2}c_1 x^2 + \left(1 + c_1^3\right)x + c_2$.

A singular solution is given by $x = -3t^2$ and $u = 1 + t^3 - t\left(-3t^2\right) = 1 + 4t^3$. Eliminating the

parameter we obtain $u = 1 + 4\left(-\dfrac{x}{3}\right)^{3/2}$, $y = x - \dfrac{24}{5}\left(-\dfrac{x}{3}\right)^{5/2}$.

22. Let $u = y'$ so that $u' = y''$. The equation becomes $u' = 1 + u^2$. Separating variables we obtain

$$\frac{du}{1 + u^2} = dx \implies \tan^{-1} u = x + c_1 \implies u = \tan(x + c_1) \implies y = -\ln|\cos(x + c_1)| + c_2.$$

23. Let $u = y'$ so that $u' = y''$. The equation becomes $xu' = u$. Separating variables we obtain

$$\frac{du}{u} = \frac{1}{x}\,dx \implies \ln|u| = \ln|x| + c \implies u = c_1 x \implies y = c_2 x^2 + c_3.$$

24. Let $u = y'$ so that $u' = y''$. The equation becomes $u' + u\tan x = 0$. Separating variables we obtain

$$\frac{du}{u} = -(\tan x)\,dx \implies \ln|u| = \ln|\cos x| + c \implies u = c_1 \cos x \implies y = c_1 \sin x + c_2.$$

25. Let $u = y'$ so that $y'' = u\dfrac{du}{dy}$. The equation becomes $u\dfrac{du}{dy} + 2yu^3 = 0$. Separating variables we obtain

$$\frac{du}{u^2} + 2y\,dy = 0 \implies -\frac{1}{u} + y^2 = c \implies u = \frac{1}{y^2 + c_1} \implies y' = \frac{1}{y^2 + c_1}$$

$$\implies \left(y^2 + c_1\right)dy = dx \implies \frac{1}{3}y^3 + c_1 y = x + c_2.$$

26. Let $u = y'$ so that $y'' = u\dfrac{du}{dy}$. The equation becomes $y^2 u\dfrac{du}{dy} = u$. Separating variables we obtain

$$du = \frac{dy}{y^2} \implies u = -\frac{1}{y} + c_1 \implies y' = \frac{c_1 y - 1}{y} \implies \frac{y}{c_1 y - 1}\,dy = dx$$

$$\implies \frac{1}{c_1}\left(1 + \frac{1}{c_1 y - 1}\right)dy = dx \text{ (for } c_1 \neq 0) \implies \frac{1}{c_1}y + \frac{1}{c_1^2}\ln|y - 1| = x + c_2.$$

If $c_1 = 0$, then $y\,dy = -dx$ and another solution is $\frac{1}{2}y^2 = -x + c_2$.

27. We need to solve $\left[1 + (y')^2\right]^{3/2} = y''$. Let $u = y'$ so that $u' = y''$. The equation becomes $\left(1 + u^2\right)^{3/2} = u'$ or $\left(1 + u^2\right)^{3/2} = \dfrac{du}{dx}$. Separating variables and using the substitution $u = \tan\theta$ we have

$$\frac{du}{(1 + u^2)^{3/2}} = dx \implies \int \frac{\sec^2\theta}{\left(1 + \tan^2\theta\right)^{3/2}}\,d\theta = x \implies \int \frac{\sec^2\theta}{\sec^3\theta}\,d\theta = x$$

$$\implies \int \cos\theta\,d\theta = x \implies \sin\theta = x \implies \frac{u}{\sqrt{1 + u^2}} = x$$

$$\implies \frac{y'}{\sqrt{1 + (y')^2}} = x \implies (y')^2 = x^2\left[1 + (y')^2\right] = \frac{x^2}{1 - x^2}$$

$$\implies y' = \frac{x}{\sqrt{1 - x^2}} \text{ (for } x > 0) \implies y = -\sqrt{1 - x^2}\,.$$

1. Identify $x_0 = 0$, $y_0 = 1$, and $f(t, y_{n-1}(t)) = -y_{n-1}(t)$. Picard's formula is $y_n(x) = 1 - \int_0^x y_{n-1}(t)\, dt$ for $n = 1, 2, 3, \ldots$. Iterating we find

$$y_1(x) = 1 - x \qquad\qquad y_3(x) = 1 - x + \frac{1}{2}x^2 - \frac{1}{6}x^3$$

$$y_2(x) = 1 - x + \frac{1}{2}x^2 \qquad\qquad y_4(x) = 1 - x + \frac{1}{2}x^2 - \frac{1}{6}x^3 + \frac{1}{24}x^4.$$

As $n \to \infty$, $y_n(x) \to e^{-x}$.

2. Identify $x_0 = 0$, $y_0 = 1$, and $f(t, y_{n-1}(t)) = t + y_{n-1}(t)$. Picard's formula is

$$y_n(x) = 1 + \int_0^x (t + y_{n-1}(t))\, dt$$

for $n = 1, 2, 3, \ldots$. Iterating we find

$$y_1(x) = 1 + x + \frac{1}{2}x^2 \qquad\qquad y_3(x) = 1 + x + x^2 + \frac{1}{3}x^3 + \frac{1}{24}x^4$$

$$y_2(x) = 1 + x + x^2 + \frac{1}{6}x^3 \qquad\qquad y_4(x) = 1 + x + x^2 + \frac{1}{3}x^3 + \frac{1}{12}x^4 + \frac{1}{120}x^5.$$

As $n \to \infty$, $y_n(x) \to -1 - x + 2e^x$.

3. Identify $x_0 = 0$, $y_0 = 1$, and $f(t, y_{n-1}(t)) = 2ty_{n-1}(t)$. Picard's formula is

$$y_n(x) = 1 + 2\int_0^x ty_{n-1}(t)\, dt$$

for $n = 1, 2, 3, \ldots$. Iterating we find

$$y_1(x) = 1 + x^2 \qquad\qquad y_3(x) = 1 + x^2 + \frac{1}{2}x^4 + \frac{1}{6}x^6$$

$$y_2(x) = 1 + x^2 + \frac{1}{2}x^4 \qquad\qquad y_4(x) = 1 + x^2 + \frac{1}{2}x^4 + \frac{1}{6}x^6 + \frac{1}{24}x^8.$$

As $n \to \infty$, $y_n(x) \to e^{x^2}$.

4. Identify $x_0 = 0$, $y_0 = 0$, and $f(t, y_{n-1}(t)) = t - 2ty_{n-1}(t)$. Picard's formula is

$$y_n(x) = \frac{1}{2}x^2 - 2\int_0^x ty_{n-1}(t)\, dt$$

for $n = 1, 2, 3, \ldots$. Iterating we find

$$y_1(x) = \frac{1}{2}x^2 \qquad\qquad y_3(x) = \frac{1}{2}x^2 - \frac{1}{4}x^4 + \frac{1}{12}x^6$$

$$y_2(x) = \frac{1}{2}x^2 - \frac{1}{4}x^4 \qquad\qquad y_4(x) = \frac{1}{2}x^2 - \frac{1}{4}x^4 + \frac{1}{12}x^6 - \frac{1}{48}x^8.$$

As $n \to \infty$, $y_n(x) \to \dfrac{1}{2} - \dfrac{1}{2}e^{-x^2}$.

5. Identify $x_0 = 0$, $y_0 = 0$, and $f(t, y_{n-1}(t)) = -y_{n-1}^2(t)$. Picard's formula is $y_n(x) = -\displaystyle\int_0^x y_{n-1}^2(t)\, dt$

for $n = 1, 2, 3, \ldots$. Iterating we find $y_1(x) = y_2(x) = y_3(x) = y_4(x) = 0$. As $n \to \infty$, $y_n(x) \to 0$.

6. Identify $x_0 = 0$, $y_0 = 1$, and $f(t, y_{n-1}(t)) = 2e^t - y_{n-1}(t)$. Picard's formula is

$$y_n(x) = 2e^x - 1 - \int_0^x y_{n-1}(t)\, dt$$

for $n = 1, 2, 3, \ldots$. Iterating we find

$$y_1(x) = 2e^x - 1 - x \qquad\qquad y_3(x) = 2e^x - 1 - x - \frac{1}{2}x^2 - \frac{1}{6}x^3$$

$$y_2(x) = 1 + x + \frac{1}{2}x^2 \qquad\qquad y_4(x) = 1 + x + \frac{1}{2}x^2 + \frac{1}{6}x^3 + \frac{1}{24}x^4.$$

As $n \to \infty$, $y_n(x) \to e^x$.

7. (a) Identify $x_0 = 0$, $y_0 = 0$, and $f(t, y_{n-1}(t)) = 1 + y_{n-1}^2(t)$. Picard's formula is

$$y_n(x) = x + \int_0^x y_{n-1}^2(t)\, dt \quad \text{for } n = 1, 2, 3, \ldots . \text{ Iterating we find}$$

$$y_1(x) = x, \qquad y_2(x) = x + \frac{1}{3}x^3, \qquad y_3(x) = x + \frac{1}{3}x^3 + \frac{2}{15}x^5 + \frac{1}{63}x^7.$$

(b) From $dy = \left(1 + y^2\right) dx$ and $y(0) = 0$ we use separation of variables to obtain $y = \tan x$.

(c) The Maclaurin series for $\tan x$ is $x + \dfrac{1}{3}x^3 + \dfrac{2}{15}x^5 + \dfrac{17}{315}x^7 + \cdots$ for $|x| < \pi/2$.

8. (a) If $y_0 = k$ then the iterants are k times the iterants given in Problem 3.

(b) If $y_0(x) = x$ then

$$y_1(x) = x + \frac{2}{3}x^3 \qquad\qquad y_3(x) = x + \frac{2}{3}x^3 + \frac{4}{15}x^5 + \frac{8}{105}x^7$$

$$y_2(x) = x + \frac{2}{3}x^3 + \frac{4}{15}x^5 \qquad\qquad y_4(x) = x + \frac{2}{3}x^3 + \frac{4}{15}x^5 + \frac{8}{105}x^7 + \frac{16}{945}x^9.$$

———— Chapter 2 Review Exercises ————

1. For $f(x, y) = \left(25 - x^2 - y^2\right)^{-1}$ we obtain $f_y(x, y) = 2y\left(25 - x^2 - y^2\right)^{-2}$ so there will be a unique solution for any point (x_0, y_0) in the region $x^2 + y^2 < 25$ or $x^2 + y^2 > 25$.

2. $y = 0$

3. False; since $y = 0$ is a solution.

4. True; since $f(x, y) = (y - 1)^3$ and $f_y(x, y) = 3(y - 1)^2$ are continuous everywhere in the plane.

5. (a) linear in x (b) linear in y, homogeneous, exact

(c) Clairaut (d) Bernoulli in x

(e) separable (f) separable, Ricatti

(g) linear in x (h) homogeneous

(i) Bernoulli (j) homogeneous, exact, Bernoulli

(k) linear in x and y, exact, separable, homogeneous

(l) exact, linear in y (m) homogeneous

(n) separable (o) Clairaut

(p) Ricatti

6. Separating variables we obtain

$$\cos^2 x\, dx = \frac{y}{y^2 + 1}\, dy \implies \frac{1}{2}x + \frac{1}{4}\sin 2x = \frac{1}{2}\ln\left(y^2 + 1\right) + c \implies 2x + \sin 2x = 2\ln\left(y^2 + 1\right) + c.$$

7. Separating variables we obtain

$$y \ln y\, dy = xe^x dx \implies \frac{1}{2}y^2 \ln|y| - \frac{1}{4}y^2 = xe^x - e^x + c.$$

If $y(1) = 1$, $c = -1/4$. The solution is $2y^2 \ln|y| - y^2 = 4xe^x - 4e^x - 1$.

8. Write the differential equation in the form $y \ln \dfrac{x}{y}\, dx = \left(x \ln \dfrac{x}{y} - y\right) dy$. This is a homogeneous equation, so let $x = uy$. Then $dx = u\, dy + y\, du$ and the differential equation becomes

$$y \ln u(u\, dy + y\, du) = (uy \ln u - y)\, dy \quad \text{or} \quad y \ln u\, du = -dy.$$

Separating variables we obtain

$$\ln u\, du = -\frac{dy}{y} \implies u \ln|u| - u = -\ln|y| + c \implies \frac{x}{y}\ln\left|\frac{x}{y}\right| - \frac{x}{y} = -\ln|y| + c$$

$$\implies x(\ln x - \ln y) - x = -y \ln|y| + cy.$$

9. The equation is homogeneous, so let $y = ux$. Then $dy = u\, dx + x\, du$ and the differential equation becomes $ux^2(u\, dx + x\, du) = \left(3u^2x^2 + x^2\right) dx$ or $ux\, du = \left(2u^2 + 1\right) dx$. Separating variables we obtain

$$\frac{u}{2u^2 + 1}\, du = \frac{dx}{x} \implies \frac{1}{4}\ln\left(2u^2 + 1\right) = \ln x + c \implies 2u^2 + 1 = c_1 x^4$$

$$\implies 2\frac{y^2}{x^2} + 1 = c_1 x^4 \implies 2y^2 + x^2 = c_1 x^6.$$

If $y(-1) = 2$ then $c_1 = 9$ and the solution of the initial-value problem is $2y^2 + x^2 = 9x^6$.

49

10. The differential equation $\dfrac{dy}{dx} + \dfrac{2}{6x+1}y = -\dfrac{3x^2}{6x+1}y^{-2}$ is Bernoulli. Using $w = y^3$ we obtain

$\dfrac{dw}{dx} + \dfrac{6}{6x+1}w = -\dfrac{9x^2}{6x+1}$. An integrating factor is $6x+1$, so

$$\dfrac{d}{dx}\left[(6x+1)w\right] = -9x^2 \implies w = -\dfrac{3x^3}{6x+1} + \dfrac{c}{6x+1} \implies (6x+1)y^3 = -3x^3 + c.$$

(Note: The differential equation is also exact.)

11. Let $u = xy$ so that $\dfrac{du}{dy} = x + y\dfrac{dx}{dy}$. The differential equation becomes $e^u\left(\dfrac{du}{dy} - x\right) + xe^u = 12y^2$

or $e^u\dfrac{du}{dy} = 12y^2$. Separating variables we obtain

$$e^u\,du = 12y^2\,dy \implies e^u = 4y^3 + c \implies e^{xy} = 4y^3 + c.$$

If $y(0) = -1$ then $c = 5$ and the solution of the initial-value problem is $e^{xy} = 4y^3 + 5$.

12. Let $u = xy$ so that $du = x\,dy + y\,dx$. The differential equation becomes

$$du - y\,dx + \left(u + y - x^2 - 2x\right)dx = 0 \quad \text{or} \quad \dfrac{du}{dx} + u = x^2 + 2x.$$

An integrating factor is e^x, so

$$\dfrac{d}{dx}[e^x u] = \left(x^2 + 2x\right)e^x \implies e^x u = x^2 e^x + c \implies y = x + \dfrac{c}{x}e^{-x}.$$

13. Write the equation in the form $\dfrac{dy}{dx} + \dfrac{8x}{x^2+4}y = \dfrac{2x}{x^2+4}$. An integrating factor is $\left(x^2+4\right)^4$, so

$$\dfrac{d}{dx}\left[\left(x^2+4\right)^4 y\right] = 2x\left(x^2+4\right)^3 \implies \left(x^2+4\right)^4 y = \dfrac{1}{4}\left(x^2+4\right)^4 + c \implies y = \dfrac{1}{4} + c\left(x^2+4\right)^{-4}.$$

If $y(0) = -1$ then $c = -320$ and $y = \dfrac{1}{4} - 320\left(x^2+4\right)^{-4}$.

14. Write the equation in the form $\dfrac{dx}{dy} - 2x = y$. An integrating factor is e^{-2y}, so

$$\dfrac{d}{dy}\left[e^{-2y}x\right] = ye^{-2y} \implies e^{-2y}x = -\dfrac{1}{2}ye^{-2y} - \dfrac{1}{4}e^{-2y} + c \implies x = -\dfrac{1}{2}y - \dfrac{1}{4} + ce^{2y}.$$

15. The differential equation is Bernoulli. Using $w = y^{-1}$ we obtain $-xy^2\dfrac{dw}{dx} + 4y = x^4y^2$ or

$\dfrac{dw}{dx} - \dfrac{4}{x}w = -x^3$. An integrating factor is x^{-4}, so

$$\dfrac{d}{dx}\left[x^{-4}w\right] = -\dfrac{1}{x} \implies x^{-4}w = -\ln x + c \implies w = -x^4\ln x + cx^4 \implies y = \left(cx^4 - x^4\ln x\right)^{-1}.$$

If $y(1) = 1$ then $c = 1$ and $y = \left(x^4 - x^4\ln x\right)^{-1}$.

50

16. Writing the differential equation in the form $y = xy' + (y' + 1)^2$ we see that it is a Clairaut equation with $f(t) = (t + 1)^2$. A family of solutions is $y = cx + (c + 1)^2$. If $y(0) = 0$ then $c = -1$ and the solution of the initial-value problem is $y = -x$.

17. Write the equation in the form $\dfrac{1}{y^3}\left(\cos\dfrac{1}{y^2}\right)\dfrac{dy}{dx} + x = 0$ and let $u = \dfrac{1}{y^2}$. Then $-\dfrac{1}{2}\dfrac{du}{dx} = \dfrac{1}{y^3}\dfrac{dy}{dx}$ and

the differential equation becomes $-\dfrac{1}{2}(\cos u)\dfrac{du}{dx} + x = 0$. Separating variables we obtain

$$\cos u\,du = 2x\,dx \implies \sin u = x^2 + c \implies \sin\frac{1}{y^2} = x^2 + c.$$

18. Let $u = y'$ so that $u' = y''$. The equation becomes $u' = x - u$ or $u' + u = x$. An integrating factor is e^x, so

$$\frac{d}{dx}[e^x u] = xe^x \implies e^x u = xe^x - e^x + c_1 \implies y' = x - 1 + c_1 e^{-x} \implies y = \frac{1}{2}x^2 - x - c_1 e^{-x} + c_2.$$

19. Identify $x_0 = 0$, $y_0 = 1$, and $f(t, y_{n-1}(t)) = t^2 + y_{n-1}^2(t)$. Picard's formula is

$$y_n(x) = 1 + \frac{1}{3}x^3 + \int_0^x y_{n-1}^2(t)\,dt$$

for $n = 1, 2, 3, \ldots$. Iterating we find

$$y_1(x) = 1 + x + \frac{1}{3}x^3$$

$$y_2(x) = 1 + x + x^2 + \frac{2}{3}x^3 + \frac{1}{6}x^4 + \frac{2}{15}x^5 + \frac{1}{63}x^7.$$

20. From $dy = (4 - 2y)\,dx$ and $y(0) = 3$ we obtain $y = 2 + e^{-2x}$. Picard's formula is

$$y_n(x) = 3 + 4x - 2\int_0^x y_{n-1}(t)\,dt$$

for $n = 1, 2, 3, \ldots$ so that

$$y_1(x) = 3 - 2x$$

$$y_2(x) = 3 - 2x + 2x^2$$

$$y_3(x) = 3 - 2x + 2x^2 - \frac{4}{3}x^3$$

$$y_4(x) = 3 - 2x + 2x^2 - \frac{4}{3}x^3 + \frac{2}{3}x^4 = 2 + \left[1 - 2x + \frac{(2x)^2}{2!} - \frac{(2x)^3}{3!} + \frac{(2x)^4}{4!}\right],$$

and $y_n(x) \to 2 + e^{-2x}$ as $n \to \infty$.

3 Applications of First-Order Differential Equations

——————— **Exercises 3.1** ———————

1. From $y = c_1 x$ we obtain $y' = \dfrac{y}{x}$ so that the differential equation of the orthogonal family is $y' = -\dfrac{x}{y}$.

   Then $y\,dy = -x\,dx$ and $y^2 + x^2 = c_2$.

2. From $3x + 4y = c_1$ we obtain $y' = -\dfrac{3}{4}$ so that the differential equation of the orthogonal family is

   $y' = \dfrac{4}{3}$. Then $3y - 4x = c_2$.

3. From $y = c_1 x^2$ we obtain $y' = \dfrac{2y}{x}$ so that the differential equation of the orthogonal family is

   $y' = -\dfrac{x}{2y}$. Then $2y\,dy = -x\,dx$ and $2y^2 + x^2 = c_2$.

4. From $y = (x - c_1)^2$ we obtain $y' = 2\sqrt{y}$ so that the differential equation of the orthogonal family is

   $y' = -\dfrac{1}{2\sqrt{y}}$. Then $2\sqrt{y}\,dy = -dx$ and $4y^{3/2} + 3x = c_2$.

5. From $c_1 x^2 + y^2 = 1$ we obtain $y' = \dfrac{y^2 - 1}{xy}$ so that the differential equation of the orthogonal family is

   $y' = \dfrac{xy}{1 - y^2}$. Then $\left(\dfrac{1}{y} - y\right) dy = x\,dx$ and $2\ln|y| = x^2 + y^2 + c_2$.

6. From $2x^2 + y^2 = c_1^2$ we obtain $y' = -\dfrac{2x}{y}$ so that the differential equation of the orthogonal family

   is $y' = \dfrac{y}{2x}$. Then $\dfrac{1}{y}\,dy = \dfrac{1}{2x}\,dx$ and $y^2 = c_2 x$.

7. From $y = c_1 e^{-x}$ we obtain $y' = -y$ so that the differential equation of the orthogonal family is

   $y' = \dfrac{1}{y}$. Then $y\,dy = dx$ and $y^2 = 2x + c_2$.

8. From $y = e^{c_1 x}$ we obtain $y' = \dfrac{y \ln y}{x}$ so that the differential equation of the orthogonal family is

   $y' = -\dfrac{x}{y \ln y}$. Then $y \ln y\,dy = -x\,dx$ and $2y^2 \ln y - y^2 = -2x^2 + c_2$.

9. From $y^2 = c_1 x^3$ we obtain $y' = \dfrac{3y}{2x}$ so that the differential equation of the orthogonal family is

   $y' = -\dfrac{2x}{3y}$. Then $3y\,dy = -2x\,dx$ and $3y^2 + 2x^2 = c_2$.

10. From $y^a = c_1 x^b$ we obtain $y' = \dfrac{by}{ax}$ so that the differential equation of the orthogonal family is

$y' = -\dfrac{ax}{by}$. Then $by\,dy = -ax\,dx$ and $by^2 + ax^2 = c_2$.

11. From $y = \dfrac{x}{1 + c_1 x}$ we obtain $y' = \dfrac{y^2}{x^2}$ so that the differential equation of the orthogonal family is

$y' = -\dfrac{x^2}{y^2}$. Then $y^2\,dy = -x^2\,dx$ and $x^3 + y^3 = c_2$.

12. From $y = \dfrac{1 + c_1 x}{1 - c_1 x}$ we obtain $y' = \dfrac{y^2 - 1}{2x}$ so that the differential equation of the orthogonal family

is $y' = \dfrac{2x}{1 - y^2}$. Then $\left(1 - y^2\right) dy = 2x\,dx$ and $3y - 3x^2 - y^3 = c_2$.

13. From $2x^2 + y^2 = 4c_1 x$ we obtain $y' = \dfrac{y^2 - 2x^2}{2xy}$ so that the differential equation of the orthogonal

family is $y' = \dfrac{2xy}{2x^2 - y^2}$. This is a homogeneous differential equation . Let $y = ux$ so that

$y' = u + xu'$. Then

$$\dfrac{2 - u^2}{u^3}\,du = \dfrac{dx}{x} \implies -u^{-2} - \ln|u| = \ln|x| + c \implies -\dfrac{x^2}{y^2} - \left(\ln|y| - \ln|x|\right) = \ln x + c$$

$$\implies x^2 + y^2 \ln|y| = c_1 y^2.$$

14. From $x^2 + y^2 = 2c_1 x$ we obtain $y' = \dfrac{y^2 - x^2}{2xy}$ so that the differential equation of the orthogonal family

is $y' = \dfrac{2xy}{x^2 - y^2}$. This is a homogeneous differential equation . Let $x = vy$ so that $\dfrac{dx}{dv} = v + y\dfrac{dv}{dy}$.

Then

$$\dfrac{dy}{y} + \dfrac{2v\,dv}{1 + v^2} = 0 \implies \ln|y| + \ln\left(1 + v^2\right) = c \implies y\left(1 + v^2\right) = c_1$$

$$\implies y\left(1 + \dfrac{x^2}{y^2}\right) = c_2 \implies x^2 + y^2 = c_2 y.$$

15. From $y^3 + 3x^2 y = c_1$ we obtain $y' = -\dfrac{2xy}{x^2 + y^2}$ so that the differential equation of the orthogonal

family is $y' = \dfrac{x^2 + y^2}{2xy}$. This is a homogeneous differential equation . Let $y = ux$ so that $y' = u + xu'$.

Then

$$\dfrac{2u}{1 - u^2}\,du = \dfrac{dx}{x} \implies -\ln\left|1 - u^2\right| = \ln|x| + c \implies x\left(1 - \dfrac{y^2}{x^2}\right) = c_1 \implies x^2 - y^2 = c_1 x.$$

16. From $y^2 - x^2 = c_1 x^3$ we obtain $y' = \dfrac{3y^2 - x^2}{2xy}$ so that the differential equation of the orthogonal family is $y' = \dfrac{2xy}{x^2 - 3y^2}$. This is a homogeneous differential equation . Let $y = ux$ so that $y' = u + xu'$. Then

$$\frac{1 - 3u^2}{u + 3u^3}\, du = \frac{dx}{x} \implies \frac{1 + 9u^2 - 12u^2}{u + 3u^3}\, du = \frac{dx}{x} \implies \ln \left| u + 3u^3 \right| - 2\ln \left(1 + 3u^2 \right) = \ln |x| + c$$

$$\implies \frac{y}{x} + \frac{3y^3}{x^3} = c_1 x \left(1 + 6\frac{y^2}{x^2} + 9\frac{y^4}{x^4} \right) \implies x^2 y + 3y^3 = c_1 \left(x^4 + 6x^2 y^2 + 9y^4 \right)$$

$$\implies y \left(x^2 + 3y^2 \right) = c_1 \left(x^2 + 3y^2 \right)^2 \implies y = c_1 \left(x^2 + 3y^2 \right).$$

17. From $y = \dfrac{c_1}{1 + x^2}$ we obtain $y' = -\dfrac{2xy}{1 + x^2}$ so that the differential equation of the orthogonal family is $y' = \dfrac{1 + x^2}{2xy}$. Then

$$2y\, dy = \frac{1 + x^2}{x}\, dx \implies y^2 = \ln |x| + \frac{1}{2}x^2 + c \implies 2y^2 = 2\ln |x| + x^2 + c_1.$$

18. From $y = \dfrac{1}{c_1 + x}$ we obtain $y' = -y^2$ so that the differential equation of the orthogonal family is $y' = \dfrac{1}{y^2}$. Then $y^2\, dy = dx$ and $y^3 = 3x + c$.

19. From $4y + x^2 + 1 + c_1 e^{2y} = 0$ we obtain $y' = \dfrac{x}{4y + x^2 - 1}$ so that the differential equation of the orthogonal family is $y' + \dfrac{4}{x}y = \dfrac{1}{x} - x$. An integrating factor is x^4, so

$$\frac{d}{dx}\left[x^4 y \right] = x^3 - x^5 \implies x^4 y = \frac{1}{4}x^4 - \frac{1}{6}x^6 + c \implies y = \frac{1}{4} - \frac{1}{6}x^2 + cx^{-4}.$$

20. From $y = -x - 1 + c_1 e^x$ we obtain $y' = y + x$ so that the differential equation of the orthogonal family is $\dfrac{dy}{dx} = -\dfrac{1}{y + x}$ or $\dfrac{dx}{dy} + x = -y$. An integrating factor is e^y, so

$$\frac{d}{dy}[e^y x] = -ye^y \implies e^y x = -ye^y + e^y + c \implies x = -y + 1 + ce^{-y}.$$

21. From $y = \dfrac{1}{\ln c_1 x}$ we obtain $y' = -\dfrac{y^2}{x}$ so that the differential equation of the orthogonal family is $y' = \dfrac{x}{y^2}$. Then $y^2\, dy = x\, dx$ and $2y^3 = 3x^2 + c$.

22. From $y = \ln(c_1 + \tan x)$ we obtain $y' = e^{-y}\sec^2 x$ so that the differential equation of the orthogonal family is $y' = -e^y \cos^2 x$. Then $e^{-y}\, dy = -\cos^2 x\, dx$ and $4e^{-y} = 2x + \sin 2x + c_2$.

23. From $\sinh y = c_1 x$ we obtain $y' = \dfrac{\tanh y}{x}$ so that the differential equation of the orthogonal family is $y' = -\dfrac{x}{\tanh y}$. Then $\tanh y\, dy = -x\, dx$ and $2\ln |\cosh y| + x^2 = c_2$.

24. From $y = c_1 \sin x$ we obtain $y' = y \cot x$ so that the differential equation of the orthogonal family is $y' = -\dfrac{\tan x}{y}$. Then $y\,dy = -\tan x\,dx$ and $y^2 = 2\ln|\cos x| + c_2$.

25. From $x^{1/3} + y^{1/3} = c_1$ we obtain $y' = -\dfrac{y^{2/3}}{x^{2/3}}$ so that the differential equation of the orthogonal family is $y' = \dfrac{x^{2/3}}{y^{2/3}}$. Then $y^{2/3}\,dy = x^{2/3}\,dx$ and $y^{5/3} = x^{5/3} + c_2$.

26. From $x^a + y^a = c_1$ we obtain $y' = -\dfrac{x^{a-1}}{y^{a-1}}$ so that the differential equation of the orthogonal family is $y' = \dfrac{y^{a-1}}{x^{a-1}}$. Then $y^{1-a}\,dy = x^{1-a}\,dx$ and $y^{2-a} = x^{2-a} + c_2$.

27. From $x + y = c_1 e^y$ we obtain $y' = \dfrac{1}{x+y-1}$ so that the differential equation of the orthogonal family is $y' = 1 - x - y$. Then $y' + y = 1 - x$. An integrating factor is e^x, so

$$\frac{d}{dx}[e^x y] = e^x - xe^x \implies e^x y = 2e^x - xe^x + c \implies y = 2 - x + ce^{-x}.$$

If $y(0) = 5$ then $c = 3$ and $y = 2 - x + 3e^{-x}$.

28. From $3xy^2 = 2 + 3c_1 x$ we obtain $y' = -\dfrac{1}{3x^2 y}$ so that the differential equation of the orthogonal family is $y' = 3x^2 y$. Then $dy = 3x^2 y\,dx$ and $y = ce^{x^3}$. If $y(0) = 10$ then $c = 10$ and $y = 10e^{x^3}$.

29. From $r = 2c_1 \cos\theta$ we obtain $r\dfrac{d\theta}{dr} = -\cot\theta$ so that the differential equation of the orthogonal family is $r\dfrac{d\theta}{dr} = \tan\theta$. Then

$$\cot\theta\,d\theta = \frac{dr}{r} \implies \ln|\sin\theta| = \ln|r| + c \implies r = c_1 \sin\theta.$$

30. From $r = c_1(1 + \cos\theta)$ we obtain $r\dfrac{d\theta}{dr} = -\dfrac{1 + \cos\theta}{\sin\theta}$ so that the differential equation of the orthogonal family is $r\dfrac{d\theta}{dr} = \dfrac{\sin\theta}{1 + \cos\theta}$. Then

$$\frac{1 + \cos\theta}{\sin\theta}\,d\theta = \frac{dr}{r} \implies \frac{\sin\theta}{1 - \cos\theta}\,d\theta = \frac{dr}{r} \implies \ln|1 - \cos\theta| = \ln|r| + c \implies r = c_1(1 - \cos\theta).$$

31. From $r^2 = c_1 \sin 2\theta$ we obtain $r\dfrac{d\theta}{dr} = \tan 2\theta$ so that the differential equation of the orthogonal family is $r\dfrac{d\theta}{dr} = -\cot 2\theta$. Then

$$-\tan 2\theta\,d\theta = \frac{dr}{r} \implies \frac{1}{2}\ln|\cos 2\theta| = \ln r + c \implies r^2 = c_1 \cos 2\theta.$$

32. From $r = \dfrac{c_1}{1 + \cos\theta}$ we obtain $r\dfrac{d\theta}{dr} = \dfrac{1 + \cos\theta}{\sin\theta}$ so that the differential equation of the orthogonal

family is $r\dfrac{d\theta}{dr} = -\dfrac{\sin\theta}{1 + \cos\theta}$. Then

$$-\frac{1 + \cos\theta}{\sin\theta}\, d\theta = \frac{dr}{r} \implies -\frac{\sin\theta}{1 - \cos\theta}\, d\theta = \frac{dr}{r} \implies -\ln|1 - \cos\theta| = \ln r + c \implies r = c_1\frac{1}{1 - \cos\theta}.$$

33. From $r = c_1 \sec\theta$ we obtain $r\dfrac{d\theta}{dr} = \cot\theta$ so that the differential equation of the orthogonal family is

$r\dfrac{d\theta}{dr} = -\tan\theta$. Then

$$-\cot\theta = \frac{dr}{r} \implies -\ln|\sin\theta| = \ln|r| + c \implies r = c_1 \csc\theta.$$

34. From $r = c_1 e^{\theta}$ we obtain $r\dfrac{d\theta}{dr} = 1$ so that the differential equation of the orthogonal family is

$r\dfrac{d\theta}{dr} = -1$. Then

$$-d\theta = \frac{dr}{r} \implies -\theta = \ln|r| + c \implies r = c_1 e^{-\theta}.$$

35. See the figures for this problem in the answer section in the text. Let β be the angle of inclination, measured from the positive x-axis, of the tangent line to a member of the given family, and ψ the angle of inclination of the tangent to a trajectory. At the point where the curves intersect, the angle between the tangents is α. Now, the slope of the tangent line to a trajectory is $dy/dx = \tan\phi$. Depending on how the angle α is chosen, we will either have $\beta + \alpha = \phi + \pi$ or $\beta - \alpha = \phi - \pi$. In any event, using the π-periodicity of the tangent function and the fact that $f(x, y) = \tan\beta$,

$$\frac{dy}{dx} = \tan\psi = \tan(\beta \pm \alpha) = \frac{\tan\beta \pm \tan\alpha}{1 \mp \tan\beta \tan\alpha} = \frac{f(x, y) \pm \tan\alpha}{1 \mp f(x, y)\tan\alpha}.$$

36. Since the differential equation of the original family is $f(x, y) = \dfrac{y}{x}$, the differential equation of the

isogonal family is $y' = \dfrac{y/x \pm 1}{1 \mp y/x} = \dfrac{y \pm x}{x \mp y}$. This is homogeneous so let $y = ux$. Then $y' = u + xu'$ and

$$xu' = \frac{\pm 1 \pm u^2}{1 \mp u} \implies \pm\frac{1 \mp u}{1 + u^2}\, du = \frac{dx}{x} \implies \pm\tan^{-1}u - \frac{1}{2}\ln\left(1 + u^2\right) = \ln|x| + c$$

$$\implies \pm 2\tan^{-1}\frac{y}{x} - \ln\left(1 + \frac{y^2}{x^2}\right) = 2\ln|x| + c_1 \implies \pm 2\tan\frac{y}{x} - \ln\left(x^2 + y^2\right) = c_1.$$

37. Since the differential equation of the original family is $f(x, y) = \dfrac{y}{x}$, the differential equation of

the isogonal family is $y' = \dfrac{y/x \pm \sqrt{3}}{1 \mp \sqrt{3}\,y/x} = \dfrac{y \pm \sqrt{3}\,x}{x \mp \sqrt{3}\,y}$. This is homogeneous so let $y = ux$. Then

$y' = u + xu'$ and

$$xu' = \frac{\pm\sqrt{3} \pm \sqrt{3}\,u^2}{1 \mp \sqrt{3}\,u} \implies \pm\frac{1}{\sqrt{3}}\,\frac{1 \mp \sqrt{3}\,u}{1 + u^2}\,du = \frac{dx}{x}$$

$$\implies \pm\frac{1}{\sqrt{3}}\tan^{-1}u - \frac{1}{2}\ln\left(1 + u^2\right) = \ln|x| + c$$

$$\implies \pm\frac{2}{\sqrt{3}}\tan^{-1}\frac{y}{x} - \ln\left(1 + \frac{y^2}{x^2}\right) = 2\ln|x| + c_1$$

$$\implies \pm\frac{2}{\sqrt{3}}\tan^{-1}\frac{y}{x} - \ln\left(x^2 + y^2\right) = c_1.$$

38. Since the differential equation of the original family is $f(x, y) = \dfrac{y}{x}$, the differential equation of

the isogonal family is $y' = \dfrac{y/x \pm 1/\sqrt{3}}{1 \mp y/\sqrt{3}\,x} = \dfrac{y \pm x/\sqrt{3}}{x \mp y/\sqrt{3}}$. This is homogeneous so let $y = ux$. Then

$y' = u + xu'$ and

$$xu' = \frac{\pm 1/\sqrt{3} \pm u^2/\sqrt{3}}{1 \mp u/\sqrt{3}} \implies \pm\sqrt{3}\,\frac{1 \mp u/\sqrt{3}}{1 + u^2}\,du = \frac{dx}{x}$$

$$\implies \pm\sqrt{3}\tan^{-1}u - \frac{1}{2}\ln\left(1 + u^2\right) = \ln|x| + c$$

$$\implies \pm 2\sqrt{3}\tan^{-1}\frac{y}{x} - \ln\left(1 + \frac{y^2}{x^2}\right) = 2\ln|x| + c_1$$

$$\implies \pm 2\sqrt{3}\tan^{-1}\frac{y}{x} - \ln\left(x^2 + y^2\right) = c_1.$$

39. From $y^2 = c_1(2x + c_1)$ we obtain $c_1 = -x \pm \sqrt{x^2 + y^2}$ and

$$y' = -\frac{x}{y} + \sqrt{\left(\frac{x}{y}\right)^2 + 1} \quad \text{or} \quad y' = -\frac{x}{y} - \sqrt{\left(\frac{x}{y}\right)^2 + 1}.$$

Self–orthogonality follows from the fact that the product of these derivatives is -1.

40. From $\dfrac{x^2}{c_1 + 1} + \dfrac{y^2}{c_1} = 1$ we obtain $c_1 = -\dfrac{yy'}{x + yy'}$ and $(x + yy')(xy' - y) = y'$. Replacing y' by $-\dfrac{1}{y'}$

results in exactly the same equation. This shows that the family is self–orthogonal.

41. From $x = c_1 e^t \cos t$ and $y = c_1 e^t \sin t$ we obtain $\dfrac{dy}{dx} = \dfrac{x + y}{x - y}$. Then the differential equation of the

orthogonal family is $\dfrac{dy}{dx} = \dfrac{y - x}{y + x}$. This is satisfied by $x = c_2 e^{-t} \cos t$ and $y = c_2 e^{-t} \sin t$.

42. We have $\psi_1 - \psi_2 = \dfrac{\pi}{2}$ so that $\tan \psi_1 = \tan\left(\psi_2 + \dfrac{\pi}{2}\right) = -\cot \psi_2 = -\dfrac{1}{\tan \psi_2}$.

Exercises 3.2

1. Let $P = P(t)$ be the population at time t, and P_0 the initial population. From $dP/dt = kP$ we obtain $P = P_0 e^{kt}$. Using $P(5) = 2P_0$ we find $k = \frac{1}{5}\ln 2$ and $P = P_0 e^{(\ln 2)t/5}$. Setting $P(t) = 3P_0$ we have

$$3 = e^{(\ln 2)t/5} \implies \ln 3 = \frac{(\ln 2)t}{5} \implies t = \frac{5\ln 3}{\ln 2} \approx 7.9 \text{ years.}$$

Setting $P(t) = 4P_0$ we have

$$4 = e^{(\ln 2)t/5} \implies \ln 4 = \frac{(\ln 2)t}{5} \implies t = 10 \text{ years.}$$

2. Setting $P = 10{,}000$ and $t = 3$ in Problem 1 we obtain

$$10{,}000 = P_0 e^{(\ln 2)3/5} \implies P_0 = 10{,}000 e^{-0.6\ln 2} \approx 6597.5.$$

Then $P(10) = P_0 e^{2\ln 2} = 4P_0 \approx 26{,}390$.

3. Let $P = P(t)$ be the population at time t. From $dP/dt = kt$ and $P(0) = P_0 = 500$ we obtain $P = 500e^{kt}$. Using $P(10) = 575$ we find $k = \frac{1}{10}\ln 1.15$. Then $P(30) = 500e^{3\ln 1.15} \approx 760$ years.

4. Let $N = N(t)$ be the number of bacteria at time t and N_0 the initial number. From $dN/dt = kN$ we obtain $N = N_0 e^{kt}$. Using $N(3) = 400$ and $N(10) = 2000$ we find $400 = N_0 e^{3k}$ or $e^k = (400/N_0)^{1/3}$. From $N(10) = 2000$ we then have

$$2000 = N_0 e^{10k} = N_0 \left(\frac{400}{N_0}\right)^{10/3} \implies \frac{2000}{400^{10/3}} = N_0^{-7/3} \implies N_0 = \left(\frac{2000}{400^{10/3}}\right)^{-3/7} \approx 201.$$

5. Let $N = N(t)$ be the amount of lead at time t. From $dN/dt = kN$ and $N(0) = 1$ we obtain $N = e^{kt}$. Using $N(3.3) = 1/2$ we find $k = \frac{1}{3.3}\ln 1/2$. When 90% of the lead has decayed, 0.1 grams will remain. Setting $N(t) = 0.1$ we have

$$e^{t(1/3.3)\ln(1/2)} = 0.1 \implies \frac{t}{3.3}\ln\frac{1}{2} = \ln 0.1 \implies t = \frac{3.3\ln 0.1}{\ln 1/2} \approx 10.96 \text{ hours.}$$

6. Let $N = N(t)$ be the amount at time t. From $dN/dt = kt$ and $N(0) = 100$ we obtain $N = 100e^{kt}$. Using $N(6) = 97$ we find $k = \frac{1}{6}\ln 0.97$. Then $N(24) = 100e^{(1/6)(\ln 0.97)24} = 100(0.97)^4 \approx 88.5$ mg.

7. Setting $N(t) = 50$ in Problem 6 we obtain

$$50 = 100e^{kt} \implies kt = \ln\frac{1}{2} \implies t = \frac{\ln 1/2}{(1/6)\ln 0.97} \approx 136.5 \text{ hours.}$$

8. The solution of $dA/dt = kA$ is $A(t) = A_0 e^{kt}$. Then $A_1 = A(t_1) = A_0 e^{kt_1}$, $A_2 = A(t_2) = A_0 e^{kt_2}$ and

$$\frac{A_1}{A_2} = e^{k(t_1 - t_2)} \implies k(t_1 - t_2) = \ln\frac{A_1}{A_2} \implies k = \frac{1}{(t_1 - t_2)} \ln\frac{A_1}{A_2}.$$

Solving $A_0/2 = A_0 e^{kt}$ for t, we obtain $t = -(\ln 2)/k$. It follows that $t = \dfrac{(t_2 - t_1)\ln 2}{\ln(A_1/A_2)}$.

9. Let $I = I(t)$ be the intensity, t the thickness, and $I(0) = I_0$. If $dI/dt = kI$ and $I(3) = .25I_0$ then $I = I_0 e^{kt}$, $k = \frac{1}{3}\ln .25$, and $I(15) = .00098I_0$.

10. From $dS/dt = rS$ we obtain $S = S_0 e^{rt}$ where $S(0) = S_0$.
    (a) If $S_0 = \$5000$ and $r = 5.75\%$ then $S(5) = \$6665.45$.
    (b) If $S(t) = \$10,000$ then $t = 12\,\text{years}$.
    (c) $S \approx \$6651.82$

11. Assume that $A = A_0 e^{kt}$ and $k = -.00012378$. If $A(t) = .145A_0$ then $t \approx 15{,}600$ years.

12. Assume that $dT/dt = k(T - 5)$ so that $T = 5 + ce^{kt}$. If $T(1) = 55°$ and $T(5) = 30°$ then $k = -\frac{1}{4}\ln 2$ and $c = 59.4611$ so that $T(0) = 64.4611°$.

13. Assume that $dT/dt = k(T - 10)$ so that $T = 10 + ce^{kt}$. If $T(0) = 70°$ and $T(1/2) = 50°$ then $c = 60$ and $k = 2\ln(2/3)$ so that $T(1) = 36.67°$. If $T(t) = 15°$ then $t = 3.06\,\text{minutes}$.

14. Assume that $dT/dt = k(T - 100)$ so that $T = 100 + ce^{kt}$. If $T(0) = 20°$ and $T(1) = 22°$ then $c = -80$ and $k = \ln(39/40)$ so that $T(t) = 90°$ implies $t = 82.1\,\text{seconds}$. If $T(t) = 98°$ then $t = 145.7\,\text{seconds}$.

15. Assume $L\,di/dt + Ri = E(t)$, $L = .1$, $R = 50$, and $E(t) = 50$ so that $i = \frac{3}{5} + ce^{-500t}$. If $i(0) = 0$ then $c = -3/5$ and $\lim_{t\to\infty} i(t) = 3/5$.

16. Assume $L\,di/dt + Ri = E(t)$, $E(t) = E_0 \sin\omega t$, and $i(0) = i_0$ so that

$$i = \frac{E_0 R}{L^2\omega^2 + R^2}\sin\omega t - \frac{E_0 L\omega}{L^2\omega^2 + R^2}\cos\omega t + ce^{-Rt/L}.$$

Since $i(0) = i_0$ we obtain $c = i_0 + \dfrac{E_0 L\omega}{L^2\omega^2 + R^2}$.

17. Assume $R\,dq/dt + (1/c)q = E(t)$, $R = 200$, $C = 10^{-4}$, and $E(t) = 100$ so that $q = 1/100 + ce^{-50t}$. If $q(0) = 0$ then $c = -1/100$ and $i = \frac{1}{2}e^{-50t}$.

18. Assume $R\,dq/dt + (1/c)q = E(t)$, $R = 1000$, $C = 5 \times 10^{-6}$, and $E(t) = 200$ so that $q = 1/1000 + ce^{-200t}$ and $i = -200ce^{-200t}$. If $i(0) = .4$ then $c = -1/500$, $q(.005) = .003\,\text{coulombs}$, and $i(.005) = .1472\,\text{amps}$. As $t \to \infty$ we have $q \to 1/1000$.

19. For $0 \le t \le 20$ the differential equation is $20\,di/dt + 2i = 120$. An integrating factor is $e^{t/10}$, so $\dfrac{d}{dt}\left[e^{t/10}i\right] = 6e^{t/10}$ and $i = 60 + c_1 e^{-t/10}$. If $i(0) = 0$ then $c_1 = -60$ and $i = 60 - 60e^{-t/10}$.

For $t > 20$ the differential equation is $20\, di/dt + 2i = 0$ and $i = c_2 e^{-t/10}$.

At $t = 20$ we want $c_2 e^{-2} = 60 - 60e^{-2}$ so that $c_2 = 60\left(e^2 - 1\right)$. Thus

$$i(t) = \begin{cases} 60 - 60e^{-t/10}, & 0 \le t \le 20; \\ 60\left(e^2 - 1\right)e^{-t/10}, & t > 20. \end{cases}$$

20. Separating variables we obtain

$$\frac{dq}{E_0 - q/C} = \frac{dt}{k_1 + k_2 t} \implies -C\ln\left|E_0 - \frac{q}{C}\right| = \frac{1}{k_2}\ln|k_1 + k_2 t| + c_1 \implies \frac{(E_0 - q/C)^{-C}}{(k_1 + k_2 t)^{1/k_2}} = c_2.$$

Setting $q(0) = q_0$ we find $c_2 = \dfrac{(E_0 - q_0/C)^{-C}}{k_1^{1/k_2}}$, so

$$\frac{(E_0 - q/C)^{-C}}{(k_1 + k_2 t)^{1/k_2}} = \frac{(E_0 - q_0/C)^{-C}}{k_1^{1/k_2}} \implies \left(E_0 - \frac{q}{C}\right)^{-C} = \left(E_0 - \frac{q_0}{C}\right)^{-C}\left(\frac{k_1}{k + k_2 t}\right)^{-1/k_2}$$

$$\implies E_0 - \frac{q}{C} = \left(E_0 - \frac{q_0}{C}\right)\left(\frac{k_1}{k + k_2 t}\right)^{1/Ck_2}$$

$$\implies q = E_0 C + (q_0 - E_0 C)\left(\frac{k_1}{k + k_2 t}\right)^{1/Ck_2}.$$

21. From $dA/dt = 4 - A/50$ we obtain $A = 200 + ce^{-t/50}$. If $A(0) = 30$ then $c = -170$ and $A = 200 - 170e^{-t/50}$.

22. From $dA/dt = 0 - A/50$ we obtain $A = ce^{-t/50}$. If $A(0) = 30$ then $c = 30$ and $A = 30e^{-t/50}$.

23. From $dA/dt = 10 - A/100$ we obtain $A = 1000 + ce^{-t/100}$. If $A(0) = 0$ then $c = -1000$ and $A = 1000 - 1000e^{-t/100}$.

24. From $\dfrac{dA}{dt} = 10 - \dfrac{10A}{500 - (10 - 5)t} = 10 - \dfrac{2A}{100 - t}$ we obtain $A = 1000 - 10t + c(100 - t)^2$. If $A(0) = 0$ then $c = -\dfrac{1}{10}$. The tank is empty in 100 minutes.

25. From $\dfrac{dA}{dt} = 3 - \dfrac{4A}{100 + (6 - 4)t} = 3 - \dfrac{2A}{50 + t}$ we obtain $A = 50 + t + c(50 + t)^{-2}$. If $A(0) = 10$ then $c = -100{,}000$ and $A(30) = 64.38$ pounds.

26. From $dA/dt = 0.18 - 4A/(400 - t)$ we obtain $A = .06(400 - t) + c(400 - t)^4$. If $A(0) = 12$ then $c = -12/400^4$ and $A(60) = 14.1$ gallons. The percentage of alcohol after 60 minutes is 4.1%. The tank is empty after 400 minutes.

27. (a) From $m\,dv/dt = mg - kv$ we obtain $v = gm/k + ce^{-kt/m}$. If $v(0) = v_0$ then $c = v_0 - gm/k$ and the solution of the initial-value problem is

$$v = \frac{gm}{k} + \left(v_0 - \frac{gm}{k}\right)e^{-kt/m}.$$

(b) As $t \to \infty$ the limiting velocity is gm/k.

(c) From $ds/dt = v$ and $s(0) = s_0$ we obtain

$$s = \frac{gm}{k}t - \frac{m}{k}\left(v_0 - \frac{gm}{k}\right)e^{-kt/m} + s_0 + \frac{m}{k}\left(v_0 - \frac{gm}{k}\right).$$

28. From $dX/dt = A - Bx$ and $X(0) = 0$ we obtain $x = A/B - (A/B)e^{-Bt}$ so that $x \to A/B$ as $t \to \infty$. If $X(T) = A/2B$ then $T = (\ln 2)/B$.

29. From $dE/dt = -E/RC$ and $E(t_1) = E_0$ we obtain $E = E_0 e^{(t_1 - t)/RC}$.

30. From $V\,dC/dt = kA(C_s - C)$ and $C(0) = C_0$ we obtain $C = C_s + (C_0 - C_s)e^{-kAt/V}$.

31. (a) From $dP/dt = (k_1 - k_2)P$ we obtain $P = P_0 e^{(k_1 - k_2)t}$ where $P_0 = P(0)$.

(b) If $k_1 > k_2$ then $P \to \infty$ as $t \to \infty$. If $k_1 = k_2$ then $P = P_0$ for every t. If $k_1 < k_2$ then $P \to 0$ as $t \to \infty$.

32. Separating variables we obtain

$$\frac{dP}{P} = k\cos t\,dt \implies \ln|P| = k\sin t + c \implies P = c_1 e^{k\sin t}.$$

If $P(0) = P_0$ then $c_1 = P_0$ and $P = P_0 e^{k\sin t}$.

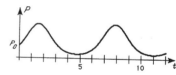

33. From $r^2 d\theta = (L/m)\,dt$ we obtain $A = \dfrac{1}{2}\displaystyle\int_{\theta_1}^{\theta_2} r^2 d\theta = \dfrac{1}{2}\dfrac{L}{m}\displaystyle\int_a^b dt = \dfrac{1}{2}\dfrac{L}{m}(b - a).$

34. Write the differential equation in the form $dA/dt + (k_1 + k_2)A = k_1 M$. Then an integrating factor is $e^{(k_1 + k_2)t}$, and

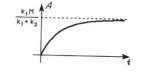

$$\frac{d}{dt}\left[e^{(k_1 + k_2)t}A\right] = k_1 M e^{(k_1 + k_2)t} \implies e^{(k_1 + k_2)t}A = \frac{k_1 M}{k_1 + k_2}e^{(k_1 + k_2)t} + c$$

$$\implies A = \frac{k_1 M}{k_1 + k_2} + ce^{-(k_1 + k_2)t}.$$

Using $A(0) = 0$ we find $c = -\dfrac{k_1 M}{k_1 + k_2}$ and $A = \dfrac{k_1 M}{k_1 + k_2}\left(1 - e^{-(k_1 + k_2)t}\right)$. As $t \to \infty$, $A \to \dfrac{k_1 M}{k_1 + k_2}$.

If $k_2 > 0$, the material will never be completely memorized.

Exercises 3.3

1. From $\dfrac{dC}{dt} = C(1 - .0005C)$ and $C(0) = 1$ we obtain $\left(\dfrac{1}{C} + \dfrac{.0005}{1 - .0005C}\right) dC = dt$ and

$C = \dfrac{1.0005e^t}{1 + .0005e^t}$. Then $C(10) = 1834$ supermarkets, and $C \rightarrow 2000$ as $t \rightarrow \infty$.

2. From $\dfrac{dN}{d} = N(a - bN)$ and $N(0) = 500$ we obtain $N = \dfrac{500a}{500b + (a - 500b)e^{-at}}$. Since

$\lim\limits_{t \to \infty} N = \dfrac{a}{b} = 50{,}000$ and $N(1) = 1000$ we have $a = .7033$, $b = .00014$, and $N = \dfrac{50{,}000}{1 + 99e^{-.7033t}}$.

3. From $\dfrac{dP}{dt} = P\left(10^{-1} - 10^{-7}P\right)$ and $P(0) = 5000$ we obtain $P = \dfrac{500}{.0005 + .0995e^{-.1t}}$ so that

$P \rightarrow 1{,}000{,}000$ as $t \rightarrow \infty$. If $P(t) = 500{,}000$ then $t = 52.9\,\text{months}$.

4. From $\dfrac{dP}{dt} = P(a - bP)\left(1 - cP^{-1}\right)$ we obtain $\left(\dfrac{b/(a - bc)}{a - bP} + \dfrac{1/(a - bc)}{P - c}\right) dP = dt$ and

$P = \dfrac{c + aEe^{(a-bc)t}}{1 + bEe^{(a-bc)t}}$ where E is an arbitrary constant.

5. (a) From $\dfrac{dP}{dt} = P(a - b \ln P)$ we obtain $\dfrac{-1}{b} \ln |a - b \ln P| = t + c_1$ so that $P = e^{a/b}e^{-ce^{-bt}}$.

(b) If $P(0) = P_0$ then $c = \dfrac{a}{b} - \ln P_0$.

6. From Problem 5 we have $P = e^{a/b}e^{-ce^{-bt}}$ so that

$$\dfrac{dP}{dt} = bce^{a/b-bt}e^{-ce^{-bt}} \quad \text{and} \quad \dfrac{d^2 P}{dt^2} = b^2 ce^{a/b-bt}e^{-ce^{-bt}}\left(ce^{-bt} - 1\right).$$

Setting $d^2P/dt^2 = 0$ and using $c = a/b - \ln P_0$ we obtain $t = (1/b)\ln(a/b - \ln P_0)$ and $P = e^{a/b-1}$.

7. Let $X = X(t)$ be the amount of C at time t and $\dfrac{dX}{dt} = k(120 - 2X)(150 - X)$. If $X(0) = 0$ and

$X(5) = 10$ then $X = \dfrac{150 - 150e^{180kt}}{1 - 2.5e^{180kt}}$ where $k = .0001259$, and $X(20) = 29.3\,\text{grams}$. Now $X \rightarrow 60$

as $t \rightarrow \infty$, so that the amount of $A \rightarrow 0$ and the amount of $B \rightarrow 30$ as $t \rightarrow \infty$.

8. From $\dfrac{dX}{dt} = k(150 - X)^2$, $X(0) = 0$, and $X(5) = 10$ we obtain $X = 150 - \dfrac{150}{150kt + 1}$ where $k = .000095238$. Then $X(20) = 33.3\,\text{grams}$ and $X \rightarrow 150$ as $t \rightarrow \infty$ so that the amount of $A \rightarrow 0$ and the amount of $B \rightarrow 0$ as $t \rightarrow \infty$. If $X(t) = 75$ then $t = 70\,\text{minutes}$.

9. If $\alpha \neq \beta$, $\dfrac{dX}{dt} = k(\alpha - X)(\beta - X)$, and $X(0) = 0$ then $\left(\dfrac{1/(\beta - \alpha)}{\alpha - X} + \dfrac{1/(\alpha - \beta)}{\beta - X}\right) dX = k\,dt$ so that

$$X = \frac{\alpha\beta - \alpha\beta e^{(\alpha-\beta)kt}}{\beta - \alpha e^{(\alpha-\beta)kt}}. \text{ If } \alpha = \beta \text{ then } \frac{1}{(\alpha - X)^2}\,dX = k\,dt \quad \text{and} \quad X = \alpha - \frac{1}{kt + c}.$$

10. From $\dfrac{dX}{dt} = k(\alpha - X)(\beta - X)(\gamma - X)$ we obtain

$$\left(\frac{1}{(\beta - \alpha)(\gamma - \alpha)} \cdot \frac{1}{\alpha - X} + \frac{1}{(\alpha - \beta)(\gamma - \beta)} \cdot \frac{1}{\beta - X} + \frac{1}{(\alpha - \gamma)(\beta - \gamma)} \cdot \frac{1}{\gamma - X}\right) dX = k\,dt$$

so that

$$\frac{-1}{((\beta - \alpha)(\gamma - \alpha)}\ln|\alpha - X| + \frac{-1}{(\alpha - \beta)(\gamma - \beta)}\ln|\beta - X| + \frac{-1}{(\alpha - \gamma)(\beta - \gamma)}\ln|\gamma - X| = kt + c.$$

11. (a) As $y \to \infty$ we assume that $v \to 0^+$. Then $v_0^2 = 2gR$ and $v_0 = \sqrt{2gR}$.

(b) Using $g = 32$ ft/s and $R = 4000(5280)$ ft we find

$$v_0 = \sqrt{2(32)(4000)(5280)} \approx 36765.2 \text{ ft/s} \approx 25067 \text{ mi/hr.}$$

(c) $v_0 = \sqrt{2(0.165)(32)(1080)} \approx 7760$ ft/s ≈ 5291 mi/hr

12. From $\dfrac{d^2y}{dx^2} = \dfrac{w}{T_1}\sqrt{1 + \left(\dfrac{dy}{dx}\right)^2}$, $p = \dfrac{dy}{dx}$, and $y'(0) = 0$ we obtain $p + \sqrt{1 + p^2} = e^{wx/T_1}$ so that

$p = \sinh\dfrac{w}{T_1}x$. From $y(0) = 1$ it follows that $y = \dfrac{T_1}{w}\cosh\dfrac{w}{T_1}x + 1 - \dfrac{T_1}{w}$.

13. From $x\dfrac{d^2y}{dx^2} = \dfrac{v_1}{v_2}\sqrt{1 + \left(\dfrac{dy}{dx}\right)^2}$, $p = \dfrac{dy}{dx}$, and $y'(1) = 0$ we obtain $p = \dfrac{1}{2}\left(x^{v_1/v_2} - x^{-v_1/v_2}\right)$. If

$y(1) = 0$ and $v_1 = v_2$ then $y = \dfrac{1}{4}x^2 - \dfrac{1}{2}\ln|x| - \dfrac{1}{4}$. If $y(1) = 0$ and $v_1 \ne v_2$ then

$$y = \frac{1}{2}\left[\frac{x^{v_1/v_2+1}}{v_1/v_2 + 1} - \frac{x^{1-v_1/v_2}}{1 - v_1/v_2}\right] + \frac{v_1v_2}{v_2^2 - v_1^2}.$$

14. From $\dfrac{dT}{dt} = k\left(T^4 - T_m^4\right)$ we obtain

$$\left[\frac{1/\left(4T_m^3\right)}{T - T_m} - \frac{1/\left(4T_m^3\right)}{T + T_m} - \frac{1/\left(2T_m^2\right)}{T^2 + T_m^2}\right] dT = k\,dt$$

so that
$$\ln\left|\frac{T - T_m}{T + T_m}\right| - 2\tan^{-1}\frac{T}{T_m} = 4T_m^3 kt + c.$$

15. From $\dfrac{dh}{dt} = -\dfrac{\sqrt{h}}{25}$ and $h(0) = 20$ we obtain $h = \left(\sqrt{20} - \dfrac{t}{50}\right)^2$. If $h(t) = 0$ then $t = 50\sqrt{20}$ seconds.

16. If $h = 0$ then $r^{1/2} = \sqrt{2\mu}\, dt$ so that $\frac{2}{3}r^{3/2} = \sqrt{2\mu}\, t + c$. If $h > 0$ then $\dfrac{r^{1/2}}{\sqrt{2\mu + 2hr}}\, dr = dt$. From a table of integrals we find

$$\frac{1}{2h}\left(2\mu r + 2hr^2\right)^{1/2} - \frac{2\mu}{(2h)^{3/2}}\ln\left(\sqrt{\mu + hr} + \sqrt{hr}\right) = t + c.$$

17. From $\dfrac{dy}{dx} = \dfrac{-y}{\sqrt{100 - y^2}}$ and $h(0) = 10$ we obtain $10\displaystyle\int (\csc\theta - \sin\theta)\, d\theta = -dx$ where $y = 10\sin\theta$.

Then

$$10\ln\left|\frac{10}{y} + \frac{\sqrt{100 - y^2}}{y}\right| - \sqrt{100 - y^2} = x.$$

18. From $m\dfrac{dv}{dt} = mg - kv^2$ and $v(0) = v_0$ we obtain

$$\left[\frac{1/2g}{1 - \sqrt{k/mg}\, v} + \frac{1/2g}{1 + \sqrt{k/mg}\, v}\right] dv = dt$$

so that

$$\frac{v + \sqrt{mg/k}}{v - \sqrt{mg/k}} = \frac{v_0 + \sqrt{mg/k}}{v_0 - \sqrt{mg/k}}\, e^{2\sqrt{gk/m}\, t}.$$

Divide this equation by $e^{2\sqrt{gk/m}\, t}$ and multiply by $v - \sqrt{mg/k}$ to see that $v \to \sqrt{mg/k}$ as $t \to \infty$.

19. Let $x\left(\dfrac{dx}{dy}\right)^2 + 2y\dfrac{dx}{dy} = x$ and $w = x^2$ so that $\dfrac{dw}{dy} = 2x\dfrac{dx}{dy}$ and $w = y\dfrac{dw}{dy} + \dfrac{1}{4}\left(\dfrac{dw}{dy}\right)^2$, a Clairaut equation. The solution is $x^2 = cy + \dfrac{1}{4}c^2$, which is a family of parabolas.

20. From $x\left(\dfrac{dx}{dy}\right)^2 + 2y\dfrac{dx}{dy} - x = 0$ and the quadratic formula we obtain

$$\frac{dx}{dy} = \frac{-y \pm \sqrt{x^2 + y^2}}{x} \quad\text{or}\quad \frac{x}{\sqrt{x^2 + y^2}}\, dx + \frac{y}{\sqrt{x^2 + y^2}}\, dy = \pm dy.$$

Then $\sqrt{x^2 + y^2} = \pm y + c$.

21. Using $\dfrac{dy}{dx} = \dfrac{dy}{dt}\Big/\dfrac{dx}{dt}$ we obtain $\left(\dfrac{-\gamma + \delta y}{y}\right) dy = \left(\dfrac{\alpha - \beta x}{x}\right) dx$. Using $x \geq 0$ and $y \geq 0$ we have $-\gamma\ln y + \delta y = \alpha\ln x - \beta x + c$.

22. From $y\left[1 + (y')^2\right] = k$ we obtain $dx = \dfrac{\sqrt{y}}{\sqrt{k - y}}\, dy$. If $y = k\sin^2\theta$ then

$$dy = 2k\sin\theta\cos\theta\, d\theta, \quad dx = 2k\left(\frac{1}{2} - \frac{1}{2}\cos 2\theta\right) d\theta, \quad\text{and}\quad x = k\theta - \frac{k}{2}\sin 2\theta + c.$$

If $x = 0$ when $\theta = 0$ then $c = 0$.

23. (a) From $2\dfrac{d\theta}{dt}\dfrac{d^2\theta}{dt^2}\,dt = -\dfrac{2g}{l}\sin\theta\,d\theta$ and $\dfrac{d\theta}{dt}\Big|_{t=0} = 0$, $\theta(0) = \theta_0$ we obtain

$$\left(\frac{d\theta}{dt}\right)^2 = \frac{2g}{l}(\cos\theta - \cos\theta_0).$$

(b) Solving $\left(\dfrac{d\theta}{dt}\right)^2 = \dfrac{2g}{l}(\cos\theta - \cos\theta_0)$ for $\dfrac{d\theta}{dt}$ and separating variables we obtain

$$\int_{\theta_0}^0 \sqrt{\frac{l}{2g}}\cdot\frac{1}{\sqrt{\cos\theta - \cos\theta_0}}\,d\theta = \int_0^{T/4} dt \quad\text{or}\quad T = 2\sqrt{\frac{2l}{g}}\int_0^{\theta_0}\frac{d\theta}{\sqrt{\cos\theta - \cos\theta_0}}.$$

———— Chapter 3 Review Exercises ————

1. From $y\left(x^3 + c_1\right) = 3$ we obtain $y' = -x^2 y^2$ so that the differential equation of the orthogonal family is $y' = \dfrac{1}{x^2 y^2}$. The orthogonal trajectories are $y^3 + \dfrac{3}{x} = c_2$.

2. From $y = 4x + 1 + c_1 e^{4x}$ we obtain $y = 4y - 16x$ so that the differential equation of the orthogonal family is $Y' = \dfrac{1}{16x - 4y}$. Then $\dfrac{dx}{dy} - 16x = -4y$ and $x = \dfrac{1}{4}y + \dfrac{1}{64} + c_2 e^{16y}$. If $x(0) = 0$ then $c_2 = -\dfrac{1}{64}$.

3. From $y - 2 = c_1(x-1)^2$ we obtain $y' = \dfrac{2(y-2)}{x-1}$ so that the differential equation of the orthogonal family is $y' = \dfrac{1-x}{2(y-2)}$. The orthogonal trajectories are $(y-2)^2 = x - \dfrac{1}{2}x^2 + c_2$.

4. From $\dfrac{dP}{dt} = kP$ and $P(0) = P_0$ we obtain $P = P_0 e^{kt}$. If $P(T) = 2P_0$ then $T = \dfrac{1}{k}\ln 2$.

5. From $\dfrac{dP}{dt} = 0.018P$ and $P(0) = 4$ billion we obtain $P = 4e^{.018t}$ so that $P(45) = 8.99$ billion.

6. Let $A = A(t)$ be the volume of CO_2 at time t. From $\dfrac{dA}{dt} = 1.2 - \dfrac{A}{4}$ and $A(0) = 16\,\text{ft}^3$ we obtain $A = 4.8 + 11.2e^{-t/4}$. Since $A(10) = 5.7\,\text{ft}^3$, the concentration is 0.017%. As $t \to \infty$ we have $A \to 4.8\,\text{ft}^3$ or 0.06%.

7. From $\dfrac{dx}{dt} = k_1 x(\alpha - x)$ we obtain $\left(\dfrac{1/\alpha}{x} + \dfrac{1/\alpha}{\alpha - x}\right)dx = k_1\,dt$ so that $x = \dfrac{\alpha c_1 e^{\alpha k_1 t}}{1 + c_1 e^{\alpha k_1 t}}$. From $\dfrac{dy}{dt} = k_2 xy$ we obtain

$$\ln|y| = \frac{k_2}{k_1}\ln\left|1 + c_1 e^{\alpha k_1 t}\right| + c \quad\text{or}\quad y = c_2\left(1 + c_1 e^{\alpha k_1 t}\right)^{k_2/k_1}.$$

8. (a) Let $\dfrac{dv}{dt} = v\dfrac{dv}{dy}$ so that $m\dfrac{dv}{dt} = -mg - kv^2$ becomes $mv\dfrac{dv}{dy} = -mg - kv^2$. Using $y(0) = 0$

and $v(0) = v_0$ it follows that $v^2 = \dfrac{mg + kv_0^2}{k}e^{-2ky/m} - \dfrac{mg}{k}$. If $v = 0$ then the maximum

height is $h = \dfrac{m}{2k}\ln\dfrac{mg + kv_0^2}{mg}$. From $mv\dfrac{dv}{dy} = mg - kv^2$, $v(0) = 0$, and $y(0) = 0$ we find that

$v^2 = \dfrac{mg}{k}\left(1 - e^{-2ky/m}\right)$. Letting $y \to \infty$ we see that the terminal velocity is $v = \sqrt{mg/k}$.

This is the square root of the result obtained in Problem 27 of Exercises 3.2.

(b) Setting $y = h$ we see that the velocity at impact is $v_i = \dfrac{v_0}{\sqrt{1 + \frac{k}{mg}v_0^2}}$.

9. (a) The differential equation is

$$\dfrac{dT}{dt} = k[T - T_2 - B(T_1 - T)] = k[(1 + B)T - (BT_1 + T_2)].$$

Separating variables we obtain $\dfrac{dT}{(1 + B)T - (BT_1 + T_2)} = k\,dt$. Then

$$\dfrac{1}{1 + B}\ln|(1 + B)T - (BT_1 + T_2)| = kt + c \quad \text{and} \quad T(t) = \dfrac{BT_1 + T_2}{1 + B} + c_3 e^{k(1+B)t}.$$

Since $T(0) = T_1$ we must have $c_3 = \dfrac{T_1 - T_2}{1 + B}$ and so

$$T(t) = \dfrac{BT_1 + T_2}{1 + B} + \dfrac{T_1 - T_2}{1 + B}e^{k(1+B)t}.$$

(b) Since $k < 0$, $\displaystyle\lim_{t\to\infty} e^{k(1+B)t} = 0$ and $\displaystyle\lim_{t\to\infty} T(t) = \dfrac{BT_1 + T_2}{1 + B}$.

(c) Since $T_s = T_2 + B(T_1 - T)$, $\displaystyle\lim_{t\to\infty} T_s = T_2 + BT_1 - B\left(\dfrac{BT_1 + T_2}{1 + B}\right) = \dfrac{BT_1 + T_2}{1 + B}$.

10. We first solve $\left(1 - \dfrac{t}{10}\right)\dfrac{di}{dt} + 0.2i = 4$. Separating variables we obtain

$\dfrac{di}{40 - 2i} = \dfrac{dt}{10 - t}$. Then

$$-\dfrac{1}{2}\ln|40 - 2i| = -\ln|10 - t| + c \quad \text{or} \quad \sqrt{40 - 2i} = c_1(10 - t).$$

Since $i(0) = 0$ we must have $c_1 = 2/\sqrt{10}$. Solving for i we get $i(t) = 4t - \frac{1}{5}t^2$,

$0 \le t < 10$. For $t \ge 10$ the equation for the current becomes $0.2i = 4$ or $i = 20$. Thus

$$i(t) = \begin{cases} 4t - \frac{1}{5}t^2, & 0 \le t < 10 \\ 20, & t \ge 10 \end{cases}.$$

4 Linear Differential Equations of Higher Order

Exercises 4.1

1. From $y = c_1 e^x + c_2 e^{-x}$ we find $y' = c_1 e^x - c_2 e^{-x}$. Then $y(0) = c_1 + c_2 = 0$, $y'(0) = c_1 - c_2 = 1$ so that $c_1 = 1/2$ and $c_2 = -1/2$. The solution is $y = \frac{1}{2}e^x - \frac{1}{2}e^{-x}$.

2. We have $y(0) = c_1 + c_2 = 0$, $y'(0) = c_1 e + c_2 e^{-1} = 1$ so that $c_1 = e/\left(e^2 - 1\right)$ and $c_2 = -e/\left(e^2 - 1\right)$. The solution is $y = e\left(e^x - e^{-x}\right)/\left(e^2 - 1\right)$.

3. From $y = c_1 e^{4x} + c_2 e^{-x}$ we find $y' = 4c_1 e^{4x} - c_2 e^{-x}$. Then $y(0) = c_1 + c_2 = 1$, $y'(0) = 4c_1 - c_2 = 2$ so that $c_1 = 3/5$ and $c_2 = 2/5$. The solution is $y = \frac{3}{5}e^{4x} + \frac{2}{5}e^{-x}$.

4. From $y = c_1 + c_2 \cos x + c_3 \sin x$ we find $y' = -c_2 \sin x + c_3 \cos x$ and $y'' = -c_2 \cos x - c_3 \sin x$. Then $y(\pi) = c_1 - c_2 = 0$, $y'(\pi) = -c_3 = 2$, $y''(\pi) = c_2 = -1$ so that $c_1 = -1$, $c_2 = -1$, and $c_3 = -2$. The solution is $y = -1 - \cos x - 2 \sin x$.

5. From $y = c_1 x + c_2 x \ln x$ we find $y' = c_1 + c_2(1 + \ln x)$. Then $y(1) = c_1 = 3$, $y'(1) = c_1 + c_2 = -1$ so that $c_1 = 3$ and $c_2 = -4$. The solution is $y = 3x - 4x \ln x$.

6. From $y = c_1 + c_2 x^2$ we find $y' = 2c_2 x$. Then $y(0) = c_1 = 0$, $y'(0) = 2c_2 \cdot 0 = 0$ and $y'(0) = 1$ is not possible. Since $a_2(x) = x$ is 0 at $x = 0$, Theorem 4.1 is not violated.

7. In this case we have $y(0) = c_1 = 0$, $y'(0) = 2c_2 \cdot 0 = 0$ so $c_1 = 0$ and c_2 is arbitrary. Two solutions are $y = x^2$ and $y = 2x^2$.

8. In this case we have $y(0) = c_1 = 1$, $y'(1) = 2c_2 = 6$ so that $c_1 = 1$ and $c_2 = 3$. The solution is $y = 1 + 3x^2$. Theorem 4.1 does not apply because y and y' are evaluated at different points.

9. From $y = c_1 e^x \cos x + c_2 e^x \sin x$ we find $y' = c_1 e^x(-\sin x + \cos x) + c_2 e^x(\cos x + \sin x)$.

    (a) We have $y(0) = c_1 = 1$, $y'(0) = c_1 + c_2 = 0$ so that $c_1 = 1$ and $c_2 = -1$. The solution is $y = e^x \cos x - e^x \sin x$.

    (b) We have $y(0) = c_1 = 1$, $y(\pi) = -c_1 e^\pi = -1$, which is not possible.

    (c) We have $y(0) = c_1 = 1$, $y(\pi/2) = c_2 e^{\pi/2} = 1$ so that $c_1 = 1$ and $c_2 = e^{-\pi/2}$. The solution is $y = e^x \cos x + e^{-\pi/2} e^x \sin x$.

    (d) We have $y(0) = c_1 = 0$, $y(\pi) = -c_1 e^\pi = 0$ so that $c_1 = 0$ and c_2 is arbitrary. Solutions are $y = c_2 e^x \sin x$, for any real numbers c_2.

10. (a) We have $y(-1) = c_1 + c_2 + 3 = 0$, $y(1) = c_1 + c_2 + 3 = 4$, which is not possible.

(b) We have $y(0) = c_1 \cdot 0 + c_2 \cdot 0 + 3 = 1$, which is not possible.

(c) We have $y(0) = c_1 \cdot 0 + c_2 \cdot 0 + 3 = 3$, $y(1) = c_1 + c_2 + 3 = 0$ so that c_1 is arbitrary and $c_2 = -3 - c_1$. Solutions are $y = c_1 x^2 - (c_1 + 3)x^4 + 3$.

(d) We have $y(1) = c_1 + c_2 + 3 = 3$, $y(2) = 4c_1 + 16c_2 + 3 = 15$ so that $c_1 = -1$ and $c_2 = 1$. The solution is $y = -x^2 + x^4 + 3$.

11. Since $a_2(x) = x - 2$ and $x_0 = 0$ the problem has a unique solution for $-\infty < x < 2$.

12. Since $a_1(x) = \tan x$ and $x_0 = 0$ the problem has a unique solution for $-\pi/2 < x < \pi/2$.

13. From $y = c_1 \cos \lambda x + c_2 \sin \lambda x$ we have $y(0) = c_1 = 0$, $y(\pi) = c_1 \cos \lambda \pi + c_2 \sin \lambda \pi = 0$, so that $c_1 = 0$ and $c_2 \sin \lambda \pi = 0$. The problem will have nontrivial solutions when $c_2 \neq 0$. Thus we require that $\sin \lambda \pi = 0$ or λ be a nonzero integer. (If $\lambda = 0$, the family of solutions is $y = c_1 = 0$.)

14. From $y = c_1 \cos \lambda x + c_2 \sin \lambda x$ we have $y(0) = c_1 = 0$, $y(5) = c_1 \cos 5\lambda + c_2 \sin 5\lambda = 0$, so that $c_1 = 0$ and $c_2 \sin 5\lambda = 0$. The problem will have nontrivial solutions when $c_2 \neq 0$. Thus we require that $\sin 5\lambda = 0$ or $\lambda = n\pi/5$ for n a nonzero integer. (If $\lambda = 0$, the family of solutions is $y = c_1 = 0$.)

15. Since $(-4)x + (3)x^2 + (1)(4x - 3x^2) = 0$ the functions are linearly dependent.

16. Since $(1)0 + (0)x + (0)e^x = 0$ the functions are linearly dependent. A similar argument shows that any set of functions containing $f(x) = 0$ will be linearly dependent.

17. Since $(-1/5)5 + (1) \cos^2 x + (1) \sin^2 x = 0$ the functions are linearly dependent.

18. Since $(1) \cos 2x + (1)1 + (-2) \cos^2 x = 0$ the functions are linearly dependent.

19. Since $(-4)x + (3)(x - 1) + (1)(x + 3) = 0$ the functions are linearly dependent.

20. From the graphs of $f_1(x) = 2 + x$ and $f_2(x) = 2 + |x|$ we see that the functions are linearly independent since they can not be multiples of each other.

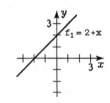 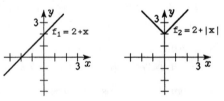

21. The functions are linearly independent since $W\left(1 + x, x, x^2\right) = \begin{vmatrix} 1 + x & x & x^2 \\ 1 & 1 & 2x \\ 0 & 0 & 2 \end{vmatrix} = 2 \neq 0.$

22. Since $(-1/2)e^x + (1/2)e^{-x} + (1) \sinh x = 0$ the functions are linearly dependent.

23. $W\left(x^{1/2}, x^2\right) = \begin{vmatrix} x^{1/2} & x^2 \\ \frac{1}{2}x^{-1/2} & 2x \end{vmatrix} = \frac{3}{2}x^{3/2} \neq 0$ for $0 < x < \infty$.

24. $W\left(1+x, x^3\right) = \begin{vmatrix} 1+x & x^3 \\ 1 & 3x^2 \end{vmatrix} = x^2(3+2x) \neq 0$ for $-\infty < x < \infty$.

25. $W(\sin x, \csc x) = \begin{vmatrix} \sin x & \csc x \\ \cos x & -\csc x \cot x \end{vmatrix} = -2\cot x \neq 0$ for $0 < x < \pi$.

26. $W(\tan x, \cot x) = \begin{vmatrix} \tan x & \cot x \\ \sec^2 x & -\csc^2 x \end{vmatrix} = -2\sec x \csc x \neq 0$ for $0 < x < \pi/2$.

27. $W\left(e^x, e^{-x}, e^{4x}\right) = \begin{vmatrix} e^x & e^{-x} & e^{4x} \\ e^x & -e^{-x} & 4e^{4x} \\ e^x & e^{-x} & 16e^{4x} \end{vmatrix} = -30e^{4x} \neq 0$ for $-\infty < x < \infty$.

28. $W\left(x, x\ln x, x^2\ln x\right) = \begin{vmatrix} x & x\ln x & x^2\ln x \\ 1 & 1+\ln x & x+2x\ln x \\ 0 & \frac{1}{x} & 3+2\ln x \end{vmatrix} = x(2+\ln x) \neq 0$ for $0 < x < \infty$.

29. No, this does not imply that f_1 and f_2 are linearly dependent on any interval containing $x=0$. We need $c_1 f(x) + c_2 f(x) = 0$ for *all* values of x in the interval.

30. **(a)** The graphs of f_1 and f_2 are as shown. Obviously, neither function is a constant multiple of the other on $-\infty < x < \infty$. Hence, f_1 and f_2 are linearly independent on $(-\infty, \infty)$.

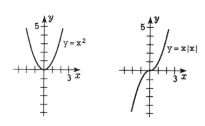

(b) For $x \geq 0$, $f_2 = x^2$ and so $W(f_1, f_2) = \begin{vmatrix} x^2 & x^2 \\ 2x & 2x \end{vmatrix} = 2x^3 - 2x^3 = 0$. For $x < 0$, $f_2 = -x^2$ and

$W(f_1, f_2) = \begin{vmatrix} x^2 & -x^2 \\ 2x & -2x \end{vmatrix} = -2x^3 + 2x^3 = 0$. We conclude that $W(f_1, f_2) = 0$ for all real values of x.

31. **(a)** If $y = 1/x$ then $y' = -1/x^2$ and $y'' = 2/x^3$ so that $y'' - 2y^3 = 0$.

(b) If $y = c/x$ then $y'' - 2y^3 = 0$ implies that $c^3 - c = 0$ so that $c = 0, +1$, or -1.

32. **(a)** Clearly $y_1 = 1$ and $y_2 = \ln x$ satisfy $y'' + (y')^2 = 0$.

(b) If $y = y_1 + y_2 = 1 + \ln x$ then $y'' + (y')^2 = \dfrac{-1}{x^2} + \dfrac{1}{x^2} = 0$. If $y = c_1 y_1 + c_2 y_2 = c_1 + c_2 \ln x$ then

$y'' + (y')^2 = \dfrac{-c_2}{x^2} + \dfrac{c_2^2}{x^2} \neq 0$ for $c_2 \neq 0$ or 1.

33. The functions satisfy the differential equation and are linearly independent since

$$W\left(e^{-3x}, e^{4x}\right) = 7e^x \neq 0$$

for $-\infty < x < \infty$. The general solution is

$$y = c_1 e^{-3x} + c_2 e^{4x}.$$

34. The functions satisfy the differential equation and are linearly independent since

$$W(\cosh 2x, \sinh 2x) = 2$$

for $-\infty < x < \infty$. The general solution is

$$y = c_1 \cosh 2x + c_2 \sinh 2x.$$

35. The functions satisfy the differential equation and are linearly independent since

$$W\left(e^x \cos 2x, e^x \sin 2x\right) = 2e^{2x} \neq 0$$

for $-\infty < x < \infty$. The general solution is $y = c_1 e^x \cos 2x + c_2 e^x \sin 2x$.

36. The functions satisfy the differential equation and are linearly independent since

$$W\left(e^{x/2}, xe^{x/2}\right) = e^x \neq 0$$

for $-\infty < x < \infty$. The general solution is

$$y = c_1 e^{x/2} + c_2 x e^{x/2}.$$

37. The functions satisfy the differential equation and are linearly independent since

$$W\left(x^3, x^4\right) = x^6 \neq 0$$

for $0 < x < \infty$. The general solution is

$$y = c_1 x^3 + c_2 x^4.$$

38. The functions satisfy the differential equation and are linearly independent since

$$W\left(\cos(\ln x), \sin(\ln x)\right) = 1/x \neq 0$$

for $0 < x < \infty$. The general solution is

$$y = c_1 \cos(\ln x) + c_2 \sin(\ln x).$$

39. The functions satisfy the differential equation and are linearly independent since

$$W\left(x, x^{-2}, x^{-2} \ln x\right) = 9x^{-6} \neq 0$$

for $0 < x < \infty$. The general solution is

$$y = c_1 x + c_2 x^{-2} + c_3 x^{-2} \ln x.$$

70

40. The functions satisfy the differential equation and are linearly independent since

$$W(1, x, \cos x, \sin x) = 1$$

for $-\infty < x < \infty$. The general solution is

$$y = c_1 + c_2 x + c_3 \cos x + c_4 \sin x.$$

41. The functions $y_1 = e^{2x}$ and $y_2 = e^{5x}$ form a fundamental set of solutions of the homogeneous equation, and $y_p = 6e^x$ is a particular solution of the nonhomogeneous equation.

42. The functions $y_1 = \cos x$ and $y_2 = \sin x$ form a fundamental set of solutions of the homogeneous equation, and $y_p = x \sin x + (\cos x) \ln(\cos x)$ is a particular solution of the nonhomogeneous equation.

43. The functions $y_1 = e^{2x}$ and $y_2 = xe^{2x}$ form a fundamental set of solutions of the homogeneous equation, and $y_p = x^2 e^{2x} + x - 2$ is a particular solution of the nonhomogeneous equation.

44. The functions $y_1 = x^{-1/2}$ and $y_2 = x^{-1}$ form a fundamental set of solutions of the homogeneous equation, and $y_p = \frac{1}{15}x^2 - \frac{1}{6}x$ is a particular solution of the nonhomogeneous equation.

45. (a) From the graphs of $y_1 = x^3$ and $y_2 = |x|^3$ we see that the functions are linearly independent since they cannot be multiples of each other. It is easily shown that $y_1 = x^3$ solves $x^2 y'' - 4xy' + 6y = 0$. To show that $y_2 = |x|^3$ is a solution let $y_2 = x^3$ for $x \geq 0$ and let $y_2 = -x^3$ for $x < 0$.

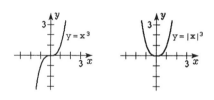

(b) If $x \geq 0$ then $y_2 = x^3$ and $W(y_1, y_2) = \begin{vmatrix} x^3 & x^3 \\ 3x^2 & 3x^2 \end{vmatrix} = 0$. If $x < 0$ then $y_2 = -x^3$ and

$$W(y_1, y_2) = \begin{vmatrix} x^3 & -x^3 \\ 3x^2 & -3x^2 \end{vmatrix} = 0.$$

(c) Part (b) does not violate Theorem 4.4 since $a_2(x) = x^2$ is zero at $x = 0$.

(d) The functions $Y_1 = x^3$ and $Y_2 = x^2$ are solutions of $x^2 y'' - 4xy' + 6y = 0$. They are linearly independent since $W\left(x^3, x^2\right) = x^4 \neq 0$ for $-\infty < x < \infty$.

(e) The function $y = x^3$ satisfies $y(0) = 0$ and $y'(0) = 0$.

(f) Neither is the general solution since we form a general solution on an interval for which $a_2(x) \neq 0$ for every x in the interval.

46. Assume y_1 satisfies $y(x_0) = 1$ and $y'(x_0) = 0$ and y_2 satisfies $y(x_0) = 0$ and $y'(x_0) = 1$. By Theorem 4.2 they are linearly independent since $W(y_1, y_2) = y_1(x)y_2'(x) - y_1'(x)y_2(x) = 1$ at $x = x_0$. Thus, y_1 and y_2 form a fundamental set of solutions on I.

47. (a) Assume y_1 and y_2 are solutions of $a_2 y'' + a_1 y' + a_0 y = 0$. If $W(y_1, y_2) = y_1 y_2' - y_1' y_2$ then

$$a_2 \frac{dW}{dx} + a_1 W = a_2 \left(y_1 y_2'' - y_1'' y_2 \right) + a_1 \left(y_1 y_2' - y_1' y_2 \right) + a_0 y_1 y_2 - a_0 y_1 y_2$$

$$= y_1 \left(a_2 y_2'' + a_1 y_2' + a_0 y_2 \right) - y_2 \left(a_2 y_1'' + a_1 y_1' + a_0 y_1 \right)$$

$$= y_1(0) - y_2(0) = 0.$$

(b) The equation in part **(a)** is first-order linear. The solution is $W = ce^{-\int [a_1(x)/a_2(x)] \, dx}$, where c is a constant.

(c) Let $x = x_0$ in $W = ce^{-\int_{x_0}^{x} [a_1(t)/a_2(t)] \, dt}$, obtaining $c = W(x_0)$.

(d) From part **(c)** we see that if $W(x_0) = 0$ then $W = 0$ for every x in I. If $W(x_0) \neq 0$ then $W \neq 0$ for every x in I since W is an exponential function.

48. We identify $a_2(x) = 1 - x^2$ and $a_1(x) = -2x$. Then from Abel's formula in Problem 47 we have

$$W = ce^{-\int [a_1(x)/a_2(x)] \, dx} = ce^{-\int [-2x/(1-x^2)] \, dx} = ce^{-\ln(1-x^2)} = \frac{c}{1 - x^2}.$$

49. We identify $a_2(x) = x$ and $a_1(x) = 1$. Then from the alternative form of Abel's formula in Problem 47(c) we have

$$W = W(x_0) e^{-\int_{x_0}^{x} (1/t) \, dt} = \begin{vmatrix} k_1 & k_3 \\ k_2 & k_4 \end{vmatrix} e^{-\ln t \big|_{x_0}^{x}} = (k_1 k_4 - k_2 k_3) e^{-\ln x + \ln x_0}$$

$$= (k_1 k_4 - k_2 k_3) e^{\ln(x_0/x)} = \frac{(k_1 k_4 - k_2 k_3) x_0}{x}.$$

50. We have $a_2 y_1'' + a_1 y_1' + a_0 = E_1$ and $a_2 y_2'' + a_1 y_2' + a_0 = E_2$. Then

$$a_2 (y_1 + y_2)'' + a_1 (y_1 + y_2)' + a_0 = (a_2 y_1'' + a_1 y_1' + a_0) + (a_2 y_2'' + a_1 y_2' + a_0) = E_1 + E_2$$

and $y_1 + y_2$ is a response of the system to the input $E_1 + E_2$.

Exercises 4.2

In Problems 1-10 we use reduction of order to find a secoond solution. In Problems 11-30 we use formula (4) from the text.

1. Define $y = u(x) \cdot 1$ so

$$y' = u', \quad y'' = u'', \quad \text{and} \quad y'' + 5y' = u'' + 5u' = 0.$$

If $w = u'$ we obtain the first-order equation $w' + 5w = 0$ which has the integrating factor $e^{5 \int dx} = e^{5x}$.

Now
$$\frac{d}{dx} [e^{5x} w] = 0 \quad \text{gives} \quad e^{5x} w = c.$$

Therefore $w = u' = ce^{-5x}$ and $u = c_1 e^{-5x}$. A second solution is $y_2 = e^{-5x}$.

2. Define $y = u(x) \cdot 1$ so

$$y' = u', \quad y'' = u'', \quad \text{and} \quad y'' - y' = u'' - u' = 0.$$

If $w = u'$ we obtain the first-order equation $w' - w = 0$ which has the integrating factor $e^{-\int dx} = e^{-x}$.

Now
$$\frac{d}{dx}[e^{-x}w] = 0 \quad \text{gives} \quad e^{-x}w = c.$$

Therefore $w = u' = ce^x$ and $u = ce^x$. A second solution is $y_2 = e^x$.

3. Define $y = u(x)e^{2x}$ so

$$y' = 2ue^{2x} + u'e^{2x}, \quad y'' = e^{2x}u'' + 4e^{2x}u' + 4e^{2x}u, \quad \text{and} \quad y'' - 4y' + 4y = 4e^{2x}u'' = 0.$$

Therefore $u'' = 0$ and $u = c_1 x + c_2$. Taking $c_1 = 1$ and $c_2 = 0$ we see that a second solution is $y_2 = xe^{2x}$.

4. Defing $y = u(x)xe^{-x}$ so

$$y' = (1-x)e^{-x}u + xe^{-x}u', \quad y'' = xe^{-x}u'' + 2(1-x)e^{-x}u' - (2-x)e^{-x}u,$$

and
$$y'' + 2y' + y = e^{-x}(xu'' + 2u') = 0 \quad \text{or} \quad u'' + \frac{2}{x}u' = 0.$$

If $w = u'$ we obtain the first-order equation $w' + \frac{2}{x}w = 0$ which has the integrating factor $e^{2\int dx/x} = x^2$. Now

$$\frac{d}{dx}[x^2 w] = 0 \quad \text{gives} \quad x^2 w = c.$$

Therefore $w = u' = c/x^2$ and $u = c_1/x$. A second solution is $y_2 = \frac{1}{x}xe^{-x} = e^{-x}$.

5. Define $y = u(x)\cos 4x$ so

$$y' = -4u\sin 4x + u'\cos 4x, \quad y'' = u''\cos 4x - 8u'\sin 4x - 16u\cos 4x$$

and
$$y'' + 16y = (\cos 4x)u'' - 8(\sin 4x)u' = 0 \quad \text{or} \quad u'' - 8(\tan 4x)u' = 0.$$

If $w = u'$ we obtain the first-order equation $w' - 8(\tan 4x)w = 0$ which has the integrating factor $e^{-8\int \tan 4x \, dx} = \cos^2 4x$. Now

$$\frac{d}{dx}[(\cos^2 4x)w] = 0 \quad \text{gives} \quad (\cos^2 4x)w = c.$$

Therefore $w = u' = c\sec^2 4x$ and $u = c_1 \tan 4x$. A second solution is $y_2 = \tan 4x \cos 4x = \sin 4x$.

6. Define $y = u(x)\sin 3x$ so

$$y' = 3u\cos 3x + u'\sin 3x, \quad y'' = u''\sin 3x + 6u'\cos 3x - 9u\sin 3x,$$

and

$$y'' + 9y = (\sin 3x)u'' + 6(\cos 3x)u' = 0 \quad \text{or} \quad u'' + 9(\cot 3x)u' = 0.$$

If $w = u'$ we obtain the first-order equation $w' + 6(\cot 3x)w = 0$ which has the integrating factor $e^{6 \int \cot 3x\, dx} = \sin^2 3x$. Now

$$\frac{d}{dx}[(\sin^2 3x)w] = 0 \quad \text{gives} \quad (\sin^2 3x)w = c.$$

Therefore $w = u' = c \csc^2 3x$ and $u = c_1 \cot 3x$. A second solution is $y_2 = \cot 3x \sin 3x = \cos 3x$.

7. Define $y = u(x)\cosh x$ so

$$y' = u \sinh x + u' \cosh x, \quad y'' = u'' \cosh x + 2u' \sinh x + u \cosh x$$

and

$$y'' - y = (\cosh x)u'' + 2(\sinh x)u' = 0 \quad \text{or} \quad u'' + 2(\tanh x)u' = 0.$$

If $w = u'$ we obtain the first-order equation $w' + 2(\tanh x)w = 0$ which has the integrating factor $e^{2 \int \tanh x\, dx} = \cosh^2 x$. Now

$$\frac{d}{dx}[(\cosh^2 x)w] = 0 \quad \text{gives} \quad (\cosh^2 x)w = c.$$

Therefore $w = u' = c \operatorname{sech}^2 x$ and $u = c_1 \tanh x$. A second solution is $y_2 = \tanh x \cosh x = \sinh x$.

8. Define $y = u(x)e^{5x}$ so

$$y' = 5e^{5x}u + e^{5x}u', \quad y'' = e^{5x}u'' + 10e^{5x}u' + 25e^{5x}u$$

and

$$y'' - 25y = e^{5x}(u'' + 10u') = 0 \quad \text{or} \quad u'' + 10u' = 0.$$

If $w = u'$ we obtain the first-order equation $w' + 10w = 0$ which has the integrating factor $e^{10 \int dx} = e^{10x}$. Now

$$\frac{d}{dx}[e^{10x}w] = 0 \quad \text{gives} \quad e^{10x}w = c.$$

Therefore $w = u' = ce^{-10x}$ and $u = c_1 e^{-10x}$. A second solution is $y_2 = e^{-10x}e^{5x} = e^{-5x}$.

9. Define $y = u(x)e^{2x/3}$ so

$$y' = \frac{2}{3}e^{2x/3}u + e^{2x/3}u', \quad y'' = e^{2x/3}u'' + \frac{4}{3}e^{2x/3}u' + \frac{4}{9}e^{2x/3}u$$

and

$$9y'' - 12y' + 4y = 9e^{2x/3}u'' = 0.$$

Therefore $u'' = 0$ and $u = c_1 x + c_2$. Taking $c_1 = 1$ and $c_2 = 0$ we see that a second solution is $y_2 = xe^{2x/3}$.

10. Define $y = u(x)e^{x/3}$ so

$$y' = \frac{1}{3}e^{x/3}u + e^{x/3}u', \quad y'' = e^{x/3}u'' + \frac{2}{3}e^{x/3}u' + \frac{1}{9}e^{x/3}u$$

and

$$6y'' + y' - y = e^{x/3}(6u'' + 5u') = 0 \quad \text{or} \quad u'' + \frac{5}{6}u' = 0.$$

If $w = u'$ we obtain the first-order equation $w' + \frac{5}{6}w = 0$ which has the integrating factor $e^{(5/6)\int dx} = e^{5x/6}$. Now

$$\frac{d}{dx}[e^{5x/6}w] = 0 \quad \text{gives} \quad e^{5x/6}w = c.$$

Therefore $w = u' = ce^{-5x/6}$ and $u = c_1e^{-5x/6}$. A second solution is $y_2 = e^{-5x/6}e^{x/3} = e^{-x/2}$.

11. Identifying $P(x) = -7/x$ we have

$$y_2 = x^4 \int \frac{e^{-\int -(7/x)\,dx}}{x^8}\,dx = x^4 \int \frac{1}{x}\,dx = x^4 \ln|x|.$$

A second solution is $y_2 = x^4 \ln|x|$.

12. Identifying $P(x) = 2/x$ we have

$$y_2 = x^2 \int \frac{e^{-\int (2/x)\,dx}}{x^4}\,dx = x^2 \int x^{-6}\,dx = -\frac{1}{5}x^{-3}.$$

A second solution is $y_2 = x^{-3}$.

13. Identifying $P(x) = 1/x$ we have

$$y_2 = \ln x \int \frac{e^{-\int dx/x}}{(\ln x)^2}\,dx = \ln x \int \frac{dx}{x(\ln x)^2} = \ln x \left(-\frac{1}{\ln x}\right) = -1.$$

A second solution is $y_2 = 1$.

14. Identifying $P(x) = 0$ we have

$$y_2 = x^{1/2}\ln x \int \frac{e^{-\int 0\,dx}}{x(\ln x)^2} = x^{1/2}\ln x \left(-\frac{1}{\ln x}\right) = -x^{1/2}.$$

A second solution is $y_2 = x^{1/2}$.

15. Identifying $P(x) = 2(1+x)/\left(1 - 2x - x^2\right)$ we have

$$y_2 = (x+1) \int \frac{e^{-\int 2(1+x)dx/(1-2x-x^2)}}{(x+1)^2}\,dx = (x+1) \int \frac{e^{\ln(1-2x-x^2)}}{(x+1)^2}\,dx$$

$$= (x+1) \int \frac{1-2x-x^2}{(x+1)^2}\,dx = (x+1) \int \left[\frac{2}{(x+1)^2} - 1\right]dx$$

$$= (x+1)\left[-\frac{2}{x+1} - x\right] = -2 - x^2 - x.$$

75

A second solution is $y_2 = x^2 + x + 2$.

16. Identifying $P(x) = -2x/\left(1 - x^2\right)$ we have

$$y_2 = \int e^{-\int -2x\,dx/(1-x^2)}\,dx = \int e^{-\ln(1-x^2)}\,dx = \int \frac{1}{1-x^2}\,dx = \frac{1}{2}\ln\left|\frac{1+x}{1-x}\right|.$$

A second solution is $y_2 = \ln\left|(1+x)/(1-x)\right|$.

17. Identifying $P(x) = -1/x$ we have

$$y_2 = x\sin(\ln x)\int \frac{e^{-\int -dx/x}}{x^2\sin^2(\ln x)}\,dx = x\sin(\ln x)\int \frac{x}{x^2\sin^2(\ln x)}\,dx$$

$$= [x\sin(\ln x)]\left[-\cot(\ln x)\right] = -x\cos(\ln x).$$

A second solution is $y_2 = x\cos(\ln x)$.

18. Identifying $P(x) = -3/x$ we have

$$y_2 = x^2\cos(\ln x)\int \frac{e^{-\int -3\,dx/x}}{x^4\cos^2(\ln x)}\,dx = x^2\cos(\ln x)\int \frac{x^3}{x^4\cos^2(\ln x)}\,dx$$

$$= x^2\cos(\ln x)\tan(\ln x) = x^2\sin(\ln x).$$

A second solution is $y_2 = x^2\sin(\ln x)$.

19. Identifying $P(x) = 4x/(1+2x)$ we have

$$y_2 = e^{-2x}\int \frac{e^{-\int 4x\,dx/(1+2x)}}{e^{-4x}}\,dx = e^{-2x}\int \frac{e^{-2x+\ln(1+2x)}}{e^{-4x}}\,dx$$

$$= e^{-2x}\int (1+2x)e^{2x}\,dx = e^{-2x}\left[\frac{1}{2}e^{2x} + xe^{2x} - \frac{1}{2}e^{2x}\right] = x.$$

A second solution is $y_2 = x$.

20. Identifying $P(x) = x/(1+x)$ we have

$$y_2 = x\int \frac{e^{-\int x\,dx/(1+x)}}{x^2}\,dx = x\int \frac{e^{-x+\ln(1+x)}}{x^2}\,dx = x\int \frac{(1+x)e^{-x}}{x^2}\,dx = x\int \left(\frac{e^{-x}}{x^2} + \frac{e^{-x}}{x}\right)dx$$

$$= x\int \frac{e^{-x}}{x^2}\,dx + x\int \frac{e^{-x}}{x}\,dx \qquad \boxed{u = e^{-x},\ \ du = -e^{-x}\,dx,\ \ dv = \frac{1}{x^2}\,dx,\ v = -\frac{1}{x}}$$

$$= x\left(-\frac{1}{x}e^{-x} - \int \frac{e^{-x}}{x}\,dx\right) + x\int \frac{e^{-x}}{x}\,dx = -e^{-x}.$$

A second solution is $y_2 = e^{-x}$.

21. Identifying $P(x) = -1/x$ we have

$$y_2 = x\int \frac{e^{-\int -dx/x}}{x^2}\,dx = x\int \frac{dx}{x} = x\ln|x|.$$

A second solution is $y_2 = x \ln |x|$.

22. Identifying $P(x) = 0$ we have

$$y_2 = x^{-4} \int \frac{e^{-\int 0 \, dx}}{x^{-8}} \, dx = x^{-4} \left(\frac{1}{9} x^9 \right) = \frac{1}{9} x^5.$$

A second solution is $y_2 = x^5$.

23. Identifying $P(x) = -5/x$ we have

$$y_2 = x^3 \ln x \int \frac{e^{-\int -5 \, dx/x}}{x^6 (\ln x)^2} \, dx = x^3 \ln x \int \frac{x^5}{x^6 (\ln x)^2} \, dx = x^3 \ln x \left(-\frac{1}{\ln x} \right) = -x^3.$$

A second solution is $y_2 = x^3$.

24. Identifying $P(x) = 1/x$ we have

$$y_2 = \cos(\ln x) \int \frac{e^{-\int dx/x}}{\cos^2(\ln x)} \, dx = \cos(\ln x) \int \frac{1/x}{\cos^2(\ln x)} \, dx = \cos(\ln x) \tan(\ln x) = \sin(\ln x).$$

A second solution is $y_2 = \sin(\ln x)$.

25. Identifying $P(x) = -4/x$ we have

$$y_2 = \left(x^2 + x^3 \right) \int \frac{e^{-\int -4 \, dx/x}}{\left(x^2 + x^3 \right)^2} \, dx = \left(x^2 + x^3 \right) \int \frac{x^4}{\left(x^2 + x^3 \right)^2} \, dx$$

$$= \left(x^2 + x^3 \right) \int \frac{dx}{(1+x)^2} = \left(x^2 + x^3 \right) \left(-\frac{1}{1+x} \right) = -x^2.$$

A second solution is $y_2 = x^2$.

26. Identifying $P(x) = -7/x$ we have

$$y_2 = x^{10} \int \frac{e^{-\int -7 \, dx/x}}{x^{20}} \, dx = x^{10} \int \frac{x^7}{x^{20}} \, dx = x^{10} \left(-\frac{1}{12} x^{-12} \right) = -\frac{1}{12} x^{-2}.$$

A second solution is $y_2 = x^{-2}$.

27. Identifying $P(x) = -(9x + 6)/(3x + 1)$ we have

$$y_2 = e^{3x} \int \frac{e^{-\int -(9x+6) \, dx/(3x+1)}}{e^{6x}} \, dx = e^{3x} \int \frac{e^{\int [3+3/(3x+1)] \, dx}}{e^{6x}} \, dx = e^{3x} \int \frac{e^{3x+\ln(3x+1)}}{e^{6x}} \, dx$$

$$= e^{3x} \int \frac{(3x+1)e^{3x}}{e^{6x}} \, dx = e^{3x} \int (3x+1)e^{-3x} \, dx = e^{3x} \left(-xe^{-3x} - \frac{2}{3} e^{-3x} \right) = -x - \frac{2}{3}.$$

A second solution is $y_2 = 3x + 2$.

28. Identifying $P(x) = -(x + 1)/x$ we have

$$y_2 = e^x \int \frac{e^{-\int -(x+1) \, dx/x}}{e^{2x}} \, dx = e^x \int \frac{e^{x+\ln x}}{e^{2x}} \, dx = e^x \int x e^{-x} \, dx = e^x (-xe^{-x} - e^{-x}) = -x - 1.$$

A second solution is $y_2 = x + 1$.

29. Identifying $P(x) = -3\tan x$ we have

$$y_2 = \int e^{-\int -3\tan x\, dx}\, dx = \int e^{3\ln\sec x}\, dx = \int \sec^3 x\, dx$$

$$= \frac{1}{2}\sec x \tan x + \frac{1}{2}\ln|\sec x + \tan x|.$$

A second solution is $y_2 = \sec x \tan x + \ln|\sec x + \tan x|$.

30. Identifying $P(x) = -(2+x)/x$ we have

$$y_2 = \int e^{-\int -(2+x)dx/x}\, dx = \int e^{2\ln x + x}\, dx = \int x^2 e^x\, dx = \left(x^2 - 2x + 2\right)e^x.$$

A second solution is $y_2 = \left(x^2 - 2x + 2\right)e^x$.

31. Identifying $P(x) = 0$ we have

$$y_2 = e^{-2x}\int \frac{e^{-\int 0\, dx}}{e^{-4x}}\, dx = e^{-2x}\frac{1}{4}e^{4x} = \frac{1}{4}e^{2x}.$$

A second solution is $y_2 = e^{2x}$. We see by observation that a particular solution is $y_p = -1/2$. The general solution is

$$y = c_1 e^{-2x} + c_2 e^{2x} - \frac{1}{2}.$$

32. Identifying $P(x) = 1$ we have $y_2 = \int e^{-\int dx}\, dx = e^{-x}$. We see by observation that a particular solution is $y_p = x$. The general solution is

$$y = c_1 + c_2 e^{-x} + x.$$

33. Identifying $P(x) = -3$ we have

$$y_2 = e^x \int \frac{e^{-\int -3\, dx}}{e^{2x}}\, dx = e^x \int e^x\, dx = e^{2x}.$$

To find a particular solution we try $y_p = Ae^{3x}$. Then $y' = 3Ae^{3x}$, $y'' = 9Ae^{3x}$, and $9Ae^{3x} - 3\left(3Ae^{3x}\right) + 2Ae^{3x} = 5e^{3x}$. Thus $A = 5/2$ and $y_p = \frac{5}{2}e^{3x}$. The general solution is

$$y = c_1 e^x + c_2 e^{2x} + \frac{5}{2}e^{3x}.$$

34. Identifying $P(x) = -4$ we have

$$y_2 = e^x \int \frac{e^{-\int -4\, dx}}{e^{2x}}\, dx = e^x \int \frac{e^{4x}}{e^{2x}}\, dx = e^x \left(\frac{1}{2}e^{2x}\right) = \frac{1}{2}e^{3x}.$$

A second solution is e^{3x}. To find a particular solution we try $y_p = ax + b$. Then $y_p' = a$, $y_p'' = 0$, and $0 - 4a + 3(ax + b) = 3ax - 4a + 3b = x$. Then $3a = 1$ and $-4a + 3b = 0$ so $a = 1/3$ and $b = 4/9$. A particular solution is $y_p = \frac{1}{3}x + \frac{4}{9}$ and the general solution is

$$y = c_1 e^x + c_2 e^{3x} + \frac{1}{3}x + \frac{4}{9}.$$

35. If $y_2 = y_1 \displaystyle\int \frac{e^{-\int P\,dx}}{y_1^2}\,dx$ then

$$y_2' = \frac{1}{y_1}e^{-\int P\,dx} + y_1' \int \frac{e^{-\int P\,dx}}{y_1^2}\,dx$$

and

$$y_2'' = \frac{-P}{y_1}e^{-\int P\,dx} - \frac{y_1'}{y_1^2}e^{-\int P\,dx} + \frac{y_1'}{y_1^2}e^{-\int P\,dx} + y_1'' \int \frac{e^{-\int P\,dx}}{y_1^2}\,dx$$

so that

$$y_2'' + Py_2' + Qy_2 = \left(y_1'' + Py_1' + Qy_1\right) \int \frac{e^{-\int P\,dx}}{y_1^2}\,dx = 0.$$

Exercises 4.3

1. From $4m^2 + m = 0$ we obtain $m = 0$ and $m = -1/4$ so that $y = c_1 + c_2 e^{-x/4}$.

2. From $2m^2 - 5m = 0$ we obtain $m = 0$ and $m = 5/2$ so that $y = c_1 + c_2 e^{5x/2}$.

3. From $m^2 - 36 = 0$ we obtain $m = 6$ and $m = -6$ so that $y = c_1 e^{6x} + c_2 e^{-6x}$.

4. From $m^2 - 8 = 0$ we obtain $m = 2\sqrt{2}$ and $m = -2\sqrt{2}$ so that $y = c_1 e^{2\sqrt{2}\,x} + c_2 e^{-2\sqrt{2}\,x}$.

5. From $m^2 + 9 = 0$ we obtain $m = 3i$ and $m = -3i$ so that $y = c_1 \cos 3x + c_2 \sin 3x$.

6. From $3m^2 + 1 = 0$ we obtain $m = i/\sqrt{3}$ and $m = -i/\sqrt{3}$ so that $y = c_1 \cos x/\sqrt{3} + c_2 \sin x/\sqrt{3}$.

7. From $m^2 - m - 6 = 0$ we obtain $m = 3$ and $m = -2$ so that $y = c_1 e^{3x} + c_2 e^{-2x}$.

8. From $m^2 - 3m + 2 = 0$ we obtain $m = 1$ and $m = 2$ so that $y = c_1 e^x + c_2 e^{2x}$.

9. From $m^2 + 8m + 16 = 0$ we obtain $m = -4$ and $m = -4$ so that $y = c_1 e^{-4x} + c_2 x e^{-4x}$.

10. From $m^2 - 10m + 25 = 0$ we obtain $m = 5$ and $m = 5$ so that $y = c_1 e^{5x} + c_2 x e^{5x}$.

11. From $m^2 + 3m - 5 = 0$ we obtain $m = -3/2 \pm \sqrt{29}/2$ so that $y = c_1 e^{(-3+\sqrt{29})x/2} + c_2 e^{(-3-\sqrt{29})x/2}$.

12. From $m^2 + 4m - 1 = 0$ we obtain $m = -2 \pm \sqrt{5}$ so that $y = c_1 e^{(-2+\sqrt{5})x} + c_2 e^{(-2-\sqrt{5})x}$.

13. From $12m^2 - 5m - 2 = 0$ we obtain $m = -1/4$ and $m = 2/3$ so that $y = c_1 e^{-x/4} + c_2 e^{2x/3}$.

14. From $8m^2 + 2m - 1 = 0$ we obtain $m = 1/4$ and $m = -1/2$ so that $y = c_1 e^{x/4} + c_2 e^{-x/2}$.

15. From $m^2 - 4m + 5 = 0$ we obtain $m = 2 \pm i$ so that $y = e^{2x}(c_1 \cos x + c_2 \sin x)$.

16. From $2m^2 - 3m + 4 = 0$ we obtain $m = 3/4 \pm \sqrt{23}\,i/4$ so that
$$y = e^{3x/4}\left(c_1 \cos \sqrt{23}\,x/4 + c_2 \sin \sqrt{23}\,x/4\right).$$

17. From $3m^2 + 2m + 1 = 0$ we obtain $m = -1/3 \pm \sqrt{2}\,i/3$ so that
$$y = e^{-x/3}\left(c_1 \cos \sqrt{2}\,x/3 + c_2 \sin \sqrt{2}\,x/3\right).$$

18. From $2m^2 + 2m + 1 = 0$ we obtain $m = -1/2 \pm i/2$ so that
$$y = e^{-x/2}(c_1 \cos x/2 + c_2 \sin x/2).$$

19. From $m^3 - 4m^2 - 5m = 0$ we obtain $m = 0$, $m = 5$, and $m = -1$ so that
$$y = c_1 + c_2 e^{5x} + c_3 e^{-x}.$$

20. From $4m^3 + 4m^2 + m = 0$ we obtain $m = 0$, $m = -1/2$, and $m = -1/2$ so that
$$y = c_1 + c_2 e^{-x/2} + c_3 x e^{-x/2}.$$

21. From $m^3 - 1 = 0$ we obtain $m = 1$ and $m = -1/2 \pm \sqrt{3}\,i/2$ so that
$$y = c_1 e^x + e^{-x/2}\left(c_2 \cos \sqrt{3}\,x/2 + c_3 \sin \sqrt{3}\,x/2\right).$$

22. From $m^3 + 5m^2 = 0$ we obtain $m = 0$, $m = 0$, and $m = -5$ so that
$$y = c_1 + c_2 x + c_3 e^{-5x}.$$

23. From $m^3 - 5m^2 + 3m + 9 = 0$ we obtain $m = -1$, $m = 3$, and $m = 3$ so that
$$y = c_1 e^{-x} + c_2 e^{3x} + c_3 x e^{3x}.$$

24. From $m^3 + 3m^2 - 4m - 12 = 0$ we obtain $m = -2$, $m = 2$, and $m = -3$ so that
$$y = c_1 e^{-2x} + c_2 e^{2x} + c_3 e^{-3x}.$$

25. From $m^3 + m^2 - 2 = 0$ we obtain $m = 1$ and $m = -1 \pm i$ so that
$$y = c_1 e^x + e^{-x}(c_2 \cos x + c_3 \sin x).$$

26. From $m^3 - m^2 - 4 = 0$ we obtain $m = 2$ and $m = -1/2 \pm \sqrt{7}\,i/2$ so that
$$y = c_1 e^{2x} + e^{-x/2}\left(c_2 \cos \sqrt{7}\,x/2 + c_3 \sin \sqrt{7}\,x/2\right).$$

27. From $m^3 + 3m^2 + 3m + 1 = 0$ we obtain $m = -1$, $m = -1$, and $m = -1$ so that
$$y = c_1 e^{-x} + c_2 x e^{-x} + c_3 x^2 e^{-x}.$$

80

28. From $m^3 - 6m^2 + 12m - 8 = 0$ we obtain $m = 2$, $m = 2$, and $m = 2$ so that
$$y = c_1 e^{2x} + c_2 x e^{2x} + c_3 x^2 e^{2x}.$$

29. From $m^4 + m^3 + m^2 = 0$ we obtain $m = 0$, $m = 0$, and $m = -1/2 \pm \sqrt{3}\,i/2$ so that
$$y = c_1 + c_2 x + e^{-x/2} \left(c_3 \cos \sqrt{3}\,x/2 + c_4 \sin \sqrt{3}\,x/2 \right).$$

30. From $m^4 - 2m^2 + 1 = 0$ we obtain $m = 1$, $m = 1$, $m = -1$, and $m = -1$ so that
$$y = c_1 e^x + c_2 x e^x + c_3 e^{-x} + c_4 x e^{-x}.$$

31. From $16m^4 + 24m^2 + 9 = 0$ we obtain $m = \pm\sqrt{3}\,i/2$ and $m = \pm\sqrt{3}\,i/2$ so that
$$y = c_1 \cos \sqrt{3}\,x/2 + c_2 \sin \sqrt{3}\,x/2 + c_3 x \cos \sqrt{3}\,x/2 + c_4 x \sin \sqrt{3}\,x/2.$$

32. From $m^4 - 7m^2 - 18 = 0$ we obtain $m = 3$, $m = -3$, and $m = \pm\sqrt{2}\,i$ so that
$$y = c_1 e^{3x} + c_2 e^{-3x} + c_3 \cos \sqrt{2}\,x + c_4 \sin \sqrt{2}\,x.$$

33. From $m^5 - 16m = 0$ we obtain $m = 0$, $m = 2$, $m = -2$, and $m = \pm 2i$ so that
$$y = c_1 + c_2 e^{2x} + c_3 e^{-2x} + c_4 \cos 2x + c_5 \sin 2x.$$

34. From $m^5 - 2m^4 + 17m^3 = 0$ we obtain $m = 0$, $m = 0$, $m = 0$, and $m = 1 \pm 4i$ so that
$$y = c_1 + c_2 x + c_3 x^2 + e^x (c_4 \cos 4x + c_5 \sin 4x).$$

35. From $m^5 + 5m^4 - 2m^3 - 10m^2 + m + 5 = 0$ we obtain $m = -1$, $m = -1$, $m = 1$, and $m = 1$, and $m = -5$ so that
$$y = c_1 e^{-x} + c_2 x e^{-x} + c_3 e^x + c_4 x e^x + c_5 e^{-5x}.$$

36. From $2m^5 - 7m^4 + 12m^3 + 8m^2 = 0$ we obtain $m = 0$, $m = 0$, $m = -1/2$, and $m = 2 \pm 2i$ so that
$$y = c_1 + c_2 x + c_3 e^{-x/2} + e^{2x} (c_4 \cos 2x + c_5 \sin 2x).$$

37. From $m^2 + 16 = 0$ we obtain $m = \pm 4i$ so that $y = c_1 \cos 4x + c_2 \sin 4x$. If $y(0) = 2$ and $y'(0) = -2$ then $c_1 = 2$, $c_2 = -1/2$, and $y = 2 \cos 4x - \frac{1}{2} \sin 4x$.

38. From $m^2 - 1 = 0$ we obtain $m = 1$ and $m = -1$ so that $y = c_1 e^x + c_2 e^{-x}$. If $y(0) = 1$ and $y'(0) = 1$ then $c_1 + c_2 =$, $c_1 - c_2 = 1$, so $c_1 = 1$, $c_2 = 0$, and $y = e^x$.

39. From $m^2 + 6m + 5 = 0$ we obtain $m = -1$ and $m = -5$ so that $y = c_1 e^{-x} + c_2 e^{-5x}$. If $y(0) = 0$ and $y'(0) = 3$ then $c_1 + c_2 = 0$, $-c_1 - 5c_2 = 3$, so $c_1 = 3/4$, $c_2 = -3/4$, and $y = \frac{3}{4} e^{-x} - \frac{3}{4} e^{-5x}$.

40. From $m^2 - 8m + 17 = 0$ we obtain $m = 4 \pm i$ so that $y = e^{4x}(c_1 \cos x + c_2 \sin x)$. If $y(0) = 4$ and $y'(0) = -1$ then $c_1 = 4$, $4c_1 + c_2 = -1$, so $c_1 = 4$, $c_2 = -17$, and $y = e^{4x}(4 \cos x - 17 \sin x)$.

41. From $2m^2 - 2m + 1 = 0$ we obtain $m = 1/2 \pm i/2$ so that $y = e^{x/2}(c_1 \cos x/2 + c_2 \sin x/2)$. If $y(0) = -1$ and $y'(0) = 0$ then $c_1 = -1$, $\frac{1}{2}c_1 + \frac{1}{2}c_2 = 0$, so $c_1 = -1$, $c_2 = 1$, and $y = e^{x/2}\left(\sin \frac{1}{2}x - \cos \frac{1}{2}x\right)$.

42. From $m^2 - 2m + 1 = 0$ we obtain $m = 1$ and $m = 1$ so that $y = c_1 e^x + c_2 x e^x$. If $y(0) = 5$ and $y'(0) = 10$ then $c_1 = 5$, $c_1 + c_2 = 10$ so $c_1 = 5$, $c_2 = 5$, and $y = 5e^x + 5xe^x$.

43. From $m^2 + m + 2 = 0$ we obtain $m = -1/2 \pm \sqrt{7}\,i/2$ so that $y = e^{-x/2}\left(c_1 \cos \sqrt{7}\,x/2 + c_2 \sin \sqrt{7}\,x/2\right)$. If $y(0) = 0$ and $y'(0) = 0$ then $c_1 = 0$ and $c_2 = 0$ so that $y = 0$.

44. From $4m^2 - 4m - 3 = 0$ we obtain $m = -1/2$ and $m = 3/2$ so that $y = c_1 e^{-x/2} + c_2 e^{3x/2}$. If $y(0) = 1$ and $y'(0) = 5$ then $c_1 + c_2 = 1$, $-\frac{1}{2}c_1 + \frac{3}{2}c_2 = 5$, so $c_1 = -7/4$, $c_2 = 11/4$, and $y = -\frac{7}{4}e^{-x/2} + \frac{11}{4}e^{3x/2}$.

45. From $m^2 - 3m + 2 = 0$ we obtain $m = 1$ and $m = 2$ so that $y = c_1 e^x + c_2 e^{2x}$. If $y(1) = 0$ and $y'(1) = 1$ then $c_1 e + c_2 e^2 = 0$, $c_1 e + 2c_2 e^2 = 0$ so $c_1 = -e^{-1}$, $c_2 = e^{-2}$, and $y = -e^{x-1} + e^{2x-2}$.

46. From $m^2 + 1 = 0$ we obtain $m = \pm i$ so that $y = c_1 \cos x + c_2 \sin x$. If $y(\pi/3) = 0$ and $y'(\pi/3) = 2$ then $\frac{1}{2}c_1 + \frac{\sqrt{3}}{2}c_2 = 0$, $-\frac{\sqrt{3}}{2}c_1 + \frac{1}{2}c_2 = 2$, so $c_1 = -\sqrt{3}$, $c_2 = 1$, and $y = -\sqrt{3}\cos x + \sin x$.

47. From $m^3 + 12m^2 + 36m = 0$ we obtain $m = 0$, $m = -6$, and $m = -6$ so that $y = c_1 + c_2 e^{-6x} + c_3 x e^{-6x}$. If $y(0) = 0$, $y'(0) = 1$, and $y''(0) = -7$ then

$$c_1 + c_2 = 0, \quad -6c_2 + c_3 = 1, \quad 36c_2 - 12c_3 = -7,$$

so $c_1 = 5/36$, $c_2 = -5/36$, $c_3 = 1/6$, and $y = \frac{5}{36} - \frac{5}{36}e^{-6x} + \frac{1}{6}xe^{-6x}$.

48. From $m^3 + 2m^2 - 5m - 6 = 0$ we obtain $m = -1$, $m = 2$, and $m = -3$ so that

$$y = c_1 e^{-x} + c_2 e^{2x} + c_3 e^{-3x}.$$

If $y(0) = 0$, $y'(0) = 0$, and $y''(0) = 1$ then

$$c_1 + c_2 + c_3 = 0, \quad -c_1 + 2c_2 - 3c_3 = 0, \quad c_1 + 4c_2 + 9c_3 = 1,$$

so $c_1 = -1/6$, $c_2 = 1/15$, $c_3 = 1/10$, and

$$y = -\frac{1}{6}e^{-x} + \frac{1}{15}e^{2x} + \frac{1}{10}e^{-3x}.$$

49. From $m^3 - 8 = 0$ we obtain $m = 2$ and $m = -1 \pm \sqrt{3}\,i$ so that

$$y = c_1 e^{2x} + e^{-x}\left(c_2 \cos \sqrt{3}\,x + c_3 \sin \sqrt{3}\,x\right).$$

If $y(0) = 0$ and $y'(0) = -1$, and $y''(0) = 0$ then

$$c_1 + c_2 = 0, \quad 2c_1 - c_2 + \sqrt{3}\,c_3 = -1, \quad 4c_1 - 2c_2 - 2\sqrt{3}\,c_3 = 0,$$

so $c_1 = -1/6$, $c_2 = 1/6$, $c_3 = -1/2\sqrt{3}$, and

$$y = -\frac{1}{6}e^{2x} + e^{-x}\left(\frac{1}{6}\cos \sqrt{3}\,x - \frac{1}{2\sqrt{3}}\sin \sqrt{3}\,x\right).$$

50. From $m^4 = 0$ we obtain $y = c_1 + c_2 x + c_3 x^2 + c_4 x^3$. If $y(0) = 2$, $y'(0) = 3$, $y''(0) = 4$, and $y'''(0) = 5$ then $c_1 = 2$, $c_2 = 3$, $2c_3 = 4$, $6c_4 = 5$, and

$$y = 2 + 3x + 2x^2 + \frac{5}{6}x^3.$$

51. From $m^4 - 3m^3 + 3m^2 - m = 0$ we obtain $m = 0$, $m = 1$, $m = 1$, and $m = 1$ so that $y = c_1 + c_2 e^x + c_3 x e^x + c_4 x^2 e^x$. If $y(0) = 0$, $y'(0) = 0$, $y''(0) = 1$, and $y'''(0) = 1$ then

$$c_1 + c_2 = 0, \quad c_2 + c_3 = 0, \quad c_2 + 2c_3 + 2c_4 = 1, \quad c_2 + 3c_3 + 6c_4 = 1,$$

so $c_1 = 2$, $c_2 = -2$, $c_3 = 2$, $c_4 = -1/2$, and

$$y = 2 - 2e^x + 2xe^x - \frac{1}{2}x^2 e^x.$$

52. From $m^4 - 1 = 0$ we obtain $m = 1$, $m = -1$, and $m = \pm i$ so that $y = c_1 e^x + c_2 e^{-x} + c_3 \cos x + c_4 \sin x$. If $y(0) = 0$, $y'(0) = 0$, $y''(0) = 0$, and $y'''(0) = 1$ then

$$c_1 + c_2 + c_3 = 0, \quad c_1 - c_2 + c_4 = 0, \quad c_1 + c_2 - c_3 = 0, \quad c_1 - c_2 - c_4 = 1,$$

so $c_1 = 1/4$, $c_2 = -1/4$, $c_3 = 0$, $c_4 = -1/2$, and

$$y = \frac{1}{4}e^x - \frac{1}{4}e^{-x} - \frac{1}{2}\sin x.$$

53. From $m^2 - 10m + 25 = 0$ we obtain $m = 5$ and $m = 5$ so that $y = c_1 e^{5x} + c_2 x e^{5x}$. If $y(0) = 1$ and $y(1) = 0$ then $c_1 = 1$, $c_1 e^5 + c_2 e^5 = 0$, so $c_1 = 1$, $c_2 = -1$, and $y = e^{5x} - x e^{5x}$.

54. From $m^2 + 4 = 0$ we obtain $m = \pm 2i$ so that $y = c_1 \cos 2x + c_2 \sin 2x$. If $y(0) = 0$ and $y(\pi) = 0$ then $c_1 = 0$ and $y = c_2 \sin 2x$.

55. From $m^2 + 1 = 0$ we obtain $m = \pm i$ so that $y = c_1 \cos x + c_2 \sin x$. If $y'(0) = 0$ and $y'(\pi/2) = 2$ then $c_1 = -2$, $c_2 = 0$ and $y = -2\cos x$.

56. From $m^2 - 1 = 0$ we obtain $m = 1$ and $m = -1$ so that $y = c_1 e^x + c_2 e^{-x}$ or $y = c_3 \cosh x + c_4 \sinh x$. If $y(0) = 1$ and $y'(1) = 0$ then $c_1 = 1$, $c_1 \sinh 1 + c_2 \cosh 1 = 0$, so $c_1 = 1$, $c_2 = -\sinh 1/\cosh 1$ and

$$y = \cosh x - \frac{\sinh 1}{\cosh 1}\sinh x = \frac{\cosh x \cosh 1 - \sinh x \sinh 1}{\cosh 1} = \frac{\cosh(x-1)}{\cosh 1}.$$

57. Since $(m-4)(m+5)^2 = m^3 + 6m^2 - 15m - 100$ the differential equation is $y''' + 6y'' - 15y' - 100y = 0$.

58. Since $\left(m + \frac{1}{2}\right)\left(m^2 - 6m + 10\right) = m^3 - \frac{11}{2}m^2 + 7m + 5$ the differential equation is

$$y''' - \frac{11}{2}y'' + 7y' + 5y = 0.$$

59. From the solution $y_1 = e^x$ we conclude that $m_1 = 1$ is a root of the auxiliary equation. Now, dividing the polynomial $m^3 - 9m^2 + 25m - 17$ by $m - 1$ gives $m^2 - 8m + 17$. Therefore $m = 4 \pm i$ are the remaining roots of the auxiliary equation, and the general solution of the differential equation is

$$y = c_1 e^x + e^{4x}(c_2 \cos x + c_3 \sin x).$$

60. From the solution $y_1 = e^{-4x} \cos x$ we conclude that $m_1 = -4 + i$ and $m_2 = -4 - i$ are roots of the auxiliary equation. Hence another solution must be $y_2 = e^{-4x} \sin x$. Now dividing the polynomial $m^3 + 6m^2 + m - 34$ by $[m - (-4 + i)][m - (-4 - i)] = m^2 + 8m + 17$ gives $m - 2$. Therefore $m_3 = 2$ is the third root of the auxiliary equation, and the general solution of the differential equation is

$$y = c_1 e^{-4x} \cos x + c_2 e^{-4x} \sin x + c_3 e^{2x}.$$

61. Since $(m - 6)(m + 3) = m^2 - 3m - 18$, a differential equation is $y'' - 3y' - 18y = 0$.

62. From $m^2 + 16 = 0$ a differential equation is $y'' + 16y = 0$.

63. Since $m^2(m - 7) = m^3 - 7m^2$, a differential equation is $y''' - 7y'' = 0$.

64. Since $(m - 3)(m + 3) = m^2 - 9$, a differential equation is $y'' - 9y = 0$.

65. From $m^4 + 1 = \left(m^2 - \sqrt{2}\,m + 1\right)\left(m^2 + \sqrt{2}\,m + 1\right)$ we obtain

$$m = 1/\sqrt{2} \pm i/\sqrt{2} \quad \text{and} \quad m = -1/\sqrt{2} \pm i/\sqrt{2}$$

so that

$$y = e^{x/\sqrt{2}}\left(c_1 \cos \frac{1}{\sqrt{2}} x + c_2 \sin \frac{1}{\sqrt{2}} x\right) + e^{-x/\sqrt{2}}\left(c_3 \cos \frac{1}{\sqrt{2}} x + c_4 \sin \frac{1}{\sqrt{2}} x\right).$$

Exercises 4.4

1. From $m^2 + 3m + 2 = 0$ we find $m_1 = -1$ and $m_2 = -2$. Then $y_c = c_1 e^{-x} + c_2 e^{-2x}$ and we assume $y_p = A$. Substituting into the differential equation we obtain $2A = 6$. Then $A = 3$, $y_p = 3$ and

$$y = c_1 e^{-x} + c_2 e^{-2x} + 3.$$

2. From $4m^2 + 9 = 0$ we find $m_1 = -\frac{3}{2} i$ and $m_2 = \frac{3}{2} i$. Then $y_c = c_1 \cos \frac{3}{2} x + c_2 \sin \frac{3}{2} x$ and we assume $y_p = A$. Substituting into the differential equation we obtain $9A = 15$. Then $A = \frac{5}{3}$, $y_p = \frac{5}{3}$ and

$$y = c_1 \cos \frac{3}{2} x + c_2 \sin \frac{3}{2} x + \frac{5}{3}.$$

3. From $m^2 - 10m + 25 = 0$ we find $m_1 = m_2 = 5$. Then $y_c = c_1 e^{5x} + c_2 x e^{5x}$ and we assume $y_p = Ax + B$. Substituting into the differential equation we obtain $25A = 30$ and $-10A + 25B = 3$. Then $A = \frac{6}{5}$, $B = \frac{6}{5}$, $y_p = \frac{6}{5} x + \frac{6}{5}$, and

$$y = c_1 e^{5x} + c_2 x e^{5x} + \frac{6}{5} x + \frac{6}{5}.$$

4. From $m^2 + m - 6 = 0$ we find $m_1 = -3$ and $m_2 = 2$. Then $y_c = c_1 e^{-3x} + c_2 e^{2x}$ and we assume $y_p = Ax + B$. Substituting into the differential equation we obtain $-6A = 2$ and $A - 6B = 0$. Then $A = -\frac{1}{3}$, $B = -\frac{1}{18}$, $y_p = \frac{1}{3}x - \frac{1}{18}$, and

$$y = c_1 e^{-3x} + c_2 e^{2x} + \frac{1}{3}x - \frac{1}{18}.$$

5. From $\frac{1}{4}m^2 + m + 1 = 0$ we find $m_1 = m_2 = 0$. Then $y_c = c_1 e^{-2x} + c_2 x e^{-2x}$ and we assume $y_p = Ax^2 + Bx + C$. Substituting into the differential equation we obtain $A = 1$, $2A + B = -2$, and $\frac{1}{2}A + B + C = 0$. Then $A = 1$, $B = -4$, $C = \frac{7}{2}$, $y_p = x^2 - 4x + \frac{7}{2}$, and

$$y = c_1 e^{-2x} + c_2 x e^{-2x} + x^2 - 4x + \frac{7}{2}.$$

6. From $m^2 - 8m + 20 = 0$ we find $m_1 = 2 + 4i$ and $m_2 = 2 - 4i$. Then $y_c = e^{2x}(c_1 \cos 4x + c_2 \sin 4x)$ and we assume $y_p = Ax^2 + Bx + C + (Dx + E)e^x$. Substituting into the differential equation we obtain

$$2A - 8B + 20C = 0$$

$$-6D + 13E = 0$$

$$-16A + 20B = 0$$

$$13D = -26$$

$$20A = 100.$$

Then $A = 5$, $B = 4$, $C = \frac{11}{10}$, $D = -2$, $E = -\frac{12}{13}$, $y_p = 5x^2 + 4x + \frac{11}{10} + \left(-2x - \frac{12}{13}\right)e^x$ and

$$y = e^{2x}(c_1 \cos 4x + c_2 \sin 4x) + 5x^2 + 4x + \frac{11}{10} + \left(-2x - \frac{12}{13}\right)e^x.$$

7. From $m^2 + 3 = 0$ we find $m_1 = \sqrt{3}\,i$ and $m_2 = -\sqrt{3}\,i$. Then $y_c = c_1 \cos \sqrt{3}\,x + c_2 \sin \sqrt{3}\,x$ and we assume $y_p = (Ax^2 + Bx + C)e^{3x}$. Substituting into the differential equation we obtain $2A + 6B + 12C = 0$, $12A + 12B = 0$, and $12A = -48$. Then $A = -4$, $B = 4$, $C = -\frac{4}{3}$, $y_p = \left(-4x^2 + 4x - \frac{4}{3}\right)e^{3x}$ and

$$y = c_1 \cos \sqrt{3}\,x + c_2 \sin \sqrt{3}\,x + \left(-4x^2 + 4x - \frac{4}{3}\right)e^{3x}.$$

8. From $4m^2 - 4m - 3 = 0$ we find $m_1 = \frac{3}{2}$ and $m_2 = -\frac{1}{2}$. Then $y_c = c_1 e^{3x/2} + c_2 e^{-x/2}$ and we assume $y_p = A\cos 2x + B\sin 2x$. Substituting into the differential equation we obtain $-19 - 8B = 1$ and $8A - 19B = 0$. Then $A = -\frac{19}{425}$, $B = -\frac{8}{425}$, $y_p = -\frac{19}{425}\cos 2x - \frac{8}{425}\sin 2x$, and

$$y = c_1 e^{3x/2} + c_2 e^{-x/2} - \frac{19}{425}\cos 2x - \frac{8}{425}\sin 2x.$$

9. From $m^2 - m = 0$ we find $m_1 = 1$ and $m_2 = 0$. Then $y_c = c_1 e^x + c_2$ and we assume $y_p = Ax$. Substituting into the differential equation we obtain $-A = -3$. Then $A = 3$, $y_p = 3x$ and $y = c_1 e^x + c_2 + 3x$.

10. From $m^2 + 2m = 0$ we find $m_1 = -2$ and $m_2 = 0$. Then $y_c = c_1 e^{-2x} + c_2$ and we assume $y_p = Ax^2 + Bx + Cxe^{-2x}$. Substituting into the differential equation we obtain $2A + 2B = 5$, $4A = 2$, and $-2C = -1$. Then $A = \frac{1}{2}$, $B = 2$, $C = \frac{1}{2}$, $y_p = \frac{1}{2}x^2 + 2x + \frac{1}{2}xe^{-2x}$, and

$$y = c_1 e^{-2x} + c_2 + \frac{1}{2}x^2 + 2x + \frac{1}{2}xe^{-2x}.$$

11. From $m^2 - m + \frac{1}{4} = 0$ we find $m_1 = m_2 = \frac{1}{2}$. Then $y_c = c_1 e^{x/2} + c_2 x e^{x/2}$ and we assume $y_p = A + Bx^2 e^{x/2}$. Substituting into the differential equation we obtain $\frac{1}{4}A = 3$ and $2B = 1$. Then $A = 12$, $B = \frac{1}{2}$, $y_p = 12 + \frac{1}{2}x^2 e^{x/2}$, and

$$y = c_1 e^{x/2} + c_2 x e^{x/2} + 12 + \frac{1}{2}x^2 e^{x/2}.$$

12. From $m^2 - 16 = 0$ we find $m_1 = 4$ and $m_2 = -4$. Then $y_c = c_1 e^{4x} + c_2 e^{-4x}$ and we assume $y_p = Axe^{4x}$. Substituting into the differential equation we obtain $8A = 2$. Then $A = \frac{1}{4}$, $y_p = \frac{1}{4}xe^{4x}$ and

$$y = c_1 e^{4x} + c_2 e^{-4x} + \frac{1}{4}xe^{4x}.$$

13. From $m^2 + 4 = 0$ we find $m_1 = 2i$ and $m_2 = -2i$. Then $y_c = c_1 \cos 2x + c_2 \sin 2x$ and we assume $y_p = Ax \cos 2x + Bx \sin 2x$. Substituting into the differential equation we obtain $4B = 0$ and $-4A = 3$. Then $A = -\frac{3}{4}$, $B = 0$, $y_p = -\frac{3}{4}x \cos 2x$, and

$$y = c_1 \cos 2x + c_2 \sin 2x - \frac{3}{4}x \cos 2x.$$

14. From $m^2 + 4 = 0$ we find $m_1 = 2i$ and $m_2 = -2i$. Then $y_c = c_1 \cos 2x + c_2 \sin 2x$ and we assume $y_p = (Ax^3 + Bx^2 + Cx) \cos 2x + (Dx^3 + Ex^2 + Fx) \sin 2x$. Substituting into the differential equation we obtain

$$2B + 4F = 0$$

$$6A + 8E = 0$$

$$12D = 0$$

$$-4C + 2E = -3$$

$$-8B + 6D = 0$$

$$-12A = 1.$$

86

Then $A = -\frac{1}{12}$, $B = 0$, $C = \frac{25}{32}$, $D = 0$, $E = \frac{1}{16}$, $F = 0$, $y_p = \left(-\frac{1}{12}x^3 + \frac{25}{32}x\right)\cos 2x + \frac{1}{16}x^2 \sin 2x$, and

$$y = c_1 \cos 2x + c_2 \sin 2x + \left(-\frac{1}{12}x^3 + \frac{25}{32}x\right)\cos 2x + \frac{1}{16}x^2 \sin 2x.$$

15. From $m^2 + 1 = 0$ we find $m_1 = i$ and $m_2 = -i$. Then $y_c = c_1 \cos x + c_2 \sin x$ and we assume $y_p = (Ax^2 + Bx)\cos x + (Cx^2 + Dx)\sin x$. Substituting into the differential equation we obtain $4C = 0$, $2A + 2D = 0$, $-4A = 2$, and $-2B + 2C = 0$. Then $A = -\frac{1}{2}$, $B = 0$, $C = 0$, $D = \frac{1}{2}$, $y_p = -\frac{1}{2}x^2 \cos x + \frac{1}{2}x \sin x$, and

$$y = c_1 \cos x + c_2 \sin x - \frac{1}{2}x^2 \cos x + \frac{1}{2}x \sin x.$$

16. From $m^2 - 5m = 0$ we find $m_1 = 5$ and $m_2 = 0$. Then $y_c = c_1 e^{5x} + c_2$ and we assume $y_p = Ax^4 + Bx^3 + Cx^2 + Dx$. Substituting into the differential equation we obtain $-20A = 2$, $12A - 15B = -4$, $6B - 10C = -1$, and $2C - 5D = 6$. Then $A = -\frac{1}{10}$, $B = \frac{14}{75}$, $C = \frac{53}{250}$, $D = -\frac{697}{625}$, $y_p = -\frac{1}{10}x^4 + \frac{14}{75}x^3 + \frac{53}{250}x^2 - \frac{697}{625}x$, and

$$y = c_1 e^{5x} + c_2 - \frac{1}{10}x^4 + \frac{14}{75}x^3 + \frac{53}{250}x^2 - \frac{697}{625}x.$$

17. From $m^2 - 2m + 5 = 0$ we find $m_1 = 1 + 2i$ and $m_2 = 1 - 2i$. Then $y_c = e^x(c_1 \cos 2x + c_2 \sin 2x)$ and we assume $y_p = Axe^x \cos 2x + Bxe^x \sin 2x$. Substituting into the differential equation we obtain $4B = 1$ and $-4A = 0$. Then $A = 0$, $B = \frac{1}{4}$, $y_p = \frac{1}{4}xe^x \sin 2x$, and

$$y = e^x(c_1 \cos 2x + c_2 \sin 2x) + \frac{1}{4}xe^x \sin 2x.$$

18. From $m^2 - 2m + 2 = 0$ we find $m_1 = 1 + i$ and $m_2 = 1 - i$. Then $y_c = e^x(c_1 \cos x + c_2 \sin x)$ and we assume $y_p = Ae^{2x} \cos x + Be^{2x} \sin x$. Substituting into the differential equation we obtain $A + 2B = 1$ and $-2A + B = -3$. Then $A = \frac{7}{5}$, $B = -\frac{1}{5}$, $y_p = \frac{7}{5}e^{2x} \cos x - \frac{1}{5}e^{2x} \sin x$ and

$$y = e^x(c_1 \cos x + c_2 \sin x) + \frac{7}{5}e^{2x} \cos x - \frac{1}{5}e^{2x} \sin x.$$

19. From $m^2 + 2m + 1 = 0$ we find $m_1 = m_2 = -1$. Then $y_c = c_1 e^{-x} + c_2 xe^{-x}$ and we assume $y_p = A \cos x + B \sin x + C \cos 2x + D \sin 2x$. Substituting into the differential equation we obtain $2B = 0$, $-2A = 1$, $-3C + 4D = 3$, and $-4C - 3D = 0$. Then $A = -\frac{1}{2}$, $B = 0$, $C = -\frac{9}{25}$, $D = \frac{12}{25}$, $y_p = -\frac{1}{2}\cos x - \frac{9}{25}\cos 2x + \frac{12}{25}\sin 2x$, and

$$y = c_1 e^{-x} + c_2 xe^{-x} - \frac{1}{2}\cos x - \frac{9}{25}\cos 2x + \frac{12}{25}\sin 2x.$$

20. From $m^2 + 2m - 24 = 0$ we find $m_1 = -6$ and $m_2 = 4$. Then $y_c = c_1 e^{-6x} + c_2 e^{4x}$ and we assume $y_p = A + (Bx^2 + Cx)e^{4x}$. Substituting into the differential equation we obtain $-24A = 16$,

$2B+10C = -2$, and $20B = -1$. Then $A = -\frac{2}{3}$, $B = -\frac{1}{20}$, $C = -\frac{19}{100}$, $y_p = -\frac{2}{3} - \left(\frac{1}{20}x^2 + \frac{19}{100}x\right)e^{4x}$, and

$$y = c_1 e^{-6x} + c_2 e^{4x} - \frac{2}{3} - \left(\frac{1}{20}x^2 + \frac{19}{100}x\right)e^{4x}.$$

21. From $m^3 - 6m^2 = 0$ we find $m_1 = m_2 = 0$ and $m_3 = 6$. Then $y_c = c_1 + c_2 x + c_3 e^{6x}$ and we assume $y_p = Ax^2 + B\cos x + C\sin x$. Substituting into the differential equation we obtain $-12A = 3$, $6B - C = -1$, and $B + 6C = 0$. Then $A = -\frac{1}{4}$, $B = -\frac{6}{37}$, $C = \frac{1}{37}$, $y_p = -\frac{1}{4}x^2 - \frac{6}{37}\cos x + \frac{1}{37}\sin x$, and

$$y = c_1 + c_2 x + c_3 e^{6x} - \frac{1}{4}x^2 - \frac{6}{37}\cos x + \frac{1}{37}\sin x.$$

22. From $m^3 - 2m^2 - 4m + 8 = 0$ we find $m_1 = m_2 = 2$ and $m_3 = -2$. Then $y_c = c_1 e^{2x} + c_2 x e^{2x} + c_3 e^{-2x}$ and we assume $y_p = (Ax^3 + Bx^2)e^{2x}$. Substituting into the differential equation we obtain $24A = 6$ and $6A + 8B = 0$. Then $A = \frac{1}{4}$, $B = -\frac{3}{16}$, $y_p = \left(\frac{1}{4}x^3 - \frac{3}{16}x^2\right)e^{2x}$, and

$$y = c_1 e^{2x} + c_2 x e^{2x} + c_3 e^{-2x} + \left(\frac{1}{4}x^3 - \frac{3}{16}x^2\right)e^{2x}.$$

23. From $m^3 - 3m^2 + 3m - 1 = 0$ we find $m_1 = m_2 = m_3 = 1$. Then $y_c = c_1 e^x + c_2 x e^x + c_3 x^2 e^x$ and we assume $y_p = Ax + B + Cx^3 e^x$. Substituting into the differential equation we obtain $-A = 1$, $3A - B = 0$, and $6C = -4$. Then $A = -1$, $B = -3$, $C = -\frac{2}{3}$, $y_p = -x - 3 - \frac{2}{3}x^3 e^x$, and

$$y = c_1 e^x + c_2 x e^x + c_3 x^2 e^x - x - 3 - \frac{2}{3}x^3 e^x.$$

24. From $m^3 - m^2 - 4m + 4 = 0$ we find $m_1 = 1$, $m_2 = 2$, and $m_3 = -2$. Then $y_c = c_1 e^x + c_2 e^{2x} + c_3 e^{-2x}$ and we assume $y_p = A + Bx e^x + Cx e^{2x}$. Substituting into the differential equation we obtain $4A = 5$, $-3B = -1$, and $4C = 1$. Then $A = \frac{5}{4}$, $B = \frac{1}{3}$, $C = \frac{1}{4}$, $y_p = \frac{5}{4} + \frac{1}{3}x e^x + \frac{1}{4}x e^{2x}$, and

$$y = c_1 e^x + c_2 e^{2x} + c_3 e^{-2x} + \frac{5}{4} + \frac{1}{3}x e^x + \frac{1}{4}x e^{2x}.$$

25. From $m^4 + 2m^2 + 1 = 0$ we find $m_1 = m_3 = i$ and $m_2 = m_4 = -i$. Then $y_c = c_1 \cos x + c_2 \sin x + c_3 x \cos x + c_4 x \sin x$ and we assume $y_p = Ax^2 + Bx + C$. Substituting into the differential equation we obtain $A = 1$, $B = -2$, and $4A + C = 1$. Then $A = 1$, $B = -2$, $C = -3$, $y_p = x^2 - 2x - 3$, and

$$y = c_1 \cos x + c_2 \sin x + c_3 x \cos x + c_4 x \sin x + x^2 - 2x - 3.$$

26. From $m^4 - m^2 = 0$ we find $m_1 = m_2 = 0$, $m_3 = 1$, and $m_4 = -1$. Then $y_c = c_1 + c_2 x + c_3 e^x + c_4 e^{-x}$ and we assume $y_p = Ax^3 + Bx^2 + (Cx^2 + Dx)e^{-x}$. Substituting into the differential equation we obtain $-6A = 4$, $-2B = 0$, $10C - 2D = 0$, and $-4C = 2$. Then $A = -\frac{2}{3}$, $B = 0$, $C = -\frac{1}{2}$, $D = -\frac{5}{2}$, $y_p = -\frac{2}{3}x^3 - \left(\frac{1}{2}x^2 + \frac{5}{2}x\right)e^{-x}$, and

$$y = c_1 + c_2 x + c_3 e^x + c_4 e^{-x} - \frac{2}{3}x^3 - \left(\frac{1}{2}x^2 + \frac{5}{2}x\right)e^{-x}.$$

27. We write $8\sin^2 x = 4 - 4\cos 2x$. From $m^2 + 1 = 0$ we find $m_1 = i$ and $m_2 = -i$. Then $y_c = c_1 \cos x + c_2 \sin x$ and we assume $y_p = A + B\cos 2x + C\sin 2x$. Substituting into the differential equation we obtain $A = 4$, $-3B = -4$, and $-3C = 0$. Then $A = 4$, $B = \frac{4}{3}$, $C = 0$, and $y_p = 4 + \frac{4}{3}\cos 2x$.

28. We write $\sin x \cos 2x = \frac{1}{2}\sin 3x - \frac{1}{2}\sin x$. From $m^2 + 1 = 0$ we find $m_1 = i$ and $m_2 = -i$. Then $y_c = c_1 \cos x + c_2 \sin x$ and we assume $y_p = A\cos 3x + B\sin 3x + Cx\cos x + Dx\sin x$. Substituting into the differential equation we obtain $-8A = 0$, $-8B = \frac{1}{2}$, $2D = 0$, and $-2C = -\frac{1}{2}$. Then $A = 0$, $B = -\frac{1}{16}$, $C = \frac{1}{4}$, $D = 0$, and $y_p = -\frac{1}{16}\sin 3x + \frac{1}{4}x\cos x$.

29. We have $y_c = c_1 \cos 2x + c_2 \sin 2x$ and we assume $y_p = A$. Substituting into the differential equation we find $A = -\frac{1}{2}$. Thus $y = c_1 \cos 2x + c_2 \sin 2x - \frac{1}{2}$. From the initial conditions we obtain $c_1 = 0$ and $c_2 = \sqrt{2}$, so $y = \sqrt{2}\sin 2x - \frac{1}{2}$.

30. We have $y_c = c_1 e^{-2x} + c_2 e^{x/2}$ and we assume $y_p = Ax^2 + Bx + C$. Substituting into the differential equation we find $A = -7$, $B = -19$, and $C = -37$. Thus $y = c_1 e^{-2x} + c_2 e^{x/2} - 7x^2 - 19x - 37$. From the initial conditions we obtain $c_1 = -\frac{1}{5}$ and $c_2 = \frac{186}{5}$, so

$$y = -\frac{1}{5}e^{-2x} + \frac{186}{5}e^{x/2} - 7x^2 - 19x - 37.$$

31. We have $y_c = c_1 e^{-x/5} + c_2$ and we assume $y_p = Ax^2 + Bx$. Substituting into the differential equation we find $A = -3$ and $B = 30$. Thus $y = c_1 e^{-x/5} + c_2 - 3x^2 + 30x$. From the initial conditions we obtain $c_1 = 200$ and $c_2 = -200$, so

$$y = 200^{-x/5} - 200 - 3x^2 + 30x.$$

32. We have $y_c = c_1 e^{-2x} + c_2 x e^{-2x}$ and we assume $y_p = (Ax^3 + Bx^2)e^{-2x}$. Substituting into the differential equation we find $A = \frac{1}{6}$ and $B = \frac{3}{2}$. Thus $y = c_1 e^{-2x} + c_2 x e^{-2x} + \left(\frac{1}{6}x^3 + \frac{3}{2}x^2\right)e^{-2x}$. From the initial conditions we obtain $c_1 = 2$ and $c_2 = 9$, so

$$y = 2e^{-2x} + 9x e^{-2x} + \left(\frac{1}{6}x^3 + \frac{3}{2}x^2\right)e^{-2x}.$$

33. We have $y_c = e^{-2x}(c_1 \cos x + c_2 \sin x)$ and we assume $y_p = Ae^{-4x}$. Substituting into the differential equation we find $A = 5$. Thus $y = e^{-2x}(c_1 \cos x + c_2 \sin x) + 7e^{-4x}$. From the initial conditions we obtain $c_1 = -10$ and $c_2 = 9$, so

$$y = e^{-2x}(-10\cos x + 9\sin x + 7e^{-4x}).$$

34. We have $y_c = c_1 e^x + c_2 e^{-x}$ and we assume $y_p = Axe^x + Bxe^{-x}$. Substituting into the differential equation we find $A = \frac{1}{4}$ and $B = -\frac{1}{4}$. Thus

$$y = c_1 e^x + c_2 e^{-x} + \frac{1}{4}xe^x - \frac{1}{4}xe^{-x} = c_1 e^x + c_2 e^{-x} + \frac{1}{2}\sinh x.$$

From the initial conditions we obtain $c_1 = 7$ and $c_2 = -5$, so

$$y = 7e^x - 5e^{-x} + \frac{1}{2}\sinh x.$$

35. We have $x_c = c_1 \cos\omega t + c_2 \sin\omega t$ and we assume $x_p = At \cos\omega t + Bt \sin\omega t$. Substituting into the differential equation we find $A = -F_0/2\omega$ and $B = 0$. Thus $x = c_1 \cos\omega t + c_2 \sin\omega t - (F_0/2\omega)t \cos\omega t$. From the initial conditions we obtain $c_1 = 0$ and $c_2 = F_0/2\omega^2$, so

$$x = (F_0/2\omega^2)\sin\omega t - (F_0/2\omega)t \cos\omega t.$$

36. We have $x_c = c_1 \cos\omega t + c_2 \sin\omega t$ and we assume $x_p = A \cos\gamma t + B \sin\gamma t$. Substituting into the differential equation we find $A = F_0/(\omega^2 - \gamma^2)$ and $B = 0$. Thus

$$x = c_1 \cos\omega t + c_2 \sin\omega t + \frac{F_0}{(\omega^2 - \gamma^2)}\cos\gamma t.$$

From the initial conditions we obtain $c_1 = F_0/(\omega^2 - \gamma^2)$ and $c_2 = 0$, so

$$x = \frac{F_0}{(\omega^2 - \gamma^2)}\cos\omega t + \frac{F_0}{(\omega^2 - \gamma^2)}\cos\gamma t.$$

37. We have $y_c = c_1 \cos x + c_2 \sin x$ and we assume $y_p = Ax \cos x + Bx \sin x + C \cos 2x + D \sin 2x$. Substituting into the differential equation we find $A = 0$, $B = \frac{1}{2}$, $C = 0$, and $D = \frac{1}{3}$. Thus

$$y = c_1 \cos x + c_2 \sin x + \frac{1}{2}x \sin x + \frac{1}{3}\sin 2x.$$

From the initial conditions we obtain $c_1 = -\frac{1}{6}$ and $c_2 = -\frac{\pi}{4}$, so

$$y = -\frac{1}{6}\cos x - \frac{\pi}{4}\sin x + \frac{1}{2}x \sin x + \frac{1}{3}\sin 2x.$$

38. We have $y_c = c_1 e^{-x} + c_2 e^{3x}$ and we assume $y_p = A + B \cos 2x + C \sin 2x$. Substituting into the differential equation we find $A = -\frac{1}{3}$, $B = -\frac{7}{65}$, and $C = -\frac{4}{65}$. Thus

$$y = c_1 e^{-x} + c_2 e^{3x} - \frac{1}{3} - \frac{7}{65}\cos 2x - \frac{4}{65}\sin 2x.$$

From the initial conditions we obtain $c_1 = \frac{1}{20}$ and $c_2 = \frac{3}{52}$, so

$$y = \frac{1}{20}e^{-x} + \frac{3}{52}e^{3x} - \frac{1}{3} - \frac{7}{65}\cos 2x - \frac{4}{65}\sin 2x.$$

39. We have $y_c = c_1 + c_2 e^x + c_3 x e^x$ and we assume $y_p = Ax + Bx^2 e^x + Ce^{5x}$. Substituting into the differential equation we find $A = 2$, $B = -12$, and $C = \frac{1}{2}$. Thus

$$y = c_1 + c_2 e^x + c_3 x e^x + 2x - 12x^2 e^x + \frac{1}{2}e^{5x}.$$

From the initial conditions we obtain $c_1 = 11$, $c_2 = -11$, and $c_3 = 9$, so

$$y = 11 - 11e^x + 9xe^x + 2x - 12x^2 e^x + \frac{1}{2}e^{5x}.$$

40. We have $y_c = c_1 e^{-2x} + e^x(c_2 \cos \sqrt{3}\,x + c_3 \sin \sqrt{3}\,x)$ and we assume $y_p = Ax + B + Cxe^{-2x}$. Substituting into the differential equation we find $A = \frac{1}{4}$, $B = -\frac{5}{8}$, and $C = \frac{2}{3}$. Thus

$$y = c_1 e^{-2x} + e^x(c_2 \cos \sqrt{3}\,x + c_3 \sin \sqrt{3}\,x) + \frac{1}{4}x - \frac{5}{8} + \frac{2}{3}xe^{-2x}.$$

From the initial conditions we obtain $c_1 = -\frac{23}{12}$, $c_2 = -\frac{59}{24}$, and $c_3 = \frac{17}{72}\sqrt{3}$, so

$$y = -\frac{23}{12}e^{-2x} + e^x\left(-\frac{59}{24}\cos \sqrt{3}\,x + \frac{17}{72}\sqrt{3}\sin \sqrt{3}\,x\right) + \frac{1}{4}x - \frac{5}{8} + \frac{2}{3}xe^{-2x}.$$

41. We have $y_c = c_1 \cos x + c_2 \sin x$ and we assume $y_p = A^2 + Bx + C$. Substituting into the differential equation we find $A = 1$, $B = 0$, and $C = -1$. Thus $y = c_1 \cos x + c_2 \sin x + x^2 - 1$. From $y(0) = 5$ and $y(1) = 0$ we obtain

$$c_1 - 1 = 5$$

$$(\cos 1)c_1 + \sin(1)c_2 = 0.$$

Solving this system we find $c_1 = 6$ and $c_2 = -6 \cot 1$. The solution of the boundary-value problem is

$$y = 6\cos x - 6(\cot 1)\sin x + x^2 - 1.$$

42. We have $y_c = e^x(c_1 \cos x + c_2 \sin x)$ and we assume $y_p = Ax + B$. Substituting into the differential equation we find $A = 1$ and $B = 0$. Thus $y = e^x(c_1 \cos x + c_2 \sin x) + x$. From $y(0) = 0$ and $y(\pi) = \pi$ we obtain

$$c_1 = 0$$

$$\pi - e^{\pi} c_1 = \pi.$$

Solving this system we find $c_1 = 0$ and c_2 is any real number. The solution of the boundary-value problem is

$$y = c_2 e^x \sin x + x.$$

43. We have $y_c = c_1 \cos 2x + c_2 \sin 2x$ and we assume $y_p = A\cos x + B\sin x$ on $[0, \pi/2]$. Substituting into the differential equation we find $A = 0$ and $B = \frac{1}{3}$. Thus $y = c_1 \cos 2x + c_2 \sin 2x + \frac{1}{3}\sin x$ on $[0, \pi/2]$. On $(\pi/2, \infty)$ we have $y = c_3 \cos 2x + c_4 \sin 2x$. From $y(0) = 1$ and $y'(0) = 2$ we obtain

$$c_1 = 1$$

$$\frac{1}{3} + 2c_2 = 2.$$

Solving this system we find $c_1 = 1$ and $c_2 = \frac{5}{6}$. Thus $y = \cos 2x + \frac{5}{6} \sin 2x + \frac{1}{3} \sin x$ on $[0, \pi/2]$. Now continuity of y at $x = \pi/2$ implies

$$\cos \pi + \frac{5}{6} \sin \pi + \frac{1}{3} \sin \frac{\pi}{2} = c_3 \cos \pi + c_4 \sin \pi$$

or $-1 + \frac{1}{3} = -c_3$. Hence $c_3 = \frac{2}{3}$. Continuity of y' at $x = \pi/2$ implies

$$-2 \sin \pi + \frac{5}{3} \cos \pi + \frac{1}{3} \cos \frac{\pi}{2} = -2c_3 \sin \pi + 2c_4 \cos \pi$$

or $-\frac{5}{3} = -2c_4$. Then $c_4 = \frac{5}{6}$ and the solution of the boundary-value problem is

$$y(x) = \begin{cases} \cos 2x + \frac{5}{6} \sin 2x + \frac{1}{3} \sin x, & 0 \le x \le \pi/2 \\ \frac{2}{3} \cos 2x + \frac{5}{6} \sin 2x, & x > \pi/2 \end{cases}.$$

Exercises 4.5

1. $(D+5)y = 9 \sin x$

2. $(4D+8)y = x + 3$

3. $(3D^2 - 5D + 1)y = e^x$

4. $(D^3 - 2D^2 + 7D - 6)y = 1 - \sin x$

5. $(D^3 - 4D^2 + 5D) = 4x$

6. $(D^4 - 2D^2 + D) = e^{-3x} + e^{2x}$

7. $9D^2 - 4 = (3D - 2)(3D + 2)$

8. $D^2 - 5 = \left(D - \sqrt{5}\right)\left(D + \sqrt{5}\right)$

9. $D^2 - 4D - 12 = (D - 6)(D + 2)$

10. $2D^2 - 3D - 2 = (2D + 1)(D - 2)$

11. $D^3 + 10D^2 + 25D = D(D + 5)^2$

12. $D^3 + 4D = D(D^2 + 4)$

13. $D^3 + 2D^2 - 13D + 10 = (D-1)(D-2)(D+5)$

14. $D^3 + 4D^2 + 3D = D(D + 1)(D + 3)$

15. $D^4 + 8D = D(D + 2)(D^2 - 2D + 4)$

16. $D^4 - 8D^2 + 16 = (D - 2)^2(D + 4)^2$

17. $D^4 y = D^4(10x^3 - 2x) = D^3(30x^2 - 2) = D^2(60x) = D(60) = 0$

18. $(2D - 1)y = (2D - 1)4e^{x/2} = 8De^{x/2} - 4e^{x/2} = 4e^{x/2} - 4e^{x/2} = 0$

19. $(D - 2)(D + 5)4e^{2x} = (D - 2)(8e^{2x} + 20e^{2x}) = (D - 2)28e^{2x} = 56e^{2x} - 56e^{2x} = 0$

20. $(D^2 + 64)(2 \cos 8x - 5 \sin 8x) = D(-16 \sin 8x - 40 \cos 8x) + 64(2 \cos 8x - 5 \sin 8x)$

$$= -128 \cos 8x + 320 \sin 8x + 128 \cos 8x - 320 \sin 8x = 0$$

21. D^4 because of x^3

22. D^5 because of x^4

23. $D(D-2)$ because of 1 and e^{2x}

24. $D^2(D-6)^2$ because of x and xe^{6x}

25. D^2+4 because of $\cos 2x$

26. $D(D^2+1)$ because of 1 and $\sin x$

27. $D^3(D^2+16)$ because of x^2 and $\sin 4x$

28. $D^2(D^2+1)(D^2+25)$ because of x, $\sin x$, and $\cos 5x$

29. $(D+1)(D-1)^3$ because of e^{-x} and $x^2 e^x$

30. $D(D-1)(D-2)$ because of 1, e^x, and e^{2x}

31. $D(D^2-2D+5)$ because of 1 and $e^x \cos 2x$

32. $(D^2+2D+2)(D^2-4D+5)$ because of $e^{-x}\sin x$ and $e^{2x}\cos x$

33. $1,\ x,\ x^2,\ x^3,\ x^4$

34. $D^2+4D = D(D+4);\quad 1,\ e^{-4x}$

35. $e^{6x},\ e^{-3x/2}$

36. $D^2-9D-36 = (D-12)(D+3);\quad e^{12x},\ e^{-3x}$

37. $\cos\sqrt{5}\,x,\ \sin\sqrt{5}\,x$

38. $D^2-6D+10 = D^2-2(3)D+(3^2+1^2);\quad e^{3x}\cos x,\ e^{3x}\sin x$

39. $D^3-10D^2+25D = D(D-5)^2;\quad 1,\ e^{5x},\ xe^{5x}$

40. $1,\ x,\ e^{5x},\ e^{7x}$

───────── **Exercises 4.6** ─────────────────────────

1. Applying D to the differential equation we obtain

$$D(D^2-9)y = 0.$$

Then

$$y = \underbrace{c_1 e^{3x} + c_2 e^{-3x}}_{y_c} + c_3$$

and $y_p = A$. Substituting y_p into the differential equation yields $-9A = 54$ or $A = -6$. The general solution is

$$y = c_1 e^{3x} + c_2 e^{-3x} - 6.$$

2. Applying D to the differential equation we obtain

$$D(2D^2 - 7D + 5)y = 0.$$

93

Then

$$y = \underbrace{c_1 e^{5x/2} + c_2 e^x}_{y_c} + c_3$$

and $y_p = A$. Substituting y_p into the differential equation yields $5A = -29$ or $A = -29/5$. The general solution is

$$y = c_1 e^{5x/2} + c_2 e^x - \frac{29}{5}.$$

3. Applying D to the differential equation we obtain

$$D(D^2 + D)y = D^2(D + 1)y = 0.$$

Then

$$y = \underbrace{c_1 + c_2 e^{-x}}_{y_c} + c_3 x$$

and $y_p = Ax$. Substituting y_p into the differential equation yields $A = 3$. The general solution is

$$y = c_1 + c_2 e^{-3x} + 3x.$$

4. Applying D to the differential equation we obtain

$$D(D^3 + 2D^2 + D)y = D^2(D + 1)^2 y = 0.$$

Then

$$y = \underbrace{c_1 + c_2 e^{-x} + c_3 x e^{-x}}_{y_c} + c_4 x$$

and $y_p = Ax$. Substituting y_p into the differential equation yields $A = 10$. The general solution is

$$y = c_1 + c_2 e^{-x} + c_3 x e^{-x} + 10x.$$

5. Applying D^2 to the differential equation we obtain

$$D^2(D^2 + 4D + 4)y = D^2(D + 2)^2 y = 0.$$

Then

$$y = \underbrace{c_1 e^{-2x} + c_2 x e^{-2x}}_{y_c} + c_3 + c_4 x$$

and $y_p = Ax + B$. Substituting y_p into the differential equation yields $4Ax + (4A + 4B) = 2x + 6$. Equating coefficients gives

$$4A = 2$$

$$4A + 4B = 6.$$

Then $A = 1/2$, $B = 1$, and the general solution is

$$y = c_1 e^{-2x} + c_2 x e^{-2x} + \frac{1}{2}x + 1.$$

6. Applying D^2 to the differential equation we obtain

$$D^2(D^2 + 3D)y = D^3(D + 3)y = 0.$$

Then

$$y = \underbrace{c_1 + c_2e^{-3x}}_{y_c} + c_3x^2 + c_4x$$

and $y_p = Ax^2 + Bx$. Substituting y_p into the differential equation yields $6Ax + (2A+3B) = 4x - 5$. Equating coefficients gives

$$6A = 4$$

$$2A + 3B = -5.$$

Then $A = 2/3$, $B = -19/9$, and the general solution is

$$y = c_1 + c_2e^{-3x} + \frac{2}{3}x^2 - \frac{19}{9}x.$$

7. Applying D^3 to the differential equation we obtain

$$D^3(D^3 + D^2)y = D^5(D + 1)y = 0.$$

Then

$$y = \underbrace{c_1 + c_2x + c_3e^{-x}}_{y_c} + c_4x^4 + c_5x^3 + c_6x^2$$

and $y_p = Ax^4 + Bx^3 + Cx^2$. Substituting y_p into the differential equation yields $12Ax^2 + (24A + 6B)x + (6B + 2C) = 8x^2$. Equating coefficients gives

$$12A = 8$$

$$24A + 6B = 0$$

$$6B + 2C = 0.$$

Then $A = 2/3$, $B = -8/3$, $C = 8$, and the general solution is

$$y = c_1 + c_2x + c_3e^{-x} + \frac{2}{3}x^4 - \frac{8}{3}x^3 + 8x^2.$$

8. Applying D^4 to the differential equation we obtain.

$$D^4(D^2 - 2D + 1)y = D^4(D - 1)^2y = 0.$$

Then

$$y = \underbrace{c_1e^x + c_2xe^x}_{y_c} + c_3x^3 + c_4x^2 + c_5x + c_6$$

95

and $y_p = Ax^3 + Bx^2 + Cx + D$. Substituting y_p into the differential equation yields
$Ax^3 + (B - 6A)x^2 + (6A - 4B + C)x + (2B - 2C + D) = x^3 + 4x$. Equating coefficients gives

$$A = 1$$

$$B - 6A = 0$$

$$6A - 4B + C = 4$$

$$2B - 2C + D = 0.$$

Then $A = 1$, $B = 6$, $C = 22$, $D = 32$, and the general solution is

$$y = c_1 e^x + c_2 x e^x + x^3 + 6x^2 + 22x + 32.$$

9. Applying $D - 4$ to the differential equation we obtain

$$(D - 4)(D^2 - D - 12)y = (D - 4)^2(D + 3)y = 0.$$

Then

$$y = \underbrace{c_1 e^{4x} + c_2 e^{-3x}}_{y_c} + c_3 x e^{4x}$$

and $y_p = Axe^{4x}$. Substituting y_p into the differential equation yields $7Ae^{4x} = e^{4x}$. Equating coefficients gives $A = 1/7$. The general solution is

$$y = c_1 e^{4x} + c_2 e^{-3x} + \frac{1}{7} x e^{4x}.$$

10. Applying $D - 6$ to the differential equation we obtain

$$(D - 6)(D^2 + 2D + 2)y = 0.$$

Then

$$y = \underbrace{e^{-x}(c_1 \cos x + c_2 \sin x)}_{y_c} + c_3 e^{6x}$$

and $y_p = Ae^{6x}$. Substituting y_p into the differential equation yields $50Ae^{6x} = 5e^{6x}$. Equating coefficients gives $A = 1/10$. The general solution is

$$y = e^{-x}(c_1 \cos x + c_2 \sin x) + \frac{1}{10} e^{6x}.$$

11. Applying $D(D - 1)$ to the differential equation we obtain

$$D(D - 1)(D^2 - 2D - 3)y = D(D - 1)(D + 1)(D - 3)y = 0.$$

Then

$$y = \underbrace{c_1 e^{3x} + c_2 e^{-x}}_{y_c} + c_3 e^x + c_4$$

96

and $y_p = Ae^x + B$. Substituting y_p into the differential equation yields $-4Ae^x - 3B = 4e^x - 9$. Equating coefficients gives $A = -1$ and $B = 3$. The general solution is

$$y = c_1 e^{3x} + c_2 e^{-x} - e^x + 3.$$

12. Applying $D^2(D+2)$ to the differential equation we obtain

$$D^2(D+2)(D^2 + 6D + 8)y = D^2(D+2)^2(D+4)y = 0.$$

Then

$$y = \underbrace{c_1 e^{-2x} + c_2 e^{-4x}}_{y_c} + c_3 x e^{-2x} + c_4 x + c_5$$

and $y_p = Axe^{-2x} + Bx + C$. Substituting y_p into the differential equation yields $2Ae^{-2x} + 8Bx + (6B + 8C) = 3e^{-2x} + 2x$. Equating coefficients gives

$$2A = 3$$

$$8B = 2$$

$$6B + 8C = 0.$$

Then $A = 3/2$, $B = 1/4$, $C = -3/16$, and the general solution is

$$y = c_1 e^{-2x} + c_2 e^{-4x} + \frac{3}{2}xe^{-2x} + \frac{1}{4}x - \frac{3}{16}.$$

13. Applying $D^2 + 1$ to the differential equation we obtain

$$(D^2 + 1)(D^2 + 25)y = 0.$$

Then

$$y = \underbrace{c_1 \cos 5x + c_2 \sin 5x}_{y_c} + c_3 \cos x + c_4 \sin x$$

and $y_p = A\cos x + B\sin x$. Substituting y_p into the differential equation yields $24A\cos x + 24B\sin x = 6\sin x$. Equating coefficients gives $A = 0$ and $B = 1/4$. The general solution is

$$y = c_1 \cos 5x + c_2 \sin 5x + \frac{1}{4}\sin x.$$

14. Applying $D(D^2 + 1)$ to the differential equation we obtain

$$D(D^2 + 1)(D^2 + 4)y = 0.$$

Then

$$y = \underbrace{c_1 \cos 2x + c_2 \sin 2x}_{y_c} + c_3 \cos x + c_4 \sin x + c_5$$

and $y_p = A\cos x + B\sin x + C$. Substituting y_p into the differential equation yields $3A\cos x + 3B\sin x + 4C = 4\cos x + 3\sin x - 8$. Equating coefficients gives $A = 4/3$, $B = 1$, and $C = -2$. The general solution is

$$y = c_1\cos 2x + c_2\sin 2x + \frac{4}{3}\cos x + \sin x - 2.$$

15. Applying $(D-4)^2$ to the differential equation we obtain

$$(D-4)^2(D^2 + 6D + 9)y = (D-4)^2(D+3)^2 y = 0.$$

Then

$$y = \underbrace{c_1 e^{-3x} + c_2 x e^{-3x}}_{y_c} + c_3 x e^{4x} + c_4 e^{4x}$$

and $y_p = Axe^{4x} + Be^{4x}$. Substituting y_p into the differential equation yields $49Axe^{4x} + (14A + 49B)e^{4x} = -xe^{4x}$. Equating coefficients gives

$$49A = -1$$

$$14A + 49B = 0.$$

Then $A = -1/49$, $B = 2/343$, and the general solution is

$$y = c_1 e^{-3x} + c_2 x e^{-3x} - \frac{1}{49}xe^{4x} + \frac{2}{343}e^{4x}.$$

16. Applying $D^2(D-1)^2$ to the differential equation we obtain

$$D^2(D-1)^2(D^2 + 3D - 10)y = D^2(D-1)^2(D-2)(D+5)y = 0.$$

Then

$$y = \underbrace{c_1 e^{2x} + c_2 e^{-5x}}_{y_c} + c_3 x e^x + c_4 e^x + c_5 x + c_6$$

and $y_p = Axe^x + Be^x + Cx + D$. Substituting y_p into the differential equation yields $-6Axe^x + (5A - 6B)e^x - 10Cx + (3C - 10D) = xe^x + x$. Equating coefficients gives

$$-6A = 1$$

$$5A - 6B = 0$$

$$-10C = 1$$

$$3C - 10D = 0.$$

Then $A = -1/6$, $B = -5/36$, $C = -1/10$, $D = -3/100$, and the general solution is

$$y = c_1 e^{2x} + c_2 e^{-5x} - \frac{1}{6}xe^x - \frac{5}{36}e^x - \frac{1}{10}x - \frac{3}{100}.$$

17. Applying $D(D-1)^3$ to the differential equation we obtain

$$D(D-1)^3(D^2-1)y = D(D-1)^4(D+1)y = 0.$$

Then

$$y = \underbrace{c_1 e^x + c_2 e^{-x}}_{y_c} + c_3 x^3 e^x + c_4 x^2 e^x + c_5 x e^x + c_6$$

and $y_p = Ax^3 e^x + Bx^2 e^x + Cxe^x + D$. Substituting y_p into the differential equation yields $6Ax^2 e^x + (6A+4B)xe^x + (2B+2C)e^x - D = x^2 e^x + 5$. Equating coefficients gives

$$6A = 1$$

$$6A + 4B = 0$$

$$2B + 2C = 0$$

$$-D = 5.$$

Then $A = 1/6$, $B = -1/4$, $C = 1/4$, $D = -5$, and the general solution is

$$y = c_1 e^x + c_2 e^{-x} + \frac{1}{6}x^3 e^x - \frac{1}{4}x^2 e^x + \frac{1}{4}xe^x - 5.$$

18. Applying $(D+1)^3$ to the differential equation we obtain

$$(D+1)^3(D^2+2D+1)y = (D+1)^5 y = 0.$$

Then

$$y = \underbrace{c_1 e^{-x} + c_2 xe^{-x}}_{y_c} + c_3 x^4 e^{-x} + c_4 x^3 e^{-x} + c_5 x^2 e^{-x}$$

and $y_p = Ax^4 e^{-x} + Bx^3 e^{-x} + Cx^2 e^{-x}$. Substituting y_p into the differential equation yields $12Ax^2 e^{-x} + 6Bxe^{-x} + 2Ce^{-x} = x^2 e^{-x}$. Equating coefficients gives $A = 1/12$, $B = 0$, and $C = 0$. The general solution is

$$y = c_1 e^{-x} + c_2 xe^{-x} + \frac{1}{2}x^4 e^{-x}.$$

19. Applying $D^2 - 2D + 2$ to the differential equation we obtain

$$(D^2 - 2D + 2)(D^2 - 2D + 5)y = 0.$$

Then

$$y = \underbrace{e^x(c_1 \cos 2x + c_2 \sin 2x)}_{y_c} + e^x(c_3 \cos x + c_4 \sin x)$$

and $y_p = Ae^x \cos x + Be^x \sin x$. Substituting y_p into the differential equation yields we obtain $3Ae^x \cos x + 3Be^x \sin x = e^x \sin x$. Equating coefficients gives $A = 0$ and $B = 1/3$. The general solution is

$$y = e^x(c_1 \cos 2x + c_2 \sin 2x) + \frac{1}{3}e^x \sin x.$$

20. Applying $D^2 - 2D + 10$ to the differential equation we obtain

$$(D^2 - 2D + 10)\left(D^2 + D + \frac{1}{4}\right)y = (D^2 - 2D + 10)\left(D + \frac{1}{2}\right)^2 y = 0.$$

Then

$$y = \underbrace{c_1 e^{-x/2} + c_2 x e^{-x/2}}_{y_c} + c_3 e^x \cos 3x + c_4 e^x \sin 3x$$

and $y_p = Ae^x \cos 3x + Be^x \sin 3x$. Substituting y_p into the differential equation yields $(9B - 27A/4)e^x \cos 3x - (9A + 27B/4)e^x \sin 3x = -e^x \cos 3x + e^x \sin 3x$. Equating coefficients gives

$$-\frac{27}{4}A + 9B = -1$$

$$-9A - \frac{27}{4}B = 1.$$

Then $A = -4/225$, $B = -28/225$, and the general solution is

$$y = c_1 e^{-x/2} + c_2 x e^{-x/2} - \frac{4}{225}e^x \cos 3x - \frac{28}{225}e^x \sin 3x.$$

21. Applying $D^2 + 25$ to the differential equation we obtain

$$(D^2 + 25)(D^2 + 25) = (D^2 + 25)^2 = 0.$$

Then

$$y = \underbrace{c_1 \cos 5x + c_2 \sin 5x}_{y_c} + c_3 x \cos 5x + c_4 x \cos 5x$$

and $y_p = Ax \cos 5x + Bx \sin 5x$. Substituting y_p into the differential equation yields $10B \cos 5x - 10A \sin 5x = 20 \sin 5x$. Equating coefficients gives $A = -2$ and $B = 0$. The general solution is

$$y = c_1 \cos 5x + c_2 \sin 5x - 2x \cos 5x.$$

22. Applying $D^2 + 1$ to the differential equation we obtain

$$(D^2 + 1)(D^2 + 1) = (D^2 + 1)^2 = 0.$$

Then

$$y = \underbrace{c_1 \cos x + c_2 \sin x}_{y_c} + c_3 x \cos x + c_4 x \cos x$$

and $y_p = Ax \cos x + Bx \sin x$. Substituting y_p into the differential equation yields $2B \cos x - 2A \sin x = 4 \cos x - \sin x$. Equating coefficients gives $A = 1/2$ and $B = 2$. The general solution is

$$y = c_1 \cos x + c_2 \sin x + \frac{1}{2}x \cos x - 2x \sin x.$$

23. Applying $(D^2 + 1)^2$ to the differential equation we obtain

$$(D^2 + 1)^2(D^2 + D + 1) = 0.$$

Then

$$y = e^{-x/2}\underbrace{\left[c_1 \cos \frac{\sqrt{3}}{2}x + c_2 \sin \frac{\sqrt{3}}{2}x\right]}_{y_c} + c_3 \cos x + c_4 \sin x + c_5 x \cos x + c_6 x \sin x$$

and $y_p = A \cos x + B \sin x + Cx \cos x + Dx \sin x$. Substituting y_p into the differential equation yields

$$(B + C + 2D) \cos x + Dx \cos x + (-A - 2C + D) \sin x - Cx \sin x = x \sin x.$$

Equating coefficients gives

$$B + C + 2D = 0$$

$$D = 0$$

$$-A - 2C + D = 0$$

$$-C = 1.$$

Then $A = 2$, $B = 1$, $C = -1$, and $D = 0$, and the general solution is

$$y = e^{-x/2}\left[c_1 \cos \frac{\sqrt{3}}{2}x + c_2 \sin \frac{\sqrt{3}}{2}x\right] + 2 \cos x + \sin x - x \cos x.$$

24. Writing $\cos^2 x = \frac{1}{2}(1 + \cos 2x)$ and applying $D(D^2 + 4)$ to the differential equation we obtain

$$D(D^2 + 4)(D^2 + 4) = D(D^2 + 4)^2 = 0.$$

Then

$$y = \underbrace{c_1 \cos 2x + c_2 \sin 2x}_{y_c} + c_3 x \cos 2x + c_4 x \sin 2x + c_5$$

and $y_p = Ax \cos 2x + Bx \sin 2x + C$. Substituting y_p into the differential equation yields $-4A \sin 2x + 4B \cos 2x + 4C = \frac{1}{2} + \frac{1}{2} \cos 2x$. Equating coefficients gives $A = 0$, $B = 1/8$, and $C = 1/8$. The general solution is

$$y = c_1 \cos 2x + c_2 \sin 2x + \frac{1}{8}x \sin 2x + \frac{1}{8}.$$

25. Applying D^3 to the differential equation we obtain

$$D^3(D^3 + 8D^2) = D^5(D + 8) = 0.$$

Then

$$y = \underbrace{c_1 + c_2 x + c_3 e^{-8x}}_{y_c} + c_4 x^2 + c_5 x^3 + c_6 x^4$$

and $y_p = Ax^2 + Bx^3 + Cx^4$. Substituting y_p into the differential equation yields $16A + 6B + (48B + 24C)x + 96Cx^2 = 2 + 9x - 6x^2$. Equating coefficients gives

$$16A + 6B = 2$$

$$48B + 24C = 9$$

$$96C = -6.$$

Then $A = 11/256$, $B = 7/32$, and $C = -1/16$, and the general solution is

$$y = c_1 + c_2x + c_3e^{-8x} + \frac{11}{256}x^2 + \frac{7}{32}x^3 - \frac{1}{16}x^4.$$

26. Applying $D(D-1)^2(D+1)$ to the differential equation we obtain

$$D(D-1)^2(D+1)(D^3 - D^2 + D - 1) = D(D-1)^3(D+1)(D^2 + 1) = 0.$$

Then

$$y = \underbrace{c_1e^x + c_2\cos x + c_3\sin x}_{y_c} + c_4 + c_5e^{-x} + c_6xe^x + c_7x^2e^x$$

and $y_p = A + Be^{-x} + Cxe^x + Dx^2e^x$. Substituting y_p into the differential equation yields

$$4Dxe^x + (2C + 4D)e^x - 4Be^{-x} - A = xe^x - e^{-x} + 7.$$

Equating coefficients gives

$$4D = 1$$

$$2C + 4D = 0$$

$$-4B = -1$$

$$-A = 7.$$

Then $A = -7$, $B = 1/4$, $C = -1/2$, and $D = 1/4$, and the general solution is

$$y = c_1e^x + c_2\cos x + c_3\sin x - 7 + \frac{1}{4}e^{-x} - \frac{1}{2}xe^x + \frac{1}{4}x^2e^x.$$

27. Applying $D^2(D-1)$ to the differential equation we obtain

$$D^2(D-1)(D^3 - 3D^2 + 3D - 1) = D^2(D-1)^4 = 0.$$

Then

$$y = \underbrace{c_1e^x + c_2xe^x + c_3x^2e^x}_{y_c} + c_4 + c_5x + c_6x^3e^x$$

and $y_p = A + Bx + Cx^3 e^x$. Substituting y_p into the differential equation yields $(-A + 3B) - Bx + 6Ce^x = 16 - x + e^x$. Equating coefficients gives

$$-A + 3B = 16$$

$$-B = -1$$

$$6C = 1.$$

Then $A = -13$, $B = 1$, and $C = 1/6$, and the general solution is

$$y = c_1 e^x + c_2 x e^x + c_3 x^2 e^x - 13 + x + \frac{1}{6} x^3 e^x.$$

28. Writing $(e^x + e^{-x})^2 = 2 + e^{2x} + e^{-2x}$ and applying $D(D-2)(D+2)$ to the differential equation we obtain

$$D(D-2)(D+2)(2D^3 - 3D^2 - 3D + 2) = D(D-2)^2(D+2)(D+1)(2D-1) = 0.$$

Then

$$y = \underbrace{c_1 e^{-x} + c_2 e^{2x} + c_3 e^{x/2}}_{y_c} + c_4 + c_5 x e^{2x} + c_6 e^{-2x}$$

and $y_p = A + Bx e^{2x} + Ce^{-2x}$. Substituting y_p into the differential equation yields $2A + 9Be^{2x} - 20Ce^{-2x} = 2 + e^{2x} + e^{-2x}$. Equating coefficients gives $A = 1$, $B = 1/9$, and $C = -1/20$, and the general solution is

$$y = c_1 e^{-x} + c_2 e^{2x} + c_3 e^{x/2} + 1 + \frac{1}{9} x e^{2x} - \frac{1}{20} e^{-2x}.$$

29. Applying $D(D-1)$ to the differential equation we obtain

$$D(D-1)(D^4 - 2D^3 + D^2) = D^3(D-1)^3 = 0.$$

Then

$$y = \underbrace{c_1 + c_2 x + c_3 e^x + c_4 x e^x}_{y_c} + c_5 x^2 + c_6 x^2 e^x$$

and $y_p = Ax^2 + Bx^2 e^x$. Substituting y_p into the differential equation yields $2A + 2Be^x = 1 + e^x$. Equating coefficients gives $A = 1/2$ and $B = 1/2$. The general solution is

$$y = c_1 + c_2 x + c_3 e^x + c_4 x e^x + \frac{1}{2} x^2 + \frac{1}{2} x^2 e^x.$$

30. Applying $D^3(D-2)$ to the differential equation we obtain

$$D^3(D-2)(D^4 - 4D^2) = D^5(D-2)^2(D+2) = 0.$$

Then

$$y = \underbrace{c_1 + c_2 x + c_3 e^{2x} + c_4 e^{-2x}}_{y_c} + c_5 x^2 + c_6 x^3 + c_7 x^4 + c_8 x e^{2x}$$

and $y_p = Ax^2 + Bx^3 + Cx^4 + Dxe^{2x}$. Substituting y_p into the differential equation yields $(-8A + 24C) - 24Bx - 48Cx^2 + 16De^{2x} = 5x^2 - e^{2x}$. Equating coefficients gives

$$-8A + 24C = 0$$

$$-24B = 0$$

$$-48C = 5$$

$$16D = -1.$$

Then $A = -5/16$, $B = 0$, $C = -5/48$, and $D = -1/16$, and the general solution is

$$y = c_1 + c_2 x + c_3 e^{2x} + c_4 e^{-2x} - \frac{5}{16}x^2 - \frac{5}{48}x^4 - \frac{1}{16}xe^{2x}.$$

31. Applying $(2D - 1)$ to the differential equation we obtain

$$(2D - 1)(16D^4 - 1) = (2D - 1)^2(2D - 1)(4D^2 + 1) = 0.$$

Then

$$y = \underbrace{c_1 e^{x/2} + c_2 e^{-x/2} + c_3 \cos\frac{1}{2}x + c_4 \sin\frac{1}{2}x}_{y_c} + c_5 x e^{x/2}$$

and $y_p = Axe^{x/2}$. Substituting y_p into the differential equation yields $8Ae^{x/2} = e^{x/2}$. Equating coefficients gives $A = 1/8$. The general solution is

$$y = c_1 e^{x/2} + c_2 e^{-x/2} + c_3 \cos\frac{1}{2}x + c_4 \sin\frac{1}{2}x + \frac{1}{8}xe^{x/2}.$$

32. Writing $2\cosh x = e^x + e^{-x}$ and applying $D(D - 1)(D + 1)$ to the differential equation we obtain

$$D(D - 1)(D + 1)(D^4 - 5D^2 + 4) = D(D - 1)^2(D + 1)^2(D - 2)(D + 2) = 0.$$

Then

$$y = \underbrace{c_1 e^x + c_2 e^{-x} + c_3 e^{2x} + c_4 e^{-2x}}_{y_c} + c_5 + c_6 x e^x + c_7 x e^{-x}$$

and $y_p = A + Bxe^x + Cxe^{-x}$. Substituting y_p into the differential equation yields $4A - 6Be^x + 6Ce^{-x} = -6 + e^x + e^{-x}$. Equating coefficients gives $A = -3/2$, $B = -1/6$, and $C = 1/6$. The general solution is

$$y = c_1 e^x + c_2 e^{-x} + c_3 e^{2x} + c_4 e^{-2x} - \frac{3}{2} - \frac{1}{6}xe^x + \frac{1}{6}xe^{-x}.$$

104

33. The complementary function is $y_c = c_1 e^{8x} + c_2 e^{-8x}$. Using D to annihilate 16 we find $y_p = A$. Substituting y_p into the differential equation we obtain $-64A = 16$. Thus $A = -1/4$ and

$$y = c_1 e^{8x} + c_2 e^{-8x} - \frac{1}{4}$$

$$y' = 8c_1 e^{8x} - 8c_2 e^{-8x}.$$

The initial conditions imply

$$c_1 + c_2 = \frac{5}{4}$$

$$8c_1 - 8c_2 = 0.$$

Thus $c_1 = c_2 = 5/8$ and

$$y = \frac{5}{8}e^{8x} + \frac{5}{8}e^{-8x} - \frac{1}{4}.$$

34. The complementary function is $y_c = c_1 + c_2 e^{-x}$. Using D^2 to annihilate x we find $y_p = Ax + Bx^2$. Substituting y_p into the differential equation we obtain $(A + 2B) + 2Bx = x$. Thus $A = -1$ and $B = 1/2$, and

$$y = c_1 + c_2 e^{-x} - x + \frac{1}{2}x^2$$

$$y' = -c_2 e^{-x} - 1 + x.$$

The initial conditions imply

$$c_1 + c_2 = 1$$

$$-c_2 = 1.$$

Thus $c_1 = 2$ and $c_2 = -1$, and

$$y = 2 - e^{-x} - x + \frac{1}{2}x^2.$$

35. The complementary function is $y_c = c_1 + c_2 e^{5x}$. Using D^2 to annihilate $x - 2$ we find $y_p = Ax + Bx^2$. Substituting y_p into the differential equation we obtain $(-5A + 2B) - 10Bx = -2 + x$. Thus $A = 9/25$ and $B = -1/10$, and

$$y = c_1 + c_2 e^{5x} + \frac{9}{25}x - \frac{1}{10}x^2$$

$$y' = 5c_2 e^{5x} + \frac{9}{25} - \frac{1}{5}x.$$

The initial conditions imply

$$c_1 + c_2 = 0$$

$$5c_2 = \frac{41}{125}.$$

105

Thus $c_1 = -41/125$ and $c_2 = 41/125$, and

$$y = -\frac{41}{125} + \frac{41}{125}e^{5x} + \frac{9}{25}x - \frac{1}{10}x^2.$$

36. The complementary function is $y_c = c_1 e^x + c_2 e^{-6x}$. Using $D - 2$ to annihilate $10e^{2x}$ we find $y_p = Ae^{2x}$. Substituting y_p into the differential equation we obtain $8Ae^{2x} = 10e^{2x}$. Thus $A = 5/4$ and

$$y = c_1 e^x + c_2 e^{-6x} + \frac{5}{4}e^{2x}$$

$$y' = c_1 e^x - 6c_2 e^{-6x} + \frac{5}{2}e^{2x}.$$

The initial conditions imply

$$c_1 + c_2 = -\frac{1}{4}$$

$$c_1 - 6c_2 = -\frac{3}{2}.$$

Thus $c_1 = -3/7$ and $c_2 = 5/28$, and

$$y = -\frac{3}{7}e^x + \frac{5}{28}e^{-6x} + \frac{5}{4}e^{2x}$$

37. The complementary function is $y_c = c_1 \cos x + c_2 \sin x$. Using $(D^2 + 1)(D^2 + 4)$ to annihilate $8 \cos 2x - 4 \sin x$ we find $y_p = Ax \cos x + Bx \sin x + C \cos 2x + D \sin 2x$. Substituting y_p into the differential equation we obtain $2B \cos x - 3C \cos 2x - 2A \sin x - 3D \sin 2x = 8 \cos 2x - 4 \sin x$. Thus $A = 2$, $B = 0$, $C = -8/3$, and $D = 0$, and

$$y = c_1 \cos x + c_2 \sin x + 2x \cos x - \frac{8}{3} \cos 2x$$

$$y' = -c_1 \sin x + c_2 \cos x + 2 \cos x - 2x \sin x + \frac{16}{3} \sin 2x.$$

The initial conditions imply

$$c_2 + \frac{8}{3} = -1$$

$$-c_1 - \pi = 0.$$

Thus $c_1 = -\pi$ and $c_2 = -11/3$, and

$$y = -\pi \cos x - \frac{11}{3} \sin x + 2x \cos x - \frac{8}{3} \cos 2x.$$

38. The complementary function is $y_c = c_1 + c_2 e^x + c_3 x e^x$. Using $D(D - 1)^2$ to annihilate $xe^x + 5$ we find $y_p = Ax + Bx^2 e^x + Cx^3 e^x$. Substituting y_p into the differential equation

106

we obtain $A + (2B + 6C)e^x + 6Cxe^x = xe^x + 5$. Thus $A = 5$, $B = -1/2$, and $C = 1/6$, and

$$y = c_1 + c_2 e^x + c_3 x e^x + 5x - \frac{1}{2}x^2 e^x + \frac{1}{6}x^3 e^x$$

$$y' = c_2 e^x + c_3(xe^x + e^x) + 5 - xe^x + \frac{1}{6}x^3 e^x$$

$$y'' = c_2 e^x + c_3(xe^x + 2e^x) - e^x - xe^x + \frac{1}{2}x^2 e^x + \frac{1}{6}x^3 e^x.$$

The initial conditions imply

$$c_1 + c_2 = 2$$

$$c_2 + c_3 + 5 = 2$$

$$c_2 + 2c_3 - 1 = -1.$$

Thus $c_1 = 8$, $c_2 = -6$, and $c_3 = 3$, and

$$y = 8 - 6e^x + 3xe^x + 5x - \frac{1}{2}x^2 e^x + \frac{1}{6}x^3 e^x.$$

39. The complementary function is $y_c = e^{2x}(c_1 \cos 2x + c_2 \sin 2x)$. Using D^4 to annihilate x^3 we find $y_p = A + Bx + Cx^2 + Dx^3$. Substituting y_p into the differential equation we obtain $(8A - 4B + 2C) + (8B - 8C + 6D)x + (8C - 12D)x^2 + 8Dx^3 = x^3$. Thus $A = 0$, $B = 3/32$, $C = 3/16$, and $D = 1/8$, and

$$y = e^{2x}(c_1 \cos 2x + c_2 \sin 2x) + \frac{3}{32}x + \frac{3}{16}x^2 + \frac{1}{8}x^3$$

$$y' = e^{2x}\left[c_1(2 \cos 2x - 2 \sin 2x) + c_2(2 \cos 2x + 2 \sin 2x)\right] + \frac{3}{32} + \frac{3}{8}x + \frac{3}{8}x^2.$$

The initial conditions imply

$$c_1 = 2$$

$$2c_1 + 2c_2 + \frac{3}{32} = 4.$$

Thus $c_1 = 2$, $c_2 = -3/64$, and

$$y = e^{2x}\left(2 \cos 2x - \frac{3}{64} \sin 2x\right) + \frac{3}{32}x + \frac{3}{16}x^2 + \frac{1}{8}x^3.$$

40. The complementary function is $y_c = c_1 + c_2 x + c_3 x^2 + c_4 e^x$. Using $D^2(D-1)$ to annihilate $x + e^x$ we find $y_p = Ax^3 + Bx^4 + Cxe^x$. Substituting y_p into the differential equation we obtain

$(-6A + 24B) - 24Bx + Ce^x = x + e^x$. Thus $A = -1/6$, $B = -1/24$, and $C = 1$, and

$$y = c_1 + c_2 x + c_3 x^2 + c_4 e^x - \frac{1}{6}x^3 - \frac{1}{24}x^4 + xe^x$$

$$y' = c_2 + 2c_3 x + c_4 e^x - \frac{1}{2}x^2 - \frac{1}{6}x^3 + e^x + xe^x$$

$$y'' = 2c_3 + c_4 e^x - x - \frac{1}{2}x^2 + 2e^x + xe^x.$$

$$y''' = c_4 e^x - 1 - x + 3e^x + xe^x$$

The initial conditions imply

$$c_1 + c_4 = 0$$

$$c_2 + c_4 + 1 = 0$$

$$2c_3 + c_4 + 2 = 0$$

$$2 + c_4 = 0.$$

Thus $c_1 = 2$, $c_2 = 1$, $c_3 = 0$, and $c_4 = -2$, and

$$y = 2 + x - 2e^x - \frac{1}{6}x^3 - \frac{1}{24}x^4 + xe^x.$$

41. The complementary function is $y_c = c_1 e^x + c_2 e^{-x}$. Using $(D-1)(D^2 - 2D + 5)^2$ to annihilate $e^x(2 + 3x \cos 2x)$ we obtain

$$y_p = Axe^x + Bxe^x \cos 2x + Cxe^x \sin 2x + De^x \cos 2x + Ee^x \sin 2x.$$

42. The complementary function is $y_c = c_1 + c_2 e^{-x}$. Using $D(D+1)(D^2+1)^3$ to annihilate $9 - e^{-x} + x^2 \sin x$ we obtain

$$y_p = Ax + Bxe^{-x} + C \cos x + D \sin x + Ex \cos x + Fx \sin x + Gx^2 \cos x + Hx^2 \sin x.$$

43. Applying the operators to the function x we find

$$(xD - 1)(D + 4)x = (xD^2 + 4xD - D - 4)x$$

$$= xD^2 x + 4xDx - Dx - 4x$$

$$= x(0) + 4x(1) - 1 - 4x = -1$$

and

$$(D + 4)(xD - 1)x = (D + 4)(xDx - x)$$

$$= (D + 4)(x \cdot 1 - x) = 0.$$

Thus, the operators are not the same.

44. Since $y_p^{(n)}(x) = 0$ for $n \geq 1$,

$$a_n y_p^{(n)} + a_{n-1} y_p^{(n-1)} + \cdots + a_1 y_p' + a_0 y_p = 0 + 0 + \cdots + 0 + a_0 \frac{k}{a_0} = k.$$

Exercises 4.7

The particular solution, $y_p = u_1 y_1 + u_2 y_2$, in the following problems can take on a variety of forms, especially where trigonometric functions are involved. The validity of a particular form can best be checked by substituting it back into the differential equation.

1. The auxiliary equation is $m^2 + 1 = 0$, so $y_c = c_1 \cos x + c_2 \sin x$ and

$$W = \begin{vmatrix} \cos x & \sin x \\ -\sin x & \cos x \end{vmatrix} = 1.$$

Identifying $f(x) = \sec x$ we obtain

$$u_1' = -\frac{\sin x \sec x}{1} = -\tan x$$

$$u_2' = \frac{\cos x \sec x}{1} = 1.$$

Then $u_1 = \ln|\cos x|$, $u_2 = x$, and

$$y = c_1 \cos x + c_2 \sin x + \cos x \ln|\cos x| + x \sin x$$

for $-\pi/2 < x < \pi/2$.

2. The auxiliary equation is $m^2 + 1 = 0$, so $y_c = c_1 \cos x + c_2 \sin x$ and

$$W = \begin{vmatrix} \cos x & \sin x \\ -\sin x & \cos x \end{vmatrix} = 1.$$

Identifying $f(x) = \tan x$ we obtain

$$u_1' = -\sin x \tan x = \frac{\cos^2 x - 1}{\cos x} = \cos x - \sec x$$

$$u_2' = \sin x.$$

Then $u_1 = \sin x - \ln|\sec x + \tan x|$, $u_2 = -\cos x$, and

$$y = c_1 \cos x + c_2 \sin x + \cos x \left(\sin x - \ln|\sec x + \tan x| \right) - \cos x \sin x$$

for $-\pi/2 < x < \pi/2$.

Exercises 4.7

3. The auxiliary equation is $m^2 + 1 = 0$, so $y_c = c_1 \cos x + c_2 \sin x$ and

$$W = \begin{vmatrix} \cos x & \sin x \\ -\sin x & \cos x \end{vmatrix} = 1.$$

Identifying $f(x) = \sin x$ we obtain

$$u_1' = -\sin^2 x$$

$$u_2' = \cos x \sin x.$$

Then

$$u_1 = \frac{1}{4} \sin 2x - \frac{1}{2} x = \frac{1}{2} \sin x \cos x - \frac{1}{2} x$$

$$u_2 = -\frac{1}{2} \cos^2 x.$$

and

$$y = c_1 \cos x + c_2 \sin x + \frac{1}{2} \sin x \cos^2 x - \frac{1}{2} x \cos x - \frac{1}{2} \cos^2 x \sin x$$

$$= c_1 \cos x + c_2 \sin x - \frac{1}{2} x \cos x$$

for $-\infty < x < \infty$.

4. The auxiliary equation is $m^2 + 1 = 0$, so $y_c = c_1 \cos x + c_2 \sin x$ and

$$W = \begin{vmatrix} \cos x & \sin x \\ -\sin x & \cos x \end{vmatrix} = 1.$$

Identifying $f(x) = \sec x \tan x$ we obtain

$$u_1' = -\sin x (\sec x \tan x) = -\tan^2 x = 1 - \sec^2 x$$

$$u_2' = \cos x (\sec x \tan x) = \tan x.$$

Then $u_1 = x - \tan x$, $u_2 = -\ln|\cos x|$, and

$$y = c_1 \cos x + c_2 \sin x + x \cos x - \sin x - \sin x \ln|\cos x|$$

$$= c_1 \cos x + c_3 \sin x + x \cos x - \sin x \ln|\cos x|$$

for $-\pi/2 < x < \pi/2$.

5. The auxiliary equation is $m^2 + 1 = 0$, so $y_c = c_1 \cos x + c_2 \sin x$ and

$$W = \begin{vmatrix} \cos x & \sin x \\ -\sin x & \cos x \end{vmatrix} = 1.$$

Identifying $f(x) = \cos^2 x$ we obtain

$$u_1' = -\sin x \cos^2 x$$

$$u_2' = \cos^3 x = \cos x \left(1 - \sin^2 x\right).$$

Then $u_1 = \frac{1}{3}\cos^3 x$, $u_2 = \sin x - \frac{1}{3}\sin^3 x$, and

$$y = c_1 \cos x + c_2 \sin x + \frac{1}{3}\cos^4 x + \sin^2 x - \frac{1}{3}\sin^4 x$$

$$= c_1 \cos x + c_2 \sin x + \frac{1}{3}\left(\cos^2 x + \sin^2 x\right)\left(\cos^2 x - \sin^2 x\right) + \sin^2 x$$

$$= c_1 \cos x + c_2 \sin x + \frac{1}{3}\cos^2 x + \frac{2}{3}\sin^2 x$$

$$= c_1 \cos x + c_2 \sin x + \frac{1}{3} + \frac{1}{3}\sin^2 x$$

for $-\infty < x < \infty$.

6. The auxiliary equation is $m^2 + 1 = 0$, so $y_c = c_1 \cos x + c_2 \sin x$ and

$$W = \begin{vmatrix} \cos x & \sin x \\ -\sin x & \cos x \end{vmatrix} = 1.$$

Identifying $f(x) = \sec^2 x$ we obtain

$$u_1' = -\frac{\sin x}{\cos^2 x}$$

$$u_2' = \sec x.$$

Then

$$u_1 = -\frac{1}{\cos x} = -\sec x$$

$$u_2 = \ln|\sec x + \tan x|$$

and

$$y = c_1 \cos x + c_2 \sin x - \cos x \sec x + \sin x \ln|\sec x + \tan x|$$

$$= c_1 \cos x + c_2 \sin x - 1 + \sin x \ln|\sec x + \tan x|$$

for $-\pi/2 < x < \pi/2$.

7. The auxiliary equation is $m^2 - 1 = 0$, so $y_c = c_1 e^x + c_2 e^{-x}$ and

$$W = \begin{vmatrix} e^x & e^{-x} \\ e^x & -e^{-x} \end{vmatrix} = -2.$$

Identifying $f(x) = \cosh x = \frac{1}{2}(e^{-x} + e^x)$ we obtain

$$u_1' = \frac{1}{4}e^{2x} + \frac{1}{4}$$

$$u_2' = -\frac{1}{4} - \frac{1}{4}e^{2x}.$$

111

Then

$$u_1 = -\frac{1}{8}e^{-2x} + \frac{1}{4}x$$

$$u_2 = -\frac{1}{8}e^{2x} - \frac{1}{4}x$$

and

$$y = c_1 e^x + c_2 e^{-x} - \frac{1}{8}e^{-x} + \frac{1}{4}xe^x - \frac{1}{8}e^x - \frac{1}{4}xe^{-x}$$

$$= c_3 e^x + c_4 e^{-x} + \frac{1}{4}x\left(e^x - e^{-x}\right)$$

$$= c_3 e^x + c_4 e^{-x} + \frac{1}{2}x \sinh x$$

for $-\infty < x < \infty$.

8. The auxiliary equation is $m^2 - 1 = 0$, so $y_c = c_1 e^x + c_2 e^{-x}$ and

$$W = \begin{vmatrix} e^x & e^{-x} \\ e^x & -e^{-x} \end{vmatrix} = -2.$$

Identifying $f(x) = \sinh 2x$ we obtain

$$u_1' = -\frac{1}{4}e^{-3x} + \frac{1}{4}e^x$$

$$u_2' = \frac{1}{4}e^{-x} - \frac{1}{4}e^{3x}.$$

Then

$$u_1 = \frac{1}{12}e^{-3x} + \frac{1}{4}e^x$$

$$u_2 = -\frac{1}{4}e^{-x} - \frac{1}{12}e^{3x}.$$

and

$$y = c_1 e^x + c_2 e^{-x} + \frac{1}{12}e^{-2x} + \frac{1}{4}e^{2x} - \frac{1}{4}e^{-2x} - \frac{1}{12}e^{2x}$$

$$= c_1 e^x + c_2 e^{-x} + \frac{1}{6}\left(e^{2x} - e^{-2x}\right)$$

$$= c_1 e^x + c_2 e^{-x} + \frac{1}{3}\sinh 2x$$

for $-\infty < x < \infty$.

9. The auxiliary equation is $m^2 - 4 = 0$, so $y_c = c_1 e^{2x} + c_2 e^{-2x}$ and

$$W = \begin{vmatrix} e^{2x} & e^{-2x} \\ 2e^{2x} & -2e^{-2x} \end{vmatrix} = -4.$$

Identifying $f(x) = e^{2x}/x$ we obtain $u'_1 = 1/4x$ and $u'_2 = -e^{4x}/4x$. Then

$$u_1 = \frac{1}{4}\ln|x|, \qquad u_2 = -\frac{1}{4}\int_{x_0}^x \frac{e^{4t}}{t}\,dt$$

and

$$y = c_1e^{2x} + c_2e^{-2x} + \frac{1}{4}\left(e^{2x}\ln|x| - e^{-2x}\int_{x_0}^x \frac{e^{4t}}{t}\,dt\right), \qquad x_0 > 0$$

for $x > 0$.

10. The auxiliary equation is $m^2 - 9 = 0$, so $y_c = c_1e^{3x} + c_2e^{-3x}$ and

$$W = \begin{vmatrix} e^{3x} & e^{-3x} \\ 3e^{3x} & -3e^{-3x} \end{vmatrix} = -6.$$

Identifying $f(x) = 9x/e^{3x}$ we obtain $u'_1 = \frac{3}{2}xe^{-6x}$ and $u'_2 = -\frac{3}{2}x$. Then

$$u_1 = -\frac{1}{24}e^{-6x} - \frac{1}{4}xe^{-6x}, \qquad u_2 = -\frac{3}{4}x^2$$

and

$$y = c_1e^{3x} + c_2e^{-3x} - \frac{1}{24}e^{-3x} - \frac{1}{4}xe^{-3x} - \frac{3}{4}x^2e^{-3x}$$

$$= c_1e^{3x} + c_3e^{-3x} - \frac{1}{4}xe^{-3x}(1 - 3x)$$

for $-\infty < x < \infty$.

11. The auxiliary equation is $m^2 + 3m + 2 = (m + 1)(m + 2) = 0$, so $y_c = c_1e^{-x} + c_2e^{-2x}$ and

$$W = \begin{vmatrix} e^{-x} & e^{-2x} \\ -e^{-x} & -2e^{-2x} \end{vmatrix} = -e^{-3x}.$$

Identifying $f(x) = 1/(1 + e^x)$ we obtain

$$u'_1 = \frac{e^x}{1 + e^x}$$

$$u'_2 = -\frac{e^{2x}}{1 + e^x} = \frac{e^x}{1 + e^x} - e^x.$$

Then $u_1 = \ln(1 + e^x)$, $u_2 = \ln(1 + e^x) - e^x$, and

$$y = c_1e^{-x} + c_2e^{-2x} + e^{-x}\ln(1 + e^x) + e^{-2x}\ln(1 + e^x) - e^{-x}$$

$$= c_3e^{-x} + c_2e^{-2x} + (1 + e^{-x})e^{-x}\ln(1 + e^x)$$

for $-\infty < x < \infty$.

12. The auxiliary equation is $m^2 - 3m + 2 = (m - 1)(m - 2) = 0$, so $y_c = c_1e^x + c_2e^{2x}$ and

$$W = \begin{vmatrix} e^x & e^{2x} \\ e^x & 2e^{2x} \end{vmatrix} = e^{3x}.$$

Identifying $f(x) = e^{3x}/(1 + e^x)$ we obtain

$$u_1' = -\frac{e^{2x}}{1 + e^x} = \frac{e^x}{1 + e^x} - e^x$$

$$u_2' = \frac{e^x}{1 + e^x}.$$

Then $u_1 = \ln(1 + e^x) - e^x$, $u_2 = \ln(1 + e^x)$, and

$$y = c_1 e^x + c_2 e^{2x} + e^x \ln(1 + e^x) - e^{2x} + e^{2x} \ln(1 + e^x)$$

$$= c_1 e^x + c_3 e^{2x} + (1 + e^x) e^x \ln(1 + e^x)$$

for $-\infty < x < \infty$.

13. The auxiliary equation is $m^2 + 3m + 2 = (m + 1)(m + 2) = 0$, so $y_c = c_1 e^{-x} + c_2 e^{-2x}$ and

$$W = \begin{vmatrix} e^{-x} & e^{-2x} \\ -e^{-x} & -2e^{-2x} \end{vmatrix} = -e^{-3x}.$$

Identifying $f(x) = \sin e^x$ we obtain

$$u_1' = \frac{e^{-2x} \sin e^x}{e^{-3x}} = e^x \sin e^x$$

$$u_2' = \frac{e^{-x} \sin e^x}{-e^{-3x}} = -e^{2x} \sin e^x.$$

Then $u_1 = -\cos e^x$, $u_2 = e^x \cos x - \sin e^x$, and

$$y = c_1 e^{-x} + c_2 e^{-2x} - e^{-x} \cos e^x + e^{-x} \cos e^x - e^{-2x} \sin e^x$$

$$= c_1 e^{-x} + c_2 e^{-2x} - e^{-2x} \sin e^x$$

for $-\infty < x < \infty$.

14. The auxiliary equation is $m^2 - 2m + 1 = (m - 1)^2 = 0$, so $y_c = c_1 e^x + c_2 x e^x$ and

$$W = \begin{vmatrix} e^x & x e^x \\ e^x & x e^x + e^x \end{vmatrix} = e^{2x}.$$

Identifying $f(x) = e^x \tan^{-1} x$ we obtain

$$u_1' = -\frac{x e^x e^x \tan^{-1} x}{e^{2x}} = -x \tan^{-1} x$$

$$u_2' = \frac{e^x e^x \tan^{-1} x}{e^{2x}} = \tan^{-1} x.$$

Then

$$u_1 = -\frac{1+x^2}{2}\tan^{-1}x + \frac{x}{2}$$

$$u_2 = x\tan^{-1}x - \frac{1}{2}\ln\left(1+x^2\right)$$

and

$$y = c_1 e^x + c_2 x e^x + \left(-\frac{1+x^2}{2}\tan^{-1}x + \frac{x}{2}\right)e^x + \left(x\tan^{-1}x - \frac{1}{2}\ln\left(1+x^2\right)\right)xe^x$$

$$= c_1 e^x + c_3 x e^x + \frac{1}{2}e^x\left[\left(x^2-1\right)\tan^{-1}x - \ln\left(1+x^2\right)\right]$$

for $-\infty < x < \infty$.

15. The auxiliary equation is $m^2 - 2m + 1 = (m-1)^2 = 0$, so $y_c = c_1 e^x + c_2 x e^x$ and

$$W = \begin{vmatrix} e^x & xe^x \\ e^x & xe^x + e^x \end{vmatrix} = e^{2x}.$$

Identifying $f(x) = e^x/\left(1+x^2\right)$ we obtain

$$u_1' = -\frac{xe^x e^x}{e^{2x}\left(1+x^2\right)} = -\frac{x}{1+x^2}$$

$$u_2' = \frac{e^x e^x}{e^{2x}\left(1+x^2\right)} = \frac{1}{1+x^2}.$$

Then $u_1 = -\frac{1}{2}\ln\left(1+x^2\right)$, $u_2 = \tan^{-1}x$, and

$$y = c_1 e^x + c_2 x e^x - \frac{1}{2}e^x\ln\left(1+x^2\right) + xe^x\tan^{-1}x$$

for $-\infty < x < \infty$.

16. The auxiliary equation is $m^2 - 2m + 2 = [m-(1+i)][m-(1-i)] = 0$, so $y_c = c_1 e^x\sin x + c_2 e^x\cos x$ and

$$W = \begin{vmatrix} e^x\sin x & e^x\cos x \\ e^x\cos x + e^x\sin x & -e^x\sin x + e^x\cos x \end{vmatrix} = -e^{2x}.$$

Identifying $f(x) = e^x\sec x$ we obtain

$$u_1' = -\frac{e^x\cos xe^x\sec x}{-e^{2x}} = 1$$

$$u_2' = \frac{(e^x\sin x)(e^x\sec x)}{-e^{2x}} = -\tan x.$$

Then $u_1 = x$, $u_2 = \ln|\cos x|$, and

$$y = c_1 e^x\sin x + c_2 e^x\cos x + xe^x\sin x + e^x\cos x\ln|\cos x|$$

115

for $-\pi/2 < x < \pi/2$.

17. The auxiliary equation is $m^2 + 2m + 1 = (m+1)^2 = 0$, so $y_c = c_1 e^{-x} + c_2 x e^{-x}$ and

$$W = \begin{vmatrix} e^{-x} & x e^{-x} \\ -e^{-x} & -x e^{-x} + e^{-x} \end{vmatrix} = e^{-2x}.$$

Identifying $f(x) = e^{-x} \ln x$ we obtain

$$u_1' = -\frac{x e^{-x} e^{-x} \ln x}{e^{-2x}} = -x \ln x$$

$$u_2' = \frac{e^{-x} e^{-x} \ln x}{e^{-2x}} = \ln x.$$

Then

$$u_1 = -\frac{1}{2} x^2 \ln x + \frac{1}{4} x^2$$

$$u_2 = x \ln x - x$$

and

$$y = c_1 e^{-x} + c_2 x e^{-x} - \frac{1}{2} x^2 e^{-x} \ln x + \frac{1}{4} x^2 e^{-x} + x^2 e^{-x} \ln x - x^2 e^{-x}$$

$$= c_1 e^{-x} + c_2 x e^{-x} + \frac{1}{2} x^2 e^{-x} \ln x - \frac{3}{4} x^2 e^{-x}$$

for $x > 0$.

18. The auxiliary equation is $m^2 + 10m + 25 = (m+5)^2 = 0$, so $y_c = c_1 e^{-5x} + c_2 x e^{-5x}$ and

$$W = \begin{vmatrix} e^{-5x} & x e^{-5x} \\ -5 e^{-5x} & -5x e^{-5x} + e^{-5x} \end{vmatrix} = e^{-10x}.$$

Identifying $f(x) = e^{-10x}/x^2$ we obtain

$$u_1' = -\frac{x e^{-5x} e^{-10x}}{x^2 e^{-10x}} = -\frac{e^{-5x}}{x}$$

$$u_2' = \frac{e^{-5x} e^{-10x}}{x^2 e^{-10x}} = \frac{e^{-5x}}{x^2}.$$

Then

$$u_1 = -\int_{x_0}^{x} \frac{e^{-5t}}{t}\, dt, \quad x_0 > 0$$

$$u_2 = \int_{x_0}^{x} \frac{e^{-5t}}{t^2}\, dt, \quad x_0 > 0$$

and

$$y = c_1 e^{-5x} + c_2 x e^{-5x} - e^{-5x} \int_{x_0}^{x} \frac{e^{-5t}}{t}\, dt + x e^{-5x} \int_{x_0}^{x} \frac{e^{-5t}}{t^2}\, dt$$

for $x > 0$.

19. The auxiliary equation is $3m^2 - 6m + 30 = 3[m - (1 + 3i)][m - (1 - 3i)] = 0$, so $y_c = c_1 e^x \cos 3x + c_2 e^x \sin 3x$ and

$$W = \begin{vmatrix} e^x \cos 3x & e^x \sin 3x \\ -3e^x \sin x + e^x \cos 3x & 3e^x \cos 3x + e^x \sin 3x \end{vmatrix} = 3e^{2x}.$$

Identifying $f(x) = \frac{1}{3} e^x \tan 3x$ we obtain

$$u_1' = -\frac{(e^x \sin 3x)(e^x \tan 3x)}{9e^{2x}} = -\frac{1}{9} \frac{\sin^2 3x}{\cos 3x} = \frac{1}{9}(\cos 3x - \sec 3x)$$

$$u_2' = \frac{(e^x \cos 3x)(e^x \tan 3x)}{9e^{2x}} = \frac{1}{9} \sin 3x.$$

Then

$$u_1 = \frac{1}{27} \sin 3x - \frac{1}{27} \ln |\sec 3x + \tan 3x|$$

$$u_2 = -\frac{1}{27} \cos 3x$$

and

$$y = c_1 e^x \cos 3x + c_2 e^x \sin 3x + \frac{1}{27} e^x \sin 3x \cos 3x$$

$$- \frac{1}{27} e^x \cos 3x \ln |\sec 3x + \tan 3x| - \frac{1}{27} e^x \sin 3x \cos 3x$$

$$= c_1 e^x \cos 3x + c_2 e^x \sin 3x - \frac{1}{27} e^x \cos 3x \ln |\sec 3x + \tan 3x|$$

for $-\pi/6 < x < \pi/6$.

20. The auxiliary equation is $4m^2 - 4m + 1 = (2m - 1)^2 = 0$, so $y_c = c_1 e^{x/2} + c_2 x e^{x/2}$ and

$$W = \begin{vmatrix} e^{x/2} & x e^{x/2} \\ \frac{1}{2} e^{x/2} & \frac{1}{2} x e^{x/2} + e^{x/2} \end{vmatrix} = e^x.$$

Identifying $f(x) = \frac{1}{4} e^{x/2} \sqrt{1 - x^2}$ we obtain

$$u_1' = -\frac{x e^{x/2} e^{x/2} \sqrt{1 - x^2}}{4 e^x} = -\frac{1}{4} x \sqrt{1 - x^2}$$

$$u_2' = \frac{e^{x/2} e^{x/2} \sqrt{1 - x^2}}{4 e^x} = \frac{1}{4} \sqrt{1 - x^2}.$$

Then

$$u_1 = \frac{1}{12} \left(1 - x^2\right)^{3/2}$$

$$u_2 = \frac{x}{8} \sqrt{1 - x^2} + \frac{1}{8} \sin^{-1} x$$

117

and

$$y = c_1 e^{x/2} + c_2 x e^{x/2} + \frac{1}{12} e^{x/2} \left(1 - x^2\right)^{3/2} + \frac{1}{8} x^2 e^{x/2} \sqrt{1 - x^2} + \frac{1}{8} x e^{x/2} \sin^{-1} x$$

for $-1 \leq x \leq 1$.

21. The auxiliary equation is $m^3 + m = m(m^2 + 1) = 0$, so $y_c = c_1 + c_2 \cos x + c_3 \sin x$ and

$$W = \begin{vmatrix} 1 & \cos x & \sin x \\ 0 & -\sin x & \cos x \\ 0 & -\cos x & -\sin x \end{vmatrix} = 1.$$

Identifying $f(x) = \tan x$ we obtain

$$u_1' = W_1 = \begin{vmatrix} 0 & \cos x & \sin x \\ 0 & -\sin x & \cos x \\ \tan x & -\cos x & -\sin x \end{vmatrix} = \tan x$$

$$u_2' = W_2 = \begin{vmatrix} 1 & 0 & \sin x \\ 0 & 0 & \cos x \\ 0 & \tan x & -\sin x \end{vmatrix} = -\sin x$$

$$u_3' = W_3 = \begin{vmatrix} 1 & \cos x & 0 \\ 0 & -\sin x & 0 \\ 0 & -\cos x & \tan x \end{vmatrix} = -\sin x \tan x = \frac{\cos^2 x - 1}{\cos x} = \cos x - \sec x.$$

Then

$$u_1 = -\ln|\cos x|$$

$$u_2 = \cos x$$

$$u_3 = \sin x - \ln|\sec x + \tan x|$$

and

$$y = c_1 + c_2 \cos x + c_3 \sin x - \ln|\cos x| + \cos^2 x$$

$$+ \sin^2 x - \sin x \ln|\sec x + \tan x|$$

$$= c_4 + c_2 \cos x + c_3 \sin x - \ln|\cos x| - \sin x \ln|\sec x + \tan x|$$

for $-\infty < x < \infty$.

22. The auxiliary equation is $m^3 + 4m = m\left(m^2 + 4\right) = 0$, so $y_c = c_1 + c_2 \cos 2x + c_3 \sin 2x$ and

$$W = \begin{vmatrix} 1 & \cos 2x & \sin 2x \\ 0 & -2\sin 2x & 2\cos 2x \\ 0 & -4\cos 2x & -4\sin 2x \end{vmatrix} = 8.$$

Identifying $f(x) = \sec 2x$ we obtain

$$u_1' = \frac{1}{8}W_1 = \frac{1}{8}\begin{vmatrix} 0 & \cos 2x & \sin 2x \\ 0 & -2\sin 2x & 2\cos 2x \\ \sec 2x & -4\cos 2x & -4\sin 2x \end{vmatrix} = \frac{1}{4}\sec 2x$$

$$u_2' = \frac{1}{8}W_2 = \frac{1}{8}\begin{vmatrix} 1 & 0 & \sin 2x \\ 0 & 0 & 2\cos 2x \\ 0 & \sec 2x & -4\sin 2x \end{vmatrix} = -\frac{1}{4}$$

$$u_3' = \frac{1}{8}W_3 = \frac{1}{8}\begin{vmatrix} 1 & \cos 2x & 0 \\ 0 & -2\sin 2x & 0 \\ 0 & -4\cos 2x & \sec 2x \end{vmatrix} = -\frac{1}{4}\tan 2x.$$

Then

$$u_1 = \frac{1}{8}\ln|\sec 2x + \tan 2x|$$

$$u_2 = -\frac{1}{4}x$$

$$u_3 = \frac{1}{8}\ln|\cos 2x|$$

and

$$y = c_1 + c_2\cos 2x + c_3\sin 2x + \frac{1}{8}\ln|\sec 2x + \tan 2x| - \frac{1}{4}x\cos 2x + \frac{1}{8}\sin 2x\ln|\cos 2x|$$

for $-\pi/4 < x < \pi/4$.

23. The auxiliary equation is $m^3 - 2m^2 - m + 2 = (m-1)(m-2)(m+1) = 0$, so $y_c = c_1 e^x + c_2 e^{2x} + c_3 e^{-x}$ and

$$W = \begin{vmatrix} e^x & e^{2x} & e^{-x} \\ e^x & 2e^{2x} & -e^{-x} \\ e^x & 4e^{2x} & e^{-x} \end{vmatrix} = 6e^{2x}.$$

Identifying $f(x) = e^{3x}$ we obtain

$$u_1' = \frac{1}{6e^{2x}}W_1 = \frac{1}{6e^{2x}}\begin{vmatrix} 0 & e^{2x} & e^{-x} \\ 0 & 2e^{2x} & -e^{-x} \\ e^{3x} & 4e^{2x} & e^{-x} \end{vmatrix} = \frac{-3e^{4x}}{6e^{2x}} = -\frac{1}{2}e^{2x}$$

$$u_2' = \frac{1}{6e^{2x}}W_2 = \frac{1}{6e^{2x}}\begin{vmatrix} e^x & 0 & e^{-x} \\ e^x & 0 & -e^{-x} \\ e^x & e^{3x} & e^{-x} \end{vmatrix} = \frac{2e^{3x}}{6e^{2x}} = \frac{1}{3}e^x$$

119

$$u_3' = \frac{1}{6e^{2x}} W_1^3 = \frac{1}{6e^{2x}} \begin{vmatrix} e^x & e^{2x} & 0 \\ e^x & 2e^{2x} & 0 \\ e^x & 4e^{2x} & e^{3x} \end{vmatrix} = \frac{e^{6x}}{6e^{2x}} = \frac{1}{6}e^{4x}.$$

Then $u_1 = -\frac{1}{4}e^{2x}$, $u_2 = \frac{1}{3}e^x$, and $u_3 = \frac{1}{24}e^{4x}$, and

$$y = c_1 e^x + c_2 e^{2x} + c_3 e^{-x} - \frac{1}{4}e^{3x} + \frac{1}{3}e^{3x} + \frac{1}{24}e^{3x}$$

$$= c_1 e^x + c_2 e^{2x} + c_3 e^{-x} + \frac{1}{8}e^{3x}$$

for $-\infty < x < \infty$.

24. The auxiliary equation is $2m^3 - 6m^2 = 2m^2(m-3) = 0$, so $y_c = c_1 + c_2 x + c_3 e^{3x}$ and

$$W = \begin{vmatrix} 1 & x & e^{3x} \\ 0 & 1 & 3e^{3x} \\ 0 & 0 & 9e^{3x} \end{vmatrix} = 9e^{3x}.$$

Identifying $f(x) = x^2/2$ we obtain

$$u_1' = \frac{1}{9e^{3x}} W_1 = \frac{1}{9e^{3x}} \begin{vmatrix} 0 & x & e^{3x} \\ 0 & 1 & 3e^{3x} \\ x^2/2 & 0 & 9e^{3x} \end{vmatrix} = \frac{\frac{3}{2}x^3 e^{3x} - \frac{1}{2}x^2 e^{3x}}{9e^{3x}} = \frac{1}{6}x^3 - \frac{1}{18}x^2$$

$$u_2' = \frac{1}{9e^{3x}} W_2 = \frac{1}{9e^{3x}} \begin{vmatrix} 1 & 0 & e^{3x} \\ 0 & 0 & 3e^{3x} \\ 0 & x^2/2 & 9e^{3x} \end{vmatrix} = \frac{-\frac{3}{2}x^2 e^{3x}}{9e^{3x}} = -\frac{1}{6}x^2$$

$$u_3' = \frac{1}{9e^{3x}} W_3 = \frac{1}{9e^{3x}} \begin{vmatrix} 1 & x & 0 \\ 0 & 1 & 0 \\ 0 & 0 & x^2/2 \end{vmatrix} = \frac{\frac{1}{2}x^2}{9e^{3x}} = \frac{1}{18}x^2 e^{-3x}.$$

Then

$$u_1 = \frac{1}{24}x^4 - \frac{1}{54}x^3$$

$$u_2 = -\frac{1}{18}x^3$$

$$u_3 = -\frac{1}{54}x^2 e^{-3x} - \frac{1}{81}xe^{-3x} - \frac{1}{243}e^{-3x}$$

and

$$y = c_1 + c_2 x + c_3 e^{3x} + \frac{1}{24}x^4 - \frac{1}{54}x^3 - \frac{1}{18}x^4 - \frac{1}{54}x^2 - \frac{1}{81}x - \frac{1}{243}$$

$$= c_4 + c_5 x + c_3 e^{3x} - \frac{1}{72}x^4 - \frac{1}{54}x^3 - \frac{1}{54}x^2$$

for $-\infty < x < \infty$.

25. The auxiliary equation is $4m^2 - 1 = (2m-1)(2m+1) = 0$, so $y_c = c_1 e^{x/2} + c_2 e^{-x/2}$ and

$$W = \begin{vmatrix} e^{x/2} & e^{-x/2} \\ \frac{1}{2}e^{x/2} & -\frac{1}{2}e^{-x/2} \end{vmatrix} = -1.$$

Identifying $f(x) = x e^{x/2}/4$ we obtain $u_1' = x/4$ and $u_2' = -x e^x/4$. Then $u_1 = x^2/8$ and $u_2 = -x e^x/4 + e^x/4$. Thus

$$y = c_1 e^{x/2} + c_2 e^{-x/2} + \frac{1}{8}x^2 e^{x/2} - \frac{1}{4}x e^{x/2} + \frac{1}{4}e^{x/2}$$

$$= c_3 e^{x/2} + c_2 e^{-x/2} + \frac{1}{8}x^2 e^{x/2} - \frac{1}{4}x e^{x/2}$$

and

$$y' = \frac{1}{2}c_3 e^{x/2} - \frac{1}{2}c_2 e^{-x/2} + \frac{1}{16}x^2 e^{x/2} + \frac{1}{8}x e^{x/2} - \frac{1}{4}e^{x/2}.$$

The initial conditions imply

$$c_3 + c_2 = 1$$

$$\frac{1}{2}c_3 - \frac{1}{2}c_2 - \frac{1}{4} = 0.$$

Thus $c_3 = 3/4$ and $c_2 = 1/4$, and

$$y = \frac{3}{4}e^{x/2} + \frac{1}{4}e^{-x/2} + \frac{1}{8}x^2 e^{x/2} - \frac{1}{4}x e^{x/2}.$$

26. The auxiliary equation is $2m^2 + m - 1 = (2m-1)(m+1) = 0$, so $y_c = c_1 e^{x/2} + c_2 e^{-x}$ and

$$W = \begin{vmatrix} e^{x/2} & e^{-x} \\ \frac{1}{2}e^{x/2} & -e^{-x} \end{vmatrix} = -\frac{3}{2}e^{-x/2}.$$

Identifying $f(x) = (x+1)/2$ we obtain

$$u_1' = \frac{1}{3}e^{-x/2}(x+1)$$

$$u_2' = -\frac{1}{3}e^x(x+1).$$

Then

$$u_1 = -e^{-x/2}\left(\frac{2}{3}x - 2\right)$$

$$u_2 = -\frac{1}{3}x e^x.$$

Thus

$$y = c_1 e^{x/2} + c_2 e^{-x} - x - 2$$

and

$$y' = \frac{1}{2}c_1 e^{x/2} - c_2 e^{-x} - 1.$$

The initial conditions imply

$$c_1 - c_2 - 2 = 1$$

$$\frac{1}{2}c_1 - c_2 - 1 = 0.$$

Thus $c_1 = 8/3$ and $c_2 = 1/3$, and

$$y = \frac{8}{3}e^{x/2} + \frac{1}{3}e^{-x} - x - 2.$$

27. The auxiliary equation is $m^2 + 2m - 8 = (m-2)(m+4) = 0$, so $y_c = c_1 e^{2x} + c_2 e^{-4x}$ and

$$W = \begin{vmatrix} e^{2x} & e^{-4x} \\ 2e^{2x} & -4e^{-4x} \end{vmatrix} = -6e^{-2x}.$$

Identifying $f(x) = 2e^{-2x} - e^{-x}$ we obtain

$$u_1' = \frac{1}{3}e^{-4x} - \frac{1}{6}e^{-3x}$$

$$u_2' = -\frac{1}{6}e^{3x} - \frac{1}{3}e^{2x}.$$

Then

$$u_1 = -\frac{1}{12}e^{-4x} + \frac{1}{18}e^{-3x}$$

$$u_2 = \frac{1}{18}e^{3x} - \frac{1}{6}e^{2x}.$$

Thus

$$y = c_1 e^{2x} + c_2 e^{-4x} - \frac{1}{12}e^{-2x} + \frac{1}{18}e^{-x} + \frac{1}{18}e^{-x} - \frac{1}{6}e^{-2x}$$

$$= c_1 e^{2x} + c_2 e^{-4x} - \frac{1}{4}e^{-2x} + \frac{1}{9}e^{-x}$$

and

$$y' = 2c_1 e^{2x} - 4c_2 e^{-4x} + \frac{1}{2}e^{-2x} - \frac{1}{9}e^{-x}.$$

The initial conditions imply

$$c_1 + c_2 - \frac{5}{36} = 1$$

$$2c_1 - 4c_2 + \frac{7}{18} = 0.$$

Thus $c_1 = 25/36$ and $c_2 = 4/9$, and

$$y = \frac{25}{36}e^{2x} + \frac{4}{9}e^{-4x} - \frac{1}{4}e^{-2x} + \frac{1}{9}e^{-x}.$$

28. The auxiliary equation is $m^2 - 4m + 4 = (m-2)^2 = 0$, so $y_c = c_1 e^{2x} + c_2 x e^{2x}$ and

$$W = \begin{vmatrix} e^{2x} & x e^{2x} \\ 2e^{2x} & 2xe^{2x} + e^{2x} \end{vmatrix} = e^{4x}.$$

Identifying $f(x) = \left(12x^2 - 6x\right) e^{2x}$ we obtain

$$u_1' = 6x^2 - 12x^3$$

$$u_2' = 12x^2 - 6x.$$

Then

$$u_1 = 2x^3 - 3x^4$$

$$u_2 = 4x^3 - 3x^2.$$

Thus

$$y = c_1 e^{2x} + c_2 x e^{2x} + \left(2x^3 - 3x^4\right) e^{2x} + \left(4x^3 - 3x^2\right) x e^{2x}$$

$$= c_1 e^{2x} + c_2 x e^{2x} + e^{2x} \left(x^4 - x^3\right)$$

and

$$y' = 2c_1 e^{2x} + c_2 \left(2x e^{2x} + e^{2x}\right) + e^{2x}\left(4x^3 - 3x^2\right) + 2e^{2x}\left(x^4 - x^3\right).$$

The initial conditions imply

$$c_1 \quad\quad = 1$$

$$2c_1 + c_2 = 0.$$

Thus $c_1 = 1$ and $c_2 = -2$, and

$$y = e^{2x} - 2x e^{2x} + e^{2x}\left(x^4 - x^3\right)$$

$$= e^{2x}\left(x^4 - x^3 - 2x + 1\right).$$

29. Write the equation in the form

$$y'' - \frac{1}{x} y' + \frac{1}{x^2} y = \frac{4}{x}\ln x$$

and identify $f(x) = (4\ln x)/x$. From $y_1 = x$ and $y_2 = x\ln x$ we compute

$$W(y_1, y_2) = \begin{vmatrix} x & x\ln x \\ 1 & 1 + \ln x \end{vmatrix} = x.$$

Now

$$u_1' = -\frac{4}{x}(\ln x)^2 \quad \text{so} \quad u_1 = -\frac{4}{3}(\ln x)^3,$$

and

$$u_2' = \frac{4}{x}\ln x \quad \text{so} \quad u_2 = 2(\ln x)^2.$$

123

Thus

$$y_p = -\frac{4}{3}x(\ln x)^3 + 2x(\ln x)^3 = \frac{2}{3}x(\ln x)^3$$

and

$$y = c_1 x + c_2 x \ln x + \frac{2}{3}x(\ln x)^3.$$

30. Write the equation in the form

$$y'' - \frac{4}{x}y' + \frac{6}{x^2}y = \frac{1}{x^3}$$

and identify $f(x) = 1/x^3$. From $y_1 = x^2$ and $y_2 = x^3$ we compute

$$W(y_1, y_2) = \begin{vmatrix} x^2 & x^3 \\ 2x & 3x^2 \end{vmatrix} = 3x^4 - 2x^4 = x^4.$$

Now

$$u_1' = -\frac{x^3/x^3}{x^4} = -\frac{1}{x^4} \quad \text{so} \quad u_1 = \frac{1}{3x^3},$$

and

$$u_2' = \frac{x^2/x^3}{x^4} = \frac{1}{x^5} \quad \text{so} \quad u_2 = \frac{1}{4x^4}.$$

Thus

$$y_p = \frac{x^2}{3x^3} - \frac{x^3}{4x^4} = \frac{1}{12x}$$

and

$$y = y_c + y_p = c_1 x^2 + c_2 x^3 + \frac{1}{12x}.$$

31. Write the equation in the form

$$y'' + \frac{1}{x}y' + \left(1 - \frac{1}{4x^2}\right)y = x^{-1/2}$$

and identify $f(x) = x^{-1/2}$. From $y_1 = x^{-1/2}\cos x$ and $y_2 = x^{-1/2}\sin x$ we compute

$$W(y_1, y_2) = \begin{vmatrix} x^{-1/2}\cos x & x^{-1/2}\sin x \\ -x^{-1/2}\sin x - \frac{1}{2}x^{-3/2}\cos x & x^{-1/2}\cos x - \frac{1}{2}x^{-3/2}\sin x \end{vmatrix} = \frac{1}{x}.$$

Now

$$u_1' = \sin x \quad \text{so} \quad u_1 = \cos x,$$

and

$$u_2' = \cos x \quad \text{so} \quad u_2 = \sin x.$$

Thus

$$y = c_1 x^{-1/2}\cos x + c_2 x^{-1/2}\sin x + x^{-1/2}\cos^2 x + x^{-1/2}\sin^2 x$$

$$= c_1 x^{-1/2}\cos x + c_2 x^{-1/2}\sin x + x^{-1/2}.$$

32. (a) Write the equation in the form

$$y'' + \frac{1}{x}y' + \frac{1}{x^2}y = \frac{\sec(\ln x)}{x^2}$$

and identify $f(x) = \sec(\ln x)/x^2$. From $y_1 = \cos(\ln x)$ and $y_2 = \sin(\ln x)$ we compute

$$W = \begin{vmatrix} \cos(\ln x) & \sin(\ln x) \\ -\dfrac{\sin(\ln x)}{x} & \dfrac{\cos(\ln x)}{x} \end{vmatrix} = \frac{1}{x}.$$

Now

$$u_1' = -\frac{\tan(\ln x)}{x} \quad \text{so} \quad u_1 = \ln|\cos(\ln x)|,$$

and

$$u_2' = \frac{1}{x} \quad \text{so} \quad u_2 = \ln x.$$

Thus, a particular solution is

$$y_p = \cos(\ln x)\ln|\cos(\ln x)| + (\ln x)\sin(\ln x).$$

(b) The general solution is

$$y = c_1\cos(\ln x) + c_2\sin(\ln x) + \cos(\ln x)\ln|\cos(\ln x)| + (\ln x)\sin(\ln x)$$

for $-\pi/2 < \ln x < \pi/2$ or $e^{-\pi/2} < x < e^{\pi/2}$. The bounds on $\ln x$ are due to the presence of $\sec(\ln x)$ in the differential equation .

33. (a) We have $y_c = c_1 e^{-x} + c_2 x e^{-x}$ and we assume $y_p = Ax^2 + Bx + C$. Substituting into the differential equation we find

$$A = 4$$

$$4A + B = 0$$

$$2A + 2B + C = -3$$

so that $A = 4$, $B = -16$, and $C = 21$. A particular solution is $y_p = 4x^2 - 16x + 21$.

(b) We have $y_c = c_1 e^{-x} + c_2 x e^{-x}$ and

$$W = \begin{vmatrix} e^{-x} & xe^{-x} \\ -e^{-x} & -xe^{-x} + e^{-x} \end{vmatrix} = e^{-2x}.$$

Identifying $f(x) = e^{-x}/x$ we obtain

$$u_1' = -\frac{xe^{-x}e^{-x}/x}{e^{-2x}} = -1$$

$$u_2' = \frac{e^{-x}e^{-x}/x}{e^{-2x}} = \frac{1}{x}.$$

125

Then $u_1 = -x$, $u_2 = \ln x$ and

$$y_p = -xe^{-x} + xe^{-x}\ln x.$$

Since $-xe^{-x}$ is a solution of the homogeneous differential equation, we take $y_p = xe^{-x}\ln x$.

(c) Adding the results of (a) and (b) we have

$$y_p = 4x^2 - 16x + 21 + xe^{-x}\ln x.$$

34. We have $y_c = c_1\cos x + c_2\sin x$. We use undetermined coefficients to find a particular solution of $y'' + y = 2x - e^{3x}$. Assuming $y_{p_1} = Ax + B + Ce^{3x}$ and substituting into the differential equation we find $A = 0$, $B = 0$, and $C = -\frac{1}{10}$. Thus $y_{p_1} = 2x - \frac{1}{10}e^{3x}$. Next we use variation of parameters to find a particular solution of $y'' + y = \cot x$. We have

$$W = \begin{vmatrix} \cos x & \sin x \\ -\sin x & \cos x \end{vmatrix} = 1.$$

Identifying $f(x) = \cot x$ we obtain

$$u_1' = -\frac{\sin x \cot x}{1} = -\cos x$$

$$u_2' = \frac{\cos x \cot x}{1} = \frac{\cos^2 x}{\sin x} = \csc x - \sin x.$$

Then

$$u_1 = \sin x$$

$$u_2 = \ln|\csc x - \cot x| + \cos x$$

and

$$y_{p_2} = \sin x \cos x + \sin x \ln|\csc x - \cot x| + \sin x \cos x = 2\sin x \cos x + \sin x \ln|\csc x - \cot x|.$$

Using the superposition principle we have that a particular solution of $y'' + y = 2x - e^{3x} + \cot x$ is

$$y_p = y_{p_1} + y_{p_2} = 2x - \frac{1}{10}e^{3x} + 2\sin x \cos x + \sin x \ln|\csc x - \cot x|.$$

Chapter 4 Review Exercises

1. $y = 0$

2. False; see Problem 45, Section 4.1.

3. False; consider $f_1(x) = 0$ and $f_2(x) = x$. These are linearly dependent even though x is not a multiple of 0. The statement would be true if it read "Two functions $f_1(x)$ and $f_2(x)$ are linearly independent on an interval if *neither* is a constant multiple of the other."

4. dependent; $-3x^2 + (-2)\left(1 - x^2\right) + \left(2 + x^2\right) = 0$

5. $(-\infty, \infty)$; $(0, \infty)$ or $(-\infty, 0)$

6. True

7. False; see Problem 31, Section 4.1.

8. $x = 2$

9. $A + Bxe^x$

10. $(D - 2)^2 \left(D^2 - 4D + 5\right)$

11. Identifying $P(x) = 0$ we have

$$y_2 = \cos 2x \int \frac{e^{-\int 0\,dx}}{\cos^2 2x}\,dx = \cos 2x \int \sec^2 2x\,dx$$

$$= \cos 2x \left(\frac{1}{2}\tan 2x\right)$$

$$= \frac{1}{2}\sin 2x.$$

12. Identifying $P(x) = -2 - 2/x$ we have $\int P\,dx = -2x - 2\ln x$ and

$$y_2 = e^x \int \frac{e^{2x + \ln x^2}}{e^{2x}}\,dx = e^x \int x^2\,dx = \frac{1}{3}x^3 e^x.$$

13. From $m^2 - 2m - 2 = 0$ we obtain $m = 1 \pm \sqrt{3}$ so that

$$y = c_1 e^{(1+\sqrt{3})x} + c_2 e^{(1-\sqrt{3})x}.$$

14. From $2m^2 + 2m + 3 = 0$ we obtain $m = -1/2 \pm \sqrt{5}/2$ so that

$$y = e^{-x/2}\left(c_1 \cos\frac{\sqrt{5}}{2}x + c_2 \sin\frac{\sqrt{5}}{2}x\right).$$

15. From $m^3 + 10m^2 + 25m = 0$ we obtain $m = 0$, $m = -5$, and $m = -5$ so that

$$y = c_1 + c_2 e^{-5x} + c_3 xe^{-5x}.$$

16. From $2m^3 + 9m^2 + 12m + 5 = 0$ we obtain $m = -1$, $m = -1$, and $m = -5/2$ so that

$$y = c_1 e^{-5x/2} + c_2 e^{-x} + c_3 x e^{-x}.$$

17. From $3m^3 + 10m^2 + 15m + 4 = 0$ we obtain $m = -1/3$ and $m = -3/2 \pm \sqrt{7}/2$ so that

$$y = c_1 e^{-x/3} + e^{-3x/2} \left(c_2 \cos \frac{\sqrt{7}}{2} x + c_3 \sin \frac{\sqrt{7}}{2} x \right).$$

18. From $2m^4 + 3m^3 + 2m^2 + 6m - 4 = 0$ we obtain $m = 1/2$, $m = -2$, and $m = \pm\sqrt{2}\,i$ so that

$$y = c_1 e^{x/2} + c_2 e^{-2x} + c_3 \cos \sqrt{2}\,x + c_4 \sin \sqrt{2}\,x.$$

19. Applying D^4 to the differential equation we obtain $D^4(D^2 - 3D + 5) = 0$. Then

$$y = \underbrace{e^{3x/2} \left(c_1 \cos \frac{\sqrt{11}}{2} x + c_2 \sin \frac{\sqrt{11}}{2} x \right)}_{y_c} + c_3 + c_4 x + c_5 x^2 + c_6 x^3$$

and $y_p = A + Bx + Cx^2 + Dx^3$. Substituting y_p into the differential equation yields

$$(5A - 3B + 2C) + (5B - 6C + 6D)x + (5C - 9D)x^2 + 5Dx^3 = -2x + 4x^3.$$

Equating coefficients gives $A = -222/625$, $B = 46/125$, $C = 36/25$, and $D = 4/5$. The general solution is

$$y = e^{3x/2} \left(c_1 \cos \frac{\sqrt{11}}{2} x + c_2 \sin \frac{\sqrt{11}}{2} x \right) - \frac{222}{625} + \frac{46}{125} x + \frac{36}{25} x^2 + \frac{4}{5} x^3.$$

20. Applying $(D - 1)^3$ to the differential equation we obtain $(D - 1)^3(D - 2D + 1) = (D - 1)^5 = 0$. Then

$$y = \underbrace{c_1 e^x + c_2 x e^x}_{y_c} + c_3 x^2 e^x + c_4 x^3 e^x + c_5 x^4 e^x$$

and $y_p = Ax^2 e^x + Bx^3 e^x + Cx^4 e^x$. Substituting y_p into the differential equation yields

$$12Cx^2 e^x + 6Bx e^x + 2Ae^x = x^2 e^x.$$

Equating coefficients gives $A = 0$, $B = 0$, and $C = 1/12$. The general solution is

$$y = c_1 e^x + c_2 x e^x + \frac{1}{12} x^4 e^x.$$

21. Applying $D(D^2 + 1)$ to the differential equation we obtain

$$D(D^2 + 1)(D^3 - 5D^2 + 6D) = D^2(D^2 + 1)(D - 2)(D - 3) = 0.$$

Then

$$y = \underbrace{c_1 + c_2 e^{2x} + c_3 e^{3x}}_{y_c} + c_4 x + c_5 \cos x + c_6 \sin x$$

and $y_p = Ax + B\cos x + C\sin x$. Substituting y_p into the differential equation yields

$$6A + (5B + 5C)\cos x + (-5B + 5C)\sin x = 8 + 2\sin x.$$

Equating coefficients gives $A = 4/3$, $B = -1/5$, and $C = 1/5$. The general solution is

$$y = c_1 + c_2 e^{2x} + c_3 e^{3x} + \frac{4}{3}x - \frac{1}{5}\cos x + \frac{1}{5}\sin x.$$

22. Applying D to the differential equation we obtain $D(D^3 - D^2) = D^3(D - 1) = 0$. Then

$$y = \underbrace{c_1 + c_2 x + c_3 e^x}_{y_c} + c_4 x^2$$

and $y_p = Ax^2$. Substituting y_p into the differential equation yields $-2A = 6$. Equating coefficients gives $A = -3$. The general solution is

$$y = c_1 + c_2 x + c_3 e^x - 3x^2.$$

23. The auxiliary equation is $m^2 - 2m + 2 = 0$ so that $m = 1 \pm i$ and $y = e^x(c_1 \cos x + c_2 \sin x)$. Setting $y(\pi/2) = 0$ and $y(\pi) = -1$ we obtain $c_1 = e^{-\pi}$ and $c_2 = 0$. Thus, $y = e^{x-\pi}\cos x$.

24. The auxiliary equation is $m^2 - 1 = (m - 1)(m + 1) = 0$ so that $m = \pm 1$ and $y = c_1 e^x + c_2 e^{-x}$. Assuming $y_p = Ax + B + C\sin x$ and substituting into the differential equation we find $A = -1$, $B = 0$, and $C = -\frac{1}{2}$. Thus $y_p = -x - \frac{1}{2}\sin x$ and

$$y = c_1 e^x + c_2 e^{-x} - x - \frac{1}{2}\sin x.$$

Setting $y(0) = 2$ and $y'(0) = 3$ we obtain

$$c_1 + c_2 = 2$$

$$c_1 - c_2 - \frac{3}{2} = 3.$$

Solving this system we find $c_1 = \frac{13}{4}$ and $c_2 = -\frac{5}{4}$. The solution of the initial-value problem is

$$y = \frac{13}{4}e^x - \frac{5}{4}e^{-x} - x - \frac{1}{2}\sin x.$$

25. The auxiliary equation is $m^2 - 2m + 2 = [m - (1+i)][m - (1-i)] = 0$, so $y_c = c_1 e^x \sin x + c_2 e^x \cos x$ and

$$W = \begin{vmatrix} e^x \sin x & e^x \cos x \\ e^x \cos x + e^x \sin x & -e^x \sin x + e^x \cos x \end{vmatrix} = -e^{2x}.$$

Identifying $f(x) = e^x \tan x$ we obtain

$$u_1' = -\frac{(e^x \cos x)(e^x \tan x)}{-e^{2x}} = \sin x$$

$$u_2' = \frac{(e^x \sin x)(e^x \tan x)}{-e^{2x}} = -\frac{\sin^2 x}{\cos x} = \cos x - \sec x.$$

Then $u_1 = -\cos x$, $u_2 = \sin x - \ln|\sec x + \tan x|$, and

$$y = c_1 e^x \sin x + c_2 e^x \cos x - e^x \sin x \cos x + e^x \sin x \cos x - e^x \cos x \ln|\sec x + \tan x|$$

$$= c_1 e^x \sin x + c_2 e^x \cos x - e^x \cos x \ln|\sec x + \tan x|.$$

26. The auxiliary equation is $m^2 - 1 = 0$, so $y_c = c_1 e^x + \overset{\cdot}{c_2} e^{-x}$ and

$$W = \begin{vmatrix} e^x & e^{-x} \\ e^x & -e^{-x} \end{vmatrix} = -2.$$

Identifying $f(x) = 2e^x/(e^x + e^{-x})$ we obtain

$$u_1' = \frac{1}{e^x + e^{-x}} = \frac{e^x}{1 + e^{2x}}$$

$$u_2' = -\frac{e^{2x}}{e^x + e^{-x}} = -\frac{e^{3x}}{1 + e^{2x}} = -e^x + \frac{e^x}{1 + e^{2x}}.$$

Then $u_1 = \tan^{-1} e^x$, $u_2 = -e^x + \tan^{-1} e^x$, and

$$y = c_1 e^x + c_2 e^{-x} + e^x \tan^{-1} e^x - 1 + e^{-x} \tan^{-1} e^x.$$

27. The auxiliary equation is $2m^3 - 13m^2 + 24m - 9 = (2m - 1)(m - 3)^2 = 0$ so that

$$y_c = c_1 e^{x/2} + c_2 e^{3x} + c_3 x e^{3x}.$$

A particular solution is $y_p = -4$ and the general solution is

$$y = c_1 e^{x/2} + c_2 e^{3x} + c_3 x e^{3x} - 4.$$

Setting $y(0) = -4$, $y'(0) = 0$, and $y''(0) = \frac{5}{2}$ we obtain

$$c_1 + c_2 - 4 = -4$$

$$\frac{1}{2} c_1 + 3c_2 + c_3 = 0$$

$$\frac{1}{4} c_1 + 9c_2 + 6c_3 = \frac{5}{2}.$$

Solving this system we find $c_1 = \frac{2}{5}$, $c_2 = -\frac{2}{5}$, and $c_3 = 1$. Thus

$$y = \frac{2}{5} e^{x/2} - \frac{2}{5} e^{3x} + x e^{3x} - 4.$$

28. The auxiliary equation is $m^2 + 1 = 0$, so $y_c = c_1 \cos x + c_2 \sin x$ and

$$W = \begin{vmatrix} \cos x & \sin x \\ -\sin x & \cos x \end{vmatrix} = 1.$$

Identifying $f(x) = \sec^3 x$ we obtain

$$u_1' = -\sin x \sec^3 x = -\frac{\sin x}{\cos^3 x}$$

$$u_2' = \cos x \sec^3 x = \sec^2 x.$$

Then

$$u_1 = -\frac{1}{2}\frac{1}{\cos^2 x} = -\frac{1}{2}\sec^2 x$$

$$u_2 = \tan x.$$

Thus

$$y = c_1 \cos x + c_2 \sin x - \frac{1}{2}\cos x \sec^2 x + \sin x \tan x$$

$$= c_1 \cos x + c_2 \sin x - \frac{1}{2}\sec x + \frac{1 - \cos^2 x}{\cos x}$$

$$= c_3 \cos x + c_2 \sin x + \frac{1}{2}\sec x.$$

and

$$y_p' = -c_3 \sin x + c_2 \cos x + \frac{1}{2}\sec x \tan x.$$

The initial conditions imply

$$c_3 + \frac{1}{2} = 1$$

$$c_2 = \frac{1}{2}.$$

Thus $c_3 = c_2 = 1/2$ and

$$y = \frac{1}{2}\cos x + \frac{1}{2}\sin x + \frac{1}{2}\sec x.$$

5 Applications of Second-Order Differential Equations: Vibrational Models

1. A weight of 4 lb (1/8 slug), attached to a spring, is released from a point 3 feet above the equilibrium position with an initial upward velocity of 2 ft/s. The spring constant is 3 lb/ft.

2. A weight of 2 lb (1/16 slug), attached to a spring, is released at rest from a point 0.7 feet below the equilibrium position. The spring constant is 4 lb/ft.

3. Applying the initial conditions to $x(t) = c_1 \cos 5t + c_2 \sin 5t$ and $x'(t) = -5c_1 \sin 5t + 5c_2 \cos 5t$ gives

$$x(0) = c_1 = -2 \quad \text{and} \quad x'(0) = 5c_2 = 10.$$

Then $c_1 = -2$, $c_2 = 2$, and

$$A = \sqrt{4+4} = 2\sqrt{2} \quad \text{and} \quad \tan\phi = \frac{-2}{2} = -1.$$

Since $\sin\phi < 0$ and $\cos\phi > 0$, ϕ is a fourth quadrant angle and $\phi = -\pi/4$. Thus $x(t) = 2\sqrt{2} \sin(5t - \pi/4)$.

4. Applying the initial conditions to $x(t) = c_1 \cos 4t + c_2 \sin 4t$ and $x'(t) = -4c_1 \sin 4t + 4c_2 \cos 4t$ gives

$$x(0) = c_1 = 1 \quad \text{and} \quad x'(0) = 4c_2 = -2.$$

Then $c_1 = 1$, $c_2 = -1/2$, and

$$A = \sqrt{1+1/4} = \frac{\sqrt{5}}{2} \quad \text{and} \quad \tan\phi = \frac{1}{-1/2} = -2.$$

Since $\sin\phi > 0$ and $\cos\phi < 0$, ϕ is a second quadrant angle and

$$\phi = \tan^{-1}(-2) + \pi \approx -1.107 + \pi \approx 2.034.$$

Thus $x(t) \approx \frac{\sqrt{5}}{2} \sin(4t + 2.034)$.

5. Applying the initial conditions to $x(t) = c_1 \cos \sqrt{2}\,t + c_2 \sin \sqrt{2}\,t$ and $x'(t) = -\sqrt{2}\,c_1 \sin \sqrt{2}\,t + \sqrt{2}\,c_2 \cos \sqrt{2}\,t$ gives

$$x(0) = c_1 = -1 \quad \text{and} \quad x'(0) = \sqrt{2}\,c_2 = -2\sqrt{2}.$$

Then $c_1 = -1$, $c_2 = -2$, and

$$A = \sqrt{1+4} = \sqrt{5} \quad \text{and} \quad \tan\phi = \frac{-1}{-2} = \frac{1}{2}.$$

Since $\sin\phi < 0$ and $\cos\phi < 0$, ϕ is a third quadrant angle and $\phi = \tan^{-1}\frac{1}{2} + \pi \approx 0.464 + \pi \approx 3.605$. Thus $x(t) \approx \sqrt{5}\sin\left(\sqrt{2}\,t + 3.605\right)$.

6. Applying the initial conditions to $x(t) = c_1\cos 8t + c_2\sin 8t$ and $x'(t) = -8c_1\sin 8t + 8c_2\cos 8t$ gives

$$x(0) = c_1 = 4 \quad \text{and} \quad x'(0) = 8c_2 = 16.$$

Then $c_1 = 4$, $c_2 = 2$, and

$$A = \sqrt{16+4} = 2\sqrt{5} \quad \text{and} \quad \tan\phi = \frac{4}{2} = 2.$$

Since $\sin\phi > 0$ and $\cos\phi > 0$, ϕ is a first quadrant angle and $\phi = \tan^{-1}2 \approx 1.107$. Thus $x(t) \approx 2\sqrt{5}\sin(8t + 1.107)$.

7. Applying the initial conditions to $x(t) = c_1\cos 10t + c_2\sin 10t$ and $x'(t) = -10c\sin 10t + 10c_2\cos 10t$ gives

$$x(0) = c_1 = 1 \quad \text{and} \quad x'(0) = 10c_2 = 1.$$

Then $c_1 = 1$, $c_2 = 1/10$, and

$$A = \sqrt{1 + .01} = \sqrt{1.01} \quad \text{and} \quad \tan\phi = \frac{1}{1/10} = 10.$$

Since $\sin\phi > 0$ and $\cos\phi > 0$, ϕ is a first quadrant angle and $\phi = \tan^{-1}10 \approx 1.471$. Thus $x(t) \approx \sqrt{1.01}\sin(10t + 1.471)$.

8. Applying the initial conditions to $x(t) = c_1\cos t + c_2\sin t$ and $x'(t) = -c_1\sin t + c_2\cos t$ gives

$$x(0) = c_1 = -4 \quad \text{and} \quad x'(0) = c_2 = 3.$$

Then $c_1 = -4$, $c_2 = 3$, and

$$A = \sqrt{16+9} = 5 \quad \text{and} \quad \tan\phi = \frac{-4}{3}.$$

Since $\sin\phi < 0$ and $\cos\phi > 0$, ϕ is a fourth quadrant angle and $\phi = \tan^{-1}\left(-\frac{4}{3}\right) \approx -0.927$. Thus $x(t) = 5\sin(t - 0.927)$.

9. From $mx'' + 16x = 0$ we obtain

$$x = c_1\cos\frac{4}{\sqrt{m}}t + c_2\sin\frac{4}{\sqrt{m}}t$$

so that the period $\pi/4 = \pi\sqrt{m}/2$, $m = 1/4$ slug, and the weight is 8 lb.

10. From $mx'' + 120x = 0$ we obtain $x = c_1\cos 2\sqrt{30/m}\,t + c_2\sin\sqrt{30/m}\,t$ so that the period

Exercises 5.1

$1 = \pi\sqrt{30/m}$, m=$30/\pi^2$ slugs, and the weight is approximately 97.3 lb.

11. From $\frac{1}{8}x'' + 16x = 0$ we obtain

$$x = c_1 \cos 8\sqrt{2}\, t + c_2 \sin 8\sqrt{2}\, t$$

so that the period of motion is $2\pi/8\sqrt{2} = \sqrt{2}\,\pi/8$ seconds.

12. From $20x'' + kx = 0$ we obtain

$$x = c_1 \cos \frac{1}{2}\sqrt{\frac{k}{5}}\, t + c_2 \sin \frac{1}{2}\sqrt{\frac{k}{5}}\, t$$

so that the frequency $2/\pi = \frac{1}{4}\sqrt{k/5}\,\pi$ and $k = 320$ N/m. If $80x'' + 320x = 0$ then $x = c_1 \cos 2t + c_2 \sin 2t$ so that the frequency is $2/2\pi = 1/\pi$ vibrations/second.

13. From $\frac{3}{4}x'' + 72x = 0$, $x(0) = -1/4$, and $x'(0) = 0$ we obtain $x = -\frac{1}{4}\cos 4\sqrt{6}\, t$.

14. From $\frac{3}{4}x'' + 72x = 0$, $x(0) = 0$, and $x'(0) = 2$ we obtain $x = \frac{\sqrt{6}}{12}\sin 4\sqrt{6}\, t$.

15. From $\frac{5}{8}x'' + 40x = 0$, $x(0) = 1/2$, and $x'(0) = 0$ we obtain $x = \frac{1}{2}\cos 8t$.

    (a) $x(\pi/12) = -1/4$, $x(\pi/8) = -1/2$, $x(\pi/6) = -1/4$, $x(\pi/8) = 1/2$, $x(9\pi/32) = \sqrt{2}/4$.

    (b) $x' = -4\sin 8t$ so that $x'(3\pi/16) = 4$ ft/s directed downward.

    (c) If $x = \frac{1}{2}\cos 8t = 0$ then $t = (2n+1)\pi/16$ for $n = 0, 1, 2, \ldots$.

16. From $50x'' + 200x = 0$, $x(0) = 0$, and $x'(0) = -10$ we obtain $x = -5\sin 2t$ and $x' = -10\cos 2t$.

17. From $20x'' + 20x = 0$, $x(0) = 0$, and $x'(0) = -10$ we obtain $x = -10\sin t$ and $x' = -10\cos t$.

    (a) The 20 kg mass has the larger amplitude.

    (b) 20 kg: $x'(\pi/4) = -5\sqrt{2}$ m/s, $x'(\pi/2) = 0$ m/s;   50 kg: $x'(\pi/4) = 0$ m/s, $x'(\pi/2) = 10$ m/s

    (c) If $-5\sin 2t = -10\sin t$ then $2\sin t(\cos t - 1) = 0$ so that $t = n\pi$ for $n = 0, 1, 2, \ldots$, placing both masses at the equilibrium position. The 50 kg mass is moving upward; the 20 kg mass is moving upward when n is even and downward when n is odd.

18. From $x'' + 16x = 0$, $x(0) = -1$, and $x'(0) = -2$ we obtain

$$x = -\cos 4t - \frac{1}{2}\sin 4t = \frac{\sqrt{5}}{2}\cos(4t - 3.6).$$

The period is $\pi/2$ seconds and the amplitude is $\sqrt{5}/2$ feet. In 4π seconds it will make 8 complete vibrations.

19. From $\frac{1}{4}x'' + x = 0$, $x(0) = 1/2$, and $x'(0) = 3/2$ we obtain

$$x = \frac{1}{2}\cos 2t + \frac{3}{4}\sin 2t = \frac{\sqrt{13}}{4}\sin(2t + 0.588).$$

20. From $1.6x'' + 40x = 0$, $x(0) = -1/3$, and $x'(0) = 5/4$ we obtain

$$x = -\frac{1}{3}\cos 5t + \frac{1}{4}\sin 5t = \frac{5}{12}\sin(5t + 0.927).$$

If $x = 5/24$ then $t = \frac{1}{5}\left(\frac{\pi}{6} + 0.927 + 2n\pi\right)$ and $t = \frac{1}{5}\left(\frac{5\pi}{6} + 0.927 + 2n\pi\right)$ for $n = 0, 1, 2, \ldots$.

21. From $2x'' + 200x = 0$, $x(0) = -2/3$, and $x'(0) = 5$ we obtain

(a) $x = -\frac{2}{3}\cos 10t + \frac{1}{2}\sin 10t = \frac{5}{6}\sin(10t - 0.927)$.

(b) The amplitude is $5/6$ ft and the period is $2\pi/10 = \pi/5$

(c) $3\pi = \pi k/5$ and $k = 15$ cycles.

(d) If $x = 0$ and the weight is moving downward for the second time, then $10t - 0.927 = 2\pi$ or $t = 0.721$ s.

(e) If $x' = \frac{25}{3}\cos(10t - 0.927) = 0$ then $10t - 0.927 = \pi/2 + n\pi$ or $t = (2n+1)\pi/20 + 0.0927$ for $n = 0, 1, 2, \ldots$.

(f) $x(3) = -0.597$ ft

(g) $x'(3) = -5.814$ ft/s

(h) $x''(3) = 59.702$ ft/s^2

(i) If $x = 0$ then $t = \frac{1}{10}(0.927 + n\pi)$ for $n = 0, 1, 2, \ldots$ and $x'(t) = \pm\frac{25}{3}$ ft/s.

(j) If $x = 5/12$ then $t = \frac{1}{10}(\pi/6 + 0.927 + 2n\pi)$ and $t = \frac{1}{10}(5\pi/6 + 0.927 + 2n\pi)$ for $n = 0, 1, 2, \ldots$.

(k) If $x = 5/12$ and $x' < 0$ then $t = \frac{1}{10}(5\pi/6 + 0.927 + 2n\pi)$ for $n = 0, 1, 2, \ldots$.

22. From $x'' + 9x = 0$, $x(0) = -1$, and $x'(0) = -\sqrt{3}$ we obtain

$$x = -\cos 3t - \frac{\sqrt{3}}{3}\sin 3t = \frac{2}{\sqrt{3}}\sin\left(37 + \frac{4\pi}{3}\right)$$

and $x' = 2\sqrt{3}\cos(3t + 4\pi/3)$. If $x' = 3$ then $t = -7\pi/18 + 2n\pi/3$ and $t = -\pi/2 + 2n\pi/3$ for $n = 1, 2, 3, \ldots$.

23. From $k_1 = 40$ and $k_2 = 120$ we compute the effective spring constant $k = 4(40)(120)/160 = 120$. Now, $m = 20/32$ so $k/m = 120(32)/20 = 192$ and $x'' + 192x = 0$. Using $x(0) = 0$ and $x'(0) = 2$ we obtain $x(t) = \frac{\sqrt{3}}{12}\sin 8\sqrt{3}\,t$.

24. Let m denote the mass in slugs of the first weight. Let k_1 and k_2 be the spring constants and $k = 4k_1k_2/(k_1 + k_2)$ the effective spring constant of the system. Now, the numerical value of the first weight is $W = mg = 32m$, so

$$32m = k_1\left(\frac{1}{3}\right) \quad \text{and} \quad 32m = k_2\left(\frac{1}{2}\right).$$

From these equations we find $2k_1 = 3k_2$. The given period of the combined system is $2\pi/w = \pi/15$, so $w = 30$. Since the mas of an 8-pound weight is $1/4$ slug, we have from $w^2 = k/m$

$$30^2 = \frac{k}{1/4} = 4k \quad \text{or} \quad k = 225.$$

We now have the system of equations

$$\frac{4k_1k_2}{k_1 + k_2} = 225$$

$$2k_1 = 3k_2.$$

Solving the second equation for k_1 and substituting in the first equation, we obtain

$$\frac{4(3k_2/2)k_2}{3k_2/2 + k_2} = \frac{12k_2^2}{5k_2} = \frac{12k_2}{5} = 225.$$

Thus, $k_2 = 375/4$ and $k_1 = 1125/8$. Finally, the value of the first weight is

$$W = 32m = \frac{k_1}{3} = \frac{1125/8}{3} = \frac{375}{8} \approx 46.88 \text{ lb.}$$

25. From $x = c_1 \cos \omega t + c_2 \sin \omega t$, $x(0) = x_0$, and $x'(0) = v_0$ we obtain

$$x = x_0 \cos \omega t + \frac{v_0}{\omega} \sin \omega t$$

so that the amplitude is $A = \sqrt{x_0^2 + (v_0/\omega)^2}$.

26. Let $A = \sqrt{c_1^2 + c_2^2}$ so that

$$x = A \left[\frac{c_1}{A} \cos \omega t - \frac{-c_2}{A} \sin \omega t \right].$$

If $\cos \phi = c_1/A$ and $\sin \phi = -c_2/A$ then $x = A \cos(\omega t + \phi)$.

27. $x = 2\sqrt{2} \left[\frac{-1}{\sqrt{2}} \cos 5t - \frac{-1}{\sqrt{2}} \sin 5t \right] = 2\sqrt{2} \cos(5t + 5\pi/4)$.

28. If $x = A \cos(\omega t + \phi)$ then the minimum and maximum velocities occur when $x'' = -A\omega^2 \cos(\omega t + \phi)$ is zero; that is, when $x = 0$.

29. From $x(t) = A \sin(\omega t + \phi)$ we compute the acceleration $a(t) = x''(t) = -\omega^2 A \sin(\omega t + \phi)$. Differentiating we find $a'(t) = -\omega^3 A \cos(\omega t + \phi)$. Thus $a'(t) = 0$ when $\cos(\omega t + \phi) = 0$ or $\sin(\omega t + \phi) = \pm 1$. Thus, maximum acceleration occurs when the displacement is $\pm A$. Using $T = 2\pi/\omega$ or $\omega = 2\pi/T$ we see that the magnitude of maximum acceleration is $\omega^2 A = (2\pi/T)^2 A = 4\pi^2 A/T^2$.

30. If $x = A \sin(\omega t + \phi)$ the extremes for x occur when $x' = A\omega \cos(\omega t + \phi) = 0$, or $t = (\pi/2 - \phi + 2n\pi)\frac{1}{\omega}$ and $t = (-\pi/2 - \phi + 2n\pi)$ for $n = 0, 1, 2, \ldots$. Thus, the time interval between successive maxima is $2\pi/\omega$.

———————— **Exercises 5.2** ————————

1. A 2-lb weight is attached to a spring whose constant is 1 lb/ft. The system is damped with a resisting force numerically equal to 2 times the instantaneous velocity. The weight starts from the equailibrium position with an upward velocity of 1.5 ft/s.

2. A 16-lb weight is attached to a spring whose constant is 2-lb/ft. The system is damped with a resisting force numerically equal to the instantaneous velocity. The weight starts 2 feet above the equilibrium position with a downward velocity of 1 ft/s.

3. (a) above   (b) heading upward

4. (a) below   (b) from rest

5. (a) below   (b) heading upward

6. (a) above   (b) heading downward

7. From $\frac{1}{8}x'' + x' + 2x = 0$, $x(0) = -1$, and $x'(0) = 8$ we obtain $x = 4te^{-4t} - e^{-4t}$ and $x' = 8e^{-4t} - 16te^{-4t}$. If $x = 0$ then $t = 1/4$ second. If $x' = 0$ then $t = 1/2$ second and the extreme displacement is $x = e^{-2}$ feet.

8. From $\frac{1}{4}x'' + \sqrt{2}\,x' + 2x = 0$, $x(0) = 0$, and $x'(0) = 5$ we obtain $x = 5te^{-2\sqrt{2}t}$ and $x' = 5e^{-2\sqrt{2}t}\left(1 - 2\sqrt{2}t\right)$. If $x' = 0$ then $t = \sqrt{2}/4$ second and the extreme displacement is $x = 5\sqrt{2}\,e^{-1}/4$ feet.

9. (a) From $x'' + 10x' + 16x = 0$, $x(0) = 1$, and $x'(0) = 0$ we obtain $x = \frac{4}{3}e^{-2t} - \frac{1}{3}e^{-8t}$.

   (b) From $x'' + x' + 16x = 0$, $x(0) = 1$, and $x'(0) = -12$ then $x = -\frac{2}{3}e^{-2t} + \frac{5}{3}e^{-8t}$.

10. (a) $x = \frac{1}{3}e^{-8t}\left(4e^{6t} - 1\right)$ is never zero; the extreme displacement is $x(0) = 1$ meter.

    (b) $x = \frac{1}{3}e^{-8t}\left(5 - 2e^{6t}\right) = 0$ when $t = \frac{1}{6}\ln\frac{5}{2} \approx 0.153$ second; if $x' = \frac{4}{3}e^{-8t}\left(e^{6t} - 10\right) = 0$ then $t = \frac{1}{6}\ln 10 \approx 0.384$ second and the extreme displacement is $x = -0.232$ meter.

11. (a) From $0.1x'' + 0.4x' + 2x = 0$, $x(0) = -1$, and $x'(0) = 0$ we obtain $= e^{-2t}\left[-\cos 4t - \frac{1}{2}\sin 4t\right]$.

    (b) $x = e^{-2t}\frac{\sqrt{5}}{2}\left[-\frac{2}{\sqrt{5}}\cos 4t - \frac{1}{\sqrt{5}}\sin 4t\right] = \frac{\sqrt{5}}{2}e^{-2t}\sin(4t + 4.25)$.

    (c) If $x = 0$ then $4t + 4.25 = 2\pi, 3\pi, 4\pi, \ldots$ so that the first time heading upward is $t = 1.294$ seconds.

12. (a) From $\frac{1}{4}x'' + x' + 5x = 0$, $x(0) = 1/2$, and $x'(0) = 1$ we obtain $x = e^{-2t}\left(\frac{1}{2}\cos 4t + \frac{1}{2}\sin 4t\right)$.

(b) $x = e^{-2t} \dfrac{1}{\sqrt{2}} \left(\dfrac{\sqrt{2}}{2} \cos 4t + \dfrac{\sqrt{2}}{2} \sin 4t \right) = \dfrac{1}{\sqrt{2}} e^{-2t} \sin \left(4t + \dfrac{\pi}{4} \right).$

(c) If $x = 0$ then $4t + \pi/4 = \pi,\ 2\pi,\ 3\pi,\ \ldots$ so that the times heading downward are $t = (7 + 8n)\pi/16$ for $n = 0, 1, 2, \ldots$.

(d)

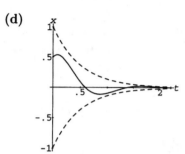

13. From $\frac{5}{16}x'' + \beta x' + 5x = 0$ we find that the roots of the auxiliary equation are $m = -\frac{8}{5}\beta \pm \frac{4}{5}\sqrt{4\beta^2 - 25}$.

   (a) If $4\beta^2 - 25 > 0$ then $\beta > 5/2$.

   (b) If $4\beta^2 - 25 = 0$ then $\beta = 5/2$.

   (c) If $4\beta^2 - 25 < 0$ then $0 < \beta < 5/2$.

14. From $0.75x'' + \beta x' + 6x = 0$ and $\beta > 3\sqrt{2}$ we find that the roots of the auxiliary equation are

$$m = -\frac{2\beta}{3} \pm \frac{2}{3}\sqrt{\beta^2 - 18} \text{ and}$$

$$x = e^{-2\beta t/3}\left[c_1 \cosh \frac{2}{3}\sqrt{\beta^2 - 18}\,t + c_2 \sinh \frac{2}{3}\sqrt{\beta^2 - 18}\,t \right].$$

   If $x(0) = 0$ and $x'(0) = -2$ then $c_1 = 0$ and $c_2 = -3/\sqrt{\beta^2 - 18}$.

15. From $40x'' + 560x' + 3920x = 0$, $x(0) = 0$, and $x'(0) = 2$ we obtain

$$x = \frac{2}{7}e^{-7t} \sin 7t.$$

16. From $40x'' + 1120x' + 3920x = 0$, $x(0) = 0$, and $x'(0) = 2$ we obtain

$$x = -\frac{\sqrt{2}}{14}e^{(-14+7\sqrt{2})t} + \frac{\sqrt{2}}{14}e^{(-14-7\sqrt{2})t}.$$

17. From $x'' + 6x' + 9 = 0$, $x(0) = -2/3$, and $x'(0) = v_0$ we obtain

$$x = -\frac{2}{3}e^{-3t} + (v_0 - 2)te^{-3t}.$$

   If $x = 0$ then $t = 2/3(v_0 - 2)$ so that $v_0 > 2$ ft/s.

18. From $x'' + \beta x' + 25x = 0$ we see that the roots of the auxiliary equation are $m = -\frac{\beta}{2} \pm \frac{1}{2}\sqrt{100 - \beta^2}\ i$. The quasi-period is $\pi/2 = 2\pi \Big/ \frac{1}{2}\sqrt{100 - \beta^2}$ so that $\beta = 6$.

19. For underdamped motion

$$x = e^{-\lambda t}\left[c_1 \cos \sqrt{\omega^2 - \lambda^2}\,t + c_2 \sin \sqrt{\omega^2 - \lambda^2}\,t\right] = Ae^{-\lambda t}\sin\left[\sqrt{\omega^2 - \lambda^2}\,t + \theta\right]$$

for some constants A and θ and

$$x' = Be^{-\lambda t}\sin\left[\sqrt{\omega^2 - \lambda^2}\,t + \gamma\right]$$

for some constants B and γ. The difference in times between two successive maxima is $2\pi/\sqrt{\omega^2 - \lambda^2}$, the quasi-period of x'.

20. The time interval between successive intercepts

$$t = \frac{(n+1)\pi - \phi}{\sqrt{\omega^2 - \lambda^2}} - \frac{n\pi - \phi}{\sqrt{\omega^2 - \lambda^2}} = \frac{\pi}{\sqrt{\omega^2 - \lambda^2}}.$$

21. The time interval between successive values of t for which (15) touches the graphs of $y = \pm Ae^{-\lambda t}$

is
$$t = \frac{(2n+3)\pi/2 - \phi}{\sqrt{\omega^2 - \lambda^2}} - \frac{(2n+1)\pi/2 - \phi}{\sqrt{\omega^2 - \lambda^2}} = \frac{\pi}{\sqrt{\omega^2 - \lambda^2}}.$$

22. From equation (17)

$$\frac{(2n+1)\pi/2 - \phi}{\sqrt{\omega^2 - \lambda^2}} - \frac{n\pi - \phi}{\sqrt{\omega^2 - \lambda^2}} = \frac{\pi/2}{\sqrt{\omega^2 - \lambda^2}},$$

which is half of the quasi-period. The period of $x = e^{-t}\sin(t + \pi/4)$ is 2π; if $x = 0$ then $t = \frac{3}{4}\pi$, $\frac{7}{4}\pi$, $\frac{11}{4}\pi$, ... and if $x' = 0$ then $t = \pi$, 2π, 3π, ..., so that the time interval between intercepts and extrema is $\pi/4$.

23. The quasi-period of $x = Ae^{-\lambda t}\sin\left(\sqrt{\omega^2 - \lambda^2}\,t + \phi\right)$ is $2\pi/\sqrt{\omega^2 - \lambda^2}$ so that the ratio of consecutive maxima is the ratio of the values at t and $t + 2\pi/\sqrt{\omega^2 - \lambda^2}$, that is

$$\frac{e^{-\lambda t}}{e^{-\lambda\left(t + 2\pi/\sqrt{\omega^2 - \lambda^2}\right)}} = e^{2\pi\lambda/\sqrt{\omega^2 - \lambda^2}}.$$

24. (a) If $\delta > 0$ is very small then x_n is slightly larger than x_{n+2} and the rate of damping is slow.

(b) If $x = \frac{1}{\sqrt{2}}e^{-2t}\sin(4t + \pi/4)$ then $\delta = 2\pi\lambda/\sqrt{\omega^2 - \lambda^2} = 4\pi/4 = \pi$.

Exercises 5.3

1. If $\frac{1}{2}x'' + \frac{1}{2}x' + 6x = 10\cos 3t$, $x(0) = -2$, and $x'(0) = 0$ then

$$x_c = e^{-t/2}\left(c_1\cos\frac{\sqrt{47}}{2}t + c_2\sin\frac{\sqrt{47}}{2}t\right)$$

and $x_p = \frac{10}{3}(\cos 3t + \sin 3t)$ so that the equation of motion is

$$x = e^{-t/2}\left(-\frac{4}{3}\cos\frac{\sqrt{47}}{2}t - \frac{64}{3\sqrt{47}}\sin\frac{\sqrt{47}}{2}t\right) + \frac{10}{3}(\cos 3t + \sin 3t).$$

2. (a) If $x'' + 2x' + 5x = 12\cos 2t + 3\sin 2t$, $x(0) = -1$, and $x'(0) = 5$ then $x_c = e^{-t}(c_1\cos 2t + c_2\sin 2t)$ and $x_p = 3\sin 2t$ so that the equation of motion is

$$x = e^{-t}\cos 2t + 3\sin 2t.$$

(b)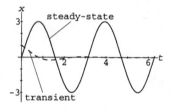

(c)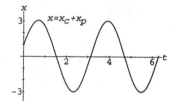

3. From $x'' + 8x' + 16x = 8\sin 4t$, $x(0) = 0$, and $x'(0) = 0$ we obtain $x_c = c_1 e^{-4t} + c_2 t e^{-4t}$ and $x_p = -\frac{1}{4}\cos 4t$ so that the equation of motion is

$$x = \frac{1}{4}e^{-4t} + te^{-4t} - \frac{1}{4}\cos 4t.$$

4. From $x'' + 8x' + 16x = e^{-t}\sin 4t$, $x(0) = 0$, and $x'(0) = 0$ we obtain $x_c = c_1 e^{-4t} + c_2 t e^{-4t}$ and $x_p = -\frac{24}{625}e^{-t}\cos 4t - \frac{7}{625}e^{-t}\sin 4t$ so that

$$x = \frac{1}{625}e^{-4t}(24 + 100t) - \frac{1}{625}e^{-t}(24\cos 4t + 7\sin 4t).$$

As $t \to \infty$ the displacement $x \to 0$.

5. From $2x'' + 32x = 68e^{-2t}\cos 4t$, $x(0) = 0$, and $x'(0) = 0$ we obtain $x_c = c_1\cos 4t + c_2\sin 4t$ and $x_p = \frac{1}{2}e^{-2t}\cos 4t - 2e^{-2t}\sin 4t$ so that

$$x = -\frac{1}{2}\cos 4t + \frac{9}{4}\sin 4t + \frac{1}{2}e^{-2t}\cos 4t - 2e^{-2t}\sin 4t.$$

6. Since $x = \frac{\sqrt{85}}{4}\sin(4t - 0.219) - \frac{\sqrt{17}}{2}e^{-2t}\sin(4t - 2.897)$, the amplitude approaches $\sqrt{85}/4$ as $t \to \infty$.

7. By Hooke's law the external force is $F(t) = kh(t)$ so that $mx'' + \beta x' + kx = kh(t)$.

8. From $\frac{1}{2}x'' + 2x' + 4x = 20\cos t$, $x(0) = 0$, and $x'(0) = 0$ we obtain $x_c = e^{-2t}(c_1 \cos 2t + c_2 \sin 2t)$ and $x_p = \frac{56}{13}\cos t + \frac{32}{13}\sin t$ so that

$$x = e^{-2t}\left(-\frac{56}{13}\cos 2t - \frac{72}{13}\sin 2t\right) + \frac{56}{13}\cos t + \frac{32}{13}\sin t.$$

9. (a) From $100x'' + 1600x = 1600\sin 8t$, $x(0) = 0$, and $x'(0) = 0$ we obtain $x_c = c_1 \cos 4t + c_2 \sin 4t$ and $x_p = -\frac{1}{3}\sin 8t$ so that

$$x = \frac{2}{3}\sin 4t - \frac{1}{3}\sin 8t.$$

(b) If $x = \frac{1}{3}\sin 4t(2 - 2\cos 4t) = 0$ then $t = n\pi/4$ for $n = 0$, 1, 2, ...

(c) If $x' = \frac{8}{3}\cos 4t - \frac{8}{3}\cos 8t = \frac{8}{3}(1 - \cos 4t)(1 + 2\cos 4t) = 0$ then $t = \pi/3 + n\pi/2$ and $t = \pi/6 + n\pi/2$ for $n = 0$, 1, 2, ... at the extreme values. *Note*: There are many other values of t for which $x' = 0$.

(d) $x(\pi/6 + n\pi/2) = \sqrt{3}/2$ cm. and $x(\pi/3 + n\pi/2) = -\sqrt{3}/2$ cm.

(e)

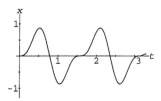

10. If $x'' + 2\lambda x' + \omega^2 x = F_0 \sin\gamma t$ describes underdamped motion then

$$x_c = e^{-\lambda t}\left[c_1 \cos\sqrt{\omega^2 - \lambda^2}\,t + c_2 \sin\sqrt{\omega^2 - \lambda^2}\,t\right]$$

and

$$x_p = \frac{F_0\left(\omega^2 - \gamma^2\right)}{4\lambda^2\gamma^2 + \left(\omega^2 - \gamma^2\right)^2}\sin\gamma t + \frac{-2\lambda\gamma F_0}{4\lambda^2\gamma^2 + \left(\omega^2 - \gamma^2\right)^2}\cos\gamma t.$$

If $\sin\phi = c_1/\sqrt{c_1^2 + c_2^2}$, $\cos\phi = c_2/\sqrt{c_1^2 + c_2^2}$, $\sin\theta = -2\lambda\gamma/\sqrt{\left(\omega^2 - \gamma^2\right)^2 + 4\lambda^2\gamma^2}$, and

$\cos\theta = \left(\omega^2 - \gamma^2\right)/\sqrt{\left(\omega^2 - \gamma^2\right)^2 + 4\lambda^2\gamma^2}$ then the equation of motion is

$$x = \sqrt{c_1^2 + c_2^2}\,e^{-\lambda t}\sin\left(\sqrt{\omega^2 - \lambda^2}\,t + \phi\right) + \frac{F_0}{\sqrt{\left(\omega^2 - \lambda^2\right)^2 + 4\lambda^2\gamma^2}}\sin(\gamma t + \theta).$$

11. (a) If $g'(\gamma) = 0$ then $\gamma\left(\gamma^2 + 2\lambda^2 - \omega^2\right) = 0$ so that $\gamma = 0$ or $\gamma = \sqrt{\omega^2 - 2\lambda^2}$. The first derivative test shows that g has a maximum value at $\gamma = \sqrt{\omega^2 - 2\lambda^2}$.

(b) The maximum value of g is $g\left(\sqrt{\omega^2 - 2\lambda^2}\right) = F_0/2\lambda\sqrt{\omega^2 - \lambda^2}$.

12. (a) If $x'' + \beta x' + 3x = 0$ and $0 < \beta < 2\sqrt{3}$ then the roots of the auxiliary equation are

$m = \frac{1}{2}\left(-\beta \pm \sqrt{\beta^2 - 12}\right)$; this is underdamped motion. The system is in resonance when

$\gamma = \sqrt{3 - \beta^2/2}$, where we require that $3 - \beta/2 > 0$, or $0 < \beta < \sqrt{6}$.

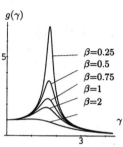

(b) When $F_0 = 3$, the resonance curve is given by

$$g(\gamma) = \frac{3}{\sqrt{(3 - \gamma^2)^2 + \beta^2\gamma^2}},$$

and the family of graphs is shown for various values of β.

13. If $\frac{1}{2}x'' + 2x' + 6x = 40\sin 2t$ then

$$x_p = -5\cos 2t + 5\sin 2t = 5\sqrt{2}\sin(2t - \pi/4).$$

14. $\gamma = \sqrt{\omega^2 - 2\lambda^2} = 2$ and $g(\gamma) = 80/2.2\sqrt{12 - 4} = 5\sqrt{2}$, the amplitude of x_p.

15. (a) From $x'' + \omega^2 x = F_0\cos\gamma t$, $x(0) = 0$, and $x'(0) = 0$ we obtain $x_c = c_1\cos\omega t + c_2\sin\omega t$ and $x_p = (F_0\cos\gamma t)/\left(\omega^2 - \gamma^2\right)$ so that

$$x = -\frac{F_0}{\omega^2 - \gamma^2}\cos\omega t + \frac{F_0}{\omega^2 - \gamma^2}\cos\gamma t.$$

(b) $\displaystyle\lim_{\gamma \to \omega}\frac{F_0}{\omega^2 - \gamma^2}(\cos\gamma t - \cos\omega t) = \lim_{\gamma \to \omega}\frac{-F_0 t\sin\gamma t}{-2\gamma} = \frac{F_0}{2\omega}t\sin\omega t.$

16. From $x'' + \omega^2 x = F_0\cos\omega t$, $x(0) = 0$, and $x'(0) = 0$ we obtain $x_c = c_1\cos\omega t + c_2\sin\omega t$ and $x_p = (F_0 t/2\omega)\sin\omega t$ so that $x = (F_0 t/2\omega)\sin\omega t$ and $\displaystyle\lim_{\gamma \to \omega}\frac{F_0}{2\omega}t\sin\omega t = \frac{F_0}{2\omega}t\sin\omega t.$

17. From $x'' + 4x = -5\sin 2t + 3\cos 2t$, $x(0) = -1$, and $x'(0) = 1$ we obtain $x_c = c_1\cos 2t + c_2\sin 2t$, $x_p = \frac{3}{4}t\sin 2t + \frac{5}{4}t\cos 2t$, and

$$x = -\cos 2t - \frac{1}{8}\sin 2t + \frac{3}{4}t\sin 2t + \frac{5}{4}t\cos 2t.$$

18. From $x'' + 9x = 5\sin 3t$, $x(0) = 2$, and $x'(0) = 0$ we obtain $x_c = c_1\cos 3t + c_2\sin 3t$, $x_p = -\frac{5}{6}t\cos 3t$, and

$$x = 2\cos 3t + \frac{5}{18}\sin 3t - \frac{5}{6}t\cos 3t.$$

19. (a) From $\cos(u - v) = \cos u\cos v + \sin u\sin v$ and $\cos(u + v) = \cos u\cos v - \sin u\sin v$ we obtain $\sin u\sin v = \frac{1}{2}[\cos(u - v) - \cos(u + v)]$. Letting $u = \frac{1}{2}(\gamma - \omega)t$ and $v = \frac{1}{2}(\gamma + \omega)t$, the result follows.

(b) If $\epsilon = \frac{1}{2}(\gamma - \omega)$ then $\gamma \approx \omega$ so that $x = (F_0/2\epsilon\gamma)\sin \epsilon t \sin \gamma t$.

(c) $\displaystyle \lim_{\epsilon \to 0} \frac{F_0}{2\epsilon\gamma}\sin \epsilon t \sin \gamma t = \lim_{\epsilon \to 0} \frac{F_0 t}{2\gamma}\cos \epsilon t \sin \gamma t = \frac{F_0 t}{2\gamma}\sin \gamma t$.

20. From $x'' + 25x = 10\cos 7t$, $x(0) = 0$, and $x'(0) = 0$ we obtain

$$x = -\frac{5}{12}(\cos 7t - \cos 5t) = -\frac{5}{12}[\cos 6t \cos t - \sin 6t \sin t - \cos 6t \cos t - \sin 6t \sin t] = \frac{5}{6}\sin 6t \sin t.$$

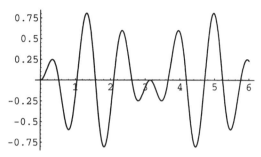

Exercises 5.4

1. Solving the differential equation $q'' + 16q = 60$ we obtain $q(t) = c_1 \cos 4t + c_2 \sin 4t + 15/4$. The initial conditions $q(0) = q'(0) = 0$ imply $c_1 = -15/4$ and $c_2 = 0$. Thus,

$$q(t) = -\frac{15}{4}\cos 4t + \frac{15}{4} \quad \text{and} \quad i(t) = 15\sin 4t.$$

2. Solving the differential equation $5q'' + 100q = 20t$ we obtain $q(t) = c_1 \cos 2\sqrt{5}\,t + c_2 \sin 2\sqrt{5}\,t + t/5$. The initial conditions $q(0) = q'(0) = 0$ imply $c_1 = 0$ and $c_2 = \sqrt{5}/50$. Thus

$$q(t) = \frac{\sqrt{5}}{50}\sin 2\sqrt{5}\,t + \frac{1}{5}t \quad \text{and} \quad i(t) = \frac{1}{5}\cos 2\sqrt{5}\,t + \frac{1}{5}.$$

3. Since $R^2 - 4L/C = -20 < 0$, the circuit is underdamped.

4. Since $R^2 - L/C = 0$, the circuit is critically damped.

5. Solving $\frac{1}{20}q'' + 2q' + 100q = 0$ we obtain $q(t) = e^{-20t}(c_1 \cos 40t + c_2 \sin 40t)$. The initial conditions $q(0) = 5$ and $q'(0) = 0$ imply $c_1 = 5$ and $c_2 = 5/2$. Thus

$$q(t) = e^{-20t}\left(5\cos 40t + \frac{5}{2}\sin 40t\right) \approx \sqrt{25 + 25/4}\,e^{-20t}\sin(40t + 1.1071)$$

and $q(0.01) \approx 4.5676$ coulombs. The charge is zero for the first time when $40t + 0.4636 = \pi$ or $t \approx 0.0509$ second.

6. Solving $\frac{1}{4}q'' + 20q' + 300q = 0$ we obtain $q(t) = c_1 e^{-20t} + c_2 e^{-60t}$. The initial conditions $q(0) = 4$ and $q'(0) = 0$ imply $c_1 = 6$ and $c_2 = -2$. Thus

$$q(t) = 6e^{-20t} - 2e^{-60t}.$$

Setting $q = 0$ we find $e^{40t} = 1/3$ which implies $t < 0$. Therefore the charge is never 0.

7. Solving $\frac{5}{3}q'' + 10q' + 30q = 300$ we obtain $q(t) = e^{-3t}(c_1 \cos 3t + c_2 \sin 3t) + 10$. The initial conditions $q(0) = q'(0) = 0$ imply $c_1 = c_2 = -10$. Thus

$$q(t) = 10 - 10e^{-3t}(\cos 3t + \sin 3t) \quad \text{and} \quad i(t) = 60e^{3t} \sin 3t.$$

Solving $i(t) = 0$ we see that the maximum charge occurs when $t = \pi/3$ and $q(\pi/3) \approx 10.432$ coulombs.

8. Solving $q'' + 100q' + 2500q = 30$ we obtain $q(t) = c_1 e^{-50t} + c_2 t e^{-50t} + 0.012$. The initial conditions $q(0) = 0$ and $q'(0) = 2$ imply $c_1 = -0.012$ and $c_2 = 1.4$. Thus

$$q(t) = -0.012e^{-50t} + 1.4te^{-50t} + 0.012 \quad \text{and} \quad i(t) = 2e^{-50t} - 70te^{-50t}.$$

Solving $i(t) = 0$ we see that the maximum charge occurs when $t = 1/35$ and $q(1/35) \approx 0.01871$.

9. Solving $q'' + 2q' + 4q = 0$ we obtain $y_c = e^{-t}\left(\cos \sqrt{3}\,t + \sin \sqrt{3}\,t\right)$. The steady-state charge has the form $y_p = A \cos t + B \sin t$. Substituting into the differential equation we find

$$(3A + 2B)\cos t + (3B - 2A)\sin t = 50 \cos t.$$

Thus, $A = 150/13$ and $B = 100/13$. The steady-state charge is

$$q_p(t) = \frac{150}{13} \cos t + \frac{100}{13} \sin t$$

and the steady-state current is

$$i_p(t) = -\frac{150}{13} \sin t + \frac{100}{13} \cos t.$$

10. From

$$i_p(t) = \frac{E_0}{Z}\left(\frac{R}{Z} \sin \gamma t - \frac{X}{Z} \cos \gamma t\right)$$

and $Z = \sqrt{X^2 + R^2}$ we see that the amplitude of $i_p(t)$ is

$$A = \sqrt{\frac{E_0^2 R^2}{Z^4} + \frac{E_0^2 X^2}{Z^4}} = \frac{E_0}{Z^2}\sqrt{R^2 + X^2} = \frac{E_0}{Z}.$$

11. The differential equation is $\frac{1}{2}q'' + 20q' + 1000q = 100 \sin t$. To use Example 3 in the text we identify $E_0 = 100$ and $\gamma = 60$. Then

$$X = L\gamma - \frac{1}{c\gamma} = \frac{1}{2}(60) - \frac{1}{0.001(60)} \approx 13.3333,$$

$$Z = \sqrt{X^2 + R^2} = \sqrt{X^2 + 400} \approx 24.0370,$$

and

$$\frac{E_0}{Z} = \frac{100}{Z} \approx 4.1603.$$

From Problem 10, then

$$i_p(t) \approx 4.1603(60t + \phi)$$

where $\sin\phi = -X/Z$ and $\cos\phi = R/Z$. Thus $\tan\phi = -X/R \approx -0.6667$ and ϕ is a fourth quadrant angle. Now $\phi \approx -0.5880$ and

$$i_p(t) \approx 4.1603(60t - 0.5880).$$

12. Solving $\frac{1}{2}q'' + 20q' + 1000q = 0$ we obtain $q_c(t) = (c_1 \cos 40t + c_2 \sin 40t)$. The steady-state charge has the form $q_p(t) = A \sin 60t + B \cos 60t + C \sin 40t + D \cos 40t$. Substituting into the differential equation we find

$$(-1600A - 2400B) \sin 60t + (2400A - 1600B) \cos 60t$$

$$+ (400C - 1600D) \sin 40t + (1600C + 400D) \cos 40t$$

$$= 200 \sin 60t + 400 \cos 40t.$$

Equating coefficients we obtain $A = -1/26$, $B = -3/52$, $C = 4/17$, and $D = 1/17$. The steady-state charge is

$$q_p(t) = -\frac{1}{26} \sin 60t - \frac{3}{52} \cos 60t + \frac{4}{17} \sin 40t + \frac{1}{17} \cos 40t$$

and the steady-state current is

$$i_p(t) = -\frac{30}{13} \cos 60t + \frac{45}{13} \sin 60t + \frac{160}{17} \cos 40t - \frac{40}{17} \sin 40t.$$

13. Solving $\frac{1}{2}q'' + 10q' + 100q = 150$ we obtain $q(t) = e^{-10t}(c_1 \cos 10t + c_2 \sin 10t) + 3/2$. The initial conditions $q(0) = 1$ and $q'(0) = 0$ imply $c_1 = c_2 = -1/2$. Thus

$$q(t) = -\frac{1}{2}e^{-10t}(\cos 10t + \sin 10t) + \frac{3}{2}.$$

As $t \to \infty$, $q(t) \to 3/2$.

14. By Problem 10 the amplitude of the steady-state current is E_0/Z, where $Z = \sqrt{X^2 + R^2}$ and $X = L\gamma - 1/C\gamma$. Since E_0 is constant the amplitude will be a maximum when Z is a minimum. Since R is constant, Z will be a minimum when $X = 0$. Solving $L\gamma - 1/C\gamma = 0$ for γ we obtain $\gamma = 1/\sqrt{LC}$. The maximum amplitude will be E_0/R.

15. By Problem 10 the amplitude of the steady-state current is E_0/Z, where $Z = \sqrt{X^2 + R^2}$ and $X = L\gamma - 1/C\gamma$. Since E_0 is constant the amplitude will be a maximum when Z is a minimum. Since R is constant, Z will be a minimum when $X = 0$. Solving $L\gamma - 1/C\gamma = 0$ for C we obtain $C = 1/L\gamma^2$.

16. Solving $0.1q'' + 10q = 100 \sin \gamma t$ we obtain $q(t) = c_1 \cos 10t + c_2 \sin 10t + q_p(t)$ where $q_p(t) = A \sin \gamma t + B \cos \gamma t$. Substituting $q_p(t)$ into the differential equation we find

$$(100 - \gamma^2)A \sin \gamma t + (100 - \gamma^2)B \cos \gamma t = 100 \sin \gamma t.$$

Equating coefficients we obtain $A = 100/(100 - \gamma^2)$ and $B = 0$. Thus, $q_p(t) = \dfrac{100}{100 - \gamma^2} \sin \gamma t$. The initial conditions $q(0) = q'(0) = 0$ imply $c_1 = 0$ and $c_2 = -10\gamma/(100 - \gamma^2)$. The charge is

$$q(t) = \frac{10}{100 - \gamma^2}(10 \sin \gamma t - \gamma \sin 10t)$$

and the current is

$$i(t) = \frac{100\gamma}{100 - \gamma^2}(\cos \gamma t - \cos 10t).$$

17. From Example 1 in the text we see that $q(t) = c_1 \cos\left(t/\sqrt{LC}\right) + c_2 \sin\left(t/\sqrt{LC}\right) + q_p(t)$ where $q_p(t) = A \sin \gamma t + B \cos \gamma t$. Substituting $q_p(t)$ into the differential equation we find

$$\left(\frac{1}{C} - L\gamma^2\right) A \sin \gamma t + \left(\frac{1}{C} - L\gamma^2\right) B \cos \gamma t = E_0 \cos \gamma t.$$

Equating coefficients we obtain $A = 0$ and $B = E_0C/(1 - LC\gamma^2)$. Thus, the charge is

$$q(t) = c_1 \cos \frac{1}{\sqrt{LC}} t + c_2 \sin \frac{1}{\sqrt{LC}} t + \frac{E_0 C}{1 - LC\gamma^2} \cos \gamma t.$$

The initial conditions $q(0) = q_0$ and $q'(0) = i_0$ imply $c_1 = q_0 - E_0C/(1 - LC\gamma^2)$ and $c_2 = i_0\sqrt{LC}$. The current is

$$i(t) = -\frac{c_1}{\sqrt{LC}} \sin \frac{1}{\sqrt{LC}} t + \frac{c_2}{\sqrt{LC}} \cos \frac{1}{\sqrt{LC}} t - \frac{E_0 C\gamma}{1 - LC\gamma^2} \sin \gamma t$$

$$= i_0 \cos \frac{1}{\sqrt{LC}} t - \frac{1}{\sqrt{LC}}\left(q_0 - \frac{E_0 C}{1 - LC\gamma^2}\right) \sin \frac{1}{\sqrt{LC}} t - \frac{E_0 C\gamma}{1 - LC\gamma^2} \sin \gamma t.$$

18. When the circuit is in resonance the form of $q_p(t)$ is $q_p(t) = At \cos kt + Bt \sin kt$ where $k = 1/\sqrt{LC}$. Substituting $q_p(t)$ into the differential equation we find

$$q_p'' + k^2 q = -2kA \sin kt + 2kB \cos kt = \frac{E_0}{L} \cos kt.$$

Equating coefficients we obtain $A = 0$ and $B = E_0/2kL$. The charge is

$$q(t) = c_1 \cos kt + c_2 \sin kt + \frac{E_0}{2kL} t \sin kt.$$

The initial conditions $q(0) = q_0$ and $q'(0) = i_0$ imply $c_1 = q_0$ and $c_2 = i_0/k$. The current is

$$i(t) = -c_1 k \sin kt + c_2 k \cos kt + \frac{E_0}{2kL}(kt \cos kt + \sin kt)$$

$$= \left(\frac{E_0}{2kL} - q_0 k\right) \sin kt + i_0 \cos kt + \frac{E_0}{2L} t \cos kt.$$

19. From $\theta'' + 16\theta = 0$, $\theta(0) = 1/2$, and $\theta'(0) = 2\sqrt{3}$ we obtain

$$\theta = \frac{1}{2}\cos 4t + \frac{\sqrt{3}}{2}\sin 4t = \sin\left(4t + \frac{\pi}{6}\right).$$

The amplitude is 1, period is $\pi/2$, and frequency is 2π.

20. If $\theta = 0$ then $4t + \pi/6 = n\pi$ or $t = \frac{1}{4}(n\pi - \pi/6)$ for $n = 1, 2, 3, \ldots$. If $\theta' = 0$ then $4t + \pi/6 = \pi/2 + n\pi$ or $t = \frac{1}{4}(\pi/3 + n\pi)$ for $n = 0, 1, 2, \ldots$.

Chapter 5 Review Exercises

1. 8 ft., since $k = 4$.

2. $2\pi/5$, since $\frac{1}{4}x'' + 6.25x = 0$.

3. 5/4 m., since $x = -\cos 4t + \frac{3}{4}\sin 4t$.

4. True

5. False; since an external force may exist.

6. False

7. overdamped

8. $-\pi/4$

9. 9/2, since $x = c_1 \cos\sqrt{2k}\,t + c_2 \sin\sqrt{2k}\,t$.

10. (a) Solving $\frac{3}{8}x'' + 6x = 0$ subject to $x(0) = 1$ and $x'(0) = -4$ we obtain

$$x = \cos 4t - \sin 4t = \sqrt{2}\sin(4t + 3\pi/4).$$

    (b) The amplitude is $\sqrt{2}$, period is $\pi/2$, and frequency is $2/\pi$.

    (c) If $x = 1$ then $t = n\pi/2$ and $t = -\pi/8 + n\pi/2$ for $n = 1, 2, 3, \ldots$.

    (d) If $x = 0$ then $t = \pi/16 + n\pi/4$ for $n = 0, 1, 2, \ldots$. The motion is upward for n even and downward for n odd.

    (e) $x'(3\pi/16) = 0$

    (f) If $x' = 0$ then $4t + 3\pi/4 = \pi/2 + n\pi$ or $t = 3\pi/16 + n\pi$.

11. From $\frac{1}{4}x'' + \frac{3}{2}x' + 2x = 0$, $x(0) = 1/3$, and $x'(0) = 0$ we obtain $x = \frac{2}{3}e^{-2t} - \frac{1}{3}e^{-4t}$.

12. From $x'' + \beta x' + 64x = 0$ we see that oscillatory motion results if $\beta^2 - 256 < 0$ or $0 \le |\beta| < 16$.

13. From $mx'' + 4x' + 2x = 0$ we see that non-oscillatory motion results if $16 - 8m \ge 0$ or $0 < m \le 2$.

14. From $\frac{1}{4}x'' + x' + x = 0$, $x(0) = 4$, and $x'(0) = 2$ we obtain $x = 4e^{-2t} + 10te^{-2t}$. If $x'(t) = 0$, then $t = 1/10$, so that the maximum displacement is $x = 5e^{-0.2} \approx 4.094$.

15. Writing $\frac{1}{8}x'' + \frac{8}{3}x = \cos\gamma t + \sin\gamma t$ in the form $x'' + \frac{64}{3}x = 8\cos\gamma t + 8\sin\gamma t$ we identify $\lambda = 0$ and $\omega^2 = 64/3$. From Example 4 in Section 5.3 we see that the system is in a state of pure resonance when $\gamma = \sqrt{64/3} = 8/\sqrt{3}$.

16. Clearly $x_p = A/\omega^2$ suffices.

17. From $\frac{1}{8}x'' + x' + 3x = e^{-t}$, $x(0) = 2$, and $x'(0) = 0$ we obtain $x_c = e^{-4t}\left(c_1\cos 2\sqrt{2}\,t + c_2\sin 2\sqrt{2}\,t\right)$, $x_p = \frac{8}{17}e^{-t}$, and

$$x = e^{-4t}\left(\frac{26}{17}\cos 2\sqrt{2}\,t + \frac{28\sqrt{2}}{17}\sin 2\sqrt{2}\,t\right) + \frac{8}{17}e^{-t}.$$

18. (a) Let k be the effective spring constant and x_1 and x_2 the elongation of springs k_1 and k_2. The restoring forces satisfy $k_1 x_1 = k_2 x_2$ so $x_2 = (k_1/k_2)x_1$. From $k(x_1 + x_2) = k_1 x_1$ we have

$$k\left(x_1 + \frac{k_1}{k_2}x_2\right) = k_1 x_1$$

$$k\left(\frac{k_2 + k_1}{k_2}\right) = k_1$$

$$k = \frac{k_1 k_2}{k_1 + k_2}$$

$$\frac{1}{k} = \frac{1}{k_1} + \frac{1}{k_2}.$$

(b) From $k_1 = 2W$ and $k_2 = 4W$ we find $1/k = 1/2W + 1/4W = 3/4W$. Then $k = 4W/3 = 4mg/3$. The differential equation $mx'' + kx = 0$ then becomes $x'' + (4g/3)x = 0$. The solution is

$$x(t) = c_1 \cos 2\sqrt{\frac{g}{3}}\,t + c_2 \sin 2\sqrt{\frac{g}{3}}\,t.$$

The initial conditions $x(0) = 1$ and $x'(0) = 2/3$ imply $c_1 = 1$ and $c_2 = 1/\sqrt{3g}$.

(c) To compute the maximum speed of the weight we compute

$$x'(t) = 2\sqrt{\frac{g}{3}}\sin 2\sqrt{\frac{g}{3}}\,t + \frac{2}{3}\cos 2\sqrt{\frac{g}{3}}\,t \quad \text{and} \quad |x'(t)| = \sqrt{4\frac{g}{3} + \frac{4}{9}} = \frac{2}{3}\sqrt{3g + 1}.$$

19. From $q'' + 10^4 q = 100\sin 50t$, $q(0) = 0$, and $q'(t) = 0$ we obtain $q_c = c_1\cos 100t + c_2\sin 100t$, $q_p = \frac{1}{75}\sin 50t$, and

(a) $q = -\frac{1}{150}\sin 100t + \frac{1}{75}\sin 50t$,

(b) $i = -\frac{2}{3}\cos 100t + \frac{2}{3}\cos 50t$, and

(c) $q = 0$ when $\sin 50t(1 - \cos 50t) = 0$ or $t = n\pi/50$ for $n = 0, 1, 2, \ldots$.

20. Differentiate $L\dfrac{d^2q}{dt^2} + R\dfrac{dq}{dt} + \dfrac{1}{C}q = E(t)$ and use $q'(t) = i(t)$ to obtain the desired result.

6 Differential Equations with Variable Coefficients

━━━━━━━━ **Exercises 6.1** ━━━━━━━━

1. The auxiliary equation is $m^2 - m - 2 = (m+1)(m-2) = 0$ so that $y = c_1 x^{-1} + c_2 x^2$.

2. The auxiliary equation is $4m^2 - 4m + 1 = (2m-1)^2 = 0$ so that $y = c_1 x^{1/2} + c_2 x^{1/2} \ln x$.

3. The auxiliary equation is $m^2 = 0$ so that $y = c_1 + c_2 \ln x$.

4. The auxiliary equation is $m^2 - 2m = m(m-2) = 0$ so that $y = c_1 + c_2 x^2$.

5. The auxiliary equation is $m^2 + 4 = 0$ so that $y = c_1 \cos(2 \ln x) + c_2 \sin(2 \ln x)$.

6. The auxiliary equation is $m^2 + 4m + 3 = (m+1)(m+3) = 0$ so that $y = c_1 x^{-1} + c_2 x^{-3}$.

7. The auxiliary equation is $m^2 - 4m - 2 = 0$ so that $y = c_1 x^{2-\sqrt{6}} + c_2 x^{2+\sqrt{6}}$.

8. The auxiliary equation is $m^2 + 2m - 4 = 0$ so that $y = c_1 x^{-1+\sqrt{5}} + c_2 x^{-1-\sqrt{5}}$.

9. The auxiliary equation is $25m^2 + 1 = 0$ so that $y = c_1 \cos\left(\frac{1}{5} \ln x\right) + c_2 \sin\left(\frac{1}{5} \ln x\right)$.

10. The auxiliary equation is $4m^2 - 1 = (2m-1)(2m+1) = 0$ so that $y = c_1 x^{1/2} + c_2 x^{-1/2}$.

11. The auxiliary equation is $m^2 + 4m + 4 = (m+2)^2 = 0$ so that $y = c_1 x^{-2} + c_2 x^{-2} \ln x$.

12. The auxiliary equation is $m^2 + 7m + 6 = (m+1)(m+6) = 0$ so that $y = c_1 x^{-1} + c_2 x^{-6}$.

13. The auxiliary equation is $m^2 - 2m + 2 = 0$ so that $y = x \left[c_1 \cos(\ln x) + c_2 \sin(\ln x)\right]$.

14. The auxiliary equation is $m^2 - 8m + 41 = 0$ so that $y = x^4 \left[c_1 \cos(5 \ln x) + c_2 \sin(5 \ln x)\right]$.

15. The auxiliary equation is $3m^2 + 3m + 1 = 0$ so that $y = x^{-1/2} \left[c_1 \cos\left(\frac{\sqrt{3}}{6} \ln x\right) + c_2 \sin\left(\frac{\sqrt{3}}{6} \ln x\right)\right]$.

16. The auxiliary equation is $2m^2 - m + 1 = 0$ so that $y = x^{1/4} \left[c_1 \cos\left(\frac{\sqrt{7}}{4} \ln x\right) + c_2 \sin\left(\frac{\sqrt{7}}{4} \ln x\right)\right]$.

17. Assuming that $y = x^m$ and substituting into the differential equation we obtain

$$m(m-1)(m-2) - 6 = m^3 - 3m^2 + 2m - 6 = (m-3)(m^2 + 2) = 0.$$

Thus

$$y = c_1 x^3 + c_2 \cos\left(\sqrt{2} \ln x\right) + c_3 \sin\left(\sqrt{2} \ln x\right).$$

18. Assuming that $y = x^m$ and substituting into the differential equation we obtain

$$m(m-1)(m-2) + m - 1 = m^3 - 3m^2 + 3m - 1 = (m-1)^3 = 0.$$

Thus

$$y = c_1x + c_2x \ln x + c_3x(\ln x)^2.$$

19. Assuming that $y = x^m$ and substituting into the differential equation we obtain

$$m(m-1)(m-2) - 2m(m-1) - 2m + 8 = m^3 - 5m^2 + 2m + 8 = (m+1)(m-2)(m-4) = 0.$$

Thus

$$y = c_1x^{-1} + c_2x^2 + c_3x^4.$$

20. Assuming that $y = x^m$ and substituting into the differential equation we obtain

$$m(m-1)(m-2) - 2m(m-1) + 4m - 4 = m^3 - 5m^2 + 8m - 4 = (m-1)(m-2)^2 = 0.$$

Thus

$$y = c_1x + c_2x^2 + c_3x^2 \ln x.$$

21. Assuming that $y = x^m$ and substituting into the differential equation we obtain

$$m(m-1)(m-2)(m-3) + 6m(m-1)(m-2) = m^4 - 7m^2 + 6m = m(m-1)(m-2)(m+3) = 0.$$

Thus

$$y = c_1 + c_2x + c_3x^2 + c_4x^{-3}.$$

22. Assuming that $y = x^m$ and substituting into the differential equation we obtain

$$m(m-1)(m-2)(m-3) + 6m(m-1)(m-2) + 9m(m-1) + 3m + 1 = m^4 + 2m^2 + 1 = (m^2+1)^2 = 0.$$

Thus

$$y = c_1 \cos(\ln x) + c_2 \sin(\ln x) + c_3 \ln x \cos(\ln x) + c_4 \ln x \sin(\ln x).$$

23. The auxiliary equation is $m^2 + 2m = m(m+2) = 0$, so that

$$y = c_1 + c_2x^{-2} \quad \text{and} \quad y' = -2c_2x^{-3}.$$

The initial conditions imply

$$c_1 + c_2 = 0$$

$$-2c_2 = 4.$$

Thus, $c_1 = 2$, $c_2 = -2$, and $y = 2 - 2x^{-2}$.

24. The auxiliary equation is $m^2 - 6m + 8 = (m-2)(m-4) = 0$, so that

$$y = c_1x^2 + c_2x^4 \quad \text{and} \quad y' = 2c_1x + 4c_2x^3.$$

The initial conditions imply

$$4c_1 + 16c_2 = 32$$

$$4c_1 + 32c_2 = 0.$$

150

Thus, $c_1 = 16$, $c_2 = -2$, and $y = 16x^2 - 2x^4$.

25. The auxiliary equation is $m^2 + 1 = 0$, so that

$$y = c_1 \cos(\ln x) + c_2 \sin(\ln x) \quad \text{and} \quad y' = -c_1 \frac{1}{x} \sin(\ln x) + c_2 \frac{1}{x} \cos(\ln x).$$

The initial conditions imply $c_1 = 1$ and $c_2 = 2$. Thus $y = \cos(\ln x) + 2\sin(\ln x)$.

26. The auxiliary equation is $m^2 - 4m + 4 = (m-2)^2 = 0$, so that

$$y = c_1 x^2 + c_2 x^2 \ln x \quad \text{and} \quad y' = 2c_1 x + c_2(x + 2x \ln x).$$

The initial conditions imply $c_1 = 5$ and $c_2 + 10 = 3$. Thus $y = 5x^2 - 7x^2 \ln x$.

In the next two problems we use the substitution $t = -x$ since the initial conditions are on the interval $(-\infty, 0)$. Then

$$\frac{dy}{dt} = \frac{dy}{dx}\frac{dx}{dt} = -\frac{dy}{dx}$$

and

$$\frac{d^2 y}{dt^2} = \frac{d}{dt}\left(\frac{dy}{dt}\right) = \frac{d}{dt}\left(-\frac{dy}{dx}\right) = -\frac{d}{dt}(y') = -\frac{dy'}{dx}\frac{dx}{dt} = -\frac{d^2 y}{dx^2}\frac{dx}{dt} = \frac{d^2 y}{dx^2}.$$

27. The differential equation and initial conditions become

$$4t^2 \frac{d^2 y}{dt^2} + y = 0; \quad y(t)\Big|_{t=1} = 2, \quad y'(t)\Big|_{t=1} = -4.$$

The auxiliary equation is $4m^2 - 4m + 1 = (2m-1)^2 = 0$, so that

$$y = c_1 t^{1/2} + c_2 t^{1/2} \ln t \quad \text{and} \quad y' = \frac{1}{2}c_1 t^{-1/2} + c_2 \left(t^{-1/2} + \frac{1}{2}t^{-1/2} \ln t\right).$$

The initial conditions imply $c_1 = 2$ and $1 + c_2 = -4$. Thus

$$y = 2t^{1/2} - 5t^{1/2} \ln t = 2(-x)^{1/2} - 5(-x)^{1/2} \ln(-x), \quad x < 0.$$

28. The differential equation and initial conditions become

$$t^2 \frac{d^2 y}{dt^2} - 4t \frac{dy}{dt} + 6y = 0; \quad y(t)\Big|_{t=2} = 8, \quad y'(t)\Big|_{t=2} = 0.$$

The auxiliary equation is $m^2 - 5m + 6 = (m-2)(m-3) = 0$, so that

$$y = c_1 t^2 + c_2 t^3 \quad \text{and} \quad y' = 2c_1 t + 3c_2 t^2.$$

The initial conditions imply

$$4c_1 + 8c_2 = 8$$

$$4c_1 + 12c_2 = 0$$

from which we find $c_1 = 6$ and $c_2 = -2$. Thus

$$y = 6t^2 - 2t^3 = 6x^2 + 2x^3, \quad x < 0.$$

29. The auxiliary equation is $m^2 = 0$ so that $y_c = c_1 + c_2 \ln x$ and

$$W(1, \ln x) = \begin{vmatrix} 1 & \ln x \\ 0 & 1/x \end{vmatrix} = \frac{1}{x}.$$

Identifying $f(x) = 1$ we obtain $u_1' = -x \ln x$ and $u_2' = x$. Then $u_1 = \frac{1}{4}x^2 - \frac{1}{2}x^2 \ln x$, $u_2 = \frac{1}{2}x^2$, and

$$y = c_1 + c_2 \ln x + \frac{1}{4}x^2 - \frac{1}{2}x^2 \ln x + \frac{1}{2}x^2 \ln x = c_1 + c_2 \ln x + \frac{1}{4}x^2.$$

30. The auxiliary equation is $m^2 - 5m = m(m-5) = 0$ so that $y_c = c_1 + c_2 x^5$ and

$$W(1, x^5) = \begin{vmatrix} 1 & x^5 \\ 0 & 5x^4 \end{vmatrix} = 5x^4.$$

Identifying $f(x) = x^3$ we obtain $u_1' = -\frac{1}{5}x^4$ and $u_2' = 1/5x$. Then $u_1 = -\frac{1}{25}x^5$, $u_2 = \frac{1}{5} \ln x$, and

$$y = c_1 + c_2 x^5 - \frac{1}{25}x^5 + \frac{1}{5}x^5 \ln x = c_1 + c_3 x^5 + \frac{1}{5}x^5 \ln x.$$

31. The auxiliary equation is $2m^2 + 3m + 1 = (2m+1)(m+1) = 0$ so that $y_c = c_1 x^{-1} + c_2 x^{-1/2}$ and

$$W(x^{-1}, x^{-1/2}) = \begin{vmatrix} x^{-1} & x^{-1/2} \\ -x^{-2} & -\frac{1}{2}x^{-3/2} \end{vmatrix} = \frac{1}{2}x^{-5/2}.$$

Identifying $f(x) = \frac{1}{2} - \frac{1}{2x}$ we obtain $u_1' = x - x^2$ and $u_2' = x^{3/2} - x^{1/2}$. Then $u_1 = \frac{1}{2}x^2 - \frac{1}{3}x^3$, $u_2 = \frac{2}{5}x^{5/2} - \frac{2}{3}x^{3/2}$, and

$$y = c_1 x^{-1} + c_2 x^{-1/2} + \frac{1}{2}x - \frac{1}{3}x^2 + \frac{2}{5}x^2 - \frac{2}{3}x = c_1 x^{-1} + c_2 x^{-1/2} - \frac{1}{6}x + \frac{1}{15}x^2.$$

32. The auxiliary equation is $m^2 - 3m + 2 = (m-1)(m-2) = 0$ so that $y_c = c_1 x + c_2 x^2$ and

$$W(x, x^2) = \begin{vmatrix} x & x^2 \\ 1 & 2x \end{vmatrix} = x^2.$$

Identifying $f(x) = x^2 e^x$ we obtain $u_1' = -x^2 e^x$ and $u_2' = x e^x$. Then $u_1 = -x^2 e^x + 2x e^x - 2e^x$, $u_2 = x e^x - e^x$, and

$$y = c_1 x + c_2 x^2 - x^3 e^x + 2x^2 e^x - 2x e^x + x^3 e^x - x^2 e^x$$

$$= c_1 x + c_2 x^2 + x^2 e^x - 2x e^x.$$

33. The auxiliary equation is $m^2 - 2m + 1 = (m-1)^2 = 0$ so that $y_c = c_1 x + c_2 x \ln x$ and

$$W(x, x \ln x) = \begin{vmatrix} x & x \ln x \\ 1 & 1 + \ln x \end{vmatrix} = x.$$

Identifying $f(x) = 2/x$ we obtain $u_1' = -2\ln x/x$ and $u_2' = 2/x$. Then $u_1 = -(\ln x)^2$, $u_2 = 2\ln x$, and

$$y = c_1 x + c_2 x \ln x - x(\ln x)^2 + 2x(\ln x)^2$$

$$= c_1 x + c_2 x \ln x + x(\ln x)^2.$$

34. The auxiliary equation is $m^2 - 3m + 2 = (m-1)(m-2) = 0$ so that $y_c = c_1 x + c_2 x^2$ and

$$W(x, x^2) = \begin{vmatrix} x & x^2 \\ 1 & 2x \end{vmatrix} = x^2.$$

Identifying $f(x) = x \ln x$ we obtain $u_1' = -x\ln x$ and $u_2' = \ln x$. Then $u_1 = \frac{1}{4}x^2 - \frac{1}{2}x^2\ln x$, $u_2 = x\ln x - x$, and

$$y = c_1 x + c_2 x^2 + \frac{1}{4}x^3 - \frac{1}{2}x^3\ln x + x^3\ln x - x^3 = c_1 x + c_2 x^2 - \frac{3}{4}x^3 + \frac{1}{2}x^3\ln x.$$

In Problems 35-40 we use the following results derived in Example 6 in the text: When $x = e^t$ or $t = \ln x$,

$$\frac{dy}{dx} = \frac{1}{x}\frac{dy}{dt} \quad \text{and} \quad \frac{d^2y}{dx^2} = \frac{1}{x^2}\left[\frac{d^2y}{dt^2} - \frac{dy}{dt}\right].$$

35. Subsituting into the differential equation we obtain

$$\frac{d^2y}{dt^2} + 9\frac{dy}{dt} + 8y = e^{2t}.$$

The auxiliary equation is $m^2 + 9 + 8 = (m+1)(m+8) = 0$ so that $y_c = c_1 e^{-t} + c_2 e^{-8t}$. Using undetermined coefficients we try $y_p = Ae^{2t}$. This leads to $30Ae^{2t} = e^{2t}$, so that $A = 1/30$ and

$$y = c_1 e^{-t} + c_2 e^{-8t} + \frac{1}{30}e^{2t} = c_1 x^{-1} + c_2 x^{-8} + \frac{1}{30}x^2.$$

36. Subsituting into the differential equation we obtain

$$\frac{d^2y}{dt^2} - 5\frac{dy}{dt} + 6y = 2t.$$

The auxiliary equation is $m^2 - 5m + 6 = (m-2)(m-3) = 0$ so that $y_c = c_1 e^{2t} + c_2 e^{3t}$. Using undetermined coefficients we try $y_p = At + B$. This leads to $(-5A + 6B) + 6At = 2t$, so that $A = 1/3$, $B = 5/18$, and

$$y = c_1 e^{2t} + c_2 e^{3t} + \frac{1}{3}t + \frac{5}{18} = c_1 x^2 + c_2 x^3 + \frac{1}{3}\ln x + \frac{5}{18}.$$

37. Subsituting into the differential equation we obtain

$$\frac{d^2y}{dt^2} - 4\frac{dy}{dt} + 13y = 4 + 3e^t.$$

The auxiliary equation is $m^2 - 4m + 13 = 0$ so that $y_c = e^{2t}(c_1 \cos 3t + c_2 \sin 3t)$. Using undetermined coefficients we try $y_p = A + Be^t$. This leads to $13A + 10Be^t = 4 + 3e^t$, so that $A = 4/13$, $B = 3/10$, and

$$y = e^{2t}(c_1 \cos 3t + c_2 \sin 3t) + \frac{4}{13} + \frac{3}{10}e^t$$

$$= x^2 \left[c_1 \cos(3\ln x) + c_2 \sin(3\ln x)\right] + \frac{4}{13} + \frac{3}{10}x.$$

38. Subsituting into the differential equation we obtain

$$2\frac{d^2y}{dt^2} - 5\frac{dy}{dt} - 3y = 1 + 2e^t + e^{2t}.$$

The auxiliary equation is $2m^2 - 5m - 3 = (2m + 1)(m - 3) = 0$ so that $y_c = c_1 e^{-t/2} + c_2 e^{3t}$. Using undetermined coefficients we try $y_p = A + Be^t + Ce^{2t}$. This leads to $-3A - 6Be^t - 5Ce^{2t} = 1 + 2e^t + e^{2t}$, so that $A = -1/3$, $B = -1/3$, $C = -1/5$, and

$$y = c_1 e^{-t/2} + c_2 e^{3t} - \frac{1}{3}e^t - \frac{1}{5}e^{2t} = c_1 x^{-1/2} + c_2 x^3 - \frac{1}{3}x - \frac{1}{5}x^2.$$

39. Subsituting into the differential equation we obtain

$$\frac{d^2y}{dt^2} + 8\frac{dy}{dt} - 20y = 5e^{-3t}.$$

The auxiliary equation is $m^2 + 8m - 20 = (m + 10)(m - 2) = 0$ so that $y_c = c_1 e^{-10t} + c_2 e^{2t}$. Using undetermined coefficients we try $y_p = Ae^{-3t}$. This leads to $-35Ae^{-3t} = 5e^{-3t}$, so that $A = -1/7$ and

$$y = c_1 e^{-10t} + c_2 e^{2t} - \frac{1}{7}e^{-3t} = c_1 x^{-10} + c_2 x^2 - \frac{1}{7}x^{-3}.$$

40. From

$$\frac{d^2y}{dx^2} = \frac{1}{x^2}\left(\frac{d^2y}{dt^2} - \frac{dy}{dt}\right).$$

it follows that

$$\frac{d^3y}{dx^3} = \frac{1}{x^2}\frac{d}{dx}\left(\frac{d^2y}{dt^2} - \frac{dy}{dt}\right) - \frac{2}{x^3}\left(\frac{d^2y}{dt^2} - \frac{dy}{dt}\right)$$

$$= \frac{1}{x^2}\frac{d}{dx}\left(\frac{d^2y}{dt^2}\right) - \frac{1}{x^2}\frac{d}{dx}\left(\frac{dy}{dt}\right) - \frac{2}{x^3}\frac{d^2y}{dt^2} + \frac{2}{x^3}\frac{dy}{dt}$$

$$= \frac{1}{x^2}\frac{d^3y}{dt^3}\left(\frac{1}{x}\right) - \frac{1}{x^2}\frac{d^2y}{dt^2}\left(\frac{1}{x}\right) - \frac{2}{x^3}\frac{d^2y}{dt^2} + \frac{2}{x^3}\frac{dy}{dt}$$

$$= \frac{1}{x^3}\left(\frac{d^3y}{dt^3} - 3\frac{d^2y}{dt^2} + 2\frac{dy}{dt}\right).$$

Substituting into the differential equation we obtain

$$\frac{d^3y}{dt^3} - 3\frac{d^2y}{dt^2} + 2\frac{dy}{dt} - 3\left(\frac{d^2y}{dt^2} - \frac{dy}{dt}\right) + 6\frac{dy}{dt} - 6y = 3 + 3t$$

or

$$\frac{d^3y}{dt^3} - 6\frac{d^2y}{dt^2} + 11\frac{dy}{dt} - 6y = 3 + 3t.$$

The auxiliary equation is $m^3 - 6m^2 + 11m - 6 = (m-1)(m-2)(m-3) = 0$ so that $y_c = c_1e^t + c_2e^{2t} + c_3e^{3t}$. Using undetermined coefficients we try $y_p = A + Bt$. This leads to $(11B - 6A) - 6Bt = 3 + 3t$, so that $A = -17/12$, $B = -1/2$, and

$$y = c_1e^t + c_2e^{2t} + c_3e^{3t} - \frac{17}{12} - \frac{1}{2}t = c_1x + c_2x^2 + c_3x^3 - \frac{17}{12} - \frac{1}{2}\ln x.$$

41. The auxiliary equation is $m^2 + m = m(m+1) = 0$ so that $u(r) = c_1r^{-1} + c_2$. The boundary conditions $u(a) = u_0$ and $u(b) = u_1$ yield the system $c_1a^{-1} + c_2 = u_0$, $c_1b^{-1} + c_2 = u_1$. Solving gives

$$c_1 = \left(\frac{u_0 - u_1}{b - a}\right)ab \quad \text{and} \quad c_2 = \frac{u_1b - u_0a}{b - a}.$$

Thus

$$u(r) = \left(\frac{u_0 - u_1}{b - a}\right)\frac{ab}{r} + \frac{u_1b - u_0a}{b - a}.$$

42. The auxiliary equation is $m^2 = 0$ so that $u(r) = c_1 + c_2\ln r$. The boundary conditions $u(a) = u_0$ and $u(b) = u_1$ yield the system $c_1 + c_2\ln a = u_0$, $c_1 + c_2\ln b = u_1$. Solving gives

$$c_1 = \frac{u_1\ln a - u_0\ln b}{\ln(a/b)} \quad \text{and} \quad c_2 = \frac{u_0 - u_1}{\ln(a/b)}.$$

Thus

$$u(r) = \frac{u_1\ln a - u_0\ln b}{\ln(a/b)} + \frac{u_0 - u_1}{\ln(a/b)}\ln r = \frac{u_0\ln(r/b) - u_1\ln(r/a)}{\ln(a/b)}.$$

43. Letting $t = x - 1$ we obtain

$$\frac{dy}{dx} = \frac{dy}{dt}$$

and

$$\frac{d^2y}{dx^2} = \frac{d}{dx}\frac{dy}{dt} = \frac{d^2y}{dt^2}\frac{dt}{dx} = \frac{d^2y}{dt^2}.$$

Substituting into the differential equation we obtain

$$t^2\frac{d^2y}{dt^2} - 2t\frac{dy}{dt} - 4y = 0.$$

The auxiliary equation is $m^2 - 3m - 4 = (m-4)(m+1) = 0$ so that

$$y = c_1 t^4 + c_2 t^{-1} = c_1(x-1)^4 + c_2(x-1)^{-1}.$$

44. Letting $t = 3x + 4$ we obtain

$$\frac{dy}{dx} = \frac{dy}{dt}\frac{dt}{dx} = 3\frac{dy}{dt}$$

and

$$\frac{d^2y}{dx^2} = \frac{d}{dx}\left(3\frac{dy}{dt}\right) = 3\frac{d^2y}{dt^2}\frac{dt}{dx} = 9\frac{d^2y}{dt^2}.$$

Substituting into the differential equation we obtain

$$9t^2\frac{d^2y}{dt^2} + 30t\frac{dy}{dt} + 9y = 0.$$

The auxiliary equation is $9m^2 + 21m + 9 = 3\left(3m^2 + 7m + 3\right) = 0$ so that

$$y = c_1 t^{(-7+\sqrt{13})/6} + c_2 t^{(-7-\sqrt{13})/6}$$

$$= c_1(3x+4)^{(-7+\sqrt{13})/6} + c_2(3x+4)^{(-7+\sqrt{13})/6}.$$

45. Letting $t = x + 2$ we obtain

$$\frac{dy}{dx} = \frac{dy}{dt}$$

and

$$\frac{d^2y}{dx^2} = \frac{d}{dx}\left(\frac{dy}{dt}\right) = \frac{d^2y}{dt^2}\frac{dt}{dx} = \frac{d^2y}{dt^2}.$$

Substituting into the differential equation we obtain

$$t^2\frac{d^2y}{dt^2} + t\frac{dy}{dt} + y = 0.$$

The auxiliary equation is $m^2 + 1 = 0$ so that

$$y = c_1\cos(\ln t) + c_2\sin(\ln t) = c_1\cos\left[\ln(x+2)\right] + c_2\sin\left[\ln(x+2)\right].$$

1. $\lim\limits_{n\to\infty}\left|\dfrac{a_{n+1}}{a_n}\right| = \lim\limits_{n\to\infty}\left|\dfrac{x^{n+1}/(n+1)}{x^n/n}\right| = \lim\limits_{n\to\infty}\dfrac{n}{n+1}|x| = |x|$

The series is absolutely convergent on $(-1,1)$. At $x = -1$, the series $\sum\limits_{n=1}^{\infty}\dfrac{1}{n}$ is the harmonic series which diverges. At $x = 1$, the series $\sum\limits_{n=1}^{\infty}\dfrac{(-1)^n}{n}$ converges by the alternating series test. Thus, the given series converges on $(-1,1]$.

2. $\lim\limits_{n\to\infty}\left|\dfrac{a_{n+1}}{a_n}\right| = \lim\limits_{n\to\infty}\left|\dfrac{x^{n+1}/(n+1)^2}{x^n/n^2}\right| = \lim\limits_{n\to\infty}\left(\dfrac{n}{n+1}\right)^2|x| = |x|$

The series is absolutely convergent on $(-1,1)$. At $x = -1$, the series $\sum\limits_{n=1}^{\infty}\dfrac{(-1)^n}{n^2}$ converges by the alternating series test. At $x = 1$, the series $\sum\limits_{n=1}^{\infty}\dfrac{1}{n^2}$ is a convergent p-series. Thus, the given series converges on $[-1,1]$.

3. $\lim\limits_{n\to\infty}\left|\dfrac{a_{n+1}}{a_n}\right| = \lim\limits_{n\to\infty}\left|\dfrac{2^{n+1}x^{n+1}/(n+1)}{2^n x^n/n}\right| = \lim\limits_{n\to\infty}\dfrac{2n}{n+1}|x| = 2|x|$

The series is absolutely convergent for $2|x| < 1$ or $|x| < 1/2$. At $x = -1/2$, the series $\sum\limits_{k=1}^{\infty}\dfrac{(-1)^k}{k}$ converges by the alternating series test. At $x = 1/2$, the series $\sum\limits_{k=1}^{\infty}\dfrac{1}{k}$ is the harmonic series which diverges. Thus, the given series converges on $[-1/2, 1/2)$.

4. $\lim\limits_{n\to\infty}\left|\dfrac{a_{n+1}}{a_n}\right| = \lim\limits_{n\to\infty}\left|\dfrac{5^{n+1}x^{n+1}/(n+1)!}{5^n x^n/n!}\right| = \lim\limits_{n\to\infty}\dfrac{5}{n+1}|x| = 0$

The series is absolutely convergent on $(-\infty, \infty)$.

5. $\lim\limits_{n\to\infty}\left|\dfrac{a_{n+1}}{a_n}\right| = \lim\limits_{n\to\infty}\left|\dfrac{(x-3)^{n+1}/(n+1)^3}{(x-3)^n/n^3}\right| = \lim\limits_{n\to\infty}\left(\dfrac{n}{n+1}\right)^3|x-3| = |x-3|$

The series is absolutely convergent for $|x - 3| < 1$ or on $(2,4)$. At $x = 2$, the series $\sum\limits_{n=1}^{\infty}\dfrac{(-1)^n}{n^3}$ converges by the alternating series test. At $x = 4$, the series $\sum\limits_{n=1}^{\infty}\dfrac{1}{n^3}$ is a convergent p-series. Thus, the given series converges on $[2,4]$.

Exercises 6.2

6. $\lim\limits_{n\to\infty}\left|\dfrac{a_{n+1}}{a_n}\right| = \lim\limits_{n\to\infty}\left|\dfrac{(x+7)^{n+1}/\sqrt{n+1}}{(x+7)^n\sqrt{n}}\right| = \lim\limits_{n\to\infty}\sqrt{\dfrac{n}{n+1}}\,|x+7| = |x+7|$

The series is absolutely convergent for $|x+7| < 1$ or on $(-8,6)$. At $x = -8$, the series $\sum\limits_{n=1}^{\infty}\dfrac{(-1)^n}{\sqrt{n}}$ converges by the alternating series test. At $x = -6$, the series $\sum\limits_{n=1}^{\infty}\dfrac{1}{\sqrt{n}}$ is a divergent p-series. Thus, the given series converges on $[-8,-6)$.

7. $\lim\limits_{n\to\infty}\left|\dfrac{a_{n+1}}{a_n}\right| = \lim\limits_{n\to\infty}\left|\dfrac{(x-5)^{n+1}/10^{n+1}}{(x-5)^n/10^n}\right| = \lim\limits_{n\to\infty}\dfrac{1}{10}|x-5| = \dfrac{1}{10}|x-5|$

The series is absolutely convergent for $\dfrac{1}{10}|x-5| < 1$, $|x-5| < 10$, or on $(-5,15)$. At $x = -5$, the series $\sum\limits_{k=1}^{\infty}\dfrac{(-1)^k(-10)^k}{10^k} = \sum\limits_{k=1}^{\infty}1$ diverges by the n-th term test. At $x = 15$, the series $\sum\limits_{k=1}^{\infty}\dfrac{(-1)^k10^k}{10^k} = \sum\limits_{k=1}^{\infty}(-1)^k$ diverges by the n-th term test. Thus, the series converges on $(-5,15)$.

8. $\lim\limits_{n\to\infty}\left|\dfrac{a_{n+1}}{a_n}\right| = \lim\limits_{n\to\infty}\left|\dfrac{(n+1)(x-4)^{n+1}/(n+3)^2}{n(x-4)^n/(n+2)^2}\right| = \lim\limits_{n\to\infty}\dfrac{(n+1)(n+2)^2}{x(n+3)^2}|x-4| = |x-4|$

The series is absolutely convergent for $|x-4| < 1$ or on $(3,5)$. At $x = 3$, the series $\sum\limits_{k=1}^{\infty}\dfrac{(-1)^k k}{(k+2)^2}$ converges by the alternating series test. At $x = 5$, the series $\sum\limits_{k=1}^{\infty}\dfrac{k}{(k+2)^2}$ diverges by the limit comparison test with $\sum\limits_{k=1}^{\infty}\dfrac{1}{k}$. Thus, the series converges on $[3,5)$.

9. $\lim\limits_{n\to\infty}\left|\dfrac{a_{n+1}}{a_n}\right| = \lim\limits_{n\to\infty}\left|\dfrac{(n+1)!2^{n+1}x^{n+1}}{n!2^n x^n}\right| = \lim\limits_{n\to\infty}2(n+1)|x| = \infty, \quad x \neq 0$

The series converges only at $x = 0$.

10. $\lim\limits_{n\to\infty}\left|\dfrac{a_{n+1}}{a_n}\right| = \lim\limits_{n\to\infty}\left|\dfrac{nx^{n+1}/(n+1)^{2(n+1)}}{(n-1)x^n/n^{2n}}\right| = \lim\limits_{n\to\infty}\dfrac{nn^{2n}}{(n-1)(n+1)^{2n+2}}|x|$

$= \lim\limits_{n\to\infty}\dfrac{n}{(n-1)(n+1)^2}\left(\dfrac{n}{n+1}\right)^{2n}|x| = \lim\limits_{n\to\infty}\dfrac{n}{(n-1)(n+1)^2}\cdot\dfrac{1}{\left[\left(\dfrac{n+1}{n}\right)^n\right]^2}|x|$

$= \lim\limits_{n\to\infty}\dfrac{n}{(n-1)(n+1)^2}\cdot\dfrac{1}{[(1+1/n)^n]^2}|x| = 0\cdot\dfrac{1}{e^2}|x| = 0$

The series is convergent on $(-\infty, \infty)$.

11. $e^x \sin x = \left(1 + x + \dfrac{x^2}{2} + \dfrac{x^3}{6} + \dfrac{x^4}{24} + \cdots\right)\left(x - \dfrac{x^3}{6} + \dfrac{x^5}{120} - \cdots\right) = x + x^2 + \dfrac{x^3}{3} - \dfrac{x^5}{30} - \cdots$

12. $e^{-x} \cos x = \left(1 - x + \dfrac{x^2}{2} - \dfrac{x^3}{6} + \dfrac{x^4}{24} - \cdots\right)\left(1 - \dfrac{x^2}{2} + \dfrac{x^4}{24} - \cdots\right) = 1 - x + \dfrac{x^3}{3} - \dfrac{x^4}{6} + \cdots$

13. $\sin x \cos x = \left(x - \dfrac{x^3}{6} + \dfrac{x^5}{120} - \dfrac{x^7}{5040} + \cdots\right)\left(1 - \dfrac{x^2}{2} + \dfrac{x^4}{24} - \dfrac{x^6}{720} + \cdots\right) = x - \dfrac{2x^3}{3} + \dfrac{2x^5}{15} - \dfrac{4x^7}{315} + \cdots$

14. $e^x \ln(1 - x) = \left(1 + x + \dfrac{x^2}{2} + \dfrac{x^3}{6} + \cdots\right)\left(-x - \dfrac{x^2}{2} - \dfrac{x^3}{3} - \dfrac{x^4}{4} - \cdots\right) = -x - \dfrac{3x^2}{2} - \dfrac{4x^3}{3} - x^4 - \cdots$

15. $\left(x - \dfrac{x^3}{3} + \dfrac{x^5}{5} - \dfrac{x^7}{7} + \cdots\right)^2 = x^2 - \dfrac{2x^4}{3} + \dfrac{23x^6}{45} - \dfrac{44x^8}{105} + \cdots$

16. $\left(1 - \dfrac{x^2}{2} + \dfrac{x^4}{3} - \dfrac{x^6}{4} + \cdots\right)^2 = 1 - x^2 + \dfrac{11x^4}{12} - \dfrac{2x^6}{3} + \cdots$

17. $\tan x = \dfrac{\sin x}{\cos x} = \dfrac{x - \dfrac{x^3}{6} + \dfrac{x^5}{120} - \dfrac{x^7}{5040} + \cdots}{1 - \dfrac{x^2}{2} + \dfrac{x^4}{24} - \dfrac{x^6}{720} + \cdots} = x + \dfrac{x^3}{3} + \dfrac{2x^5}{15} + \dfrac{17x^7}{315} + \cdots$

18. $e^x + e^{-x} = \left(1 + x + \dfrac{x^2}{2} + \dfrac{x^3}{6} + \dfrac{x^4}{24} + \dfrac{x^5}{120} + \dfrac{x^6}{720} + \cdots\right)$

$$+ \left(1 - x + \dfrac{x^2}{2} - \dfrac{x^3}{6} + \dfrac{x^4}{24} - \dfrac{x^5}{120} + \dfrac{x^6}{720} - \cdots\right)$$

$$= 2 + x^2 + \dfrac{x^4}{12} + \dfrac{x^6}{360} + \cdots$$

$$\dfrac{1}{e^x + e^{-x}} = \dfrac{1}{2 + x^2 + \dfrac{x^4}{12} + \dfrac{x^6}{360} + \cdots} = \dfrac{1}{2} - \dfrac{x^2}{4} + \dfrac{5x^4}{48} - \dfrac{61x^6}{1440} + \cdots$$

19. $\dfrac{1}{1 - \dfrac{x^2}{2} + \dfrac{x^4}{3} - \dfrac{x^6}{4} + \cdots} = 1 + \dfrac{x^2}{2} - \dfrac{x^4}{12} - \dfrac{x^6}{24} + \cdots$

20. $\dfrac{1}{\left(1 - \dfrac{x^2}{2} + \dfrac{x^4}{3} - \dfrac{x^6}{4} + \cdots\right)^2} = \dfrac{1}{1 - x^2 + \dfrac{11x^4}{12} - \dfrac{2x^6}{3}} = 1 + x^2 + \dfrac{x^4}{12} - \dfrac{x^6}{6} - \cdots$

Exercises 6.2

21. Separating variables we obtain

$$\frac{dy}{y} = -dx \implies \ln|y| = -x + c \implies y = c_1 e^{-x}.$$

Substituting $y = \sum_{n=0}^{\infty} c_n x^n$ into the differential equation leads to

$$y' + y = \underbrace{\sum_{n=1}^{\infty} n c_n x^{n-1}}_{k=n-1} + \underbrace{\sum_{n=0}^{\infty} c_n x^n}_{k=n} = \sum_{k=0}^{\infty} (k+1)c_{k+1}x^k + \sum_{k=0}^{\infty} c_k x^k = \sum_{k=0}^{\infty} [(k+1)c_{k+1} + c_k]x^k = 0.$$

Thus $(k+1)c_{k+1} + c_k = 0$ and $c_{k+1} = -\frac{1}{k+1}c_k$ for $k = 0, 1, 2, \ldots$. Iterating we find

$$c_1 = -c_0$$

$$c_2 = -\frac{1}{2}c_1 = \frac{1}{2}c_0$$

$$c_3 = -\frac{1}{3}c_2 = -\frac{1}{6}c_0$$

$$c_4 = -\frac{1}{4}c_3 = \frac{1}{24}c_0$$

and so on. Therefore

$$y = c_0 - c_0 x + \frac{1}{2}c_0 x^2 - \frac{1}{6}c_0 x^3 + \frac{1}{24}c_0 x^4 - \cdots = c_0\left[1 - x + \frac{1}{2}x^2 - \frac{1}{6}x^3 + \frac{1}{24}x^4 - \cdots\right]$$

$$= c_0 \sum_{n=0}^{\infty} \frac{1}{n!}(-x)^n = c_0 e^{-x}.$$

22. Separating variables we obtain

$$\frac{dy}{y} = 2\,dx \implies \ln|y| = 2x + c \implies y = c_1 e^{2x}.$$

Substituting $y = \sum_{n=0}^{\infty} c_n x^n$ into the differential equation leads to

$$y' - 2y = \underbrace{\sum_{n=1}^{\infty} n c_n x^{n-1}}_{k=n-1} - 2\underbrace{\sum_{n=0}^{\infty} c_n x^n}_{k=n} = \sum_{k=0}^{\infty} (k+1)c_{k+1}x^k - 2\sum_{k=0}^{\infty} c_k x^k$$

$$= \sum_{k=0}^{\infty} [(k+1)c_{k+1} - 2c_k]x^k = 0.$$

Thus $(k+1)c_{k+1} - 2c_k = 0$ and $c_{k+1} = \dfrac{2}{k+1}c_k$, for $k = 0, 1, 2, \ldots$. Iterating we find

$$c_1 = 2c_0$$

$$c_2 = \frac{2}{2}c_1 = \frac{4}{2}c_0$$

$$c_3 = \frac{2}{3}c_2 = \frac{8}{6}c_0$$

$$c_4 = \frac{2}{4}c_3 = \frac{16}{24}c_0$$

and so on. Therefore

$$y = c_0 + 2c_0 x + \frac{4}{2}c_0 x^2 + \frac{8}{6}c_0 x^3 + \frac{16}{24}c_0 x^4 + \cdots$$

$$= c_0 \left[1 + 2x + \frac{1}{2}(2x)^2 + \frac{1}{6}(2x)^3 + \frac{1}{24}(2x)^4 + \cdots\right] = c_0 \sum_{n=0}^{\infty} \frac{1}{n!}(2x)^n = c_0 e^{2x}.$$

23. Separating variables we obtain

$$\frac{dy}{y} = x^2 dx \implies \ln|y| = \frac{1}{3}x^3 + c \implies y = c_1 e^{x^3/3}.$$

Substituting $y = \sum_{n=0}^{\infty} c_n x^n$ into the differential equation leads to

$$y' - x^2 y = \underbrace{\sum_{n=1}^{\infty} n c_n x^{n-1}}_{k=n-3} - \underbrace{\sum_{n=0}^{\infty} c_n x^{n+2}}_{k=n} = \sum_{k=-2}^{\infty} (k+3)c_{k+3} x^{k+2} - \sum_{k=0}^{\infty} c_k x^{k+2}$$

$$= c_1 + 2c_2 x + \sum_{k=0}^{\infty} [(k+3)c_{k+3} - c_k]x^{k+2} = 0.$$

Thus $c_1 = c_2 = 0$, $(k+3)c_{k+3} - c_k = 0$ and $c_{k+3} = \dfrac{1}{k+3}c_k$, for $k = 0, 1, 2, \ldots$. Iterating we find

$$c_3 = \frac{1}{3}c_0$$

$$c_4 = c_5 = 0$$

$$c_6 = \frac{1}{6}c_3 = \frac{1}{2} \cdot \frac{1}{3^2}c_0$$

$$c_7 = c_8 = 0$$

$$c_9 = \frac{1}{9}c_6 = \frac{1}{2 \cdot 3} \cdot \frac{1}{3^3}c_0$$

and so on. Therefore

$$y = c_0 + \frac{1}{3}c_0 x^3 + \frac{1}{2} \cdot \frac{1}{3^2} c_0 x^6 + \frac{1}{2 \cdot 3} \cdot \frac{1}{3^3} c_0 x^9 + \cdots$$

$$= c_0 \left[1 + \frac{x^3}{3} + \frac{1}{2} \left(\frac{x^3}{3} \right)^2 + \frac{1}{2 \cdot 3} \left(\frac{x^3}{3} \right)^3 + \cdots \right] = c_0 \sum_{n=0}^{\infty} \frac{1}{n!} \left(\frac{x^3}{3} \right)^n = c_0 e^{x^3/3}.$$

24. Separating variables we obtain

$$\frac{dy}{y} = -x^3 dx \implies \ln|y| = -\frac{1}{4} x^4 + c \implies y = c_1 e^{-x^4/4}.$$

Substituting $y = \sum_{n=0}^{\infty} c_n x^n$ into the differential equation leads to

$$y' + x^3 2y = \underbrace{\sum_{n=1}^{\infty} n c_n x^{n-1}}_{k=n-4} + \underbrace{\sum_{n=0}^{\infty} c_n x^{n+3}}_{k=n} = \sum_{k=-3}^{\infty} (k+4)c_{k+4} x^{k+3} - \sum_{k=0}^{\infty} c_k x^{k+3}$$

$$= c_1 + 2c_2 x + 3c_3 x^2 + \sum_{k=0}^{\infty} [(k+4)c_{k+4} + c_k] x^{k+2} = 0.$$

Thus $c_1 = c_2 = c_3 = 0$, $(k+4)c_{k+4} + c_k = 0$ and $c_{k+4} = -\frac{1}{k+4} c_k$, $k = 0, 1, 2, \ldots$. Iterating we find

$$c_4 = -\frac{1}{4} c_0$$

$$c_5 = c_6 = c_7 = 0$$

$$c_8 = -\frac{1}{8} c_4 = \frac{1}{2} \cdot \frac{1}{4^2} c_0$$

$$c_9 = c_{10} = c_{11} = 0$$

$$c_{12} = -\frac{1}{12} c_8 = -\frac{1}{2 \cdot 3} \cdot \frac{1}{4^3} c_0$$

and so on. Therefore

$$y = c_0 - \frac{1}{4} c_0 x^4 + \frac{1}{2} \cdot \frac{1}{4^2} c_0 x^8 - \frac{1}{2 \cdot 3} \cdot \frac{1}{4^3} c_0 x^{12} + \cdots$$

$$= c_0 \left[1 - \frac{x^4}{4} + \frac{1}{2} \left(\frac{x^4}{4} \right)^2 - \frac{1}{2 \cdot 3} \left(\frac{x^4}{4} \right)^3 + \cdots \right] = c_0 \sum_{n=0}^{\infty} \frac{1}{n!} \left(\frac{-x^4}{4} \right)^n = c_0 e^{-x^4/4}.$$

25. Separating variables we obtain

$$\frac{dy}{y} = \frac{dx}{1-x} \implies \ln|y| = -\ln|1-x| + c \implies y = \frac{c_1}{1-x}.$$

Substituting $y = \sum_{n=0}^{\infty} c_n x^n$ into the differential equation leads to

$$(1-x)y' - y = \underbrace{\sum_{n=1}^{\infty} nc_n x^{n-1}}_{k=n-1} - \underbrace{\sum_{n=1}^{\infty} nc_n x^n}_{k=n} - \underbrace{\sum_{n=0}^{\infty} c_n x^n}_{k=n}$$

$$= \sum_{k=0}^{\infty} (k+1)c_{k+1}x^k - \sum_{k=1}^{\infty} kc_k x^k - \sum_{k=0}^{\infty} c_k x^k$$

$$= c_1 - c_0 + \sum_{k=1}^{\infty} [(k+1)c_{k+1} - (k+1)c_k]x^k = 0.$$

Thus
$$c_1 - c_0 = 0, \qquad (k+1)c_{k+1} - (k+1)c_k = 0$$

and
$$c_1 = c_0$$

$$c_{k+1} = c_k, \quad k = 1, 2, 3, \ldots .$$

Iterating we find

$$c_1 = c_0,$$

$$c_2 = c_1 = c_0$$

$$c_3 = c_2 = c_0$$

and so on. Therefore

$$y = c_0 + c_0 x + c_0 x^2 + c_0 x^3 + \cdots = c_0 \left[1 + x + x^2 + x^3 + \cdots\right] = c_0 \sum_{n=0}^{\infty} x^n = \frac{c_0}{1-x}.$$

26. Separating variables we obtain

$$\frac{dy}{y} = \frac{2}{1+x}\, dx \implies \ln|y| = 2\ln|1+x| + c \implies y = c_1(1+x)^2.$$

Substituting $y = \sum_{n=0}^{\infty} c_n x^n$ into the differential equation leads to

$$(1+x)y' - 2y = \underbrace{\sum_{n=1}^{\infty} nc_n x^{n-1}}_{k=n-1} + \underbrace{\sum_{n=1}^{\infty} nc_n x^n}_{k=n} - 2\underbrace{\sum_{n=0}^{\infty} c_n x^n}_{k=n}$$

$$= \sum_{k=0}^{\infty} (k+1)c_{k+1}x^k + \sum_{k=1}^{\infty} kc_k x^k - 2\sum_{k=0}^{\infty} c_k x^k$$

$$= c_1 - 2c_0 + \sum_{k=1}^{\infty} [(k+1)c_{k+1} + (k-2)c_k]x^k = 0.$$

Then

$$c_1 - 2c_0 = 0$$

$$(k+1)c_{k+1} + (k-2)c_k = 0$$

and

$$c_1 = 2c_0$$

$$c_{k+1} = -\frac{k-2}{k+1}c_k, \quad k = 1, 2, 3, \ldots.$$

Iterating we find

$$c_1 = 2c_0$$

$$c_2 = \frac{1}{2}c_1 = c_0$$

$$c_3 = 0c_2 = 0$$

$$c_4 = 0$$

and so on. Therefore

$$y = c_0 + 2c_0 x + c_0 x^2 = c_0\left(1 + 2x + x^2\right) = c_0(1+x)^2.$$

27. The auxiliary equation is $m^2 + 1 = 0$, so $y = c_1 \cos x + c_2 \sin x$. Substituting $y = \sum_{n=0}^{\infty} c_n x^n$ into the differential equation leads to

$$y'' + y = \underbrace{\sum_{n=2}^{\infty} n(n-1)c_n x^{n-2}}_{k=n-2} + \underbrace{\sum_{n=0}^{\infty} c_n x^n}_{k=n} = \sum_{k=0}^{\infty} (k+2)(k+1)c_{k+2} x^k + \sum_{k=0}^{\infty} c_k x^k$$

$$= \sum_{k=0}^{\infty} [(k+2)(k+1)c_{k+2} + c_k]x^k = 0.$$

Thus

$$(k+2)(k+1)c_{k+2} + c_k = 0$$

and

$$c_{k+2} = -\frac{1}{(k+2)(k+1)} c_k, \quad k = 0, 1, 2, \ldots.$$

Iterating we find

$$c_2 = -\frac{1}{2}c_0$$

$$c_3 = -\frac{1}{3\cdot 2}c_1$$

$$c_4 = -\frac{1}{4\cdot 3}c_2 = \frac{1}{4\cdot 3\cdot 2}c_0$$

$$c_5 = -\frac{1}{5\cdot 4}c_3 = \frac{1}{5\cdot 4\cdot 3\cdot 2}c_1$$

$$c_6 = -\frac{1}{6\cdot 5}c_4 = -\frac{1}{6!}c_0$$

$$c_7 = -\frac{1}{7\cdot 6}c_5 = -\frac{1}{7!}c_1$$

and so on. Therefore

$$y = c_0 + c_1 x - \frac{1}{2}c_0 x^2 - \frac{1}{3!}c_1 x^3 + \frac{1}{4!}c_0 x^4 + \frac{1}{5!}c_1 x^5 - \cdots$$

$$= c_0\left[1 - \frac{1}{2}x^2 + \frac{1}{4!}x^4 - \cdots\right] + c_1\left[1 - \frac{1}{3!}x^3 + \frac{1}{5!}x^5 - \cdots\right]$$

$$= c_0\sum_{n=0}^{\infty}\frac{(-1)^n x^{2n}}{(2n)!} + c_1\sum_{n=0}^{\infty}\frac{(-1)^n x^{2n+1}}{(2n+1)!} = c_0\cos x + c_1\sin x.$$

28. The auxiliary equation is $m^2 - 1 = 0$, so $y = c_1 e^x + c_2 e^{-x}$. Substituting $y = \sum_{n=0}^{\infty} c_n x^n$ into the differential equation leads to

$$y'' - y = \underbrace{\sum_{n=2}^{\infty} n(n-1)c_n x^{n-2}}_{k=n-2} - \underbrace{\sum_{n=0}^{\infty} c_n x^n}_{k=n} = \sum_{k=0}^{\infty}(k+2)(k+1)c_{k+2}x^k - \sum_{k=0}^{\infty} c_k x^k$$

$$= \sum_{k=0}^{\infty}[(k+2)(k+1)c_{k+2} - c_k]x^k = 0.$$

Thus

$$(k+2)(k+1)c_{k+2} - c_k = 0, \quad k = 0,\ 1,\ 2,\ \ldots$$

and

$$c_{k+2} = \frac{c_k}{(k+2)(k+1)}, \quad k = 0,\ 1,\ 2,\ \ldots.$$

Iterating, we find

$$c_2 = \frac{c_0}{2 \cdot 1} = \frac{1}{2}c_0$$

$$c_3 = \frac{c_1}{3 \cdot 2} = \frac{1}{3 \cdot 2}c_1$$

$$c_4 = \frac{c_2}{4 \cdot 3} = \frac{1}{4 \cdot 3 \cdot 2}c_0$$

$$c_5 = \frac{c_3}{5 \cdot 4} = \frac{1}{5 \cdot 4 \cdot 3 \cdot 2}c_1$$

$$c_6 = \frac{c_4}{6 \cdot 5} = \frac{1}{6 \cdot 5 \cdot 4 \cdot 3 \cdot 2}c_0$$

$$c_7 = \frac{c_5}{7 \cdot 6} = \frac{1}{7 \cdot 6 \cdot 5 \cdot 4 \cdot 3 \cdot 2}c_1.$$

and so on. Therefore,

$$y = c_0 + c_1 x + c_2 x^2 + c_3 x^3 + \cdots$$

$$= c_0 + c_1 x + \frac{1}{2}c_0 x^2 + \frac{1}{3 \cdot 2}c_1 x^3 + \frac{1}{4 \cdot 3 \cdot 2}c_0 x^4 + \frac{1}{5 \cdot 4 \cdot 3 \cdot 2}c_1 x^5 + \cdots$$

$$= c_0 \left[1 + \frac{1}{2!}x^2 + \frac{1}{4!}x^4 + \cdots \right] + c_1 \left[x + \frac{1}{3!}x^3 + \frac{1}{5!}x^5 + \cdots \right]$$

$$= c_0 \sum_{n=0}^{\infty} \frac{1}{(2n)!}x^{2n} + c_1 \sum_{n=0}^{\infty} \frac{1}{(2n+1)!}x^{2n+1} = c_0 \cosh x + c_1 \sinh x$$

$$= c_0 \frac{e^x + e^{-x}}{2} + c_1 \frac{e^x - e^{-x}}{2} = \left(\frac{c_0 + c_1}{2} \right) e^x + \left(\frac{c_0 - c_1}{2} \right) e^{-x} = C_0 e^x + C_1 e^{-x}.$$

29. The auxiliary equation is $m^2 - m = m(m-1) = 0$, so $y = c_1 + c_2 e^x$. Substituting $y = \sum_{n=0}^{\infty} c_n x^n$ into the differential equation leads to

$$y'' - y' = \underbrace{\sum_{n=2}^{\infty} n(n-1)c_n x^{n-2}}_{k=n-2} - \underbrace{\sum_{n=1}^{\infty} nc_n x^{n-1}}_{k=n-1}$$

$$= \sum_{k=0}^{\infty} (k+2)(k+1)c_{k+2} x^k - \sum_{k=0}^{\infty} (k+1)c_{k+1} x^k$$

$$= \sum_{k=0}^{\infty} [(k+2)(k+1)c_{k+2} - (k+1)c_{k+1}]x^k = 0.$$

Thus

$$(k+2)(k+1)c_{k+2} - (k+1)c_{k+1} = 0$$

and
$$c_{k+2} = \frac{1}{(k+2)} c_{k+1}, \quad k = 0, 1, 2, \ldots.$$

Iterating we find
$$c_2 = \frac{1}{2} c_1$$

$$c_3 = \frac{1}{3} c_2 = \frac{1}{3 \cdot 2} c_1$$

$$c_4 = \frac{1}{4} c_3 = \frac{1}{4!} c_1$$

and so on. Therefore
$$y = c_0 + c_1 x + \frac{1}{2} c_1 x^2 + \frac{1}{3!} c_1 x^3 + \frac{1}{4!} c_1 x^4 + \cdots$$

$$\boxed{c_0 = C_0 + c_1}$$

$$= C_0 + c_1 \left[1 + x + \frac{1}{2} x^2 + \frac{1}{3!} x^3 + \frac{1}{4!} x^4 + \cdots \right] = C_0 + c_1 \sum_{n=0}^{\infty} \frac{1}{n!} x^n = C_0 + c_1 e^x.$$

30. The auxiliary equation is $2m^2 + m = m(2m + 1) = 0$, so $y = c_1 + c_2 e^{-x/2}$. Substituting $y = \sum_{n=0}^{\infty} c_n x^n$ into the differential equation leads to

$$2y'' + y' = 2 \underbrace{\sum_{n=2}^{\infty} n(n-1)c_n x^{n-2}}_{k=n-2} + \underbrace{\sum_{n=1}^{\infty} n c_n x^{n-1}}_{k=n-1}$$

$$= 2 \sum_{k=0}^{\infty} (k+2)(k+1)c_{k+2} x^k + \sum_{k=0}^{\infty} (k+1)c_{k+1} x^k$$

$$= \sum_{k=0}^{\infty} [2(k+2)(k+1)c_{k+2} + (k+1)c_{k+1}] x^k = 0.$$

Thus
$$2(k+2)(k+1)c_{k+2} + (k+1)c_{k+1} = 0$$

and
$$c_{k+2} = -\frac{1}{2(k+2)} c_{k+1}, \quad k = 0, 1, 2, \ldots.$$

Iterating we find
$$c_2 = -\frac{1}{2} \frac{1}{2} c_1$$

$$c_3 = -\frac{1}{2} \frac{1}{3} c_2 = \frac{1}{2^2} \frac{1}{3 \cdot 2} c_1$$

$$c_4 = -\frac{1}{2} \frac{1}{4} c_3 = \frac{1}{2^3} \frac{1}{4!} c_1$$

167

and so on. Therefore

$$y = c_0 + c_1 x - \frac{1}{2}\frac{1}{2}c_1 x^2 + \frac{1}{2^2 3!}c_1 x^3 - \frac{1}{2^3 4!}c_1 x^4 + \cdots$$

$$\boxed{\begin{array}{l} c_0 = C_0 - 2c_1 \\ c_1 = -\frac{1}{2}C_1 \end{array}}$$

$$= C_0 + \left[C_1 - \frac{1}{2}C_1 x + \frac{1}{2}\frac{1}{2}\frac{1}{2}C_1 x^2 - \frac{1}{2^2 2 \cdot 3!}\frac{1}{2}C_1 x^3 + \cdots \right]$$

$$= C_0 + C_1 \left[1 - \frac{x}{2} + \frac{1}{2}\left(\frac{x}{2}\right)^2 - \frac{1}{3!}\left(\frac{x}{3}\right)^3 + \cdots \right]$$

$$= C_0 + C_1 \sum_{n=0}^{\infty} \frac{(-1)^n}{n!}\left(\frac{x}{2}\right)^n = C_0 + C_1 \sum_{n=0}^{\infty} \frac{1}{n!}\left(-\frac{x}{n}\right)^n = C_0 + C_1 e^{-x/2}.$$

Exercises 6.3

1. Substituting $y = \sum_{n=0}^{\infty} c_n x^n$ into the differential equation we have

$$y'' - xy' = \underbrace{\sum_{n=2}^{\infty} n(n-1)c_n x^{n-2}}_{k=n-2} - \underbrace{\sum_{n=0}^{\infty} c_n x^{n+1}}_{k=n+1} = \sum_{k=0}^{\infty}(k+2)(k+1)c_{k+2}x^k - \sum_{k=1}^{\infty} c_{k-1}x^k$$

$$= 2c_2 + \sum_{k=1}^{\infty}[(k+2)(k+1)c_{k+2} - c_{k-1}]x^k = 0.$$

Thus

$$c_2 = 0$$

$$(k+2)(k+1)c_{k+2} - c_{k-1} = 0$$

and

$$c_{k+2} = \frac{1}{(k+2)(k+1)}c_{k-1}, \quad k = 1, 2, 3, \ldots.$$

Choosing $c_0 = 1$ and $c_1 = 0$ we find

$$c_3 = \frac{1}{6}$$

$$c_4 = c_5 = 0$$

$$c_6 = \frac{1}{180}$$

and so on. For $c_0 = 0$ and $c_1 = 1$ we obtain

$$c_3 = 0$$

$$c_4 = \frac{1}{12}$$

$$c_5 = c_6 = 0$$

$$c_7 = \frac{1}{504}$$

and so on. Thus, two solutions are

$$y_1 = 1 + \frac{1}{6}x^3 + \frac{1}{180}x^6 + \cdots \quad \text{and} \quad y_2 = x + \frac{1}{12}x^4 + \frac{1}{504}x^7 + \cdots .$$

2. Substituting $y = \sum_{n=0}^{\infty} c_n x^n$ into the differential equation we have

$$y'' + x^2 y = \underbrace{\sum_{n=2}^{\infty} n(n-1)c_n x^{n-2}}_{k=n-2} + \underbrace{\sum_{n=0}^{\infty} c_n x^{n+2}}_{k=n+2} = \sum_{k=0}^{\infty} (k+2)(k+1)c_{k+2}x^k + \sum_{k=2}^{\infty} c_{k-2}x^k$$

$$= 2c_2 + 6c_3 x + \sum_{k=2}^{\infty} [(k+2)(k+1)c_{k+2} + c_{k-2}]x^k = 0.$$

Thus

$$c_2 = c_3 = 0$$

$$(k+2)(k+1)c_{k+2} + c_{k-2} = 0$$

and $$c_{k+2} = -\frac{1}{(k+2)(k+1)} c_{k-2}, \quad k = 2, 3, 4, \ldots .$$

Choosing $c_0 = 1$ and $c_1 = 0$ we find

$$c_4 = -\frac{1}{12}$$

$$c_5 = c_6 = c_7 = 0$$

$$c_8 = \frac{1}{672}$$

and so on. For $c_0 = 0$ and $c_1 = 1$ we obtain

$$c_4 = 0$$

$$c_5 = -\frac{1}{20}$$

$$c_6 = c_7 = c_8 = 0$$

$$c_9 = \frac{1}{1440}$$

169

and so on. Thus, two solutions are

$$y_1 = 1 - \frac{1}{12}x^4 + \frac{1}{672}x^8 - \cdots \quad \text{and} \quad y_2 = x - \frac{1}{20}x^5 + \frac{1}{1440}x^9 - \cdots .$$

3. Substituting $y = \sum_{n=0}^{\infty} c_n x^n$ into the differential equation we have

$$y'' - 2xy' + y = \underbrace{\sum_{n=2}^{\infty} n(n-1)c_n x^{n-2}}_{k=n-2} - 2\underbrace{\sum_{n=1}^{\infty} nc_n x^n}_{k=n} + \underbrace{\sum_{n=0}^{\infty} c_n x^n}_{k=n}$$

$$= \sum_{k=0}^{\infty} (k+2)(k+1)c_{k+2}x^k - 2\sum_{k=1}^{\infty} kc_k x^k + \sum_{k=0}^{\infty} c_k x^k$$

$$= 2c_2 + c_0 + \sum_{k=1}^{\infty} [(k+2)(k+1)c_{k+2} - (2k-1)c_k]x^k = 0.$$

Thus

$$2c_2 + c_0 = 0$$

$$(k+2)(k+1)c_{k+2} - (2k-1)c_k = 0$$

and

$$c_2 = -\frac{1}{2}c_0$$

$$c_{k+2} = \frac{2k-1}{(k+2)(k+1)}c_k, \quad k = 1, 2, 3, \ldots .$$

Choosing $c_0 = 1$ and $c_1 = 0$ we find

$$c_2 = -\frac{1}{2}$$

$$c_3 = c_5 = c_7 = \cdots = 0$$

$$c_4 = -\frac{1}{8}$$

$$c_6 = -\frac{7}{336}$$

and so on. For $c_0 = 0$ and $c_1 = 1$ we obtain

$$c_2 = c_4 = c_6 = \cdots = 0$$

$$c_3 = \frac{1}{6}$$

$$c_5 = \frac{1}{24}$$

$$c_7 = \frac{1}{112}$$

and so on. Thus, two solutions are

$$y_1 = 1 - \frac{1}{2}x^2 - \frac{1}{8}x^4 - \frac{7}{336}x^6 - \cdots \quad \text{and} \quad y_2 = x + \frac{1}{6}x^3 + \frac{1}{24}x^5 + \frac{1}{112}x^7 + \cdots .$$

4. Substituting $y = \sum_{n=0}^{\infty} c_n x^n$ into the differential equation we have

$$y'' - xy' + 2y = \underbrace{\sum_{n=2}^{\infty} n(n-1)c_n x^{n-2}}_{k=n-2} - \underbrace{\sum_{n=1}^{\infty} nc_n x^n}_{k=n} + 2\underbrace{\sum_{n=0}^{\infty} c_n x^n}_{k=n}$$

$$= \sum_{k=0}^{\infty} (k+2)(k+1)c_{k+2}x^k - \sum_{k=1}^{\infty} kc_k x^k + 2\sum_{k=0}^{\infty} c_k x^k$$

$$= 2c_2 + 2c_0 + \sum_{k=1}^{\infty} [(k+2)(k+1)c_{k+2} - (k-2)c_k]x^k = 0.$$

Thus

$$2c_2 + 2c_0 = 0$$

$$(k+2)(k+1)c_{k+2} - (k-2)c_k = 0$$

and

$$c_2 = -c_0$$

$$c_{k+2} = \frac{k-2}{(k+2)(k+1)}c_k, \quad k = 1, 2, 3, \ldots .$$

Choosing $c_0 = 1$ and $c_1 = 0$ we find

$$c_2 = -1$$

$$c_3 = c_5 = c_7 = \cdots = 0$$

$$c_4 = 0$$

$$c_6 = c_8 = c_{10} = \cdots = 0.$$

For $c_0 = 0$ and $c_1 = 1$ we obtain

$$c_2 = c_4 = c_6 = \cdots = 0$$

$$c_3 = -\frac{1}{6}$$

$$c_5 = -\frac{1}{120}$$

171

and so on. Thus, two solutions are

$$y_1 = 1 - x^2 \quad \text{and} \quad y_2 = x - \frac{1}{6}x^3 - \frac{1}{120}x^5 - \cdots .$$

5. Substituting $y = \sum_{n=0}^{\infty} c_n x^n$ into the differential equation we have

$$y'' + x^2 y' + xy = \underbrace{\sum_{n=2}^{\infty} n(n-1)c_n x^{n-2}}_{k=n-2} + \underbrace{\sum_{n=1}^{\infty} nc_n x^{n+1}}_{k=n+1} + \underbrace{\sum_{n=0}^{\infty} c_n x^{n+1}}_{k=n+1}$$

$$= \sum_{k=0}^{\infty} (k+2)(k+1)c_{k+2} x^k + \sum_{k=2}^{\infty} (k-1)c_{k-1} x^k + \sum_{k=1}^{\infty} c_{k-1} x^k$$

$$= 2c_2 + (6c_3 + c_0)x + \sum_{k=2}^{\infty} [(k+2)(k+1)c_{k+2} + kc_{k-1}]x^k = 0.$$

Thus

$$c_2 = 0$$

$$6c_3 + c_0 = 0$$

$$(k+2)(k+1)c_{k+2} + kc_{k-1} = 0$$

and

$$c_3 = -\frac{1}{6}c_0$$

$$c_{k+2} = -\frac{k}{(k+2)(k+1)}c_{k-1}, \quad k = 2, 3, 4, \ldots .$$

Choosing $c_0 = 1$ and $c_1 = 0$ we find

$$c_3 = -\frac{1}{6}$$

$$c_4 = c_5 = 0$$

$$c_6 = \frac{1}{45}$$

and so on. For $c_0 = 0$ and $c_1 = 1$ we obtain

$$c_3 = 0$$

$$c_4 = -\frac{1}{6}$$

$$c_5 = c_6 = 0$$

$$c_7 = \frac{5}{252}$$

and so on. Thus, two solutions are

$$y_1 = 1 - \frac{1}{6}x^3 + \frac{1}{45}x^6 - \cdots \quad \text{and} \quad y_2 = x - \frac{1}{6}x^4 + \frac{5}{232}x^7 - \cdots .$$

6. Substituting $y = \sum_{n=0}^{\infty} c_n x^n$ into the differential equation we have

$$y'' + 2xy' + 2y = \underbrace{\sum_{n=2}^{\infty} n(n-1)c_n x^{n-2}}_{k=n-2} + 2\underbrace{\sum_{n=1}^{\infty} nc_n x^n}_{k=n} + 2\underbrace{\sum_{n=0}^{\infty} c_n x^n}_{k=n}$$

$$= \sum_{k=0}^{\infty}(k+2)(k+1)c_{k+2}x^k + 2\sum_{k=1}^{\infty} kc_k x^k + 2\sum_{k=0}^{\infty} c_k x^k$$

$$= 2c_2 + 2c_0 + \sum_{k=1}^{\infty}[(k+2)(k+1)c_{k+2} + 2(k+1)c_k]x^k = 0.$$

Thus

$$2c_2 + 2c_0 = 0$$

$$(k+2)(k+1)c_{k+2} + 2(k+1)c_k = 0$$

and

$$c_2 = -c_0$$

$$c_{k+2} = -\frac{2}{k+2}c_k, \quad k = 1, 2, 3, \ldots .$$

Choosing $c_0 = 1$ and $c_1 = 0$ we find

$$c_2 = -1$$

$$c_3 = c_5 = c_7 = \cdots = 0$$

$$c_4 = \frac{1}{2}$$

$$c_6 = -\frac{1}{6}$$

and so on. For $c_0 = 0$ and $c_1 = 1$ we obtain

$$c_2 = c_4 = c_6 = \cdots = 0$$

$$c_3 = -\frac{2}{3}$$

$$c_5 = \frac{4}{15}$$

$$c_7 = -\frac{8}{105}$$

173

and so on. Thus, two solutions are

$$y_1 = 1 - x^2 + \frac{1}{2}x^4 - \frac{1}{6}x^6 + \cdots \quad \text{and} \quad y_2 = x - \frac{2}{3}x^3 + \frac{4}{15}x^5 - \frac{8}{105}x^7 + \cdots .$$

7. Substituting $y = \sum_{n=0}^{\infty} c_n x^n$ into the differential equation we have

$$(x-1)y'' + y' = \underbrace{\sum_{n=2}^{\infty} n(n-1)c_n x^{n-1}}_{k=n-1} - \underbrace{\sum_{n=2}^{\infty} n(n-1)c_n x^{n-2}}_{k=n-2} + \underbrace{\sum_{n=1}^{\infty} nc_n x^{n-1}}_{k=n-1}$$

$$= \sum_{k=1}^{\infty} (k+1)kc_{k+1}x^k - \sum_{k=0}^{\infty} (k+2)(k+1)c_{k+2}x^k + \sum_{k=0}^{\infty} (k+1)c_{k+1}x^k$$

$$= -2c_2 + c_1 + \sum_{k=1}^{\infty} [(k+1)kc_{k+1} - (k+2)(k+1)c_{k+2} + (k+1)c_{k+1}]x^k = 0.$$

Thus

$$-2c_2 + c_1 = 0$$

$$(k+1)^2 c_{k+1} - (k+2)(k+1)c_{k+2} = 0$$

and

$$c_2 = \frac{1}{2}c_1$$

$$c_{k+2} = \frac{k+1}{k+2}c_{k+1}, \quad k = 1, 2, 3, \ldots .$$

Choosing $c_0 = 1$ and $c_1 = 0$ we find $c_2 = c_3 = c_4 = \cdots = 0$. For $c_0 = 0$ and $c_1 = 1$ we obtain

$$c_2 = \frac{1}{2}, \qquad c_3 = \frac{1}{3}, \qquad c_4 = \frac{1}{4},$$

and so on. Thus, two solutions are

$$y_1 = 1 \quad \text{and} \quad y_2 = x + \frac{1}{2}x^2 + \frac{1}{3}x^3 + \frac{1}{4}x^4 + \cdots .$$

8. Substituting $y = \sum_{n=0}^{\infty} c_n x^n$ into the differential equation we have

$$(x+2)y'' + xy' - y = \underbrace{\sum_{n=2}^{\infty} n(n-1)c_n x^{n-1}}_{k=n-1} + \underbrace{\sum_{n=2}^{\infty} 2n(n-1)c_n x^{n-2}}_{k=n-2} + \underbrace{\sum_{n=1}^{\infty} nc_n x^n}_{k=n} - \underbrace{\sum_{n=0}^{\infty} c_n x^n}_{k=n}$$

$$= \sum_{k=1}^{\infty} (k+1)kc_{k+1}x^k + \sum_{k=0}^{\infty} 2(k+2)(k+1)c_{k+2}x^k + \sum_{k=1}^{\infty} kc_k x^k - \sum_{k=0}^{\infty} c_k x^k$$

$$= 4c_2 - c_0 + \sum_{k=1}^{\infty} [(k+1)kc_{k+1} + 2(k+2)(k+1)c_{k+2} + (k-1)c_k]x^k = 0.$$

174

Thus

$$4c_2 - c_0 = 0$$

$$(k+1)kc_{k+1} + 2(k+2)(k+1)c_{k+2} + (k-1)c_k = 0, \quad k = 1, 2, 3, \ldots$$

and

$$c_2 = \frac{1}{4}c_0$$

$$c_{k+2} = -\frac{(k+1)kc_{k+1} + (k-1)c_k}{2(k+2)(k+1)}, \quad k = 1, 2, 3, \ldots .$$

Choosing $c_0 = 1$ and $c_1 = 0$ we find

$$c_1 = 0, \qquad c_2 = \frac{1}{4}, \qquad c_3 = -\frac{1}{24}, \qquad c_4 = 0, \qquad c_5 = \frac{1}{480}$$

and so on. For $c_0 = 0$ and $c_1 = 1$ we obtain

$$c_2 = 0$$

$$c_3 = 0$$

$$c_4 = c_5 = c_6 = \cdots = 0.$$

Thus, two solutions are

$$y_1 = c_0\left[1 + \frac{1}{4}x^2 - \frac{1}{24}x^3 + \frac{1}{480}x^5 + \cdots\right] \quad \text{and} \quad y_2 = c_1 x.$$

9. Substituting $y = \sum_{n=0}^{\infty} c_n x^n$ into the differential equation we have

$$\left(x^2 - 1\right)y'' + 4xy' + 2y = \underbrace{\sum_{n=2}^{\infty} n(n-1)c_n x^n}_{k=n} - \underbrace{\sum_{n=2}^{\infty} n(n-1)c_n x^{n-2}}_{k=n-2} + \underbrace{4\sum_{n=1}^{\infty} nc_n x^n}_{k=n} + \underbrace{2\sum_{n=0}^{\infty} c_n x^n}_{k=n}$$

$$= \sum_{k=2}^{\infty} k(k-1)c_k x^k - \sum_{k=0}^{\infty} (k+2)(k+1)c_{k+2}x^k + 4\sum_{k=1}^{\infty} kc_k x^k + 2\sum_{k=0}^{\infty} c_k x^k$$

$$= -2c_2 + 2c_0 + (-6c_3 + 6c_1)x + \sum_{k=2}^{\infty} \left[\left(k^2 - k + 4k + 2\right)c_k - (k+2)(k+1)c_{k+2}\right]x^k = 0.$$

Thus

$$-2c_2 + 2c_0 = 0$$

$$-6c_3 + 6c_1 = 0$$

$$\left(k^2 + 3k + 2\right)c_k - (k+2)(k+1)c_{k+2} = 0$$

and

$$c_2 = c_0$$

$$c_3 = c_1$$

$$c_{k+2} = c_k, \quad k = 2, 3, 4, \ldots .$$

Choosing $c_0 = 1$ and $c_1 = 0$ we find

$$c_2 = 1$$

$$c_3 = c_5 = c_7 = \cdots = 0$$

$$c_4 = c_6 = c_8 = \cdots = 1.$$

For $c_0 = 0$ and $c_1 = 1$ we obtain

$$c_2 = c_4 = c_6 = \cdots = 0$$

$$c_3 = c_5 = c_7 = \cdots = 1.$$

Thus, two solutions are

$$y_1 = 1 + x^2 + x^4 + \cdots \quad \text{and} \quad y_2 = x + x^3 + x^5 + \cdots .$$

10. Substituting $y = \sum_{n=0}^{\infty} c_n x^n$ into the differential equation we have

$$\left(x^2 + 1\right) y'' - 6y = \underbrace{\sum_{n=2}^{\infty} n(n-1)c_n x^n}_{k=n} + \underbrace{\sum_{n=2}^{\infty} n(n-1)c_n x^{n-2}}_{k=n-2} - \underbrace{6 \sum_{n=0}^{\infty} c_n x^n}_{k=n}$$

$$= \sum_{k=2}^{\infty} k(k-1)c_k x^k + \sum_{k=0}^{\infty} (k+2)(k+1)c_{k+2} x^k - 6 \sum_{k=0}^{\infty} c_k x^k$$

$$= 2c_2 - 6c_0 + (6c_3 - 6c_1)x + \sum_{k=2}^{\infty} \left[\left(k^2 - k - 6\right) c_k + (k+2)(k+1)c_{k+2} \right] x^k = 0.$$

Thus

$$2c_2 - 6c_0 = 0$$

$$6c_3 - 6c_1 = 0$$

$$(k-3)(k+2)c_k + (k+2)(k+1)c_{k+2} = 0$$

and

$$c_2 = 3c_0$$

$$c_3 = c_1$$

$$c_{k+2} = -\frac{k-3}{k+1} c_k, \quad k = 2, 3, 4, \ldots .$$

Choosing $c_0 = 1$ and $c_1 = 0$ we find

$$c_2 = 3$$

$$c_3 = c_5 = c_7 = \cdots = 0$$

$$c_4 = 1$$

$$c_6 = -\frac{1}{5}$$

and so on. For $c_0 = 0$ and $c_1 = 1$ we obtain

$$c_2 = c_4 = c_6 = \cdots = 0$$

$$c_3 = 1$$

$$c_5 = c_7 = c_9 = \cdots = 0.$$

Thus, two solutions are

$$y_1 = 1 + 3x^2 + x^4 - \frac{1}{5}x^6 + \cdots \quad \text{and} \quad y_2 = x + x^3.$$

11. Substituting $y = \sum_{n=0}^{\infty} c_n x^n$ into the differential equation we have

$$\left(x^2 + 2\right)y'' + 3xy' - y = \underbrace{\sum_{n=2}^{\infty} n(n-1)c_n x^n}_{k=n} + 2\underbrace{\sum_{n=2}^{\infty} n(n-1)c_n x^{n-2}}_{k=n-2} + 3\underbrace{\sum_{n=1}^{\infty} nc_n x^n}_{k=n} - \underbrace{\sum_{n=0}^{\infty} c_n x^n}_{k=n}$$

$$= \sum_{k=2}^{\infty} k(k-1)c_k x^k + 2\sum_{k=0}^{\infty} (k+2)(k+1)c_{k+2}x^k + 3\sum_{k=1}^{\infty} kc_k x^k - \sum_{k=0}^{\infty} c_k x^k$$

$$= (4c_2 - c_0) + (12c_3 + 2c_1)x + \sum_{k=2}^{\infty} \left[2(k+2)(k+1)c_{k+2} + \left(k^2 + 2k - 1\right)c_k\right]x^k = 0.$$

Thus

$$4c_2 - c_0 = 0$$

$$12c_3 + 2c_1 = 0$$

$$2(k+2)(k+1)c_{k+2} + \left(k^2 + 2k - 1\right)c_k = 0$$

and

$$c_2 = \frac{1}{4}c_0$$

$$c_3 = -\frac{1}{6}c_1$$

$$c_{k+2} = -\frac{k^2 + 2k - 1}{2(k+2)(k+1)}c_k, \quad k = 2, 3, 4, \ldots.$$

Choosing $c_0 = 1$ and $c_1 = 0$ we find

$$c_2 = \frac{1}{4}$$

$$c_3 = c_5 = c_7 = \cdots = 0$$

$$c_4 = -\frac{7}{96}$$

and so on. For $c_0 = 0$ and $c_1 = 1$ we obtain

$$c_2 = c_4 = c_6 = \cdots = 0$$

$$c_3 = -\frac{1}{6}$$

$$c_5 = \frac{7}{120}$$

and so on. Thus, two solutions are

$$y_1 = 1 + \frac{1}{4}x^2 - \frac{7}{96}x^4 + \cdots \quad \text{and} \quad y_2 = x - \frac{1}{6}x^3 + \frac{7}{120}x^5 - \cdots \,.$$

12. Substituting $y = \sum_{n=0}^{\infty} c_n x^n$ into the differential equation we have

$$\left(x^2 - 1\right) y'' + xy' - y = \underbrace{\sum_{n=2}^{\infty} n(n-1)c_n x^n}_{k=n} - \underbrace{\sum_{n=2}^{\infty} n(n-1)c_n x^{n-2}}_{k=n-2} + \underbrace{\sum_{n=1}^{\infty} nc_n x^n}_{k=n} - \underbrace{\sum_{n=0}^{\infty} c_n x^n}_{k=n}$$

$$= \sum_{k=2}^{\infty} k(k-1)c_k x^k - \sum_{k=0}^{\infty} (k+2)(k+1)c_{k+2} x^k + \sum_{k=1}^{\infty} kc_k x^k - \sum_{k=0}^{\infty} c_k x^k$$

$$= (-c_2 - c_0) - 6c_3 x + \sum_{k=2}^{\infty} \left[-(k+2)(k+1)c_{k+2} + \left(k^2 - 1\right) c_k \right] x^k = 0.$$

Thus

$$-2c_2 - c_0 = 0$$

$$-6c_3 = 0$$

$$-(k+2)(k+1)c_{k+2} + (k-1)(k+1)c_k = 0$$

and

$$c_2 = -\frac{1}{2}c_0$$

$$c_3 = 0$$

$$c_{k+2} = \frac{k-1}{k+2}c_k, \quad k = 2, 3, 4, \ldots \,.$$

Choosing $c_0 = 1$ and $c_1 = 0$ we find

$$c_2 = -\frac{1}{2}$$

$$c_3 = c_5 = c_7 = \cdots = 0$$

$$c_4 = -\frac{1}{8}$$

and so on. For $c_0 = 0$ and $c_1 = 1$ we obtain

$$c_2 = c_4 = c_6 = \cdots = 0$$

$$c_3 = c_5 = c_7 = \cdots = 0.$$

Thus, two solutions are

$$y_1 = 1 - \frac{1}{2}x^2 - \frac{1}{8}x^4 - \cdots \quad \text{and} \quad y_2 = x.$$

13. Substituting $y = \sum_{n=0}^{\infty} c_n x^n$ into the differential equation we have

$$y'' - (x+1)y' - y = \underbrace{\sum_{n=2}^{\infty} n(n-1)c_n x^{n-2}}_{k=n-2} - \underbrace{\sum_{n=1}^{\infty} nc_n x^n}_{k=n} - \underbrace{\sum_{n=1}^{\infty} nc_n x^{n-1}}_{k=n-1} - \underbrace{\sum_{n=0}^{\infty} c_n x^n}_{k=n}$$

$$= \sum_{k=0}^{\infty}(k+2)(k+1)c_{k+2}x^k - \sum_{k=1}^{\infty} kc_k x^k - \sum_{k=0}^{\infty}(k+1)c_{k+1}x^k - \sum_{k=0}^{\infty} c_k x^k$$

$$= 2c_2 - c_1 - c_0 + \sum_{k=1}^{\infty}[(k+2)(k+1)c_{k+2} - (k+1)c_{k+1} - (k+1)c_k]x^k = 0.$$

Thus

$$2c_2 - c_1 - c_0 = 0$$

$$(k+2)(k+1)c_{k+2} - (k-1)(c_{k+1} + c_k) = 0$$

and

$$c_2 = \frac{c_1 + c_0}{2}$$

$$c_{k+2} = \frac{c_{k+1} + c_k}{k+2}c_k, \quad k = 2, 3, 4, \ldots.$$

Choosing $c_0 = 1$ and $c_1 = 0$ we find

$$c_2 = \frac{1}{2}, \qquad c_3 = \frac{1}{6}, \qquad c_4 = \frac{1}{6}$$

and so on. For $c_0 = 0$ and $c_1 = 1$ we obtain

$$c_2 = \frac{1}{2}, \qquad c_3 = \frac{1}{2}, \qquad c_4 = \frac{1}{4}$$

179

and so on. Thus, two solutions are

$$y_1 = 1 + \frac{1}{2}x^2 + \frac{1}{6}x^3 + \frac{1}{6}x^4 + \cdots \quad \text{and} \quad y_2 = x + \frac{1}{2}x^2 + \frac{1}{2}x^3 + \frac{1}{4}x^4 + \cdots .$$

14. Substituting $y = \sum_{n=0}^{\infty} c_n x^n$ into the differential equation we have

$$y'' - xy' - (x+2)y = \underbrace{\sum_{n=2}^{\infty} n(n-1)c_n x^{n-2}}_{k=n-2} - \underbrace{\sum_{n=1}^{\infty} n c_n x^n}_{k=n} - \underbrace{\sum_{n=0}^{\infty} c_n x^{n+1}}_{k=n+1} - \underbrace{\sum_{n=0}^{\infty} 2c_n x^n}_{k=n}$$

$$= \sum_{k=0}^{\infty} (k+2)(k+1)c_{k+2} x^k - \sum_{k=1}^{\infty} k c_k x^k - \sum_{k=1}^{\infty} c_{k-1} x^k - \sum_{k=0}^{\infty} 2c_k x^k$$

$$= 2c_2 - 2c_0 + \sum_{k=1}^{\infty} [(k+2)(k+1)c_{k+2} - (k+2)c_k - c_{k-1}]x^k = 0.$$

Thus

$$2c_2 - 2c_0 = 0$$

$$(k+2)(k+1)c_{k+2} - (k+2)c_k - c_{k-1} = 0, \qquad k = 1, 2, 3, \ldots,$$

and

$$c_2 = c_0$$

$$c_{k+2} = \frac{c_k}{k+1} + \frac{c_{k-1}}{(k+2)(k+1)}, \qquad k = 1, 2, 3, \ldots .$$

Choosing $c_0 = 1$ and $c_1 = 0$ we find

$$c_1 = 0, \qquad c_2 = 1, \qquad c_3 = \frac{1}{6}, \qquad c_4 = \frac{1}{3}, \qquad c_5 = \frac{11}{5!}$$

and so on. For $c_0 = 0$ and $c_1 = 1$ we obtain

$$c_2 = c_0 = 0, \qquad c_3 = \frac{1}{2}, \qquad c_4 = \frac{1}{12}, \qquad c_5 = \frac{1}{8}$$

and so on. Thus, two solutions are

$$y_1 = 1 + x^2 + \frac{1}{6}x^3 + \frac{1}{3}x^4 + \frac{11}{5!}x^5 + \cdots \quad \text{and} \quad y_2 = x + \frac{1}{2}x^3 + \frac{1}{12}x^4 + \frac{1}{8}x^5 + \cdots .$$

15. Substituting $y = \sum_{n=0}^{\infty} c_n x^n$ into the differential equation we have

$$(x-1)y'' - xy' + y = \underbrace{\sum_{n=2}^{\infty} n(n-1)c_n x^{n-1}}_{k=n-1} - \underbrace{\sum_{n=2}^{\infty} n(n-1)c_n x^{n-2}}_{k=n-2} - \underbrace{\sum_{n=1}^{\infty} n c_n x^n}_{k=n} + \underbrace{\sum_{n=0}^{\infty} c_n x^n}_{k=n}$$

180

$$= \sum_{k=1}^{\infty}(k+1)kc_{k+1}x^k - \sum_{k=0}^{\infty}(k+2)(k+1)c_{k+2}x^k - \sum_{k=1}^{\infty}kc_kx^k + \sum_{k=0}^{\infty}c_kx^k$$

$$= -2c_2 + c_0 + \sum_{k=1}^{\infty}[-(k+2)(k+1)c_{k+2} + (k+1)kc_{k+1} - (k-1)c_k]x^k = 0.$$

Thus

$$-2c_2 + c_0 = 0$$

$$-(k+2)(k+1)c_{k+2} + (k-1)kc_{k+1} - (k-1)c_k = 0$$

and

$$c_2 = \frac{1}{2}c_0$$

$$c_{k+2} = \frac{kc_{k+1}}{k+2} - \frac{(k-1)c_k}{(k+2)(k+1)}, \quad k = 1, 2, 3, \ldots .$$

Choosing $c_0 = 1$ and $c_1 = 0$ we find

$$c_2 = \frac{1}{2}, \qquad c_3 = \frac{1}{6}, \qquad c_4 = 0$$

and so on. For $c_0 = 0$ and $c_1 = 1$ we obtain $c_2 = c_3 = c_4 = \cdots = 0$. Thus,

$$y = C_1\left(1 + \frac{1}{2}x^2 + \frac{1}{6}x^3 + \cdots\right) + C_2 x$$

and

$$y' = C_1\left(x + \frac{1}{2}x^2 + \cdots\right) + C_2.$$

The initial conditions imply $C_1 = -2$ and $C_2 = 6$, so

$$y = -2\left(1 + \frac{1}{2}x^2 + \frac{1}{6}x^3 + \cdots\right) + 6x = 8x - 2e^x.$$

16. Substituting $y = \sum_{n=0}^{\infty}c_nx^n$ into the differential equation we have

$$(x+1)y'' - (2-x)y' + y$$

$$= \underbrace{\sum_{n=2}^{\infty}n(n-1)c_nx^{n-1}}_{k=n-1} + \underbrace{\sum_{n=2}^{\infty}n(n-1)c_nx^{n-2}}_{k=n-2} - 2\underbrace{\sum_{n=1}^{\infty}nc_nx^{n-1}}_{k=n-1} + \underbrace{\sum_{n=1}^{\infty}nc_nx^n}_{k=n} + \underbrace{\sum_{n=0}^{\infty}c_nx^n}_{k=n}$$

$$= \sum_{k=1}^{\infty}(k+1)kc_{k+1}x^k + \sum_{k=0}^{\infty}(k+2)(k+1)c_{k+2}x^k - 2\sum_{k=0}^{\infty}(k+1)c_{k+1}x^k + \sum_{k=1}^{\infty}kc_kx^k + \sum_{k=0}^{\infty}c_kx^k$$

$$= 2c_2 - 2c_1 + c_0 + \sum_{k=1}^{\infty}[(k+2)(k+1)c_{k+2} - (k+1)c_{k+1} + (k+1)c_k]x^k = 0.$$

Thus

$$2c_2 - 2c_1 + c_0 = 0$$

$$(k+2)(k+1)c_{k+2} - (k+1)c_{k+1} + (k+1)c_k = 0$$

and

$$c_2 = c_1 - \frac{1}{2}c_0$$

$$c_{k+2} = \frac{1}{k+2}c_{k+1} - \frac{1}{k+2}c_k, \quad k = 1, 2, 3, \ldots.$$

Choosing $c_0 = 1$ and $c_1 = 0$ we find

$$c_2 = -\frac{1}{2}, \qquad c_3 = -\frac{1}{6}, \qquad c_4 = \frac{1}{12}$$

and so on. For $c_0 = 0$ and $c_1 = 1$ we obtain

$$c_2 = 1, \qquad c_3 = 0, \qquad c_4 = -\frac{1}{4}$$

and so on. Thus,

$$y = C_1\left(1 - \frac{1}{2}x^2 - \frac{1}{6}x^3 + \frac{1}{12}x^4 + \cdots\right) + C_2\left(x + x^2 - \frac{1}{4}x^4 + \cdots\right)$$

and

$$y' = C_1\left(-x - \frac{1}{2}x^2 + \frac{1}{3}x^3 + \cdots\right) + C_2\left(1 + 2x - x^3 + \cdots\right).$$

The initial conditions imply $C_1 = 2$ and $C_2 = -1$, so

$$y = 2\left(1 - \frac{1}{2}x^2 - \frac{1}{6}x^3 + \frac{1}{12}x^4 + \cdots\right) - \left(x + x^2 - \frac{1}{4}x^4 + \cdots\right)$$

$$= 2 - x - 2x^2 - \frac{1}{3}x^3 + \frac{5}{12}x^4 + \cdots.$$

17. Substituting $y = \sum_{n=0}^{\infty} c_n x^n$ into the differential equation we have

$$y'' - 2xy' + 8y = \underbrace{\sum_{n=2}^{\infty} n(n-1)c_n x^{n-2}}_{k=n-2} - 2\underbrace{\sum_{n=1}^{\infty} nc_n x^n}_{k=n} + 8\underbrace{\sum_{n=0}^{\infty} c_n x^n}_{k=n}$$

$$= \sum_{k=0}^{\infty}(k+2)(k+1)c_{k+2}x^k - 2\sum_{k=1}^{\infty} kc_k x^k + 8\sum_{k=0}^{\infty} c_k x^k$$

$$= 2c_2 + 8c_0 + \sum_{k=1}^{\infty}[(k+2)(k+1)c_{k+2} + (8-2k)c_k]x^k = 0.$$

Thus

$$2c_2 + 8c_0 = 0$$

$$(k+2)(k+1)c_{k+2} + (8-2k)c_k = 0$$

182

and

$$c_2 = -4c_0$$

$$c_{k+2} = \frac{2k-8}{(k+2)(k+1)} c_k, \quad k = 1, 2, 3, \ldots.$$

Choosing $c_0 = 1$ and $c_1 = 0$ we find

$$c_2 = -4$$

$$c_3 = c_5 = c_7 = \cdots = 0$$

$$c_4 = \frac{4}{3}$$

$$c_6 = c_8 = c_{10} = \cdots = 0.$$

For $c_0 = 0$ and $c_1 = 1$ we obtain

$$c_2 = c_4 = c_6 = \cdots = 0$$

$$c_3 = -1$$

$$c_5 = \frac{1}{10}$$

and so on. Thus,

$$y = C_1 \left(1 - 4x^2 + \frac{4}{3}x^4 \right) + C_2 \left(x - x^3 + \frac{1}{10}x^5 + \cdots \right)$$

and

$$y' = C_1 \left(-8x + \frac{16}{3}x^3 \right) + C_2 \left(1 - 3x^2 + \frac{1}{2}x^4 + \cdots \right).$$

The initial conditions imply $C_1 = 3$ and $C_2 = 0$, so

$$y = 3 \left(1 - 4x^2 + \frac{4}{3}x^4 \right) = 3 - 12x^2 + 4x^4.$$

18. Substituting $y = \sum_{n=0}^{\infty} c_n x^n$ into the differential equation we have

$$(x^2+1)y'' + 2xy' = \underbrace{\sum_{n=2}^{\infty} n(n-1)c_n x^n}_{k=n} + \underbrace{\sum_{n=2}^{\infty} n(n-1)c_n x^{n-2}}_{k=n-2} + \underbrace{\sum_{n=1}^{\infty} 2nc_n x^n}_{k=n}$$

$$= \sum_{k=2}^{\infty} k(k-1)c_k x^k + \sum_{k=0}^{\infty} (k+2)(k+1)c_{k+2} x^k + \sum_{k=1}^{\infty} 2kc_k x^k$$

$$= 2c_2 + (6c_3 + 2c_1)x + \sum_{k=2}^{\infty} [k(k+1)c_k + (k+2)(k+1)c_{k+2}]x^k = 0.$$

183

Thus

$$2c_2 = 0,$$

$$6c_3 + 2c_1 = 0,$$

$$k(k+1)c_k + (k+2)(k+1)c_{k+2} = 0$$

and

$$c_2 = 0$$

$$c_3 = -\frac{1}{3}c_1$$

$$c_{k+2} = -\frac{k}{k+2}c_k, \quad k = 2, 3, 4, \ldots .$$

Choosing $c_0 = 1$ and $c_1 = 0$ we find $c_3 = c_4 = c_5 = \cdots = 0$. For $c_0 = 0$ and $c_1 = 1$ we obtain

$$c_3 - \frac{1}{3}$$

$$c_4 = c_6 = c_8 = \cdots = 0$$

$$c_5 = -\frac{1}{5}$$

$$c_7 = \frac{1}{7}$$

and so on. Thus

$$y = c_0 + c_1 \left(x - \frac{1}{3}x^3 + \frac{1}{5}x^5 - \frac{1}{7}x^7 + \cdots \right)$$

and

$$y' = c_1 \left(1 - x^2 + x^4 - x^6 + \cdots \right).$$

The initial conditions imply $c_0 = 0$ and $c_1 = 1$, so

$$y = x - \frac{1}{3}x^3 + \frac{1}{5}x^5 - \frac{1}{7}x^7 + \cdots .$$

19. Substituting $y = \sum_{n=0}^{\infty} c_n x^n$ into the differential equation we have

$$y'' + (\sin x)y = \sum_{n=2}^{\infty} n(n-1)c_n x^{n-2} + \left(x - \frac{1}{6}x^3 + \frac{1}{120}x^5 - \cdots \right)\left(c_0 + c_1 x + c_2 x^2 + \cdots \right)$$

$$= \left[2c_2 + 6c_3 x + 12c_4 x^2 + 20c_5 x^3 + \cdots \right] + \left[c_0 x + c_1 x^2 + \left(c_2 - \frac{1}{6}c_0 \right) x^3 + \cdots \right]$$

$$= 2c_2 + (6c_3 + c_0)x + (12c_4 + c_1)x^2 + \left(20c_5 + c_2 - \frac{1}{6}c_0 \right) x^3 + \cdots = 0.$$

Thus

$$2c_2 = 0$$

$$6c_3 + c_0 = 0$$

$$12c_4 + c_1 = 0$$

$$20c_5 + c_2 - \frac{1}{6}c_0 = 0$$

and

$$c_2 = 0$$

$$c_3 = -\frac{1}{6}c_0$$

$$c_4 = -\frac{1}{12}c_1$$

$$c_5 = -\frac{1}{20}c_2 + \frac{1}{120}c_0.$$

Choosing $c_0 = 1$ and $c_1 = 0$ we find

$$c_2 = 0, \qquad c_3 = -\frac{1}{6}, \qquad c_4 = 0, \qquad c_5 = \frac{1}{120}$$

and so on. For $c_0 = 0$ and $c_1 = 1$ we obtain

$$c_2 = 0, \qquad c_3 = 0, \qquad c_4 = -\frac{1}{12}, \qquad c_5 = 0$$

and so on. Thus, two solutions are

$$y_1 = 1 - \frac{1}{6}x^3 + \frac{1}{120}x^5 + \cdots \qquad \text{and} \qquad y_2 = x - \frac{1}{12}x^4 + \cdots .$$

20. Substituting $y = \sum_{n=0}^{\infty} c_n x^n$ into the differential equation we have

$$y'' + \frac{\sin x}{x}y = \sum_{n=2}^{\infty} n(n-1)c_n x^{n-2} + \left(1 - \frac{1}{6}x^2 + \frac{1}{120}x^4 - \cdots\right)\left(c_0 + c_1 x + c_2 x^2 + c_3 x^3 + \cdots\right)$$

$$= \left[2c_2 + 6c_3 x + 12c_4 x^2 + 20c_5 x^3 + \cdots\right]$$

$$+ \left[c_0 + c_1 x + \left(c_2 - \frac{1}{6}c_0\right)x^2 + \left(c_3 - \frac{1}{6}c_1\right)x^3 + \cdots\right]$$

$$= (2c_2 + c_0) + (6c_3 + c_1)x + \left(12c_4 + c_2 - \frac{1}{6}c_0\right)x^2 + \cdots = 0.$$

Thus

$$2c_2 + c_0 = 0$$

$$6c_3 + c_1 = 0$$

$$12c_4 + c_2 - \frac{1}{6}c_0 = 0$$

and

$$c_2 = -\frac{1}{2}$$

$$c_3 = -\frac{1}{6}c_1$$

$$c_4 = -\frac{1}{12}c_2 + \frac{1}{72}c_0.$$

Choosing $c_0 = 1$ and $c_1 = 0$ we find

$$c_2 = -\frac{1}{2}, \qquad c_3 = 0, \qquad c_4 = \frac{1}{18}$$

and so on. For $c_0 = 0$ and $c_1 = 1$ we obtain

$$c_2 = 0, \qquad c_3 = -\frac{1}{6}, \qquad c_4 = 0$$

and so on. Thus, two solutions are

$$y_1 = 1 - \frac{1}{2}x^2 + \frac{1}{18}x^4 - \cdots \quad \text{and} \quad y_2 = x - \frac{1}{6}x^3 + \cdots .$$

21. Substituting $y = \sum_{n=0}^{\infty} c_n x^n$ into the differential equation we have

$$y'' + e^{-x}y = \sum_{n=2}^{\infty} n(n-1)c_n x^{n-2}$$

$$+ \left(1 - x + \frac{1}{2}x^2 - \frac{1}{6}x^3 + \frac{1}{24}x^4 - \cdots\right)\left(c_0 + c_1 x + c_2 x^2 + c_3 x^3 + \cdots\right)$$

$$= \left[2c_2 + 6c_3 x + 12c_4 x^2 + 20c_5 x^3 + \cdots\right] + \left[c_0 + (c_1 - c_0)x + \left(c_2 - c_1 + \frac{1}{2}c_0\right)x^2 + \cdots\right]$$

$$= (2c_2 + c_0) + (6c_3 + c_1 - c_0)x + (12c_4 + c_2 - c_1 + \frac{1}{2}c_0)x^2 + \cdots = 0.$$

Then

$$2c_2 + c_0 = 0$$

$$6c_3 + c_1 - c_0 = 0$$

$$12c_4 + c_2 - c_1 + \frac{1}{2}c_0 = 0$$

and

$$c_2 = -\frac{1}{2}c_0$$

$$c_3 = -\frac{1}{6}c_1 + \frac{1}{6}c_0$$

$$c_4 = -\frac{1}{12}c_2 + \frac{1}{12}c_1 - \frac{1}{24}c_0.$$

Choosing $c_0 = 1$ and $c_1 = 0$ we find

$$c_2 = -\frac{1}{2}, \qquad c_3 = \frac{1}{6}, \qquad c_4 = 0$$

and so on. For $c_0 = 0$ and $c_1 = 1$ we obtain

$$c_2 = 0, \qquad c_3 = -\frac{1}{6}, \qquad c_4 = \frac{1}{12}.$$

Thus, two solutions are

$$y_1 = 1 - \frac{1}{2}x^2 + \frac{1}{6}x^3 + \cdots \quad \text{and} \quad y_2 = x - \frac{1}{6}x^3 + \frac{1}{12}x^4 + \cdots.$$

22. Substituting $y = \sum_{n=0}^{\infty} c_n x^n$ into the differential equation we have

$$y'' + e^x y - y = \sum_{n=2}^{\infty} n(n-1)c_n x^{n-2}$$

$$+ \left(1 + x + \frac{1}{2}x^2 + \frac{1}{6}x^3 + \cdots\right)\left(c_1 + 2c_2 x + 3c_3 x^2 + 4c_4 x^3 + \cdots\right) - \sum_{n=0}^{\infty} c_n x^n$$

$$= \left[2c_2 + 6c_3 x + 12c_4 x^2 + 20c_5 x^3 + \cdots\right]$$

$$+ \left[c_1 + (2c_2 + c_1)x + \left(3c_3 + 2c_2 + \frac{1}{2}c_1\right)x^2 + \cdots\right] - \left[c_0 + c_1 x + c_2 x^2 + \cdots\right]$$

$$= (2c_2 + c_1 - c_0) + (6c_3 + 2c_2)x + \left(12c_4 + 3c_3 + c_2 + \frac{1}{2}c_1\right)x^2 + \cdots = 0.$$

Thus

$$2c_2 + c_1 - c_0 = 0$$

$$6c_3 + 2c_2 = 0$$

$$12c_4 + 3c_3 + c_2 + \frac{1}{2}c_1 = 0$$

187

and

$$c_2 = \frac{1}{2}c_0 - \frac{1}{2}c_1$$

$$c_3 = -\frac{1}{3}c_2$$

$$c_4 = -\frac{1}{4}c_3 + \frac{1}{12}c_2 - \frac{1}{24}c_1.$$

Choosing $c_0 = 1$ and $c_1 = 0$ we find

$$c_2 = \frac{1}{2}, \qquad c_3 = -\frac{1}{6}, \qquad c_4 = 0$$

and so on. For $c_0 = 0$ and $c_1 = 1$ we obtain

$$c_2 = -\frac{1}{2}, \qquad c_3 = \frac{1}{6}, \qquad c_4 = -\frac{1}{24}$$

and so on. Thus, two solutions are

$$y_1 = 1 + \frac{1}{2}x^2 - \frac{1}{6}x^3 + \cdots \quad \text{and} \quad y_2 = x - \frac{1}{2}x^2 + \frac{1}{6}x^3 - \frac{1}{24}x^4 + \cdots.$$

23. Substituting $y = \sum_{n=0}^{\infty} c_n x^n$ into the differential equation leads to

$$y'' - xy = \underbrace{\sum_{n=2}^{\infty} n(n-1)c_n x^{n-2}}_{k=n-2} - \underbrace{\sum_{n=0}^{\infty} c_n x^{n+1}}_{k=n+1} = \sum_{k=0}^{\infty} (k+2)(k+1)c_{k+2}x^k - \sum_{k=1}^{\infty} c_{k-1}x^k$$

$$= 2c_2 + \sum_{k=1}^{\infty} [(k+2)(k+1)c_{k+2} - c_{k-1}]x^k = 1.$$

Thus

$$2c_2 = 1$$

$$(k+2)(k+1)c_{k+2} - c_{k-1} = 0$$

and

$$c_2 = \frac{1}{2}$$

$$c_{k+2} = \frac{c_{k-1}}{(k+2)(k+1)}, \qquad k = 1, 2, 3, \ldots.$$

Let c_0 and c_1 be arbitrary and iterate to find

$$c_2 = \frac{1}{2}$$

$$c_3 = \frac{1}{6}c_0$$

$$c_4 = \frac{1}{12}c_1$$

$$c_5 = \frac{1}{20}c_2 = \frac{1}{40}$$

and so on. The solution is

$$y = c_0 + c_1 x + \frac{1}{2}x^2 + \frac{1}{6}c_0 x^3 + \frac{1}{12}c_1 x^4 + \frac{1}{40}c_5 + \cdots$$

$$= c_0 \left(1 + \frac{1}{6}x^3 + \cdots\right) + c_1 \left(x + \frac{1}{12}x^4 + \cdots\right) + \frac{1}{2}x^2 + \frac{1}{40}x^5 + \cdots.$$

24. Substituting $y = \sum_{n=0}^{\infty} c_n x^n$ into the differential equation leads to

$$y'' - 4xy' - 4y = \underbrace{\sum_{n=2}^{\infty} n(n-1)c_n x^{n-2}}_{k=n-2} - \underbrace{\sum_{n=1}^{\infty} 4nc_n x^n}_{k=n} - \underbrace{\sum_{n=0}^{\infty} 4c_n x^n}_{k=n}$$

$$= \sum_{k=0}^{\infty}(k+2)(k+1)c_{k+2}x^k - \sum_{k=1}^{\infty} 4kc_k x^k - \sum_{k=0}^{\infty} 4c_k x^k$$

$$= 2c_2 - 4c_0 + \sum_{k=1}^{\infty}[(k+2)(k+1)c_{k+2} - 4(k+1)c_k]x^k$$

$$= e^x = 1 + \sum_{k=1}^{\infty} \frac{1}{k!}x^k.$$

Thus

$$2c_2 - 4c_0 = 1$$

$$(k+2)(k+1)c_{k+2} - 4(k+1)c_k = \frac{1}{k!}$$

and

$$c_2 = \frac{1}{2} + 2c_0$$

$$c_{k+2} = \frac{1}{(k+2)!} + \frac{4}{k+2}c_k, \qquad k = 1, 2, 3, \ldots .$$

Let c_0 and c_1 be arbitrary and iterate to find

$$c_2 = \frac{1}{2} + 2c_0$$

$$c_3 = \frac{1}{3!} + \frac{4}{3}c_1 = \frac{1}{3!} + \frac{4}{3}c_1$$

$$c_4 = \frac{1}{4!} + \frac{4}{4}c_2 = \frac{1}{4!} + \frac{1}{2} + 2c_0 = \frac{13}{4!} + 2c_0$$

$$c_5 = \frac{1}{5!} + \frac{4}{5}c_3 = \frac{1}{5!} + \frac{4}{5 \cdot 3!} + \frac{16}{15}c_1 = \frac{17}{5!} + \frac{16}{15}c_1$$

$$c_6 = \frac{1}{6!} + \frac{4}{6}c_4 = \frac{1}{6!} + \frac{4 \cdot 13}{6 \cdot 4!} + \frac{8}{6}c_0 = \frac{261}{6!} + \frac{4}{3}c_0$$

$$c_7 = \frac{1}{7!} + \frac{4}{7}c_5 = \frac{1}{7!} + \frac{4 \cdot 17}{7 \cdot 5!} + \frac{64}{105}c_1 = \frac{409}{7!} + \frac{64}{105}c_1$$

and so on. The solution is

$$y = c_0 + c_1 x + \left(\frac{1}{2} + 2c_0\right)x^2 + \left(\frac{1}{3!} + \frac{4}{3}c_1\right)x^3 - \left(\frac{13}{4!} + 2c_0\right)x^4 + \left(\frac{17}{5!} + \frac{16}{15}c_1\right)x^5$$

$$+ \left(\frac{261}{6!} + \frac{4}{3}c_0\right)x^6 + \left(\frac{409}{7!} + \frac{64}{105}c_1\right)x^7 + \cdots$$

$$= c_0\left[1 + 2x^2 + 2x^4 + \frac{4}{3}x^6 + \cdots\right] + c_1\left[x + \frac{4}{3}x^3 + \frac{16}{15}x^5 + \frac{64}{105}x^7 + \cdots\right]$$

$$+ \frac{1}{2}x^2 + \frac{1}{3!}x^3 + \frac{13}{4!}x^4 + \frac{17}{5!}x^5 + \frac{261}{6!}x^6 + \frac{409}{7!}x^7 + \cdots.$$

25. Two power series solutions are

$$y_1 = 1 + \sum_{k=1}^{\infty}(-1)^k \frac{2^k n \cdot (n-2)\cdots(n-2k+2)}{(2k)!}x^{2k}$$

$$y_2 = x + \sum_{k=1}^{\infty}(-1)^k \frac{2^k(n-1)(n-3)\cdots(n-2k+1)}{(2k+1)!}x^{2k+1}.$$

Substituting $n = 1$ into the second series gives the polynomial solution $y_2 = x$, whereas substituting $n = 2$ into the first series gives $y_1 = 1 - 2x^2$.

26. If $t = L - x$ then $\dfrac{d\theta}{dx} = -\dfrac{d\theta}{dt}$ and $\dfrac{d^2\theta}{dx^2} = \dfrac{d^2\theta}{dt^2}$ and the boundary-value problem becomes in terms of t,

$$\frac{d^2\theta}{dt^2} + \lambda^2 t\theta = 0, \qquad \theta(L) = 0, \qquad \theta'(L) = 0.$$

Substituting $\theta = \sum\limits_{n=0}^{\infty} c_n t^n$ into the differential equation we obtain $c_2 = 0$ and

$$c_{k+2} = -\frac{\lambda^2}{(k+2)(k+1)} c_{k-1}, \quad k = 1, 2, 3, \dots.$$

Choosing $c_0 = 1$ and $c_1 = 0$ we find

$$c_2 = 0$$

$$c_3 = -\frac{\lambda^2}{6}$$

$$c_4 = c_5 = 0$$

$$c_6 = \frac{\lambda^4}{180}$$

$$c_7 = c_8 = 0$$

and so on. For $c_0 = 0$ and $c_1 = 1$ we obtain

$$c_2 = c_3 = 0$$

$$c_4 = -\frac{\lambda^2}{12}$$

$$c_5 = c_6 = 0$$

$$c_7 = \frac{\lambda^2}{504}$$

$$c_8 = c_9 = 0$$

and so on. Thus

$$\theta = C_1 \left(1 - \lambda^2 6 t^3 + \frac{\lambda^4}{180} t^6 - \cdots \right) + C_2 \left(t - \frac{\lambda^2}{12} t^4 + \frac{\lambda^4}{504} t^7 - \cdots \right).$$

Now the boundary condition $\theta'(0) = 0$ implies $C_2 = 0$. Thus

$$\theta = C_1 \left(1 - \frac{\lambda^2}{6} t^3 + \frac{\lambda^4}{180} t^6 - \cdots \right)$$

or

$$\theta = C_1 \left(1 - \frac{\lambda^2}{6} (L - x)^3 + \frac{\lambda^4}{180} (L - x)^6 - \cdots \right).$$

191

Exercises 6.4

1. Irregular singular point: $x = 0$.

2. Regular singular points: $x = 0, -3$.

3. Irregular singular point: $x = 3$. Regular singular point: $x = -3$.

4. Irregular singular point: $x = 1$. Regular singular point: $x = 0$.

5. Regular singular points: $x = 0, \pm 2i$.

6. Irregular singular point: $x = 5$. Regular singular point: $x = 0$.

7. Regular singular points: $x = -3, 2$.

8. Regular singular points: $x = 0, \pm i$.

9. Irregular singular point: $x = 0$. Regular singular points: $x = 2, \pm 5$.

10. Irregular singular point: $x = -1$. Regular singular points: $x = 0, 3$.

11. Substituting $y = \sum_{n=0}^{\infty} c_n x^{n+r}$ into the differential equation and collecting terms, we obtain

$$2xy'' - y' + 2y = \left(2r^2 - 3r\right) c_0 x^{r-1} + \sum_{k=1}^{\infty} [2(k+r-1)(k+r)c_k - (k+r)c_k + 2c_{k-1}]x^{k+r-1} = 0,$$

which implies
$$2r^2 - 3r = r(2r - 3) = 0$$

and
$$(k+r)(2k + 2r - 3)c_k + 2c_{k-1} = 0.$$

The indicial roots are $r = 0$ and $r = 3/2$. For $r = 0$ the recurrence relation is

$$c_k = -\frac{2c_{k-1}}{k(2k - 3)}, \quad k = 1, 2, 3, \ldots,$$

and
$$c_1 = 2c_0, \qquad c_2 = -2c_0, \qquad c_3 = \frac{4}{9}c_0.$$

For $r = 3/2$ the recurrence relation is

$$c_k = -\frac{2c_{k-1}}{(2k + 3)k}, \quad k = 1, 2, 3, \ldots,$$

and
$$c_1 = -\frac{2}{5}c_0, \qquad c_2 = \frac{2}{35}c_0, \qquad c_3 = -\frac{4}{945}c_0.$$

The general solution on $(0, \infty)$ is

$$y = C_1\left(1 + 2x - 2x^2 + \frac{4}{9}x^3 + \cdots\right) + C_2 x^{3/2}\left(1 - \frac{2}{5}x + \frac{2}{35}x^2 - \frac{4}{945}x^3 + \cdots\right).$$

192

12. Substituting $y = \sum_{n=0}^{\infty} c_n x^{n+r}$ into the differential equation and collecting terms, we obtain

$$2xy'' + 5y' + xy = \left(2r^2 + 3r\right) c_0 x^{r-1} + \left(2r^2 + 7r + 5\right) c_1 x^r$$

$$+ \sum_{k=2}^{\infty} [2(k+r)(k+r-1)c_k + 5(k+r)c_k + c_{k-2}]x^{k+r-1}$$

$$= 0,$$

which implies

$$2r^2 + 3r = r(2r+3) = 0,$$

$$\left(2r^2 + 7r + 5\right) c_1 = 0,$$

and

$$(k+r)(2k+2r+3)c_k + c_{k-2} = 0.$$

The indicial roots are $r = -3/2$ and $r = 0$, so $c_1 = 0$. For $r = -3/2$ the recurrence relation is

$$c_k = -\frac{c_{k-2}}{(2k-3)k}, \quad k = 2, 3, 4, \ldots,$$

and

$$c_2 = -\frac{1}{2}c_0, \quad c_3 = 0, \quad c_4 = \frac{1}{40}c_0.$$

For $r = 0$ the recurrence relation is

$$c_k = -\frac{c_{k-2}}{k(2k+3)}, \quad k = 2, 3, 4, \ldots,$$

and

$$c_2 = -\frac{1}{14}c_0, \quad c_3 = 0, \quad c_4 = \frac{1}{616}c_0.$$

The general solution on $(0, \infty)$ is

$$y = C_1 x^{-3/2}\left(1 - \frac{1}{2}x^2 + \frac{1}{40}x^4 + \cdots\right) + C_2\left(1 - \frac{1}{14}x^2 + \frac{1}{616}x^4 + \cdots\right).$$

13. Substituting $y = \sum_{n=0}^{\infty} c_n x^{n+r}$ into the differential equation and collecting terms, we obtain

$$4xy'' + \frac{1}{2}y' + y = \left(4r^2 - \frac{7}{2}r\right) c_0 x^{r-1} + \sum_{k=1}^{\infty} [4(k+r)(k+r-1)c_k + \frac{1}{2}(k+r)c_k + c_{k-1}]x^{k+r-1}$$

$$= 0,$$

which implies

$$4r^2 - \frac{7}{2}r = r\left(4r - \frac{7}{2}\right) = 0$$

and

$$\frac{1}{2}(k+r)(8k+8r-7)c_k + c_{k-1} = 0.$$

193

The indicial roots are $r = 0$ and $r = 7/8$. For $r = 0$ the recurrence relation is

$$c_k = -\frac{2c_{k-1}}{k(8k-7)}, \quad k = 1, 2, 3, \ldots,$$

and

$$c_1 = -2c_0, \quad c_2 = \frac{2}{9}c_0, \quad c_3 = -\frac{4}{459}c_0.$$

For $r = 7/8$ the recurrence relation is

$$c_k = -\frac{2c_{k-1}}{(8k+7)k}, \quad k = 1, 2, 3, \ldots,$$

and

$$c_1 = -\frac{2}{15}c_0, \quad c_2 = \frac{2}{345}c_0, \quad c_3 = -\frac{4}{32,085}c_0.$$

The general solution on $(0, \infty)$ is

$$y = C_1\left(1 - 2x + \frac{2}{9}x^2 - \frac{4}{459}x^3 + \cdots\right) + C_2 x^{7/8}\left(1 - \frac{2}{15}x + \frac{2}{345}x^2 - \frac{4}{32,085}x^3 + \cdots\right).$$

14. Substituting $y = \sum_{n=0}^{\infty} c_n x^{n+r}$ into the differential equation and collecting terms, we obtain

$$2x^2 y'' - xy' + (x^2 + 1)y = (2r^2 - 3r + 1)c_0 x^r + (2r^2 + r)c_1 x^{r+1}$$

$$+ \sum_{k=2}^{\infty} [2(k+r)(k+r-1)c_k - (k+r)c_k + c_k + c_{k-2}]x^{k+r}$$

$$= 0,$$

which implies

$$2r^2 - 3r + 1 = (2r - 1)(r - 1) = 0,$$

$$\left(2r^2 + r\right)c_1 = 0,$$

and

$$[(k+r)(2k+2r-3)+1]c_k + c_{k-2} = 0.$$

The indicial roots are $r = 1/2$ and $r = 1$, so $c_1 = 0$. For $r = 1/2$ the recurrence relation is

$$c_k = -\frac{c_{k-2}}{k(2k-1)}, \quad k = 2, 3, 4, \ldots,$$

and

$$c_2 = -\frac{1}{6}c_0, \quad c_3 = 0, \quad c_4 = \frac{1}{168}c_0.$$

For $r = 1$ the recurrence relation is

$$c_k = -\frac{c_{k-2}}{k(2k+1)}, \quad k = 2, 3, 4, \ldots,$$

194

and
$$c_2 = -\frac{1}{10}c_0, \qquad c_3 = 0, \qquad c_4 = \frac{1}{360}c_0.$$

The general solution on $(0, \infty)$ is

$$y = C_1 x^{1/2}\left(1 - \frac{1}{6}x^2 + \frac{1}{168}x^4 + \cdots\right) + C_2 x\left(1 - \frac{1}{10}x^2 + \frac{1}{360}x^4 + \cdots\right).$$

15. Substituting $y = \sum_{n=0}^{\infty} c_n x^{n+r}$ into the differential equation and collecting terms, we obtain

$$3xy'' + (2 - x)y' - y = \left(3r^2 - r\right)c_0 x^{r-1}$$

$$+ \sum_{k=1}^{\infty}[3(k+r-1)(k+r)c_k + 2(k+r)c_k - (k+r)c_{k-1}]x^{k+r-1}$$

$$= 0,$$

which implies
$$3r^2 - r = r(3r - 1) = 0$$

and
$$(k+r)(3k + 3r - 1)c_k - (k+r)c_{k-1} = 0.$$

The indicial roots are $r = 0$ and $r = 1/3$. For $r = 0$ the recurrence relation is

$$c_k = \frac{c_{k-1}}{(3k-1)}, \qquad k = 1, 2, 3, \ldots,$$

and
$$c_1 = \frac{1}{2}c_0, \qquad c_2 = \frac{1}{10}c_0, \qquad c_3 = \frac{1}{80}c_0.$$

For $r = 1/3$ the recurrence relation is

$$c_k = \frac{c_{k-1}}{3k}, \qquad k = 1, 2, 3, \ldots,$$

and
$$c_1 = \frac{1}{3}c_0, \qquad c_2 = \frac{1}{18}c_0, \qquad c_3 = \frac{1}{162}c_0.$$

The general solution on $(0, \infty)$ is

$$y = C_1\left(1 + \frac{1}{2}x + \frac{1}{10}x^2 + \frac{1}{80}x^3 + \cdots\right) + C_2 x^{1/3}\left(1 + \frac{1}{3}x + \frac{1}{18}x^2 + \frac{1}{162}x^3 + \cdots\right).$$

16. Substituting $y = \sum_{n=0}^{\infty} c_n x^{n+r}$ into the differential equation and collecting terms, we obtain

$$x^2 y'' - \left(x - \frac{2}{9}\right)y = \left(r^2 - r + \frac{2}{9}\right)c_0 x^r + \sum_{k=1}^{\infty}\left[(k+r)(k+r-1)c_k + \frac{2}{9}c_k - c_{k-1}\right]x^{k+r}$$

$$= 0,$$

which implies
$$r^2 - r + \frac{2}{9} = \left(r - \frac{2}{3}\right)\left(r - \frac{1}{3}\right) = 0$$

195

and

$$\left[(k+r)(k+r-1) + \frac{2}{9}\right] c_k - c_{k-1} = 0.$$

The indicial roots are $r = 2/3$ and $r = 1/3$. For $r = 2/3$ the recurrence relation is

$$c_k = \frac{3c_{k-1}}{3k^2 + k}, \quad k = 1, 2, 3, \cdots,$$

and

$$c_1 = \frac{3}{4}c_0, \qquad c_2 = \frac{9}{56}c_0, \qquad c_3 = \frac{9}{560}c_0.$$

For $r = 1/3$ the recurrence relation is

$$c_k = \frac{3c_{k-1}}{3k^2 - k}, \quad k = 1, 2, 3, \cdots,$$

and

$$c_1 = \frac{3}{2}c_0, \qquad c_2 = \frac{9}{20}c_0, \qquad c_3 = \frac{9}{160}c_0.$$

The general solution on $(0, \infty)$ is

$$y = C_1 x^{2/3}\left(1 + \frac{3}{4}x + \frac{9}{56}x^2 + \frac{9}{560}x^3 + \cdots\right) + C_2 x^{1/3}\left(1 + \frac{3}{2}x + \frac{9}{20}x^2 + \frac{9}{160}x^3 + \cdots\right).$$

17. Substituting $y = \sum_{n=0}^{\infty} c_n x^{n+r}$ into the differential equation and collecting terms, we obtain

$$2xy'' - (3 + 2x)y' + y = \left(2r^2 - 5r\right)c_0 x^{r-1} + \sum_{k=1}^{\infty}[2(k+r)(k+r-1)c_k$$

$$- 3(k+r)c_k - 2(k+r-1)c_{k-1} + c_{k-1}]x^{k+r-1}$$

$$= 0,$$

which implies

$$2r^2 - 5r = r(2r - 5) = 0$$

and

$$(k+r)(2k + 2r - 5)c_k - (2k + 2r - 3)c_{k-1} = 0.$$

The indicial roots are $r = 0$ and $r = 5/2$. For $r = 0$ the recurrence relation is

$$c_k = \frac{(2k - 3)c_{k-1}}{k(2k - 5)}, \quad k = 1, 2, 3, \cdots,$$

and

$$c_1 = \frac{1}{3}c_0, \qquad c_2 = -\frac{1}{6}c_0, \qquad c_3 = -\frac{1}{6}c_0.$$

For $r = 5/2$ the recurrence relation is

$$c_k = \frac{2(k + 1)c_{k-1}}{k(2k + 5)}, \quad k = 1, 2, 3, \cdots,$$

and

$$c_1 = \frac{4}{7}c_0, \qquad c_2 = \frac{4}{21}c_0, \qquad c_3 = \frac{32}{693}c_0.$$

The general solution on $(0, \infty)$ is

$$y = C_1 \left(1 + \frac{1}{3}x - \frac{1}{6}x^2 - \frac{1}{6}x^3 + \cdots \right) + C_2 x^{5/2} \left(1 + \frac{4}{7}x + \frac{4}{21}x^2 + \frac{32}{693}x^3 + \cdots \right).$$

18. Substituting $y = \sum_{n=0}^{\infty} c_n x^{n+r}$ into the differential equation and collecting terms, we obtain

$$2xy'' + xy' + \left(x^2 - \frac{4}{9} \right) y = \left(r^2 - \frac{4}{9} \right) c_0 x^r + \left(r^2 + 2r + \frac{5}{9} \right) c_1 x^{r+1}$$

$$+ \sum_{k=2}^{\infty} [(k+r)(k+r-1)c_k + (k+r)c_k - \frac{4}{9}c_k + c_{k-2}]x^{k+r}$$

$$= 0,$$

which implies

$$r^2 - \frac{4}{9} = \left(r + \frac{2}{3} \right) \left(r - \frac{2}{3} \right) = 0,$$

$$\left(r^2 + 2r + \frac{5}{9} \right) c_1 = 0,$$

and

$$\left[(k+r)^2 - \frac{4}{9} \right] c_k + c_{k-2} = 0.$$

The indicial roots are $r = -2/3$ and $r = 2/3$, so $c_1 = 0$. For $r = -2/3$ the recurrence relation is

$$c_k = -\frac{9c_{k-2}}{3k(3k-4)}, \quad k = 2, 3, 4, \ldots,$$

and

$$c_2 = -\frac{3}{4}c_0, \quad c_3 = 0, \quad c_4 = \frac{9}{128}c_0.$$

For $r = 2/3$ the recurrence relation is

$$c_k = -\frac{9c_{k-2}}{3k(3k+4)}, \quad k = 2, 3, 4, \ldots,$$

and

$$c_2 = -\frac{3}{20}c_0, \quad c_3 = 0, \quad c_4 = \frac{9}{1,280}c_0.$$

The general solution on $(0, \infty)$ is

$$y = C_1 x^{-2/3} \left(1 - \frac{3}{4}x^2 + \frac{9}{128}x^4 + \cdots \right) + C_2 x^{2/3} \left(1 - \frac{3}{20}x^2 + \frac{9}{1,280}x^4 + \cdots \right).$$

19. Substituting $y = \sum_{n=0}^{\infty} c_n x^{n+r}$ into the differential equation and collecting terms, we obtain

$$9x^2 y'' + 9x^2 y' + 2y = \left(9r^2 - 9r + 2 \right) c_0 x^r$$

$$+ \sum_{k=1}^{\infty} [9(k+r)(k+r-1)c_k + 2c_k + 9(k+r-1)c_{k-1}]x^{k+r}$$

$$= 0,$$

which implies
$$9r^2 - 9r + 2 = (3r - 1)(3r - 2) = 0$$

and
$$[9(k+r)(k+r-1) + 2]c_k + 9(k+r-1)c_{k-1} = 0.$$

The indicial roots are $r = 1/3$ and $r = 2/3$. For $r = 1/3$ the recurrence relation is

$$c_k = -\frac{(3k-2)c_{k-1}}{k(3k-1)}, \quad k = 1, 2, 3, \ldots,$$

and
$$c_1 = -\frac{1}{2}c_0, \quad c_2 = \frac{1}{5}c_0, \quad c_3 = -\frac{7}{120}c_0.$$

For $r = 2/3$ the recurrence relation is

$$c_k = -\frac{(3k-1)c_{k-1}}{k(3k+1)}, \quad k = 1, 2, 3, \ldots,$$

and
$$c_1 = -\frac{1}{2}c_0, \quad c_2 = \frac{5}{28}c_0, \quad c_3 = -\frac{1}{21}c_0.$$

The general solution on $(0, \infty)$ is

$$y = C_1 x^{1/3}\left(1 - \frac{1}{2}x + \frac{1}{5}x^2 - \frac{7}{120}x^3 + \cdots\right) + C_2 x^{2/3}\left(1 - \frac{1}{2}x + \frac{5}{28}x^2 - \frac{1}{21}x^3 + \cdots\right).$$

20. Substituting $y = \sum_{n=0}^{\infty} c_n x^{n+r}$ into the differential equation and collecting terms, we obtain

$$2x^2 y'' + 3xy' + (2x - 1)y = \left(2r^2 + r - 1\right)c_0 x^r$$

$$+ \sum_{k=1}^{\infty}[2(k+r)(k+r-1)c_k + 3(k+r)c_k - c_k + 2c_{k-1}]x^{k+r}$$

$$= 0,$$

which implies
$$2r^2 + r - 1 = (2r - 1)(r + 1) = 0$$

and
$$[(k+r)(2k+2r+1) - 1]c_k + 2c_{k-1} = 0.$$

The indicial roots are $r = -1$ and $r = 1/2$. For $r = -1$ the recurrence relation is

$$c_k = -\frac{2c_{k-1}}{k(2k-3)}, \quad k = 1, 2, 3, \ldots,$$

and
$$c_1 = 2c_0, \quad c_2 = -2c_0, \quad c_3 = \frac{4}{9}c_0.$$

For $r = 1/2$ the recurrence relation is

$$c_k = -\frac{2c_{k-1}}{k(2k+3)}, \quad k = 1, 2, 3, \ldots,$$

and
$$c_1 = -\frac{2}{5}c_0, \qquad c_2 = \frac{2}{35}c_0, \qquad c_3 = -\frac{4}{945}c_0.$$

The general solution on $(0, \infty)$ is
$$y = C_1 x^{-1}\left(1 + 2x - 2x^2 + \frac{4}{9}x^3 + \cdots\right) + C_2 x^{1/2}\left(1 - \frac{2}{5}x + \frac{2}{35}x^2 - \frac{4}{945}x^3 + \cdots\right).$$

21. Substituting $y = \sum_{n=0}^{\infty} c_n x^{n+r}$ into the differential equation and collecting terms, we obtain
$$2x^2 y'' - x(x-1)y' - y = \left(2r^2 - r - 1\right)c_0 x^r$$
$$+ \sum_{k=1}^{\infty} [2(k+r)(k+r-1)c_k + (k+r)c_k - c_k - (k+r-1)c_{k-1}]x^{k+r}$$
$$= 0,$$

which implies
$$2r^2 - r - 1 = (2r+1)(r-1) = 0$$

and
$$[(k+r)(2k+2r-1) - 1]c_k - (k+r-1)2c_{k-1} = 0.$$

The indicial roots are $r = -1/2$ and $r = 1$. For $r = -1/2$ the recurrence relation is
$$c_k = \frac{c_{k-1}}{2k}, \qquad k = 1, 2, 3, \ldots,$$

and
$$c_1 = \frac{1}{2}c_0, \qquad c_2 = \frac{1}{8}c_0, \qquad c_3 = \frac{1}{48}c_0.$$

For $r = 1$ the recurrence relation is
$$c_k = \frac{c_{k-1}}{2k+3}, \qquad k = 1, 2, 3, \ldots,$$

and
$$c_1 = \frac{1}{5}c_0, \qquad c_2 = \frac{1}{35}c_0, \qquad c_3 = \frac{1}{315}c_0.$$

The general solution on $(0, \infty)$ is
$$y = C_1 x^{-1/2}\left(1 + \frac{1}{2}x + \frac{1}{8}x^2 + \frac{1}{48}x^3 + \cdots\right) + C_2 x\left(1 + \frac{1}{5}x + \frac{1}{35}x^2 + \frac{1}{315}x^3 + \cdots\right).$$

22. Substituting $y = \sum_{n=0}^{\infty} c_n x^{n+r}$ into the differential equation and collecting terms, we obtain
$$x(x-2)y'' + y' - 2y = \left(-2r^2 + 3r\right)c_0 x^{r-1}$$
$$+ \sum_{k=0}^{\infty} [(k+r)(k+r-1)c_k - 2c_k - (k+r+1)(2k+2r-1)c_{k+1}]x^{k+r}$$
$$= 0,$$

which implies
$$-2r^2 + 3r = -r(2r - 3) = 0$$

and
$$[(k+r)(k+r-1) - 2]c_k - (k+r+1)(2k+2r-1)c_{k+1} = 0.$$

The indicial roots are $r = 3/2$ and $r = 0$. For $r = 3/2$ the recurrence relation is
$$c_{k+1} = \frac{2k-1}{4(k+1)} c_k, \quad k = 0, 1, 2, \ldots.$$

and
$$c_1 = -\frac{1}{4}c_0, \qquad c_2 = -\frac{1}{32}c_0, \qquad c_3 = -\frac{1}{128}c_0.$$

For $r = 0$ the recurrence relation is
$$c_{k+1} = \frac{k-2}{2k-1} c_k, \quad k = 0, 1, 2, \ldots,$$

and
$$c_1 = 2c_0, \qquad c_2 = -2c_0, \qquad c_3 = 0.$$

The general solution on $(0, \infty)$ is
$$y = C_1 x^{3/2} \left(1 - \frac{1}{4}x - \frac{1}{32}x^2 - \frac{1}{128}x^3 - \cdots \right) + C_2 \left(1 + 2x - 2x^2 \right).$$

23. Substituting $y = \sum_{n=0}^{\infty} c_n x^{n+r}$ into the differential equation and collecting terms, we obtain
$$xy'' + 2y' - xy = \left(r^2 + r \right) c_0 x^{r-1} + \left(r^2 + 3r + 2 \right) c_1 x^r$$

$$+ \sum_{k=2}^{\infty} [(k+r)(k+r-1)c_k + 2(k+r)c_k - c_{k-2}]x^{k+r-1}$$

$$= 0,$$

which implies
$$r^2 + r = r(r+1) = 0,$$
$$\left(r^2 + 3r + 2 \right) c_1 = 0,$$

and
$$(k+r)(k+r+1)c_k - c_{k-2} = 0.$$

The indicial roots are $r_1 = 0$ and $r_2 = -1$, so $c_1 = 0$. For $r_1 = 0$ the recurrence relation is
$$c_k = \frac{c_{k-2}}{k(k+1)}, \quad k = 2, 3, 4, \ldots,$$

and
$$c_2 = \frac{1}{3!}c_0$$

$$c_3 = c_5 = c_7 = \cdots = 0$$

$$c_4 = \frac{1}{5!}c_0$$

$$c_{2n} = \frac{1}{(2n+1)!}c_0.$$

For $r_2 = -1$ the recurrence relation is

$$c_k = \frac{c_{k-2}}{k(k-1)}, \quad k = 2, 3, 4, \ldots,$$

and

$$c_2 = \frac{1}{2!} c_0$$

$$c_3 = c_5 = c_7 = \cdots = 0$$

$$c_4 = \frac{1}{4!} c_0$$

$$c_{2n} = \frac{1}{(2n)!} c_0.$$

The general solution on $(0, \infty)$ is

$$y = C_1 \sum_{n=0}^{\infty} \frac{1}{(2n+1)!} x^{2n} + C_2 x^{-1} \sum_{n=0}^{\infty} \frac{1}{(2n)!} x^{2n}$$

$$= \frac{1}{x} \left[C_1 \sum_{n=0}^{\infty} \frac{1}{(2n+1)!} x^{2n+1} + C_2 \sum_{n=0}^{\infty} \frac{1}{(2n)!} x^{2n} \right]$$

$$= \frac{1}{x} [C_1 \sinh x + C_2 \cosh x].$$

24. Substituting $y = \sum_{n=0}^{\infty} c_n x^{n+r}$ into the differential equation and collecting terms, we obtain

$$x^2 y'' + xy' + \left(x^2 - \frac{1}{4} \right) y = \left(r^2 - \frac{1}{4} \right) c_0 x^r + \left(r^2 + 2r + \frac{3}{4} \right) c_1 x^{r+1}$$

$$+ \sum_{k=2}^{\infty} [(k+r)(k+r-1)c_k + (k+r)c_k - \frac{1}{4} c_k + c_{k-2}] x^{k+r}$$

$$= 0,$$

which implies

$$r^2 - \frac{1}{4} = \left(r - \frac{1}{2} \right) \left(r + \frac{1}{2} \right) = 0,$$

$$\left(r^2 + 2r + \frac{3}{4} \right) c_1 = 0,$$

and

$$\left[(k+r)^2 - \frac{1}{4} \right] c_k + c_{k-2} = 0.$$

The indicial roots are $r_1 = 1/2$ and $r_2 = -1/2$, so $c_1 = 0$. For $r_1 = 1/2$ the recurrence relation is

$$c_k = -\frac{c_{k-2}}{k(k+1)}, \quad k = 2, 3, 4, \ldots,$$

and
$$c_2 = -\frac{1}{3!}c_0$$

$$c_3 = c_5 = c_7 = \cdots = 0$$

$$c_4 = \frac{1}{5!}c_0$$

$$c_{2n} = \frac{(-1)^n}{(2n+1)!}c_0.$$

For $r_2 = -1/2$ the recurrence relation is

$$c_k = -\frac{c_{k-2}}{k(k-1)}, \quad k = 2, 3, 4, \ldots,$$

and
$$c_2 = -\frac{1}{2!}c_0$$

$$c_3 = c_5 = c_7 = \cdots = 0$$

$$c_4 = \frac{1}{4!}c_0$$

$$c_{2n} = \frac{(-1)^n}{(2n)!}c_0.$$

The general solution on $(0, \infty)$ is

$$y = C_1 x^{1/2} \sum_{n=0}^{\infty} \frac{(-1)^n}{(2n+1)!} x^{2n} + C_2 x^{-1/2} \sum_{n=0}^{\infty} \frac{(-1)^n}{(2n)!} x^{2n}$$

$$= C_1 x^{-1/2} \sum_{n=0}^{\infty} \frac{(-1)^n}{(2n+1)!} x^{2n+1} + C_2 x^{-1/2} \sum_{n=0}^{\infty} \frac{(-1)^n}{(2n)!} x^{2n}$$

$$= x^{-1/2}[C_1 \sin x + C_2 \cos x].$$

25. Substituting $y = \sum_{n=0}^{\infty} c_n x^{n+r}$ into the differential equation and collecting terms, we obtain

$$x(x-1)y'' + 3y' - 2y$$

$$= \left(4r - r^2\right) c_0 x^{r-1} + \sum_{k=1}^{\infty} [(k+r-1)(k+r-12)c_{k-1} - (k+r)(k+r-1)c_k$$

$$+ 3(k+r)c_k - 2c_{k-1}]x^{k+r-1}$$

$$= 0,$$

which implies
$$4r - r^2 = r(4 - r) = 0$$

and
$$-(k+r)(k+r-4)c_k + [(k+r-1)(k+r-2) - 2]c_{k-1} = 0.$$

202

The indicial roots are $r_1 = 4$ and $r_2 = 0$. For $r_2 = 0$ the recurrence relation is

$$-k(k-4)c_k + k(k-3)c_{k-1} = 0, \quad k = 1, 2, 3, \ldots,$$

or

$$-(k-4)c_k + (k-3)c_{k-1} = 0, \quad k = 1, 2, 3, \ldots.$$

Then

$$3c_1 - 2c_0 = 0$$

$$2c_2 - c_1 = 0$$

$$c_3 + 0c_2 = 0 \quad \Rightarrow \quad c_3 = 0$$

$$0c_4 + c_3 = 0 \quad \Rightarrow \quad c_4 \text{ is arbitrary}$$

and

$$c_k = \frac{(k-3)c_{k-1}}{c-4}, \quad k = 5, 6, 7, \ldots.$$

Taking $c_0 \neq 0$ and $c_4 = 0$ we obtain

$$c_1 = \frac{2}{3}c_0$$

$$c_2 = \frac{1}{3}c_0$$

$$c_3 = c_4 = c_5 = \cdots = 0.$$

Taking $c_0 = 0$ and $c_4 \neq 0$ we obtain

$$c_1 = c_2 = c_3 = 0$$

$$c_5 = 2c_4$$

$$c_6 = 3c_4$$

$$c_7 = 4c_4.$$

The general solution on $(0, \infty)$ is

$$y = C_1 \left(1 + \frac{2}{3}x + \frac{1}{3}x^2\right) + C_2 \left(x^4 + 2x^5 + 3x^6 + 4x^7 + \cdots\right)$$

$$= C_1 \left(1 + \frac{2}{3}x + \frac{1}{3}x^2\right) + C_2 \sum_{n=1}^{\infty} nx^{n+3}.$$

Exercises 6.4

26. Substituting $y = \sum_{n=0}^{\infty} c_n x^{n+r}$ into the differential equation and collecting terms, we obtain

$$y'' + \frac{3}{x}y' - 2y = \left(r^2 + 2r\right) c_0 x^{r-2} + \left(r^2 + 4r + 3\right) c_1 x^{r-1}$$

$$+ \sum_{k=2}^{\infty} [(k+r)(k+r-1)c_k + 3(k+r)c_k - 2c_{k-2}]x^{k+r-2}$$

$$= 0,$$

which implies

$$r^2 + 2r = r(r+2) = 0$$

$$\left(r^2 + 4r + 3\right) c_1 = 0$$

$$(k+r)(k+r+2)c_k - 2c_{k-2} = 0.$$

The indicial roots are $r_1 = 0$ and $r_2 = -2$, so $c_1 = 0$. For $r_1 = 0$ the recurrence relation is

$$c_k = \frac{2c_{k-2}}{k(k+2)}, \qquad k = 2, 3, 4, \ldots,$$

and

$$c_2 = \frac{1}{4}c_0$$

$$c_3 = c_5 = c_7 = \cdots = 0$$

$$c_4 = \frac{1}{48}c_0$$

$$c_6 = \frac{1}{1{,}152}c_0.$$

The result is

$$y_1 = c_0 \left(1 + \frac{1}{4}x^2 + \frac{1}{48}x^4 + \frac{1}{1{,}152}c_6 + \cdots\right).$$

A second solution is

$$y_2 = y_1 \int \frac{e^{-\int(3/x)dx}}{y_1^2} \, dx = y_1 \int \frac{dx}{x^3 \left(1 + \frac{1}{4}x^2 + \frac{1}{48}x^4 + \cdots\right)^2}$$

$$= y_1 \int \frac{dx}{x^3 \left(1 + \frac{1}{2}x^2 + \frac{5}{48}x^4 + \frac{7}{576}x^6 + \cdots\right)} = y_1 \int \frac{1}{x^3} \left(1 - \frac{1}{2}x^2 + \frac{7}{48}x^4 + \frac{19}{576}x^6 + \cdots\right)$$

$$= y_1 \int \left(\frac{1}{x^3} - \frac{1}{2x} + \frac{7}{48}x - \frac{19}{576}x^3 + \cdots \right) = y_1 \left[-\frac{1}{2x^2} - \frac{1}{2}\ln x + \frac{7}{96}x^2 - \frac{19}{2,304}x^4 + \cdots \right]$$

$$= -\frac{1}{2}y_1 \ln x + y \left[-\frac{1}{2x^2} + \frac{7}{96}x^2 - \frac{19}{2,304}x^4 + \cdots \right].$$

The general solution on $(0, \infty)$ is

$$y = C_1 y_1(x) + C_2 y_2(x).$$

27. Substituting $y = \sum_{n=0}^{\infty} c_n x^{n+r}$ into the differential equation and collecting terms, we obtain

$$xy'' + (1 - x)y' - y = r^2 c_0 x^{r-1} + \sum_{k=0}^{\infty} [(k+r)(k+r-1)c_k + (k+r)c_k - (k+r)c_{k-1}]x^{k+r-1} = 0,$$

which implies $r^2 = 0$ and

$$(k+r)^2 c_k - (k+r)c_{k-1} = 0.$$

The indicial roots are $r_1 = r_2 = 0$ and the recurrence relation is

$$c_k = \frac{c_{k-1}}{k}, \quad k = 1, 2, 3, \ldots.$$

One solution is

$$y_1 = c_0 \left(1 + x + \frac{1}{2}x^2 + \frac{1}{3!}x^3 + \cdots \right) = c_0 e^x.$$

A second solution is

$$y_2 = y_1 \int \frac{e^{-\int (1/x - 1)dx}}{e^{2x}}\, dx = e^x \int \frac{e^x/x}{e^{2x}}\, dx = e^x \int \frac{1}{x}e^{-x}dx$$

$$= e^x \int \frac{1}{x}\left(1 - x + \frac{1}{2}x^2 - \frac{1}{3!}x^3 + \cdots \right) dx = e^x \int \left(\frac{1}{x} - 1 + \frac{1}{2}x - \frac{1}{3!}x^2 + \cdots \right) dx$$

$$= e^x \left[\ln x - x + \frac{1}{2 \cdot 2}x^2 - \frac{1}{3 \cdot 3!}x^3 + \cdots \right] = e^x \ln x - e^x \sum_{n=1}^{\infty} \frac{(-1)^{n+1}}{n \cdot n!}x^n.$$

The general solution on $(0, \infty)$ is

$$y = C_1 e^x + C_2 e^x \left(\ln x - \sum_{n=1}^{\infty} \frac{(-1)^{n+1}}{n \cdot n!}x^n \right).$$

28. Substituting $y = \sum_{n=0}^{\infty} c_n x^{n+r}$ into the differential equation and collecting terms, we obtain

$$xy'' + y = \left(r^2 - r \right) c_0 x^{r-1} + \sum_{k=0}^{\infty} [(k+r+1)(k+r)c_{k+1} + c_k]x^{k+r} = 0,$$

which implies

$$r^2 - r = r(r - 1) = 0$$

$$(k+r+1)(k+r)c_{k+1} + c_k = 0.$$

The indicial roots are $r_1 = 1$ and $r_2 = 0$. For $r_1 = 1$ the recurrence relation is

$$c_{k+1} = \frac{-c_k}{(k+2)(k+1)}, \qquad k = 0, 1, 2, \ldots,$$

and

$$c_1 = -\frac{1}{2}c_0$$

$$c_2 = \frac{1}{3! \cdot 2}c_0$$

$$c_3 = -\frac{1}{4!3!}c_0$$

$$c_4 = \frac{1}{5!4!}c_0.$$

The result is

$$y_1 = c_0\left(x - \frac{1}{2}x^2 + \frac{1}{3!2}x^3 - \frac{1}{4!3!}x^4 + \frac{1}{5!4!}x^5 - \cdots\right).$$

A second solution is

$$y_2 = y_1 \int \frac{e^{\int 0\, dx}}{y_1^2}\, dx = y_1 \int \frac{1}{y_1^2}\, dx = y_1 \int \frac{dx}{\left(x - \frac{1}{2}x^2 + \frac{1}{3!2}x^3 - \frac{1}{4!3!}x^4 + \cdots\right)^2}$$

$$= y_1 \int \frac{dx}{x^2 - x^3 + \frac{5}{3!2}x^4 - \frac{14}{4!3!}x^5 + \cdots} = y_1 \int \frac{dx}{x^2\left(1 - x + \frac{5}{3!2}x^2 - \frac{14}{4!3!}x^3 + \cdots\right)}$$

$$= y_1 \int \frac{1}{x^2}\left(1 + x + \frac{7}{3!2}x^2 + \frac{38}{4!3!}x^3 + \cdots\right) dx = y_1 \int \left(\frac{1}{x^2} + \frac{1}{x} + \frac{7}{3!2} + \frac{38}{4!3!}x + \cdots\right) dx$$

$$= y_1\left(-\frac{1}{x} + \ln x + \frac{7}{3!2}x + \frac{19}{4!3!}x^2 + \cdots\right).$$

The general solution is

$$y_1(x) = C_1 y_1 + C_2 y_1\left(-\frac{1}{x} + \ln x + \frac{7}{3!2}x + \frac{19}{4!3!}x^2 + \cdots\right).$$

29. Substituting $y = \sum_{n=0}^{\infty} c_n x^{n+r}$ into the differential equation and collecting terms, we obtain

$$xy'' + y' + y = r^2 c_0 x^{r-1} + \sum_{k=1}^{\infty}[(k+r)(k+r-1)c_k + (k+r)c_k + c_{k-1}]x^{k+r-1} = 0$$

which implies $r^2 = 0$ and

$$(k+r)^2 c_k + c_{k-1} = 0.$$

The indicial roots are $r_1 = r_2 = 0$ and the recurrence relation is

$$c_k = -\frac{c_{k-1}}{k^2}, \qquad k = 1, 2, 3, \ldots.$$

One solution is

$$y_1 = c_0 \left(1 - x + \frac{1}{2^2}x^2 - \frac{1}{(3!)^2}x^3 + \frac{1}{(4!)^2}x^4 - \cdots \right) = c_0 \sum_{n=0}^{\infty} \frac{(-1)^n}{(n!)^2} x^n.$$

A second solution is

$$y_2 = y_1 \int \frac{e^{-\int (1/x)dx}}{y_1^2} \, dx = y_1 \int \frac{dx}{x \left(1 - x + \frac{1}{4}x^2 - \frac{1}{36}x^3 + \cdots \right)^2}$$

$$= y_1 \int \frac{dx}{x \left(1 - 2x + \frac{3}{2}x^2 - \frac{5}{9}x^3 + \frac{35}{288}x^4 - \cdots \right)}$$

$$= y_1 \int \frac{1}{x} \left(1 + 2x + \frac{5}{2}x^2 + \frac{23}{9}x^3 + \frac{677}{288}x^4 + \cdots \right) dx$$

$$= y_1 \int \left(\frac{1}{x} + 2 + \frac{5}{2}x + \frac{23}{9}x^2 + \frac{677}{288}x^3 + \cdots \right) dx$$

$$= y_1 \left[\ln x + 2x + \frac{5}{4}x^2 + \frac{23}{27}x^3 + \frac{677}{1,152}x^4 + \cdots \right]$$

$$= y_1 \ln x + y_1 \left(2x + \frac{5}{4}x^2 + \frac{23}{27}x^3 + \frac{677}{1,152}x^4 + \cdots \right).$$

The general solution on $(0, \infty)$ is

$$y = C_1 y_1(x) + C_2 y_2(x).$$

30. Substituting $y = \sum_{n=0}^{\infty} c_n x^{n+r}$ into the differential equation and collecting terms, we obtain

$$xy'' - xy' + y = \left(r^2 - r \right) c_0 x^{r-1} + \sum_{k=0}^{\infty} [(k+r+1)(k+r)c_{k+1} - (k+r)c_k + c_k]x^{k+r} = 0$$

which implies

$$r^2 - r = r(r-1) = 0$$

and

$$(k+r+1)(k+r)c_{k+1} - (k+r-1)c_k = 0.$$

The indicial roots are $r_1 = 1$ and $r_2 = 0$. For $r_1 = 1$ the recurrence relation is

$$c_{k+1} = \frac{kc_k}{(k+2)(k+1)}, \quad k = 0, 1, 2, \ldots,$$

and one solution is $y_1 = c_0 x$. A second solution is

$$y_2 = x \int \frac{e^{-\int -dx}}{x^2}\, dx = x \int \frac{e^x}{x^2}\, dx = x \int \frac{1}{x^2}\left(1 + x + \frac{1}{2}x^2 + \frac{1}{3!}x^3 + \cdots\right) dx$$

$$= x \int \left(\frac{1}{x^2} + \frac{1}{x} + \frac{1}{2} + \frac{1}{3!}x + \frac{1}{4!}x^2 + \cdots\right) dx = x \left[-\frac{1}{x} + \ln x + \frac{1}{2}x + \frac{1}{12}x^2 + \frac{1}{72}x^3 + \cdots\right]$$

$$= x \ln x - 1 + \frac{1}{2}x^2 + \frac{1}{12}x^3 + \frac{1}{72}x^4 + \cdots.$$

The general solution on $(0, \infty)$ is

$$y = C_1 x + C_2 y_2(x).$$

31. Substituting $y = \sum_{n=0}^{\infty} c_n x^{n+r}$ into the differential equation and collecting terms, we obtain

$$x^2 y'' + x(x-1)y' + y = \left(r^2 - 2r + 1\right) c_0 x^r$$

$$+ \sum_{k=1}^{\infty}[(k+r)(k+r-1)c_k - (k+r-1)c_k + (k+r-1)c_{k-1}]x^{k+r}$$

$$= 0$$

which implies $r^2 - 2r + 1 = (r-1)^2 = 0$

and $(k+r-1)^2 c_k + (k+r-1)c_{k-1} = 0.$

The indicial roots are $r_1 = r_2 = 1$ and the recurrence relation is

$$c_k = -\frac{c_{k-1}}{k}, \quad k = 1, 2, 3, \ldots.$$

One solution is

$$y_1 = c_0 x \left(1 - x + \frac{1}{2}x^2 - \frac{1}{3!}x^3 + \cdots\right) = c_0 x e^{-x}.$$

A second solution is

$$y_2 = y_1 \int \frac{e^{-\int(1-1/x)dx}}{x^2 e^{-2x}}\, dx = y_1 \int \frac{xe^{-x}}{x^2 e^{-2x}}\, dx = y_1 \int \frac{1}{x}e^x dx$$

$$= y_1 \int \frac{1}{x}\left(1 + x + \frac{1}{2}x^2 + \frac{1}{3!}x^3 + \cdots\right) dx = y_1 \int \left(\frac{1}{x} + 1 + \frac{1}{2}x + \frac{1}{3!}x^2 + \cdots\right) dx$$

$$= y_1 \left[\ln x + x + \frac{1}{4}x^2 + \frac{1}{18}x^3 + \cdots\right].$$

The general solution on $(0, \infty)$ is

$$y = C_1 y_1(x) + C_2 y_2(x).$$

32. Substituting $y = \sum_{n=0}^{\infty} c_n x^{n+r}$ into the differential equation and collecting terms, we obtain

$$xy'' + y' - 4xy = r^2 c_0 x^{r-1} + \left(r^2 + 2r + 1\right) c_1 x^r$$

$$+ \sum_{k=2}^{\infty} [(k+r)(k+r-1)c_k + (k+r)c_k - 4c_{k-2}] x^{k+r-1}$$

$$= 0$$

which implies

$$r^2 = 0,$$

$$\left(r^2 + 2r + 1\right) c_1 = 0,$$

and

$$(k+r)^2 c_k - 4c_{k-2} = 0.$$

The indicial roots are $r_1 = r_2 = 0$, so $c_1 = 0$ and the recurrence relation is

$$c_k = \frac{4c_{k-2}}{k^2}, \quad k = 2, 3, 4, \dots.$$

One solution is

$$y_1 = c_0 \left(1 + x^2 + \frac{1}{4}x^4 + \frac{1}{36}x^6 + \cdots\right).$$

A second solution is

$$y_2 = y_1 \int \frac{e^{-\int (1/x)dx}}{y_1^2} \, dx = y_1 \int \frac{dx}{x\left(1 + x^2 + \frac{1}{4}x^4 + \frac{1}{36}x^6 + \cdots\right)^2}$$

$$= y_1 \int \frac{dx}{x\left(1 + 2x^2 + \frac{3}{2}x^4 + \frac{5}{9}x^6 + \cdots\right)} = y_1 \int \frac{1}{x}\left(1 - 2x^2 + \frac{5}{2}x^4 - \frac{23}{9}x^6 + \cdots\right) dx$$

$$= y_1 \int \left(\frac{1}{x} - 2x + \frac{5}{2}x^3 - \frac{23}{9}x^5 + \cdots\right) dx = y_1 \left[\ln x - x^2 + \frac{5}{8}x^4 - \frac{23}{54}x^6 + \cdots\right]$$

$$= y_1 \ln x + y_1 \left(-x^2 + \frac{5}{8}x^4 - \frac{23}{54}x^6 + \cdots\right).$$

The general solution on $(0, \infty)$ is

$$y = C_1 y_1(x) + C_2 y_2(x).$$

33. Substituting $y = \sum_{n=0}^{\infty} c_n x^{n+r}$ into the differential equation and collecting terms, we obtain

$$xy'' + (x-1)y' - 2y = r^2 c_0 x^{r-1} + \sum_{k=1}^{\infty} [(k+r)(k+r-1)c_k$$

$$- (k+r)c_k + (k+r-3)c_{k-1}]x^{k+r-1}$$

$$= 0$$

which implies $r^2 = 0$ and

$$(k+r)(k+r-2)c_k + (k+r-3)c_{k-1} = 0.$$

The indicial roots are $r_1 = r_2 = 0$ and the recurrence relation is

$$k(k-2)c_k + (k-3)c_{k-1} = 0, \quad k = 1, 2, 3, \dots.$$

Then

$$-c_1 - 2c_0 = 0 \quad \Rightarrow \quad c_1 = -2c_0$$

$$0c_2 - c_1 = 0 \quad \Rightarrow \quad c_1 = 0 \text{ and } c_2 \text{ is arbitrary}$$

$$3c_3 + 0c_2 = 0 \quad \Rightarrow \quad c_3 = 0$$

and

$$c_k = -\frac{(k-3)c_{k-1}}{k(k-2)}, \quad k = 4, 5, 6, \dots.$$

Since $c_1 = 0$ and $c_1 = -2c_0$, we have $c_0 = 0$. Taking $c_2 = 0$ we obtain $c_3 = c_4 = c_5 = \cdots = 0$. Thus, $y_1 = c_2 x^2$. A second solution is

$$y_2 = x^2 \int \frac{e^{-\int(1-1/x)\,dx}}{x^4}\,dx = x^2 \int \frac{xe^{-x}}{x^4}\,dx = x^2 \int \frac{1}{x^3}\left(1 - x + \frac{1}{2}x^2 - \frac{1}{3!}x^3 + \frac{1}{4!}x^4 - \cdots\right)dx$$

$$= x^2 \int \left(\frac{1}{x^3} - \frac{1}{x^2} + \frac{1}{2x} - \frac{1}{3!} + \frac{1}{4!}x - \cdots\right)dx = x^2\left[-\frac{1}{2x^2} + \frac{1}{x} + \frac{1}{2}\ln x - \frac{1}{6}x + \frac{1}{48}x^2 - \cdots\right]$$

$$= \frac{1}{2}x^2 \ln x - \frac{1}{2} + x - \frac{1}{6}x^3 + \frac{1}{48}x^4 - \cdots.$$

34. Substituting $y = \sum_{n=0}^{\infty} c_n x^{n+r}$ into the differential equation and collecting terms, we obtain

$$xy'' - y' + x^3 y = \left(r^2 - 2r\right)c_0 x^{r-1} + \left(r^2 - 1\right)c_1 x^r$$

$$+ \left(r^2 + 2r\right)c_2 x^{r+1} + \left(r^2 + 4r + 3\right)c_3 x^{r+2}$$

$$+ \sum_{k=4}^{\infty} [(k+r)(k+r-1)c_k - (k+r)c_k + c_{k-4}]x^{k+r-1}$$

$$= 0$$

210

which implies

$$r^2 - 2r = r(r - 2) = 0,$$

$$\left(r^2 - 1\right)c_1 = 0,$$

$$r^2 + 2r = r(r + 2)c_2 = 0,$$

$$\left(r^2 + 4r + 3\right)c_3 = 0,$$

and

$$(k + r)(k + r - 2)c_k + c_{k-4} = 0.$$

The indicial roots are $r = 2$ and $r = 0$, so $c_1 = c_3 = 0$. Also, when $r = 2$, $c_2 = 0$; but when $r = 0$, c_2 is arbitrary. For $r = 0$ the recurrence relation is

$$c_k = -\frac{c_{k-4}}{k(k-2)}, \quad k = 4, 5, 6, \ldots .$$

Taking c_0 arbitrary and $c_2 = 0$ we find

$$c_4 = -\frac{1}{8}c_0$$

$$c_5 = c_6 = c_7 = 0$$

$$c_8 = \frac{1}{384}c_0$$

$$c_9 = c_{10} = c_{11} = 0.$$

One solution is

$$y_1 = c_0 \left(1 - \frac{1}{8}x^4 + \frac{1}{384}x^8 - \cdots\right).$$

Taking $c_0 = 0$ and c_2 arbitrary we find

$$c_3 = c_4 = c_5 = 0$$

$$c_6 = -\frac{1}{24}c_2$$

$$c_7 = c_8 = c_9 = 0$$

$$c_{10} = \frac{1}{1,920}c_2.$$

A second solution is

$$y_2 = c_2 \left(x^2 - \frac{1}{24}x^6 + \frac{1}{1,920}x^{10} - \cdots\right).$$

The general solution on $(0, \infty)$ is

$$y = C_1 y_1(x) + C_2 y_2(x).$$

35. Substituting $y = \sum_{n=0}^{\infty} c_n x^{n+r}$ into the differential equation and collecting terms, we obtain

$$x^3 y'' + y = c_0 x^r + \sum_{k=1}^{\infty} [c_k + (k+r-1)(k+r-2)c_{k-1}]x^{k+r} = 0.$$

It follows that $c_0 = 0$ and

$$c_k = -(k+r-1)(k+r-2)c_{k-1}.$$

The only solution we obtain is $y(x) = 0$.

36. Substituting $y = \sum_{n=0}^{\infty} c_n x^{n+r}$ into the differential equation and collecting terms, we obtain

$$x^2 y'' - y' + y = rc_0 x^{r-1} + \sum_{k=0}^{\infty} ([(k+r)(k+r-1)+1]c_k - (k+r+1)c_{k+1}) x^{k+r} = 0.$$

Thus $r = 0$ and the recurrence relation is

$$c_{k+1} = \frac{k(k-1)+1}{k+1} c_k, \qquad k = 0, 1, 2, \dots .$$

Then

$$c_1 = 0, \qquad c_2 = \frac{1}{2}c_0, \qquad c_3 = \frac{1}{2}c_0, \qquad c_4 = \frac{7}{8}c_0,$$

and so on. Therefore, one solution is

$$y(x) = c_0 \left[1 + x + \frac{1}{2}x^2 + \frac{1}{2}x^3 + \frac{7}{8}x^4 + \cdots \right].$$

37. Substituting $y = \sum_{n=0}^{\infty} c_n x^{n+r}$ into the differential equation and collecting terms, we obtain

$$x^2 y'' + 3xy' - 8y = \sum_{n=0}^{\infty} [(n+r)(n+r-1)c_n + 3(n+r)c_n - 8c_n]x^{n+r}$$

$$= [r(r-1) + 3r - 8]c_0 + \sum_{n=1}^{\infty} [(n+r)(n+r+2) - 8]c_n x^{n+r}$$

$$= 0.$$

Taking $c_0 \neq 0$ and $c_n = 0$ for $n = 1, 2, 3, \dots$, we have

$$r(r-1) + 3r - 8 = r^2 + 2r - 8 = (r+4)(r-2) = 0.$$

The general solution is $y = C_1 x^{-4} + C_2 x^2$.

38. Assume $x = 0$ is a regular singular point so that

$$xP(x) = \sum_{n=0}^{\infty} p_n x^n \quad \text{and} \quad x^2 Q(x) = \sum_{n=0}^{\infty} q_n x^n.$$

Multiplying both sides of $y'' + P(x)y' + Q(x)y = 0$ by x^2 we have

$$x^2 y'' + x(xP(x))y' + (x^2 Q(x)) y = 0$$

or

$$x^2 y'' + x \left(\sum_{n=0}^{\infty} p_n x^n \right) y' + \left(\sum_{n=0}^{\infty} q_n x^n \right) y = 0.$$

Substituting $y = \sum_{n=0}^{\infty} c_n x^{n+r}$ into the differential equation we obtain

$$x^2 \sum_{n=0}^{\infty} (n+r)(n+r-1) c_n x^{n+r-2} + x \left(\sum_{n=0}^{\infty} p_n x^n \right) \left(\sum_{n=0}^{\infty} (n+r) c_n x^{n+r-1} \right)$$

$$+ \left(\sum_{n=0}^{\infty} q_n x^n \right) \left(\sum_{n=0}^{\infty} c_n x^{n+r} \right)$$

$$= \left(\sum_{n=0}^{\infty} (n+r)(n+r-1) c_n x^{n+r} \right) + \left(\sum_{n=0}^{\infty} p_n x^n \right) \left(\sum_{n=0}^{\infty} (n+r) c_n x^{n+r} \right)$$

$$+ \left(\sum_{n=0}^{\infty} q_n x^n \right) \left(\sum_{n=0}^{\infty} c_n x^{n+r} \right)$$

$$= 0.$$

The coefficient of the lowest power of x, obtained when $n = 0$, is

$$r(r-1)c_0 + p_0 r c_0 + q_0 c_0 = [r(r-1) + p_0 r + q_0] c_0.$$

The indicial equation is then $r(r-1) + p_0 r + q_0 = 0$.

39. Identifying $p_0 = 5/3$ and $q_0 = -1/3$, the indicial equation is

$$r(r-1) + \frac{5}{3}r - \frac{1}{3} = r^2 + \frac{2}{3}r - \frac{1}{3} = (r+1)\left(r - \frac{1}{3}\right) = 0.$$

The indicial roots are -1 and $1/3$.

40. (a) Substituting $w = 1/x$, the differential equation becomes

$$w^2 \frac{d^2 y}{dw^2} + 2w \frac{dy}{dw} - 4y = 0$$

and we see that there is a singular point at ∞.

(b) Identifying $P(w) = 2w$ and $Q(w) = -4/w^2$ we see that ∞ is a regular singular point.

Exercises 6.5

1. Since $\nu^2 = 1/9$ the general solution is $y = c_1 J_{1/3}(x) + c_2 J_{-1/3}(x)$.

2. Since $\nu^2 = 1$ the general solution is $y = c_1 J_1(x) + c_2 Y_1(x)$.

3. Since $\nu^2 = 25/4$ the general solution is $y = c_1 J_{5/2}(x) + c_2 J_{-5/2}(x)$.

4. Since $\nu^2 = 1/16$ the general solution is $y = c_1 J_{1/4}(x) + c_2 J_{-1/4}(x)$.

5. Since $\nu^2 = 0$ the general solution is $y = c_1 J_0(x) + c_2 Y_0(x)$.

6. Since $\nu^2 = 4$ the general solution is $y = c_1 J_2(x) + c_2 Y_2(x)$.

7. Since $\nu^2 = 2$ the general solution is $y = c_1 J_2(3x) + c_2 Y_2(3x)$.

8. Since $\nu^2 = 1/4$ the general solution is $y = c_1 J_{1/2}(6x) + c_2 J_{-1/2}(6x)$.

9. If $y = x^{-1/2} v(x)$ then

$$y' = x^{-1/2} v'(x) - \frac{1}{2} x^{-3/2} v(x),$$

$$y'' = x^{-1/2} v''(x) - x^{-3/2} v'(x) + \frac{3}{4} x^{-5/2} v(x),$$

and

$$x^2 y'' + 2xy' + \lambda^2 x^2 y = x^{3/2} v'' + x^{1/2} v' + \left(\lambda^2 x^{3/2} - \frac{1}{4} x^{-1/2} \right) v.$$

Multiplying by $x^{1/2}$ we obtain

$$x^2 v'' + x v' + \left(\lambda^2 x^2 - \frac{1}{4} \right) v = 0,$$

whose solution is $v = c_1 J_{1/2}(\lambda x) + c_2 J_{-1/2}(\lambda x)$. Then $y = c_1 x^{-1/2} J_{1/2}(\lambda x) + c_2 x^{-1/2} J_{-1/2}(\lambda x)$.

10. From $y = x^n J_n(x)$ we find

$$y' = x^n J_n' + nx^{n-1} J_n \qquad \text{and} \qquad y'' = x^n J_n'' + 2nx^{n-1} J_n' + n(n-1)x^{n-2} J_n.$$

Substituting into the differential equation, we have

$$x^{n+1} J_n'' + 2nx^n J_n' + n(n-1)x^{n-1} J_n + (1 - 2n)(x^n J_n' + nx^{n-1} J_n) + x^{n+1} J_n$$

$$= x^{n+1} J_n'' + (2n + 1 - 2n)x^n J_n' + (n^2 - n + n - 2n^2)x^{n-1} J_n + x^{n+1} J_n$$

$$= x^{n+1} [x^2 J_n'' + x J_n' - n^2 J_n + x^2 J_n]$$

$$= x^{n+1} [x^2 J_n'' + x J_n' + (x^2 - n^2) J_n]$$

$$= x^{n-1} \cdot 0 \qquad \text{(since } J_n \text{ is a solution of Bessel's equation)}$$

$$= 0.$$

Therefore, $x^n J_n$ is a solution of the original equation.

11. From $y = x^{-n} J_n$ we find

$$y' = x^{-n} J_n' - nx^{-n-1} J_n \quad \text{and} \quad y'' = x^{-n} J_n'' - 2nx^{-n-1} J_n' + n(n+1)x^{-n-2} J_n.$$

Substituting into the differential equation, we have

$$xy'' + (1 + 2n)y' + xy = x^{-n-1}\left[x^2 J_n'' + x J_n' + \left(x^2 - n^2\right) J_n\right]$$

$$= x^{-n-1} \cdot 0 \qquad \text{(since } J_n \text{ is a solution of Bessel's equation)}$$

$$= 0.$$

Therefore, $x^{-n} J_n$ is a solution of the original equation.

12. From $y = \sqrt{x}\, J_\nu(\lambda x)$ we find

$$y' = \lambda \sqrt{x}\, J_\nu'(\lambda x) + \frac{1}{2} x^{-1/2} J_\nu(\lambda x)$$

and

$$y'' = \lambda^2 \sqrt{x}\, J_\nu''(\lambda x) + \lambda x^{-1/2} J_\nu'(\lambda x) - \frac{1}{4} x^{-3/2} J_\nu(\lambda x).$$

Substituting into the differential equation, we have

$$x^2 y'' + \left(\lambda^2 x^2 - \nu^2 + \frac{1}{4}\right) y = \sqrt{x}\left[\lambda^2 x^2 J_\nu''(\lambda x) + \lambda x J_\nu'(\lambda x) + \left(\lambda^2 x^2 - \nu^2\right) J_\nu(\lambda x)\right]$$

$$= \sqrt{x} \cdot 0 \qquad \text{(since } J_n \text{ is a solution of Bessel's equation)}$$

$$= 0.$$

Therefore, $\sqrt{x}\, J_\nu(\lambda x)$ is a solution of the original equation.

13. From Problem 10 with $n = 1/2$ we find $y = x^{1/2} J_{1/2}(x)$. From Problem 11 with $n = -1/2$ we find $y = x^{1/2} J_{-1/2}(x)$.

14. From Problem 10 with $n = 1$ we find $y = x J_1(x)$. From Problem 11 with $n = -1$ we find $y = x J_{-1}(x) = -x J_1(x)$.

15. From Problem 10 with $n = -1$ we find $y = x^{-1} J_{-1}(x)$. From Problem 11 with $n = 1$ we find $y = x^{-1} J_1(x) = -x^{-1} J_{-1}(x)$.

16. From Problem 12 with $\lambda = 2$ and $\nu = 0$ we find $y = \sqrt{x}\, J_0(2x)$.

17. From Problem 12 with $\lambda = 1$ and $\nu = \pm 3/2$ we find $y = \sqrt{x}\, J_{3/2}(x)$ and $y = \sqrt{x}\, J_{-3/2}(x)$.

18. From Problem 10 with $n = 3$ we find $y = x^3 J_3(x)$. From Problem 11 with $n = -3$ we find $y = x^3 J_{-3}(x) = -x^3 J_3(x)$.

Exercises 6.5

19. The recurrence relation follows from

$$-\nu J_\nu(x) + x J_{\nu-1}(x) = -\sum_{n=0}^{\infty} \frac{(-1)^n \nu}{n!\Gamma(1+\nu+n)} \left(\frac{x}{2}\right)^{2n+\nu} + x \sum_{n=0}^{\infty} \frac{(-1)^n}{n!\Gamma(\nu+n)} \left(\frac{x}{2}\right)^{2n+\nu-1}$$

$$= -\sum_{n=0}^{\infty} \frac{(-1)^n \nu}{n!\Gamma(1+\nu+n)} \left(\frac{x}{2}\right)^{2n+\nu} + \sum_{n=0}^{\infty} \frac{(-1)^n(\nu+n)}{n!\Gamma(1+\nu+n)} \cdot 2\left(\frac{x}{2}\right)\left(\frac{x}{2}\right)^{2n+\nu-1}$$

$$= \sum_{n=0}^{\infty} \frac{(-1)^n(2n+\nu)}{n!\Gamma(1+\nu+n)} \left(\frac{x}{2}\right)^{2n+\nu} = x J_\nu'(x).$$

20. Using

$$J_\nu(x) = \sum_{n=0}^{\infty} \frac{(-1)^n}{n!\Gamma(1+\nu+n)} \left(\frac{x}{2}\right)^{2n+\nu}$$

$$J_\nu'(x) = \sum_{n=0}^{\infty} \frac{(2n+\nu)(-1)^n}{2n!\Gamma(1+\nu+n)} \left(\frac{x}{2}\right)^{2n+\nu-1}$$

$$J_{\nu-1}(x) = \sum_{n=0}^{\infty} \frac{(-1)^n}{n!\Gamma(\nu+n)} \left(\frac{x}{2}\right)^{2n+\nu-1}$$

we obtain

$$\frac{d}{dx}[x^\nu J_\nu(x)] = x^\nu J_\nu'(x) + \nu x^{\nu-1} J_\nu(x)$$

$$= x^\nu \sum_{n=0}^{\infty} \frac{(2n+\nu)(-1)^n}{2n!\Gamma(1+\nu+n)} \left(\frac{x}{2}\right)^{2n+\nu-1}$$

$$+ \nu x^{\nu-1} \sum_{n=0}^{\infty} \frac{(-1)^n}{n!\Gamma(1+\nu+n)} \left(\frac{x}{2}\right)^{2n+\nu}$$

$$= x^\nu \sum_{n=0}^{\infty} \frac{(2n+\nu)(-1)^n}{2n!(\nu+n)\Gamma(\nu+n)} \left(\frac{x}{2}\right)^{2n+\nu-1}$$

$$+ x^\nu \sum_{n=0}^{\infty} \frac{\nu(-1)^n 2^{-1}}{n!(\nu+n)\Gamma(\nu+n)} \left(\frac{x}{2}\right)^{-1}\left(\frac{x}{2}\right)^{2n+\nu}$$

$$= x^\nu \left[\sum_{n=0}^{\infty} \frac{(2n+\nu)(-1)^n}{2n!(\nu+n)\Gamma(\nu+n)} \left(\frac{x}{2}\right)^{2n+\nu-1} \right.$$

$$\left. + \sum_{n=0}^{\infty} \frac{\nu(-1)^n}{2n!(\nu+n)\Gamma(\nu+n)} \left(\frac{x}{2}\right)^{2n+\nu-1} \right]$$

216

$$= x^\nu \sum_{n=0}^{\infty} \frac{(2n+2\nu)(-1)^n}{2n!(\nu+n)\Gamma(\nu+n)} \left(\frac{x}{2}\right)^{2n+\nu-1}$$

$$= x^\nu \sum_{n=0}^{\infty} \frac{(-1)^n}{n!\Gamma(\nu+n)} \left(\frac{x}{2}\right)^{2n+\nu-1}$$

$$= x^\nu J_{\nu-1}(x).$$

Alternatively, we can note that the formula in Problem 19 is a linear first-order differential equation in $J_\nu(x)$. An integrating factor for this equation is x^ν, so $\dfrac{d}{dx}[x^\nu J_\nu(x)] = x^\nu J_{\nu-1}(x)$.

21. The recurrence relation follows from

$$x J_{\nu+1}(x) + x J_{\nu-1}(x) = \sum_{n=0}^{\infty} \frac{(-1)^{n-1} 2n}{n!\Gamma(1+\nu+n)} \left(\frac{x}{2}\right)^{2n+\nu} + \sum_{n=0}^{\infty} \frac{(-1)^n 2(\nu+n)}{n!\Gamma(1+\nu+n)} \left(\frac{x}{2}\right)^{2n+\nu}$$

$$= \sum_{n=0}^{\infty} \frac{(-1)^n 2\nu}{n!\Gamma(1+\nu+n)} \left(\frac{x}{2}\right)^{2n+\nu} = 2\nu J_\nu(x).$$

22. The recurrence relation follows from Example 3 in the text and Problem 21:

$$2 J_\nu'(x) = \frac{1}{x}[2\nu J_\nu(x) - 2 J_{\nu+1}(x)] = \frac{1}{x}[x J_{\nu+1}(x) + x J_{\nu-1}(x)] - 2 J_{\nu+1}(x) = J_{\nu-1}(x) - J_{\nu+1}(x).$$

23. By Problem 20 $\dfrac{d}{dx}[x J_1(x)] = x J_0(x)$ so that $\displaystyle\int_0^x r J_0(r)\, dr = r J_1(r) \Big|_{r=0}^{r=x} = x J_1(x).$

24. By Problem 19 we obtain $J_0'(x) = J_{-1}(x)$ and by Problem 22

$$2 J_0'(x) = J_{-1}(x) - J_1(x) = J_0'(x) - J_1(x)$$

so that $J_0'(x) = -J_1(x)$.

25. Using Problem 20 and 24 and integration by parts we have

$$\int x^n J_0(x)\, dx = \int x^{n-1}(x J_0(x))\, dx = \int x^{n-1} \frac{d}{dx}(x J_1(x))\, dx$$

$$= x^{n-1} x J_1(x) - (n-1) \int x^{n-2} x J_1(x)\, dx$$

$$= x^n J_1(x) - (n-1) \int x^{n-1}(-J_0'(x))\, dx$$

$$= x^n J_1(x) + (n-1) x^{n-1} J_0(x) - (n-1)^2 \int x^{n-2} J_0(x)\, dx.$$

26. Using Problem 25 with $n = 3$ and Problem 23 we have

$$\int x^3 J_0(x)\, dx = x^3 J_1(x) + 2x^2 J_0(x) - 4 \int x J_0(x)\, dx$$

$$= x^3 J_1(x) + 2x^2 J_0(x) - 4x J_1(x) + c.$$

217

27. Since

$$\Gamma\left(1 - \frac{1}{2} + n\right) = \frac{(2n-1)!}{(n-1)!2^{2n-1}}$$

we obtain

$$J_{-1/2}(x) = \sum_{n=0}^{\infty} \frac{(-1)^n 2^{1/2} x^{-1/2}}{2n(2n-1)!\sqrt{\pi}} x^{2n} = \sqrt{\frac{2}{\pi x}} \cos x.$$

28. By Problem 21 we obtain $J_{1/2}(x) = xJ_{3/2}(x) + xJ_{-1/2}(x)$ so that

$$J_{3/2}(x) = \sqrt{\frac{2}{\pi x}} \left(\frac{\sin x}{x} - \cos x\right).$$

29. By Problem 21 we obtain $-J_{-1/2}(x) = xJ_{1/2}(x) + xJ_{-3/2}(x)$ so that

$$J_{-3/2}(x) = -\sqrt{\frac{2}{\pi x}} \left(\frac{\cos x}{x} + \sin x\right).$$

30. By Problem 21 we obtain $3J_{3/2}(x) = xJ_{5/2}(x) + xJ_{1/2}(x)$ so that

$$J_{5/2}(x) = \sqrt{\frac{2}{\pi x}} \left(\frac{3\sin x}{x^2} - \frac{3\cos x}{x} - \sin x\right).$$

31. By Problem 21 we obtain $-3J_{-3/2}(x) = xJ_{-1/2}(x) + xJ_{-5/2}(x)$ so that

$$J_{-5/2}(x) = \sqrt{\frac{2}{\pi x}} \left(\frac{3\cos x}{x^2} + \frac{3\sin x}{x} - \cos x\right).$$

32. By Problem 21 we obtain $5J_{5/2}(x) = xJ_{7/2}(x) + xJ_{3/2}(x)$ so that

$$J_{7/2}(x) = \sqrt{\frac{2}{\pi x}} \left(\frac{15\sin x}{x^3} - \frac{15\cos x}{x^2} - \frac{6\sin x}{x} + \cos x\right).$$

33. By Problem 21 we obtain $-5J_{-5/2}(x) = xJ_{-3/2}(x) + xJ_{-7/2}(x)$ so that

$$J_{-7/2}(x) = \sqrt{\frac{2}{\pi x}} \left(\frac{-15\cos x}{x^3} - \frac{15\sin x}{x^2} + \frac{6\cos x}{x} + \sin x\right).$$

34. Since

$$i^{-\nu}J_\nu(ix) = i^{-\nu}i^\nu \sum_{n=0}^{\infty} \frac{(-1)^n i^{2n}}{n!\Gamma(1+\nu+n)} \left(\frac{x}{2}\right)^{2n+\nu} = \sum_{n=0}^{\infty} \frac{1}{n!\Gamma(1+\nu+n)} \left(\frac{x}{2}\right)^{2n+\nu},$$

the function is real.

35. If $y_1 = I_\nu(x) = i^{-\nu}J_\nu(ix)$ then

$$y_1' = i^{-\nu+1}J_\nu'(ix),$$

$$y_1'' = -i^{-\nu}J_\nu''(ix),$$

and

$$x^2 y_1'' + x y_1' - \left(x^2 + \nu^2\right) y_1 = i^{-\nu} \left[(ix)^2 J_\nu''(ix) + (ix) J_\nu'(ix) + \left((ix)^2 - \nu^2\right) J_\nu(ix)\right] = i^{-\nu} \cdot 0 = 0.$$

Similarly, $y_2 = I_{-\nu}(x) = i^\nu J_{-\nu}(ix)$ satisfies the differential equation, and the general solution is $y = c_1 I_\nu(x) + c_2 I_{-\nu}(x)$.

36. If $y_1 = J_0(x)$ then using equation (35) on Page 299 in the text gives

$$y_2 = J_0(x) \int \frac{e^{-\int dx/x}}{(J_0(x))^2} \, dx$$

$$= J_0(x) \int \frac{dx}{x \left(1 - \dfrac{x^2}{4} + \dfrac{x^4}{64} - \dfrac{x^6}{2304} + \cdots\right)^2} \, dx$$

$$= J_0(x) \int \left(\frac{1}{x} + \frac{x}{2} + \frac{5x^3}{32} + \frac{23x^5}{576} + \cdots\right) dx$$

$$= J_0(x) \left(\ln x + \frac{x^2}{4} + \frac{5x^4}{128} + \frac{23x^6}{3456} + \cdots\right)$$

$$= J_0(x)\ln x + \left(1 - \frac{x^2}{4} + \frac{x^4}{64} - \frac{x^6}{2304} + \cdots\right)\left(\frac{x^2}{4} + \frac{5x^4}{128} + \frac{23x^6}{3456} + \cdots\right)$$

$$= J_0(x)\ln x + \frac{x^2}{4} - \frac{3x^4}{128} + \frac{11x^6}{13824} - \cdots .$$

37. Using (8) with $\nu = m$ we have

$$J_{-m}(x) = \sum_{n=0}^{\infty} \frac{(-1)^n}{n!\Gamma(1 - m + n)} \left(\frac{x}{2}\right)^{2n-m} = \sum_{n=m}^{\infty} \frac{(-1)^n}{n!\Gamma(1 - m + n)} \left(\frac{x}{2}\right)^{2n-m}$$

$$= \sum_{j=0}^{\infty} \frac{(-1)^j(-1)^m}{(j + m)!\Gamma(1 + j)} \left(\frac{x}{2}\right)^{2j+m} = (-1)^m \sum_{j=0}^{\infty} \frac{(-1)^j}{j!\Gamma(1 + m + j)} \left(\frac{x}{2}\right)^{2j+m}$$

$$= (-1)^m J_m(x).$$

38. Using (7) with $\nu = m$ we have

$$J_m(-x) = \sum_{n=0}^{\infty} \frac{(-1)^n}{n!\Gamma(1 + m + n)} \left(-\frac{x}{2}\right)^{2n+m} = (-1)^m \sum_{n=0}^{\infty} \frac{(-1)^n}{n!\Gamma(1 + m + n)} \left(\frac{x}{2}\right)^{2n+m} = (-1)^m J_m(x).$$

39. (a) Using the formulas on Page 315 in the text we obtain

$$P_6(x) = \frac{1}{16}\left(231x^6 - 315x^4 + 105x^2 - 5\right)$$

and

219

$$P_7(x) = \frac{1}{16}\left(429x^7 - 693x^5 + 315x^3 - 35x\right).$$

(b) $P_6(x)$ satisfies $\left(1 - x^2\right)y'' - 2xy' + 42y = 0$ and $P_7(x)$ satisfies $\left(1 - x^2\right)y'' - 2xy' + 56y = 0$.

40. We use the product rule for differentiation:

$$\frac{d}{dx}\left[(1 - x^2)\frac{dy}{dx}\right] + n(n+1)y = (1 - x^2)\frac{d^2y}{dx^2} + (-2x)\frac{dy}{dx} + n(n+1)y$$

$$= (1 - x^2)y'' - 2xy' + n(n+1)y = 0.$$

41. If $x = \cos\theta$ then

$$\frac{dy}{d\theta} = -\sin\theta\frac{dy}{dx},$$

$$\frac{d^2y}{d\theta^2} = \sin^2\theta\frac{d^2y}{dx^2} - \cos\frac{dy}{dx},$$

and

$$\sin\theta\frac{d^2y}{d\theta^2} + \cos\theta\frac{dy}{d\theta} + n(n+1)(\sin\theta)y = \sin\theta\left[\left(1 - \cos^2\theta\right)\frac{d^2y}{dx^2} - 2\cos\theta\frac{dy}{dx} + n(n+1)y\right] = 0.$$

That is,

$$\left(1 - x^2\right)\frac{d^2y}{dx^2} - 2x\frac{dy}{dx} + n(n+1)y = 0.$$

42. The polynomials are shown in (18) on Page 316 in the text.

43. By the binomial theorem we have

$$\left[1 + \left(t^2 - 2xt\right)\right]^{-1/2} = 1 - \frac{1}{2}\left(t^2 - 2xt\right) + \frac{3}{8}\left(t^2 - 2xt\right)^2 + \cdots = 1 + xt + \frac{1}{2}\left(3x^2 - 1\right)t^2 + \cdots.$$

44. Letting $x = 1$ in $(1 - 2xt + t^2)^{-1/2}$, we have

$$(1 - 2t + t^2)^{-1/2} = (1 - t)^{-1} = \frac{1}{1 - t} = 1 + t + t^2 + t^3 + \cdots \quad (|t| < 1)$$

$$= \sum_{n=0}^{\infty} t^n.$$

From Problem 43 we have

$$\sum_{n=0}^{\infty} P_n(1)t^n = (1 - 2t + t^2)^{-1/2} = \sum_{n=0}^{\infty} t^n.$$

Equating the coefficients of corresponding terms in the two series, we see that $P_n(1) = 1$. Similarly, letting $x = -1$ we have

$$(1 + 2t + t^2)^{-1/2} = (1 + t)^{-1} = \frac{1}{1 + t} = 1 - t + t^2 - 3t^3 + \cdots \quad (|t| < 1)$$

$$= \sum_{n=0}^{\infty}(-1)^n t^n = \sum_{n=0}^{\infty} P_n(-1)t^n,$$

so that $P_n(-1) = (-1)^n$.

45. The recurrence relation can be wrtten

$$P_{k+1}(x) = \frac{2k+1}{k+1} x P_k(x) - \frac{k}{k+1} P_{k-1}(x), \qquad k = 2, 3, 4, \ldots .$$

$k = 1$: $\quad P_2(x) = \dfrac{3}{2}x^2 - \dfrac{1}{2}$

$k = 2$: $\quad P_3(x) = \dfrac{5}{3}x \left(\dfrac{3}{2}x^2 - \dfrac{1}{2} \right) - \dfrac{2}{3}x = \dfrac{5}{2}x^3 - \dfrac{3}{2}x$

$k = 3$: $\quad P_4(x) = \dfrac{7}{4}x \left(\dfrac{5}{2}x^3 - \dfrac{3}{2}x \right) - \dfrac{3}{4} \left(\dfrac{3}{2}x^2 - \dfrac{1}{2} \right) = \dfrac{35}{8}x^4 - \dfrac{30}{8}x^2 + \dfrac{3}{8}$

$k = 4$: $\quad P_5(x) = \dfrac{9}{5}x \left(\dfrac{35}{8}x^4 - \dfrac{30}{8}x^2 + \dfrac{3}{8} \right) - \dfrac{4}{5} \left(\dfrac{5}{2}x^3 - \dfrac{3}{2}x \right) = \dfrac{63}{8}x^5 - \dfrac{35}{4}x^3 + \dfrac{15}{8}x$

$k = 5$: $\quad P_6(x) = \dfrac{11}{6}x \left(\dfrac{63}{8}x^5 - \dfrac{35}{4}x^3 + \dfrac{15}{8}x \right) - \dfrac{5}{6} \left(\dfrac{35}{8}x^4 - \dfrac{30}{8}x^2 + \dfrac{3}{8} \right) = \dfrac{231}{16}x^6 - \dfrac{315}{16}x^4 + \dfrac{105}{16}x - \dfrac{5}{16}$

46. $n = 0$: $\quad P_0(x) = 1$

$n = 1$: $\quad P_1(x) = \dfrac{1}{2} \dfrac{d}{dx} (x^2 - 1) = x$

$n = 2$: $\quad P_2(x) = \dfrac{1}{8} \dfrac{d^2}{dx^2} (x^2 - 1)^2 = \dfrac{1}{8} \dfrac{d^2}{dx^2} (x^4 - 2x^2 + 1) = \dfrac{1}{8}(12x^2 - 4) = \dfrac{3}{2}x^2 - \dfrac{1}{2}$

$n = 3$: $\quad P_3(x) = \dfrac{1}{48} \dfrac{d^3}{dx^3} (x^2 - 1)^3 = \dfrac{1}{48} \dfrac{d^3}{dx^3} (x^6 - 3x^4 + 3x^2 - 3) = \dfrac{1}{48}(120x^3 - 72x) = \dfrac{5}{2}x^3 - \dfrac{3}{2}x$

47. For $n = 0, 1, 2$, and 3 we obtain

$$\int_{-1}^{1} P_0^2(x)\, dx = 2,$$

$$\int_{-1}^{1} P_1^2(x)\, dx = \int_{-1}^{1} x^2 dx = \frac{2}{3},$$

$$\int_{-1}^{1} P_2^2(x)\, dx = \int_{-1}^{1} \frac{1}{4} \left(9x^4 - 6x^2 + 1 \right) dx = \frac{2}{5},$$

and

$$\int_{-1}^{1} P_3^2(x)\, dx = \int_{-1}^{1} \frac{1}{4} \left(25x^6 - 30x^4 + 9x^2 \right) dx = \frac{2}{7}.$$

In general,

$$\int_{-1}^{1} P_n^2(x)\, dx = \frac{2}{2n+1} \qquad \text{for } n = 0, 1, 2, \cdots.$$

48. All integrals of the form $\int_{-1}^{1} P_n(x) P_m(x)\, dx$ are 0 for $n \neq m$.

221

49. Let

$$y_2 = \frac{1}{2}x[\ln(1+x) - \ln(1-x)] - 1$$

so that

$$y_2' = \frac{1}{2}x\left[\frac{1}{1+x} + \frac{1}{1-x}\right] + \frac{1}{2}[\ln(1+x) - \ln(1-x)]$$

and

$$y_2'' = \frac{1}{2}x\left[-\frac{1}{(1+x)^2} + \frac{1}{(1-x)^2}\right] + \frac{1}{2}\left[\frac{1}{1+x} + \frac{1}{1-x}\right] + \frac{1}{2}\left[\frac{1}{1+x} + \frac{1}{1-x}\right]$$

$$= \frac{1}{2}x\left[-\frac{1}{(1+x)^2} + \frac{1}{(1-x)^2}\right] + \frac{1}{1+x} + \frac{1}{1-x}.$$

Then

$$(1-x)(1+x)y_2'' - 2xy_2' + 2y_2 = 0.$$

—————— Chapter 6 Review Exercises ——————

1. The auxiliary equation is $6m^2 - m - 1 = 0$ so that

$$y = c_1 x^{1/2} + c_2 x^{-1/3}.$$

2. The auxiliary equation is $2m^3 + 13m^2 + 24m + 9 = (m+3)^2(m+1/2) = 0$ so that

$$y = c_1 x^{-3} + c_2 x^{-3}\ln x + \frac{1}{4}x^3.$$

3. The auxiliary equation is $m^2 - 5m + 6 = (m-2)(m-3) = 0$ and a particular solution is $y_p = x^4 - x^2 \ln x$ so that

$$y = c_1 x^2 + c_2 x^3 + x^4 - x^2 \ln x.$$

4. The auxiliary equation is $m^2 - 2m + 1 = (m-1)^2 = 0$ and a particular solution is $y_p = \frac{1}{4}x^3$ so that

$$y = c_1 x + c_2 x \ln x + \frac{1}{4}x^3.$$

5. Since

$$P(x) = \frac{-2x}{(x-2)(x^2+2x+4)} \quad \text{and} \quad Q(x) = \frac{1}{(x-2)(x^2+2x+4)}$$

the singular points are $x = 0$, $x = -1 + \sqrt{3}\,i$, and $x = -1 - \sqrt{3}\,i$. All others are ordinary points.

6. Since

$$P(x) = 0 \quad \text{and} \quad Q(x) = \frac{2}{(x^2-4)(x^2+4)}$$

the singular points are $x = 2$, $x = -2$, $x = 2i$, and $x = -2i$. All others are ordinary points.

7. Since

$$P(x) = \frac{1}{x(x-5)^2} \quad \text{and} \quad Q(x) = 0$$

the regular singular point is $x = 0$ and the irregular singular point is $x = 5$.

8. Since

$$P(x) = 0 \quad \text{and} \quad Q(x) = \frac{1}{x(x-5)^2}$$

the regular singular points are $x = 0$ and $x = 5$. There are no irregular singular points.

9. Since

$$P(x) = -\frac{1}{x^2(x^2-9)} \quad \text{and} \quad Q(x) = \frac{1}{x(x^2-9)^2}$$

the regular singular points are $x = 3$ and $x = -3$. The irregular singular point is $x = 0$.

10. Since

$$P(x) = \frac{1}{x(x^2+1)^3} \quad \text{and} \quad Q(x) = -\frac{8}{(x^2+1)^3}$$

the regular singular point is $x = 0$. The irregular singular points are $x = i$ and $x = -i$.

11. Since $P(x) = -x$ and $Q(x) = 6$ the interval of convergence is $-\infty < x < \infty$.

12. Since $P(x) = -2x/\left(x^2 - 4\right)$ and $Q(x) = 9/\left(x^2 - 4\right)$ an interval of convergence is $-2 < x < 2$.

13. Substituting $y = \sum_{n=0}^{\infty} c_n x^n$ into the differential equation we obtain

$$y'' + xy = 2c_2 + \sum_{k=3}^{\infty} [k(k-1)c_k + c_{k-3}]x^{k-2} = 0$$

which implies $c_2 = 0$ and

$$c_k = -\frac{c_{k-3}}{k(k-1)}, \quad k = 3, 4, 5, \ldots.$$

Choosing $c_0 = 1$ and $c_1 = 0$ we find

$$c_3 = -\frac{1}{6}$$

$$c_4 = c_5 = 0$$

$$c_6 = \frac{1}{180}$$

and so on. For $c_0 = 0$ and $c_1 = 1$ we obtain

$$c_3 = 0$$

$$c_4 = -\frac{1}{12}$$

$$c_5 = c_6 = 0$$

$$c_7 = \frac{1}{504}$$

and so on. Thus, two solutions are

$$y_1 = c_0\left(1 - \frac{1}{6}x^3 + \frac{1}{180}x^6 - \cdots\right)$$

and

$$y_2 = c_1\left(x - \frac{1}{12}x^4 + \frac{1}{504}x^7 - \cdots\right).$$

14. Substituting $y = \sum_{n=0}^{\infty} c_n x^n$ into the differential equation we obtain

$$y'' - 4y = \sum_{k=2}^{\infty}[k(k-1)c_k - 4c_{k-2}]x^{k-2} = 0$$

which implies

$$c_k = \frac{4c_{k-2}}{k(k-1)}, \quad k = 2, 3, 4, \ldots.$$

Choosing $c_0 = 1$ and $c_1 = 0$ we find

$$c_2 = 2$$

$$c_3 = c_5 = c_7 = \cdots = 0$$

$$c_4 = \frac{2}{3}$$

$$c_6 = \frac{4}{45}$$

and so on. For $c_0 = 0$ and $c_1 = 1$ we obtain

$$c_2 = c_4 = c_6 = \cdots = 0$$

$$c_3 = \frac{2}{3}$$

$$c_5 = \frac{2}{15}$$

$$c_7 = \frac{4}{315}$$

and so on. Thus, two solutions are

$$y_1 = c_0 \left(1 + 2x^2 + \frac{2}{3}x^4 + \frac{4}{45}x^6 + \cdots \right)$$

and

$$y_2 = c_1 \left(x + \frac{2}{3}x^3 + \frac{2}{15}x^5 + \frac{4}{315}x^7 + \cdots \right).$$

15. Substituting $y = \sum_{n=0}^{\infty} c_n x^n$ into the differential equation we obtain

$$(x-1)y'' + 3y = (-2c_2 + 3c_0) + \sum_{k=3}^{\infty} (k-1)(k-2)c_{k-1} - k(k-1)c_k + 3c_{k-2}]x^{k-2} = 0$$

which implies $c_2 = 3c_0/2$ and

$$c_k = \frac{(k-1)(k-2)c_{k-1} + 3c_{k-2}}{k(k-1)}, \quad k = 3, 4, 5, \ldots .$$

Choosing $c_0 = 1$ and $c_1 = 0$ we find

$$c_2 = \frac{3}{2}, \qquad c_3 = \frac{1}{2}, \qquad c_4 = \frac{5}{8}$$

and so on. For $c_0 = 0$ and $c_1 = 1$ we obtain

$$c_2 = 0, \qquad c_3 = \frac{1}{2}, \qquad c_4 = \frac{1}{4}$$

and so on. Thus, two solutions are

$$y_1 = C_1 \left(1 + \frac{3}{2}x^2 + \frac{1}{2}x^3 + \frac{5}{8}x^4 + \cdots \right)$$

and

$$y_2 = C_2 \left(x + \frac{1}{2}x^3 + \frac{1}{4}x^4 + \cdots \right).$$

16. Substituting $y = \sum_{n=0}^{\infty} c_n x^n$ into the differential equation we obtain

$$y'' - x^2 y' + xy = 2c_2 + (6c_3 + c_0)x + \sum_{k=1}^{\infty} [(k+3)(k+2)c_{k+3} - (k-1)c_k]x^{k+1} = 0$$

which implies $c_2 = 0$, $c_3 = -c_0/6$, and

$$c_{k+3} = \frac{k-1}{(k+3)(k+2)} c_k, \quad k = 1, 2, 3, \ldots .$$

Choosing $c_0 = 1$ and $c_1 = 0$ we find

$$c_3 = -\frac{1}{6}$$

$$c_4 = c_7 = c_{10} = \cdots = 0$$

$$c_5 = c_8 = c_{11} = \cdots = 0$$

$$c_6 = -\frac{1}{90}$$

and so on. For $c_0 = 0$ and $c_1 = 1$ we obtain

$$c_3 = c_6 = c_9 = \cdots = 0$$

$$c_4 = c_7 = c_{10} = \cdots = 0$$

$$c_5 = c_8 = c_{11} = \cdots = 0$$

and so on. Thus, two solutions are

$$y_1 = c_0 \left(1 - \frac{1}{6}x^3 - \frac{1}{90}x^6 - \cdots \right) \quad \text{and} \quad y_2 = c_1 x.$$

17. Substituting $y = \sum_{n=0}^{\infty} c_n x^{n+r}$ into the differential equation we obtain

$$2x^2 y'' + xy' - (x+1)y$$

$$= \left(2r^2 - r - 1 \right) c_0 x^r + \sum_{k=1}^{\infty} [2(k+r)(k+r-1)c_k + (k+r)c_k - c_k - c_{k-1}]x^{k+r}$$

$$= 0$$

which implies

$$2r^2 - r - 1 = (2r+1)(r-1) = 0$$

and

$$[(k+r)(2k+2r-1) - 1]c_k - c_{k-1} = 0.$$

The indicial roots are $r = 1$ and $r = -1/2$. For $r = 1$ the recurrence relation is

$$c_k = \frac{c_{k-1}}{k(2k+3)}, \quad k = 1, 2, 3, \ldots,$$

so

$$c_1 = \frac{1}{5}c_0, \qquad c_2 = \frac{1}{70}c_0, \qquad c_3 = \frac{1}{1,890}c_0.$$

For $r = -1/2$ the recurrence relation is

$$c_k = \frac{c_{k-1}}{k(2k-3)}, \quad k = 1, 2, 3, \ldots,$$

so

$$c_1 = -c_0, \qquad c_2 = -\frac{1}{2}c_0, \qquad c_3 = -\frac{1}{18}c_0.$$

Two linearly independent solutions are

$$y_1 = C_1 x \left(1 + \frac{1}{5}x + \frac{1}{70}x^2 + \frac{1}{1,890}x^3 + \cdots \right)$$

and

$$y_2 = C_2 x^{-1/2} \left(1 - x - \frac{1}{2}x^2 - \frac{1}{18}x^3 - \cdots \right).$$

18. Substituting $y = \sum_{n=0}^{\infty} c_n x^{n+r}$ into the differential equation we obtain

$$2xy'' + y' + y = \left(2r^2 - r\right) c_0 x^{r-1} + \sum_{k=1}^{\infty} [2(k+r)(k+r-1)c_k + (k+r)c_k + c_{k-1}] x^{k+r-1} = 0$$

which implies

$$2r^2 - r = r(2r - 1) = 0$$

and

$$(k+r)(2k + 2r - 1)c_k + c_{k-1} = 0.$$

The indicial roots are $r = 0$ and $r = 1/2$. For $r = 0$ the recurrence relation is

$$c_k = -\frac{c_{k-1}}{k(2k-1)}, \quad k = 1, 2, 3, \ldots,$$

so

$$c_1 = -c_0, \qquad c_2 = \frac{1}{6}c_0, \qquad c_3 = -\frac{1}{90}c_0.$$

For $r = 1/2$ the recurrence relation is

$$c_k = -\frac{c_{k-1}}{k(2k+1)}, \quad k = 1, 2, 3, \ldots,$$

so

$$c_1 = -\frac{1}{3}c_0, \qquad c_2 = \frac{1}{30}c_0, \qquad c_3 = -\frac{1}{630}c_0.$$

Two linearly independent solutions are

$$y_1 = C_1 x \left(1 - x + \frac{1}{6}x^2 - \frac{1}{90}x^3 + \cdots\right)$$

and

$$y_2 = C_2 x^{1/2} \left(1 - \frac{1}{3}x + \frac{1}{30}x^2 - \frac{1}{630}x^3 + \cdots\right).$$

19. Substituting $y = \sum_{n=0}^{\infty} c_n x^{n+r}$ into the differential equation we obtain

$$x(1-x)y'' - 2y' + y = \left(r^2 - 3r\right) c_0 x^{r-1} + \sum_{k=1}^{\infty} [(k+r)(k+r-1)c_k - 2(k+r)c_k$$

$$- (k+r-1)(k+r-2)c_{k-1} + c_{k-1}] x^{k+r-1}$$

$$= 0$$

which implies

$$r^2 - 3r = r(r - 3) = 0$$

and

$$(k+r)(k+r-3)c_k - [(k+r-1)(k+r-2) - 1]c_{k-1} = 0.$$

The indicial roots are $r_1 = 3$ and $r_2 = 0$. For $r_1 = 3$ the recurrence relation is

$$c_k = \frac{\left(k^2 + 3k + 1\right) c_{k-1}}{k(k+3)}, \quad k = 1, 2, 3, \ldots,$$

so

$$c_1 = \frac{5}{4}c_0, \qquad c_2 = \frac{11}{8}c_0, \qquad c_3 = \frac{209}{144}c_0.$$

One solution is

$$y_1 = c_0 x^3 \left(1 + \frac{5}{4}x + \frac{11}{8}x^2 + \frac{209}{144}x^3 + \cdots\right).$$

A second solution is

$$y_2 = y_1 \int \frac{e^{\int [2/x(1-x)]dx}}{y_1^2}\, dx = y_1 \int \frac{x^2 dx}{(1-x)^2 x^6 \left(1 + \frac{5}{2}x + \frac{69}{16}x^2 + \frac{913}{144}x^3 + \cdots\right)}$$

$$= y_1 \int \frac{dx}{x^4 \left(1 - 2x + x^2\right)\left(1 + \frac{5}{2}x + \frac{69}{16}x^2 + \frac{913}{144}x^3 + \cdots\right)}$$

$$= y_1 \int \frac{dx}{x^4 \left(1 + \frac{1}{2}x + \frac{5}{16}x^2 + \frac{31}{144}x^3 + \cdots\right)} = y_1 \int \frac{1}{x^4}\left(1 - \frac{1}{2}x - \frac{1}{16}x^2 - \frac{1}{36}x^3 - \cdots\right) dx$$

$$= y_1 \int \left(\frac{1}{x^4} - \frac{1}{2x^3} - \frac{1}{16x^2} - \frac{1}{36x} - \cdots\right) dx = y_1 \left[-\frac{1}{3x^3} + \frac{1}{4x^2} + \frac{1}{16x} - \frac{1}{36}\ln x + \cdots\right]$$

$$= -\frac{1}{36} y_1 \ln x + y_1 \left(-\frac{1}{3x^3} + \frac{1}{4x^2} + \frac{1}{16x} + \cdots\right).$$

20. Substituting $y = \sum_{n=0}^{\infty} c_n x^{n+r}$ into the differential equation we obtain

$$x^2 y'' - xy' + \left(x^2 + 1\right) y = \left(r^2 - 2r + 1\right) c_0 x^r + r^2 c_1 x^{r+1}$$

$$+ \sum_{k=2}^{\infty} [(k+r)(k+r-1)c_k - (k+r)c_k + c_k + c_{k-2}]x^{k+r}$$

$$= 0$$

which implies

$$r^2 - 2r + 1 = (r-1)^2 = 0$$

$$r^2 c_1 = 0$$

$$[(k+r)(k+r-2) + 1]c_k + c_{k-2} = 0.$$

The indicial roots are $r_1 = r_2 = 1$, so $c_1 = 0$ and

$$c_k = -\frac{c_{k-2}}{k^2}, \quad k = 2, 3, 4, \ldots.$$

Thus

$$c_2 = -\frac{1}{4}c_0$$

$$c_3 = c_5 = c_7 = \cdots = 0$$

$$c_4 = \frac{1}{64}c_0$$

$$c_6 = -\frac{1}{2,304}c_0$$

and one solution is

$$y_1 = c_0 x \left(1 - \frac{1}{4}x^2 + \frac{1}{64}x^4 - \frac{1}{2,304}x^6 + \cdots\right).$$

A second solution is

$$y_2 = y_1 \int \frac{e^{dx/x}}{y_1^2}\, dx = y_1 \int \frac{x\, dx}{x^2\left(1 - \frac{1}{4}x^2 + \frac{1}{64}x^4 - \frac{1}{2,304}x^6 + \cdots\right)^2}$$

$$= y_1 \int \frac{dx}{x\left(1 - \frac{1}{2}x^2 + \frac{3}{32}x^4 - \frac{5}{576}x^6 + \cdots\right)}$$

$$= y_1 \int \frac{1}{x}\left(1 + \frac{1}{2}x^2 + \frac{5}{32}x^4 + \frac{23}{576}x^6 + \cdots\right) dx$$

$$= y_1 \int \left(\frac{1}{x} + \frac{1}{2}x + \frac{5}{32}x^3 + \frac{23}{576}x^5 + \cdots\right) dx$$

$$= y_1 \ln x + y_1 \left(\frac{1}{4}x^2 + \frac{5}{128}x^4 + \frac{23}{3,456}x^6 + \cdots\right).$$

21. Substituting $y = \sum_{n=0}^{\infty} c_n x^{n+r}$ into the differential equation we obtain

$$xy'' - (2x - 1)y' + (x - 1)y = r^2 c_0 x^{r-1} + \left[\left(r^2 + 2r + 1\right)c_1 - (2r + 1)c_0\right]x^r$$

$$+ \sum_{k=2}^{\infty}[(k + r)(k + r - 1)c_k + (k + r)c_k - 2(k + r - 1)c_{k-1} - c_{k-1} + c_{k-2}]x^{k+r-1}$$

$$= 0$$

which implies

$$r^2 = 0,$$

$$(r + 1)^2 c_1 - (2r + 1)c_0 = 0,$$

and

$$(k + r)^2 c_k - (2k + 2r - 1)c_{k-1} + c_{k-2} = 0.$$

The indicial roots are $r_1 = r_2 = 0$, so $c_1 = c_0$ and

$$c_k = \frac{(2k-1)c_{k-1} - c_{k-2}}{k^2}, \quad k = 2, 3, 4, \dots .$$

Thus

$$c_2 = \frac{1}{2}c_0, \qquad c_3 = \frac{1}{3!}c_0, \qquad c_4 = \frac{1}{4!}c_0$$

and one solution is

$$y_1 = c_0 \left(1 + x + \frac{1}{2}x^2 + \frac{1}{3!}x^3 + \frac{1}{4!}x^4 + \cdots \right) = c_0 e^x.$$

A second solution is

$$y_2 = e^x \int \frac{e^{\int (2-1/x)dx}}{e^{2x}} \, dx = e^x \int \frac{e^{2x} dx}{xe^{2x}} = e^x \int \frac{1}{x} \, dx = e^x \ln x.$$

22. Substituting $y = \sum_{n=0}^{\infty} c_n x^{n+r}$ into the differential equation we obtain

$$x^2 y'' - x^2 y' + \left(x^2 - 2 \right) y = \left(r^2 - r - 2 \right) c_0 x^r + \left[\left(r^2 + r - 2 \right) c_1 - rc_0 \right] x^{r+1}$$

$$+ \sum_{k=2}^{\infty} [(k+r)(k+r-1)c_k - 2c_k - (k+r-1)c_{k-1} + c_{k-2}]x^{k+r}$$

$$= 0$$

which implies

$$r^2 - r - 2 = (r-2)(r+1) = 0,$$

$$\left(r^2 + r - 2 \right) c_1 - rc_0 = 0,$$

and

$$[(k+r)(k+r-1) - 2]c_k - (k+r-1)c_{k-1} + c_{k-2} = 0.$$

The indicial roots are $r_1 = 2$ and $r_2 = -1$. For $r_2 = -1$,

$$-2c_1 + c_0 = 0 \quad \text{and} \quad k(k-3)c_k - (k-2)c_{k-1} + c_{k-2} = 0, \quad k = 2, 3, 4, \dots .$$

Thus

$$c_1 = \frac{1}{2}c_0$$

$$-2c_2 - 0 \cdot c_1 + c_0 = 0 \quad \Rightarrow \quad c_2 = \frac{1}{2}c_0$$

$$0 \cdot c_3 - c_2 + c_1 = 0 \quad \Rightarrow \quad c_2 = c_1 = \frac{1}{2}c_0 \text{ and } c_3 \text{ is arbitrary}$$

and

$$c_k = \frac{(k-2)c_{k-1} - c_{k-2}}{k(k-3)}, \quad k = 4, 5, 6, \dots .$$

Taking $c_0 = 1$ and $c_3 = 0$ we have

$$c_1 = \frac{1}{2}, \qquad c_2 = \frac{1}{2}, \qquad c_4 = -\frac{1}{8}, \qquad c_5 = -\frac{3}{80},$$

and so on. Choosing $c_0 = 0$ and $c_3 = 1$ we have

$$c_1 = c_2 = 0, \qquad c_4 = \frac{1}{2}, \qquad c_5 = \frac{3}{20},$$

and so on. Two solutions are

$$y_1 = C_1 x^{-1} \left(1 + \frac{1}{2}x + \frac{1}{2}x^2 - \frac{1}{8}x^4 - \frac{3}{80}x^5 + \cdots \right)$$

and

$$y_2 = C_2 x^{-1} \left(x^3 + \frac{1}{2}x^4 + \frac{3}{20}x^5 + \cdots \right).$$

23. Substituting $y = \sum_{n=0}^{\infty} c_n x^{n+r}$ into the differential equation we obtain

$$xy'' + y' + xy = r^2 c_0 x^r + \left(r^2 + 2r + 1 \right) c_1 x^{r+1} + \sum_{k=2}^{\infty} [(k+r)(k+r-1)c_k + (k+r)c_k + c_{k-2}]x^{k+r} = 0$$

which implies

$$r^2 = 0,$$

$$(r+1)^2 c_1 = 0,$$

and

$$(k+r)^2 c_k + c_{k-2} = 0.$$

The indicial roots are $r_1 = r_2 = 0$, so $c_1 = 0$ and the recurrence relation is

$$c_k = -\frac{c_{k-2}}{k^2}, \qquad k = 2, 3, 4, \ldots .$$

Thus

$$c_2 = -\frac{1}{4}c_0$$

$$c_3 = c_5 = c_7 = \cdots = 0$$

$$c_4 = \frac{1}{64}c_0$$

$$c_6 = -\frac{1}{2,304}c_0$$

and

$$y_1 = c_0 \left(1 - \frac{1}{4}x^2 + \frac{1}{64}x^4 - \frac{1}{2,304}x^6 + \cdots \right).$$

7 Laplace Transform

_____ Exercises 7.1 _____

1. $\mathcal{L}\{f(t)\} = \int_0^1 -e^{-st}dt + \int_1^\infty e^{-st}dt = \frac{1}{s}e^{-st}\Big|_0^1 - \frac{1}{s}e^{-st}\Big|_1^\infty$

$= \frac{1}{s}e^{-s} - \frac{1}{s} - \left(0 - \frac{1}{s}e^{-s}\right) = \frac{2}{s}e^{-s} - \frac{1}{s}, \quad s > 0$

2. $\mathcal{L}\{f(t)\} = \int_0^2 4e^{-st}dt = -\frac{4}{s}e^{-st}\Big|_0^2 = -\frac{4}{s}(e^{-2s} - 1), \quad s > 0$

3. $\mathcal{L}\{f(t)\} = \int_0^1 te^{-st}dt + \int_1^\infty e^{-st}dt = \left(-\frac{1}{s}te^{-st} - \frac{1}{s^2}e^{-st}\right)\Big|_0^1 - \frac{1}{s}e^{-st}\Big|_1^\infty$

$= \left(-\frac{1}{s}e^{-s} - \frac{1}{s^2}e^{-s}\right) - \left(0 - \frac{1}{s^2}\right) - \frac{1}{s}(0 - e^{-s}) = \frac{1}{s^2}(1 - e^{-s}), \quad s > 0$

4. $\mathcal{L}\{f(t)\} = \int_0^1 (2t + 1)e^{-st}dt = \left(-\frac{2}{s}te^{-st} - \frac{2}{s^2}e^{-st} - \frac{1}{s}e^{-st}\right)\Big|_0^1$

$= \left(-\frac{2}{s}e^{-s} - \frac{2}{s^2}e^{-s} - \frac{1}{s}e^{-s}\right) - \left(0 - \frac{2}{s^2} - \frac{1}{s}\right) = \frac{1}{s}(1 - 3e^{-s}) + \frac{2}{s^2}(1 - e^{-s}), \quad s > 0$

5. $\mathcal{L}\{f(t)\} = \int_0^\pi (\sin t)e^{-st}dt = \left(-\frac{s}{s^2+1}e^{-st}\sin t - \frac{1}{s^2+1}e^{-st}\cos t\right)\Big|_0^\pi$

$= \left(0 + \frac{1}{s^2+1}e^{-\pi s}\right) - \left(0 - \frac{1}{s^2+1}\right) = \frac{1}{s^2+1}(e^{-\pi s} + 1), \quad s > 0$

6. $\mathcal{L}\{f(t)\} = \int_{\pi/2}^\infty (\cos t)e^{-st}dt = \left(-\frac{s}{s^2+1}e^{-st}\cos t + \frac{1}{s^2+1}e^{-st}\sin t\right)\Big|_{\pi/2}^\infty$

$= 0 - \left(0 + \frac{1}{s^2+1}e^{-\pi s/2}\right) = -\frac{1}{s^2+1}e^{-\pi s/2}, \quad s > 0$

7. $f(t) = \begin{cases} 0, & 0 < t < 1 \\ t, & t > 1 \end{cases}$

$\mathcal{L}\{f(t)\} = \int_1^\infty te^{-st}\,dt = \left(-\frac{1}{s}te^{-st} - \frac{1}{s^2}e^{-st}\right)\Big|_1^\infty = \frac{1}{s}e^{-s} + \frac{1}{s^2}e^{-s}, \quad s > 0$

8. $f(t) = \begin{cases} 0, & 0 < t < 1 \\ 2t - 2, & t > 1 \end{cases}$

$\mathcal{L}\{f(t)\} = 2\int_1^\infty (t - 1)e^{-st}\,dt = 2\left(-\frac{1}{s}(t-1)e^{-st} - \frac{1}{s^2}e^{-st}\right)\Big|_1^\infty = \frac{2}{s^2}e^{-s}, \quad s > 0$

9. $f(t) = \begin{cases} 1-t, & 0 < t < 1 \\ 0, & t > 0 \end{cases}$

$$\mathcal{L}\{f(t)\} = \int_0^1 (1-t)e^{-st}\,dt = \left(-\frac{1}{s}(1-t)e^{-st} + \frac{1}{s^2}e^{-st}\right)\Big|_0^1 = \frac{1}{s^2}e^{-s} + \frac{1}{s} - \frac{1}{s^2}, \quad s > 0$$

10. $f(t) = \begin{cases} 0, & 0 < t < a \\ c, & a < t < b; \\ 0, & t > b \end{cases}$
$\quad \mathcal{L}\{f(t)\} = \int_a^b ce^{-st}\,dt = -\frac{c}{s}e^{-st}\Big|_a^b = \frac{c}{s}(e^{-sa} - e^{-sb}), \quad s > 0$

11. $\mathcal{L}\{f(t)\} = \int_0^\infty e^{t+7}e^{-st}\,dt = e^7\int_0^\infty e^{(1-s)t}\,dt = \frac{e^7}{1-s}e^{(1-s)t}\Big|_0^\infty = 0 - \frac{e^7}{1-s} = \frac{e^7}{s-1}, \quad s > 1$

12. $\mathcal{L}\{f(t)\} = \int_0^\infty e^{-2t-5}e^{-st}\,dt = e^{-5}\int_0^\infty e^{-(s+2)t}\,dt = -\frac{e^{-5}}{s+2}e^{-(s+2)t}\Big|_0^\infty = \frac{e^{-5}}{s+2}, \quad s > -2$

13. $\mathcal{L}\{f(t)\} = \int_0^\infty te^{4t}e^{-st}\,dt = \int_0^\infty te^{(4-s)t}\,dt = \left(\frac{1}{4-s}te^{(4-s)t} - \frac{1}{(4-s)^2}e^{(4-s)t}\right)\Big|_0^\infty$

$$= \frac{1}{(4-s)^2}, \quad s > 4$$

14. $\mathcal{L}\{f(t)\} = \int_0^\infty t^2 e^{3t}e^{-st}\,dt = \int_0^\infty t^2 e^{(3-s)t}\,dt$

$$= \left(\frac{1}{3-s}t^2 e^{(3-s)t} - \frac{2}{(3-s)^2}te^{(3-s)t} + \frac{2}{(3-s)^3}e^{(3-s)t}\right)\Big|_0^\infty$$

$$= -\frac{2}{(3-s)^3} = \frac{2}{(s-3)^3}, \quad s > 3$$

15. $\mathcal{L}\{f(t)\} = \int_0^\infty e^{-t}(\sin t)e^{-st}\,dt = \int_0^\infty (\sin t)e^{-(s+1)t}\,dt$

$$= \left(\frac{-(s+1)}{(s+1)^2+1}e^{-(s+1)t}\sin t - \frac{1}{(s+1)^2+1}e^{-(s+1)t}\cos t\right)\Big|_0^\infty$$

$$= \frac{1}{(s+1)^2+1} = \frac{1}{s^2+2s+2}, \quad s > -1$$

16. $\mathcal{L}\{f(t)\} = \int_0^\infty e^t(\cos t)e^{-st}\,dt = \int_0^\infty (\cos t)e^{(1-s)t}\,dt$

$$= \left(\frac{1-s}{(1-s)^2+1}e^{(1-s)t}\cos t + \frac{1}{(1-s)^2+1}e^{(1-s)t}\sin t\right)\Big|_0^\infty$$

$$= -\frac{1-s}{(1-s)^2+1} = \frac{s-1}{s^2-2s+2}, \quad s > 1$$

17. $\mathcal{L}\{f(t)\} = \displaystyle\int_0^\infty t(\cos t)e^{-st}dt$

$$= \left[\left(-\frac{st}{s^2+1} - \frac{s^2-1}{(s^2+1)^2}\right)(\cos t)e^{-st} + \left(\frac{t}{s^2+1} + \frac{2s}{(s^2+1)^2}\right)(\sin t)e^{-st}\right]_0^\infty$$

$$= \frac{s^2-1}{(s^2+1)^2}, \quad s > 0$$

18. $\mathcal{L}\{f(t)\} = \displaystyle\int_0^\infty t(\sin t)e^{-st}dt$

$$= \left[\left(-\frac{t}{s^2+1} - \frac{2s}{(s^2+1)^2}\right)(\cos t)e^{-st} - \left(\frac{st}{s^2+1} + \frac{s^2-1}{(s^2+1)^2}\right)(\sin t)e^{-st}\right]_0^\infty$$

$$= \frac{2s}{(s^2+1)^2}, \quad s > 0$$

19. $\mathcal{L}\{2t^4\} = 2\dfrac{4!}{s^5}$

20. $\mathcal{L}\{t^5\} = \dfrac{5!}{s^6}$

21. $\mathcal{L}\{4t - 10\} = \dfrac{4}{s^2} - \dfrac{10}{s}$

22. $\mathcal{L}\{7t + 3\} = \dfrac{7}{s^2} + \dfrac{3}{s}$

23. $\mathcal{L}\{t^2 + 6t - 3\} = \dfrac{2}{s^3} + \dfrac{6}{s^2} - \dfrac{3}{s}$

24. $\mathcal{L}\{-4t^2 + 16t + 9\} = -4\dfrac{2}{s^3} + \dfrac{16}{s^2} + \dfrac{9}{s}$

25. $\mathcal{L}\{t^3 + 3t^2 + 3t + 1\} = \dfrac{3!}{s^4} + 3\dfrac{2}{s^3} + \dfrac{3}{s^2} + \dfrac{1}{s}$

26. $\mathcal{L}\{8t^3 - 12t^2 + 6t - 1\} = 8\dfrac{3!}{s^4} - 12\dfrac{2}{s^3} + \dfrac{6}{s^2} - \dfrac{1}{s}$

27. $\mathcal{L}\{1 + e^{4t}\} = \dfrac{1}{s} + \dfrac{1}{s-4}$

28. $\mathcal{L}\{t^2 - e^{-9t} + 5\} = \dfrac{2}{s^3} - \dfrac{1}{s+9} + \dfrac{5}{s}$

29. $\mathcal{L}\{1 + 2e^{2t} + e^{4t}\} = \dfrac{1}{s} + \dfrac{2}{s-2} + \dfrac{1}{s-4}$

30. $\mathcal{L}\{e^{2t} - 2 + e^{-2t}\} = \dfrac{1}{s-2} - \dfrac{2}{s} + \dfrac{1}{s+2}$

31. $\mathcal{L}\{4t^2 - 5\sin 3t\} = 4\dfrac{2}{s^3} - 5\dfrac{3}{s^2+9}$

32. $\mathcal{L}\{\cos 5t + \sin 5t\} = \dfrac{s}{s^2+25} + \dfrac{5}{s^2+25}$

33. $\mathcal{L}\{\sinh kt\} = \dfrac{k}{s^2 - k^2}$

34. $\mathcal{L}\{\cosh kt\} = \dfrac{s}{s^2 - k^2}$

35. $\mathcal{L}\{e^t \sinh t\} = \mathcal{L}\left\{e^t \dfrac{e^t - e^{-t}}{2}\right\} = \mathcal{L}\left\{\dfrac{1}{2}e^{2t} - \dfrac{1}{2}\right\} = \dfrac{1}{2(s-1)} - \dfrac{1}{2s}$

36. $\mathcal{L}\{e^{-t} \cosh t\} = \mathcal{L}\left\{e^{-t} \dfrac{e^t + e^{-t}}{2}\right\} = \mathcal{L}\left\{\dfrac{1}{2} + \dfrac{1}{2}e^{-2t}\right\} = \dfrac{1}{2s} + \dfrac{1}{2(s+2)}$

37. $\mathcal{L}\{\sin 2t \cos 2t\} = \mathcal{L}\left\{\dfrac{1}{2}\sin 4t\right\} = \dfrac{2}{s^2 + 16}$

38. $\mathcal{L}\{\cos^2 t\} = \mathcal{L}\left\{\dfrac{1}{2} + \dfrac{1}{2}\cos 2t\right\} = \dfrac{1}{2s} + \dfrac{1}{2}\dfrac{s}{s^2 + 4}$

39. $\mathcal{L}\{\cos t \cos 2t\} = \mathcal{L}\left\{\dfrac{1}{2}\cos 3t + \dfrac{1}{2}\cos t\right\} = \dfrac{1}{2}\dfrac{s}{s^2 + 9} + \dfrac{1}{2}\dfrac{s}{s^2 + 1}$

40. $\mathcal{L}\{\sin t \sin 2t\} = \mathcal{L}\left\{\dfrac{1}{2}\cos t - \dfrac{1}{2}\cos 3t\right\} = \dfrac{1}{2}\dfrac{s}{s^2 + 1} - \dfrac{1}{2}\dfrac{s}{s^2 + 9}$

41. $\mathcal{L}\{\sin t \cos 2t\} = \mathcal{L}\left\{\dfrac{1}{2}\sin 3t - \dfrac{1}{2}\sin t\right\} = \dfrac{1}{2}\dfrac{3}{s^2 + 9} - \dfrac{1}{2}\dfrac{1}{s^2 + 1}$

42. $\mathcal{L}\{\sin^3 t\} = \mathcal{L}\left\{\sin t\left(\dfrac{1}{2} - \dfrac{1}{2}\cos 2t\right)\right\} = \mathcal{L}\left\{\dfrac{1}{2}\sin t - \dfrac{1}{2}\left(\dfrac{1}{2}\sin 3t - \dfrac{1}{2}\sin t\right)\right\} = \dfrac{3}{4}\dfrac{1}{s^2 + 1} - \dfrac{1}{4}\dfrac{3}{s^2 + 9}$

43. Let $u = st$ so that $du = s\,dt$ and $\mathcal{L}\{t^\alpha\} = \displaystyle\int_0^\infty e^{-st}t^\alpha\,dt = \int_0^\infty e^{-u}\left(\dfrac{u}{s}\right)^\alpha \dfrac{1}{s}\,du = \dfrac{1}{s^{\alpha+1}}\Gamma(\alpha + 1)$
for $\alpha > -1$.

44. $\mathcal{L}\{t^{-1/2}\} = \dfrac{\Gamma(1/2)}{s^{1/2}} = \sqrt{\dfrac{\pi}{s}}$

45. $\mathcal{L}\{t^{1/2}\} = \dfrac{\Gamma(3/2)}{s^{3/2}} = \dfrac{\sqrt{\pi}}{2s^{3/2}}$

46. $\mathcal{L}\{t^{3/2}\} = \dfrac{\Gamma(5/2)}{s^{5/2}} = \dfrac{3\sqrt{\pi}}{4s^{5/2}}$

47. If we attempt to compute the Laplace transform of $1/t^2$ we obtain

$$\mathcal{L}\{1/t^2\} = \int_0^1 \dfrac{1}{t^2}e^{-st}\,dt + \int_1^\infty \dfrac{1}{t^2}e^{-st}\,dt.$$

If $s = 0$ then

$$\int_0^1 \dfrac{1}{t^2}e^{-st}\,dt = \int_0^1 \dfrac{1}{t^2}\,dt,$$

which diverges. If $s < 0$ then

$$\int_0^1 \dfrac{1}{t^2}e^{-st}\,dt > \int_0^1 \dfrac{1}{t^2}\,dt,$$

which diverges. If $s > 0$ then

$$\int_0^1 \dfrac{1}{t^2}e^{-st}\,dt > e^{-s}\int_0^1 \dfrac{1}{t^2}e^{-st}\,dt,$$

which diverges. Thus, the Laplace transform of $1/t^2$ does not exist.

48. Since f and g are of exponential order there exist numbers c, d, M, and N such that $|f(t)| \leq Me^{ct}$ and $|g(t)| \leq Ne^{dt}$ for $t > T$. Then

$$|(fg)(t)| = |f(t)||g(t)| \leq Me^{ct}Ne^{dt} = MNe^{(c+d)t}$$

for $t > T$, and fg is of exponential order.

Exercises 7.2

1. $\mathcal{L}^{-1}\left\{\dfrac{1}{s^3}\right\} = \dfrac{1}{2}\mathcal{L}^{-1}\left\{\dfrac{2}{s^3}\right\} = \dfrac{1}{2}t^2$

2. $\mathcal{L}^{-1}\left\{\dfrac{1}{s^4}\right\} = \dfrac{1}{6}\mathcal{L}^{-1}\left\{\dfrac{3!}{s^4}\right\} = \dfrac{1}{6}t^3$

3. $\mathcal{L}^{-1}\left\{\dfrac{1}{s^2} - \dfrac{48}{s^5}\right\} = \mathcal{L}^{-1}\left\{\dfrac{1}{s^2} - \dfrac{48}{24}\cdot\dfrac{4!}{s^5}\right\} = t - 2t^4$

4. $\mathcal{L}^{-1}\left\{\left(\dfrac{2}{s} - \dfrac{1}{s^3}\right)^2\right\} = \mathcal{L}^{-1}\left\{4\cdot\dfrac{1}{s^2} - \dfrac{4}{6}\cdot\dfrac{3!}{s^4} + \dfrac{1}{120}\cdot\dfrac{5!}{s^6}\right\} = 4t - \dfrac{2}{3}t^3 + \dfrac{1}{120}t^5$

5. $\mathcal{L}^{-1}\left\{\dfrac{(s+1)^3}{s^4}\right\} = \mathcal{L}^{-1}\left\{\dfrac{1}{s} + 3\cdot\dfrac{1}{s^2} + \dfrac{3}{2}\cdot\dfrac{2}{s^3} + \dfrac{1}{6}\cdot\dfrac{3!}{s^4}\right\} = 1 + 3t + \dfrac{3}{2}t^2 + \dfrac{1}{6}t^3$

6. $\mathcal{L}^{-1}\left\{\dfrac{(s+2)^3}{s^3}\right\} = \mathcal{L}^{-1}\left\{\dfrac{1}{s} + 4\cdot\dfrac{1}{s^2} + 2\cdot\dfrac{2}{s^3}\right\} = 1 + 4t + 2t^2$

7. $\mathcal{L}^{-1}\left\{\dfrac{1}{s^2} - \dfrac{1}{s} + \dfrac{1}{s-2}\right\} = t - 1 + e^{2t}$

8. $\mathcal{L}^{-1}\left\{4\cdot\dfrac{1}{s} + \dfrac{1}{4}\cdot\dfrac{4!}{s^5} - \dfrac{1}{s+8}\right\} = 4 + \dfrac{1}{4}t^4 - e^{-8t}$

9. $\mathcal{L}^{-1}\left\{\dfrac{1}{4s+1}\right\} = \mathcal{L}^{-1}\left\{\dfrac{1}{4}\cdot\dfrac{1}{s+1/4}\right\} = \dfrac{1}{4}e^{-t/4}$

10. $\mathcal{L}^{-1}\left\{\dfrac{1}{5s-2}\right\} = \mathcal{L}^{-1}\left\{\dfrac{1}{5}\cdot\dfrac{1}{s-2/5}\right\} = \dfrac{1}{5}e^{2t/5}$

11. $\mathcal{L}^{-1}\left\{\dfrac{5}{s^2+49}\right\} = \mathcal{L}^{-1}\left\{\dfrac{5}{7}\cdot\dfrac{7}{s^2+49}\right\} = \dfrac{5}{7}\sin 7t$

12. $\mathcal{L}^{-1}\left\{\dfrac{10s}{s^2+16}\right\} = 10\cos 4t$

13. $\mathscr{L}^{-1}\left\{\dfrac{4s}{4s^2+1}\right\} = \mathscr{L}^{-1}\left\{\dfrac{s}{s^2+1/4}\right\} = \cos\dfrac{1}{2}t$

14. $\mathscr{L}^{-1}\left\{\dfrac{1}{4s^2+1}\right\} = \mathscr{L}^{-1}\left\{\dfrac{1}{2}\cdot\dfrac{1/2}{s^2+1/4}\right\} = \dfrac{1}{2}\sin\dfrac{1}{2}t$

15. $\mathscr{L}^{-1}\left\{\dfrac{1}{s^2-16}\right\} = \mathscr{L}^{-1}\left\{\dfrac{1/8}{s-4}-\dfrac{1/8}{s+4}\right\} = \dfrac{1}{8}e^{4t}-\dfrac{1}{8}e^{-4t} = \dfrac{1}{4}\sinh 4t$

16. $\mathscr{L}^{-1}\left\{\dfrac{10s}{s^2-25}\right\} = 10\cosh 5t$

17. $\mathscr{L}^{-1}\left\{\dfrac{2s-6}{s^2+9}\right\} = \mathscr{L}^{-1}\left\{2\cdot\dfrac{s}{s^2+9}-2\cdot\dfrac{3}{s^2+9}\right\} = 2\cos 3t - 2\sin 3t$

18. $\mathscr{L}^{-1}\left\{\dfrac{s+1}{s^2+2}\right\} = \mathscr{L}^{-1}\left\{\dfrac{s}{s^2+2}+\dfrac{1}{\sqrt{2}}\cdot\dfrac{\sqrt{2}}{s^2+2}\right\} = \cos\sqrt{2}\,t + \dfrac{1}{\sqrt{2}}\sin\sqrt{2}\,t$

19. $\mathscr{L}^{-1}\left\{\dfrac{1}{s^2+35}\right\} = \mathscr{L}^{-1}\left\{\dfrac{1}{3}\cdot\dfrac{1}{s}-\dfrac{1}{3}\cdot\dfrac{1}{s+3}\right\} = \dfrac{1}{3}-\dfrac{1}{3}e^{-3t}$

20. $\mathscr{L}^{-1}\left\{\dfrac{s+1}{s^2-4s}\right\} = \mathscr{L}^{-1}\left\{-\dfrac{1}{4}\cdot\dfrac{1}{s}+\dfrac{5}{4}\cdot\dfrac{1}{s-4}\right\} = -\dfrac{1}{4}+\dfrac{5}{4}e^{4t}$

21. $\mathscr{L}^{-1}\left\{\dfrac{s}{s^2+2s-3}\right\} = \mathscr{L}^{-1}\left\{\dfrac{1}{4}\cdot\dfrac{1}{s-1}+\dfrac{3}{4}\cdot\dfrac{1}{s+3}\right\} = \dfrac{1}{4}e^t+\dfrac{3}{4}e^{-3t}$

22. $\mathscr{L}^{-1}\left\{\dfrac{1}{s^2+s-20}\right\} = \mathscr{L}^{-1}\left\{\dfrac{1}{9}\cdot\dfrac{1}{s-4}-\dfrac{1}{9}\cdot\dfrac{1}{s+5}\right\} = \dfrac{1}{9}e^{4t}-\dfrac{1}{9}e^{-5t}$

23. $\mathscr{L}^{-1}\left\{\dfrac{0.95}{(s-0.1)(s+0.2)}\right\} = \mathscr{L}^{-1}\left\{(0.3)\cdot\dfrac{1}{s-0.1}+(0.6)\cdot\dfrac{1}{s+0.2}\right\} = 0.3e^{0.1t}+0.6e^{-0.2t}$

24. $\mathscr{L}^{-1}\left\{\dfrac{s-3}{(s-\sqrt{3})(s+\sqrt{3})}\right\} = \mathscr{L}^{-1}\left\{\dfrac{s}{s^2-3}-\sqrt{3}\cdot\dfrac{\sqrt{3}}{s^2-3}\right\} = \cosh\sqrt{3}\,t-\sqrt{3}\sinh\sqrt{3}\,t$

25. $\mathscr{L}^{-1}\left\{\dfrac{s}{(s-2)(s-3)(s-6)}\right\} = \mathscr{L}^{-1}\left\{\dfrac{1}{2}\cdot\dfrac{1}{s-2}-\dfrac{1}{s-3}+\dfrac{1}{2}\cdot\dfrac{1}{s-6}\right\} = \dfrac{1}{2}e^{2t}-e^{3t}+\dfrac{1}{2}e^{6t}$

26. $\mathscr{L}^{-1}\left\{\dfrac{s^2+1}{s(s-1)(s+1)(s-2)}\right\} = \mathscr{L}^{-1}\left\{\dfrac{1}{2}\cdot\dfrac{1}{s}-\dfrac{1}{s-1}-\dfrac{1}{3}\cdot\dfrac{1}{s+1}+\dfrac{5}{6}\cdot\dfrac{1}{s-2}\right\}$

$$= \dfrac{1}{2}-e^t-\dfrac{1}{3}e^{-t}+\dfrac{5}{6}e^{2t}$$

27. $\mathscr{L}^{-1}\left\{\dfrac{2s+4}{(s-2)(s^2+4s+3)}\right\} = \mathscr{L}^{-1}\left\{\dfrac{8}{15}\cdot\dfrac{1}{s-2}-\dfrac{1}{3}\cdot\dfrac{1}{s+1}-\dfrac{1}{5}\cdot\dfrac{1}{s+3}\right\} = \dfrac{8}{15}e^{2t}-\dfrac{1}{3}e^{-t}-\dfrac{1}{5}e^{-3t}$

Exercises 7.2

28. $\mathcal{L}^{-1}\left\{\dfrac{s+1}{(s^2-4s)(s+5)}\right\}=\mathcal{L}^{-1}\left\{-\dfrac{1}{20}\cdot\dfrac{1}{s}+\dfrac{1}{36}\cdot\dfrac{5}{s-4}-\dfrac{4}{45}\cdot\dfrac{1}{s+5}\right\}=-\dfrac{1}{20}+\dfrac{5}{36}e^{4t}-\dfrac{4}{45}e^{-5t}$

29. $\mathcal{L}^{-1}\left\{\dfrac{1}{s^2(s^2+4)}\right\}=\mathcal{L}^{-1}\left\{\dfrac{1}{4}\cdot\dfrac{1}{s^2}-\dfrac{1}{8}\cdot\dfrac{2}{s^2+4}\right\}=\dfrac{1}{4}t-\dfrac{1}{8}\sin 2t$

30. $\mathcal{L}^{-1}\left\{\dfrac{s-1}{s^2(s^2+1)}\right\}=\mathcal{L}^{-1}\left\{\dfrac{1}{s}-\dfrac{1}{s^2}-\dfrac{s}{s^2+1}+\dfrac{1}{s^2+1}\right\}=1-t-\cos t+\sin t$

31. $\mathcal{L}^{-1}\left\{\dfrac{s}{(s^2+4)(s+2)}\right\}=\mathcal{L}^{-1}\left\{\dfrac{1}{4}\cdot\dfrac{s}{s^2+4}+\dfrac{1}{4}\cdot\dfrac{2}{s^2+4}-\dfrac{1}{4}\cdot\dfrac{1}{s+2}\right\}=\dfrac{1}{4}\cos 2t+\dfrac{1}{4}\sin 2t-\dfrac{1}{4}e^{-2t}$

32. $\mathcal{L}^{-1}\left\{\dfrac{1}{s^4-9}\right\}=\mathcal{L}^{-1}\left\{\dfrac{1}{6\sqrt{3}}\cdot\dfrac{\sqrt{3}}{s^2-3}-\dfrac{1}{6\sqrt{3}}\cdot\dfrac{\sqrt{3}}{s^2-3}\right\}=\dfrac{1}{6\sqrt{3}}\sinh\sqrt{3}\,t-\dfrac{1}{6\sqrt{3}}\sin\sqrt{3}\,t$

33. $\mathcal{L}^{-1}\left\{\dfrac{1}{(s^2+1)(s^2+4)}\right\}=\mathcal{L}^{-1}\left\{\dfrac{1}{3}\cdot\dfrac{1}{s^2+1}-\dfrac{1}{6}\cdot\dfrac{2}{s^2+4}\right\}=\dfrac{1}{3}\sin t-\dfrac{1}{6}\sin 2t$

34. $\mathcal{L}^{-1}\left\{\dfrac{6s+3}{(s^2+1)(s^2+4)}\right\}=\mathcal{L}^{-1}\left\{2\cdot\dfrac{s}{s^2+1}+\dfrac{1}{s^2+1}-2\cdot\dfrac{s}{s^2+4}-\dfrac{1}{2}\cdot\dfrac{2}{s^2+4}\right\}$

$$=2\cos t+\sin t-2\cos 2t-\dfrac{1}{2}\sin 2t$$

In Problems 35 and 36 we use the fact that $\int_0^\infty f(x)\,dx=\int_0^\infty g(x)\,dx$ if both integrals exist and $f(x)\neq g(x)$ for at most finitely many values of x.

35. $\mathcal{L}\{f(t)\}=\displaystyle\int_0^\infty e^{-st}dt=\dfrac{1}{s}$ for $s>0$

36. $\mathcal{L}\{f(t)\}=\displaystyle\int_0^\infty e^{(3-s)t}dt=\dfrac{1}{s-3}$ for $s>3$

Exercises 7.3

1. $\mathcal{L}\{te^{10t}\}=\dfrac{1}{(s-10)^2}$

2. $\mathcal{L}\{te^{-6t}\}=\dfrac{1}{(s+6)^2}$

3. $\mathcal{L}\{t^3e^{-2t}\}=\dfrac{3!}{(s+2)^4}$

4. $\mathcal{L}\{t^{10}e^{-7t}\}=\dfrac{10!}{(s+7)^{11}}$

5. $\mathcal{L}\{e^t\sin 3t\}=\dfrac{3}{(s-1)^2+9}$

6. $\mathcal{L}\{e^{-2t}\cos 4t\}=\dfrac{s+2}{(s+2)^2+16}$

7. $\mathscr{L}\left\{e^{5t}\sinh 3t\right\} = \dfrac{3}{(s-5)^2-9}$

8. $\mathscr{L}\left\{e^{-t}\cosh t\right\} = \dfrac{s+1}{(s+1)^2-1}$

9. $\mathscr{L}\left\{t\left(e^t+e^{2t}\right)^2\right\} = \mathscr{L}\left\{te^{2t}+2te^{3t}+te^{4t}\right\} = \dfrac{1}{(s-2)^2}+\dfrac{2}{(s-3)^2}+\dfrac{1}{(s-4)^2}$

10. $\mathscr{L}\left\{e^{2t}(t-1)^2\right\} = \mathscr{L}\left\{t^2e^{2t}-2te^{2t}+e^{2t}\right\} = \dfrac{2}{(s-2)^3}-\dfrac{2}{(s-2)^2}+\dfrac{1}{s-2}$

11. $\mathscr{L}\left\{e^{-t}\sin^2 t\right\} = \mathscr{L}\left\{\dfrac{1}{2}e^{-t}-\dfrac{1}{2}e^{-t}\cos 2t\right\} = \dfrac{1}{2}\dfrac{1}{s+1}-\dfrac{1}{2}\dfrac{s+1}{(s+1)^2+4}$

12. $\mathscr{L}\left\{e^t\cos^2 3t\right\} = \mathscr{L}\left\{\dfrac{1}{2}e^t+\dfrac{1}{2}e^t\cos 6t\right\} = \dfrac{1}{2}\dfrac{1}{s-1}+\dfrac{1}{2}\dfrac{s-1}{(s-1)^2+36}$

13. $\mathscr{L}^{-1}\left\{\dfrac{1}{(s+2)^3}\right\} = \mathscr{L}^{-1}\left\{\dfrac{1}{2}\dfrac{2}{(s+2)^3}\right\} = \dfrac{1}{2}t^2e^{-2t}$

14. $\mathscr{L}^{-1}\left\{\dfrac{1}{(s-1)^4}\right\} = \mathscr{L}^{-1}\left\{\dfrac{1}{6}\dfrac{3!}{(s-1)^4}\right\} = \dfrac{1}{6}t^3e^t$

15. $\mathscr{L}^{-1}\left\{\dfrac{1}{s^2-6s+10}\right\} = \mathscr{L}^{-1}\left\{\dfrac{1}{(s-3)^2+1^2}\right\} = e^{3t}\sin t$

16. $\mathscr{L}^{-1}\left\{\dfrac{1}{s^2+2s+5}\right\} = \mathscr{L}^{-1}\left\{\dfrac{1}{2}\dfrac{2}{(s+1)^2+2^2}\right\} = \dfrac{1}{2}e^{-t}\sin 2t$

17. $\mathscr{L}^{-1}\left\{\dfrac{s}{s^2+4s+5}\right\} = \mathscr{L}^{-1}\left\{\dfrac{(s+2)}{(s+2)^2+1^2}-2\dfrac{1}{(s+2)^2+1^2}\right\} = e^{-2t}\cos t - 2e^{-2t}\sin t$

18. $\mathscr{L}^{-1}\left\{\dfrac{2s+5}{s^2+6s+34}\right\} = \mathscr{L}^{-1}\left\{2\dfrac{(s+3)}{(s+3)^2+5^2}-\dfrac{1}{5}\dfrac{5}{(s+3)^2+5^2}\right\} = 2e^{-3t}\cos 5t - \dfrac{1}{5}e^{-3t}\sin 5t$

19. $\mathscr{L}^{-1}\left\{\dfrac{s}{(s+1)^2}\right\} = \mathscr{L}^{-1}\left\{\dfrac{s+1-1}{(s+1)^2}\right\} = \mathscr{L}^{-1}\left\{\dfrac{1}{s+1}-\dfrac{1}{(s+1)^2}\right\} = e^{-t}-te^{-t}$

20. $\mathscr{L}^{-1}\left\{\dfrac{5s}{(s-2)^2}\right\} = \mathscr{L}^{-1}\left\{\dfrac{5(s-2)+10}{(s-2)^2}\right\} = \mathscr{L}^{-1}\left\{\dfrac{5}{s-2}+\dfrac{10}{(s-2)^2}\right\} = 5e^{2t}+10te^{2t}$

21. $\mathscr{L}^{-1}\left\{\dfrac{2s-1}{s^2(s+1)^3}\right\} = \mathscr{L}^{-1}\left\{\dfrac{5}{s}-\dfrac{1}{s^2}-\dfrac{5}{s+1}-\dfrac{4}{(s+1)^2}-\dfrac{3}{2}\dfrac{2}{(s+1)^3}\right\} = 5-t-5e^{-t}-4te^{-t}-\dfrac{3}{2}t^2e^{-t}$

22. $\mathscr{L}^{-1}\left\{\dfrac{(s+1)^2}{(s+2)^4}\right\} = \mathscr{L}^{-1}\left\{\dfrac{1}{(s+2)^2}-\dfrac{2}{(s+2)^3}+\dfrac{1}{6}\dfrac{3!}{(s+2)^4}\right\} = te^{-2t}-t^2e^{-2t}+\dfrac{1}{6}t^3e^{-2t}$

23. $\mathcal{L}\{(t-1)\,\mathcal{U}(t-1)\} = \dfrac{e^{-s}}{s^2}$

24. $\mathcal{L}\{e^{2-t}\,\mathcal{U}(t-2)\} = \mathcal{L}\left\{e^{-(t-2)}\,\mathcal{U}(t-2)\right\} = \dfrac{e^{-2s}}{s+1}$

25. $\mathcal{L}\{t\,\mathcal{U}(t-2)\} = \mathcal{L}\left\{(t-2)\,\mathcal{U}(t-2) + 2\,\mathcal{U}(t-2)\right\} = \dfrac{e^{-2s}}{s^2} + \dfrac{2e^{-2s}}{s}$

26. $\mathcal{L}\{(3t+1)\,\mathcal{U}(t-3)\} = 3\,\mathcal{L}\left\{\left(t+\dfrac{1}{3}\right)\mathcal{U}(t-3)\right\} = 3\,\mathcal{L}\left\{(t-3)\,\mathcal{U}(t-3) + \dfrac{10}{3}\,\mathcal{U}(t-3)\right\}$

$$= \dfrac{3e^{-3s}}{s^2} + \dfrac{10e^{-3s}}{s}$$

27. $\mathcal{L}\{\cos 2t\,\mathcal{U}(t-\pi)\} = \mathcal{L}\left\{\cos 2(t-\pi)\,\mathcal{U}(t-\pi)\right\} = \dfrac{se^{-\pi s}}{s^2+4}$

28. $\mathcal{L}\left\{\sin t\,\mathcal{U}\left(t-\dfrac{\pi}{2}\right)\right\} = \mathcal{L}\left\{\cos\left(t-\dfrac{\pi}{2}\right)\mathcal{U}\left(t-\dfrac{\pi}{2}\right)\right\} = \dfrac{se^{-\pi s}}{s^2+1}$

29. $\mathcal{L}\left\{(t-1)^3 e^{t-1}\,\mathcal{U}(t-1)\right\} = \dfrac{6e^{-s}}{(s-1)^4}$

30. $\mathcal{L}\left\{te^{t-5}\,\mathcal{U}(t-5)\right\} = \mathcal{L}\left\{(t-5)e^{t-5}\,\mathcal{U}(t-5) + 5e^{t-5}\,\mathcal{U}(t-5)\right\} = \dfrac{e^{-5s}}{(s-1)^2} + \dfrac{5e^{-5s}}{s-1}$

31. $\mathcal{L}^{-1}\left\{\dfrac{e^{-2s}}{s^3}\right\} = \mathcal{L}^{-1}\left\{\dfrac{1}{2}\cdot\dfrac{2}{s^3}e^{-2s}\right\} = \dfrac{1}{2}(t-2)^2\,\mathcal{U}(t-2)$

32. $\mathcal{L}^{-1}\left\{\dfrac{(1+e^{-2s})^2}{s+2}\right\} = \mathcal{L}^{-1}\left\{\dfrac{1}{s+2} + \dfrac{2e^{-2s}}{s+2} + \dfrac{e^{-4s}}{s+2}\right\} = e^{-2t} + 2e^{-2(t-2)}\,\mathcal{U}(t-2) + e^{-2(t-4)}\,\mathcal{U}(t-4)$

33. $\mathcal{L}^{-1}\left\{\dfrac{e^{-\pi s}}{s^2+1}\right\} = \sin(t-\pi)\,\mathcal{U}(t-\pi)$

34. $\mathcal{L}^{-1}\left\{\dfrac{se^{-\pi s/2}}{s^2+4}\right\} = \cos 2\left(t-\dfrac{\pi}{2}\right)\mathcal{U}\left(t-\dfrac{\pi}{2}\right)$

35. $\mathcal{L}^{-1}\left\{\dfrac{e^{-s}}{s(s+1)}\right\} = \mathcal{L}^{-1}\left\{\dfrac{e^{-s}}{s} - \dfrac{e^{-s}}{s+1}\right\} = \mathcal{U}(t-1) - e^{-(t-1)}\,\mathcal{U}(t-1)$

36. $\mathcal{L}^{-1}\left\{\dfrac{e^{-2s}}{s^2(s-1)}\right\} = \mathcal{L}^{-1}\left\{-\dfrac{e^{-2s}}{s} - \dfrac{e^{-2s}}{s^2} + \dfrac{e^{-2s}}{s-1}\right\} = -\mathcal{U}(t-2) - (t-2)\,\mathcal{U}(t-2) + e^{t-2}\,\mathcal{U}(t-2)$

37. $\mathcal{L}\{t\cos 2t\} = -\dfrac{d}{ds}\left(\dfrac{s}{s^2+4}\right) = \dfrac{s^2-4}{(s^2+4)^2}$

38. $\mathscr{L}\{t \sinh 3t\} = -\dfrac{d}{ds}\left(\dfrac{3}{s^2 - 9}\right) = \dfrac{6s}{(s^2 - 9)^2}$

39. $\mathscr{L}\{t^2 \sinh t\} = \dfrac{d^2}{ds^2}\left(\dfrac{1}{s^2 - 1}\right) = \dfrac{6s^2 + 2}{(s^2 - 1)^3}$

40. $\mathscr{L}\{t^2 \cos t\} = \dfrac{d^2}{ds^2}\left(\dfrac{s}{s^2 + 1}\right) = \dfrac{d}{ds}\left(\dfrac{1 - s^2}{(s^2 + 1)^2}\right) = \dfrac{2s\left(s^2 - 3\right)}{(s^2 + 1)^3}$

41. $\mathscr{L}\{te^{2t} \sin 6t\} = -\dfrac{d}{ds}\left(\dfrac{6}{(s - 2)^2 + 36}\right) = \dfrac{12(s - 2)}{[(s - 2)^2 + 36]^2}$

42. $\mathscr{L}\{te^{-3t} \cos 3t\} = -\dfrac{d}{ds}\left(\dfrac{s + 3}{(s + 3)^2 + 9}\right) = \dfrac{(s + 3)^2 - 9}{[(s + 3)^2 + 9]^2}$

43. $\mathscr{L}^{-1}\left\{\dfrac{s}{(s^2 + 1)^2}\right\} = \mathscr{L}^{-1}\left\{-\dfrac{1}{2} \cdot \dfrac{-2s}{(s^2 + 1)^2}\right\} = \mathscr{L}^{-1}\left\{\dfrac{1}{2}(-1)\dfrac{d}{ds}\left(\dfrac{1}{s^2 + 1}\right)\right\} = \dfrac{1}{2}t \sin t$

44. $\mathscr{L}^{-1}\left\{\dfrac{s + 1}{(s^2 + 2s + 2)^2}\right\} = \mathscr{L}^{-1}\left\{-\dfrac{1}{2} \cdot \dfrac{-2(s + 1)}{[(s + 1)^2 + 1]^2}\right\} = \mathscr{L}^{-1}\left\{\dfrac{1}{2} \cdot \dfrac{-d}{ds}\left(\dfrac{1}{(s + 1)^2 + 1}\right)\right\}$

$$= \dfrac{1}{2}te^{-t} \sin t$$

45. (c)   **46. (e)**   **47. (f)**   **48. (b)**   **49. (a)**   **50. (d)**

51. $\mathscr{L}\{2 - 4\,\mathscr{U}(t - 3)\} = \dfrac{2}{s} - \dfrac{4}{s}e^{-3s}$

52. $\mathscr{L}\{1 - \mathscr{U}(t - 4) + \mathscr{U}(t - 5)\} = \dfrac{1}{s} - \dfrac{e^{-4s}}{s} + \dfrac{e^{-5s}}{s}$

53. $\mathscr{L}\{t^2\,\mathscr{U}(t - 1)\} = \mathscr{L}\left\{\left[(t - 1)^2 + 2t - 1\right]\mathscr{U}(t - 1)\right\} = \mathscr{L}\left\{\left[(t - 1)^2 + 2(t - 1) - 1\right]\mathscr{U}(t - 1)\right\}$

$$= \left(\dfrac{2}{s^3} + \dfrac{2}{s^2} + \dfrac{1}{s}\right)e^{-s}$$

54. $\mathscr{L}\left\{\sin t\,\mathscr{U}\left(t - \dfrac{3\pi}{2}\right)\right\} = \mathscr{L}\left\{-\cos\left(t - \dfrac{3\pi}{2}\right)\mathscr{U}\left(t - \dfrac{3\pi}{2}\right)\right\} = -\dfrac{se^{-3\pi s/2}}{s^2 + 1}$

55. $\mathscr{L}\{t - t\,\mathscr{U}(t - 2)\} = \mathscr{L}\{t - (t - 2)\,\mathscr{U}(t - 2) - 2\,\mathscr{U}(t - 2)\} = \dfrac{1}{s^2} - \dfrac{e^{-2s}}{s^2} - \dfrac{2e^{-2s}}{s}$

56. $\mathscr{L}\{\sin t - \sin t\,\mathscr{U}(t - 2\pi)\} = \mathscr{L}\{\sin t - \sin(t - 2\pi)\,\mathscr{U}(t - 2\pi)\} = \dfrac{1}{s^2 + 1} - \dfrac{e^{-2\pi s}}{s^2 + 1}$

57. $\mathscr{L}\{f(t)\} = \mathscr{L}\{\mathscr{U}(t - a) - \mathscr{U}(t - b)\} = \dfrac{e^{-as}}{s} - \dfrac{e^{-bs}}{s}$

241

58. $\mathcal{L}\{f(t)\} = \mathcal{L}\{\mathcal{U}(t-1) + \mathcal{U}(t-2) + \mathcal{U}(t-3) + \cdots\} = \dfrac{e^{-s}}{s} + \dfrac{e^{-2s}}{s} + \dfrac{e^{-3s}}{s} + \cdots = \dfrac{1}{s}\dfrac{e^{-s}}{1-e^{-s}}$

59. $\mathcal{L}^{-1}\left\{\dfrac{1}{s^2} - \dfrac{e^{-s}}{s^2}\right\} = t - (t-1)\,\mathcal{U}(t-1) = \begin{cases} t, & 0 \le t < 1 \\ 1, & t \ge 1 \end{cases}$

60. $\mathcal{L}^{-1}\left\{\dfrac{2}{s} - \dfrac{3e^{-s}}{s^2} + \dfrac{5e^{-2s}}{s^2}\right\} = 2 - 3(t-1)\,\mathcal{U}(t-1) + 5(t-2)\,\mathcal{U}(t-2)$

$$= \begin{cases} 2, & 0 \le t < 1 \\ -3t + 5, & 1 \le t < 2 \\ 2t - 5, & t \ge 2 \end{cases}$$

61. $f(t) = -\dfrac{1}{t}\mathcal{L}^{-1}\left\{\dfrac{d}{ds}[\ln(s-3) - \ln(s+1)]\right\} = -\dfrac{1}{t}\mathcal{L}^{-1}\left\{\dfrac{1}{s-3} - \dfrac{1}{s+1}\right\} = -\dfrac{1}{t}\left(e^{3t} - e^{-t}\right)$

62. $f(t) = -\dfrac{1}{t}\mathcal{L}^{-1}\left\{\dfrac{d}{ds}\left[\ln\left(s^2+1\right) - \ln\left(s^2+4\right)\right]\right\} = -\dfrac{1}{t}\mathcal{L}^{-1}\left\{\dfrac{2s}{s^2+1} - \dfrac{2s}{s^2+2^2}\right\}$

$$= -\dfrac{1}{t}(2\cos t - 2\cos 2t)$$

63. $f(t) = -\dfrac{1}{t}\mathcal{L}^{-1}\left\{\dfrac{d}{ds}\left(\dfrac{\pi}{2} - \tan^{-1}\dfrac{s}{2}\right)\right\} = -\dfrac{1}{t}\mathcal{L}^{-1}\left\{-\dfrac{2}{s^2+2^2}\right\} = \dfrac{\sin 2t}{t}$

64. $f(t) = -\dfrac{1}{t}\mathcal{L}^{-1}\left\{\dfrac{d}{ds}\left(\dfrac{1}{s} - \cot^{-1}\dfrac{4}{s}\right)\right\} = -\dfrac{1}{t}\mathcal{L}^{-1}\left\{-\dfrac{1}{s^2} - \dfrac{4}{s^2+4^2}\right\} = -\dfrac{1}{t}(-t - \sin 4t) = 1 + \dfrac{\sin 4t}{t}$

Exercises 7.4

1. $\mathcal{L}\{e^t\} = \mathcal{L}\left\{\dfrac{d}{dt}e^t\right\} = s\mathcal{L}\{e^t\} - e^0 = \dfrac{s}{s-1} - 1 = \dfrac{1}{s-1}$

2. $\mathcal{L}\{-\sin 2t\} = \mathcal{L}\left\{\dfrac{d}{dt}\cos^2 t\right\} = s\mathcal{L}\left\{\cos^2 t\right\} - \cos^2 0 = s\mathcal{L}\left\{\cos^2 t\right\} - 1$

Solving for $\mathcal{L}\left\{\cos^2 t\right\}$ we obtain

$$\mathcal{L}\left\{\cos^2 t\right\} = \dfrac{1}{s}\mathcal{L}\{-\sin 2t\} + \dfrac{1}{s} = \dfrac{1}{s}\dfrac{-2}{s^2+4} + \dfrac{1}{s} = \dfrac{s^2+2}{s(s^2+4)}.$$

3. $\mathcal{L}\{y'' + 3y'\} = \mathcal{L}\{y''\} + 3\mathcal{L}\{y'\} = s^2 Y(s) - sy(0) - y'(0) + 3[sY(s) - y(0)] = (s^2 + 3s)Y(s) - s - 2$

4. $\mathcal{L}\{y'' - 4y' + 5y\} = \mathcal{L}\{y''\} - 4\mathcal{L}\{y'\} + 5\mathcal{L}\{y\}$

$$= s^2 Y(s) - sy(0) - y'(0) - 4[sY(s) - y(0)] + 5Y(s) = (s^2 - 4s + 5)Y(s) - s + 5$$

5. We solve $\mathcal{L}\{y'' - 2y' + y\} = \mathcal{L}\{0\} = 0$.

$$s^2 Y(s) - sy(0) - y'(0) - 2[sY(s) - y(0)] + Y(s) = 0$$

$$(s^2 - 2s + 1)Y(s) - 2s + 1 = 0$$

$$Y(s) = \frac{2s - 1}{(s - 1)^2}$$

6. We solve $\mathcal{L}\{y'' + y\} = \mathcal{L}\{1\} = 1/s$.

$$s^2 Y(s) - sy(0) - y'(0) + Y(s) = \frac{1}{s}$$

$$(s^2 + 1)Y(s) - 2s - 3 = \frac{1}{s}$$

$$Y(s) = \frac{1}{s(s^2 + 1)} + \frac{2s + 3}{s^2 + 1}$$

7. $\mathcal{L}\left\{\int_0^t e^\tau \, d\tau\right\} = \frac{1}{s}\mathcal{L}\{e^t\} = \frac{1}{s(s - 1)}$

8. $\mathcal{L}\left\{\int_0^t \cos\tau \, d\tau\right\} = \frac{1}{s}\mathcal{L}\{\cos t\} = \frac{s}{s(s^2 + 1)} = \frac{1}{s^2 + 1}$

9. $\mathcal{L}\left\{\int_0^t e^{-\tau}\cos\tau \, d\tau\right\} = \frac{1}{s}\mathcal{L}\left\{e^{-t}\cos t\right\} = \frac{1}{s}\frac{s + 1}{(s + 1)^2 + 1} = \frac{s + 1}{s(s^2 + 2s + 2)}$

10. $\mathcal{L}\left\{\int_0^t \tau\sin\tau \, d\tau\right\} = \frac{1}{s}\mathcal{L}\{t\sin t\} = \frac{1}{s}\left(-\frac{d}{ds}\frac{1}{s^2 + 1}\right) = -\frac{1}{s}\frac{-2s}{(s^2 + 1)^2} = \frac{2}{(s^2 + 1)^2}$

11. $\mathcal{L}\left\{\int_0^t \tau e^{t-\tau} \, d\tau\right\} = \mathcal{L}\{t\}\mathcal{L}\{e^t\} = \frac{1}{s^2(s - 1)}$

12. $\mathcal{L}\left\{\int_0^t \sin\tau\cos(t - \tau) \, d\tau\right\} = \mathcal{L}\{\sin t\}\mathcal{L}\{\cos t\} = \frac{s}{(s^2 + 1)^2}$

13. $\mathcal{L}\left\{t\int_0^t \sin\tau \, d\tau\right\} = -\frac{d}{ds}\mathcal{L}\left\{\int_0^t \sin\tau \, d\tau\right\} = -\frac{d}{ds}\left(\frac{1}{s}\frac{1}{s^2 + 1}\right) = \frac{3s^2 + 1}{s^2(s^2 + 1)^2}$

14. $\mathcal{L}\left\{t\int_0^t \tau e^{-\tau} \, d\tau\right\} = -\frac{d}{ds}\mathcal{L}\left\{t\int_0^t \tau e^{-\tau} \, d\tau\right\} = -\frac{d}{ds}\left(\frac{1}{s}\frac{1}{(s + 1)^2}\right) = \frac{3s + 1}{s^2(s + 1)^3}$

15. $\mathcal{L}\{1 * t^3\} = \dfrac{1}{s}\dfrac{3!}{s^4} = \dfrac{6}{s^5}$

16. $\mathcal{L}\{1 * e^{-2t}\} = \dfrac{1}{s(s+2)}$

17. $\mathcal{L}\{t^2 * t^4\} = \dfrac{2}{s^3}\dfrac{4!}{s^5} = \dfrac{48}{s^8}$

18. $\mathcal{L}\{t^2 * te^t\} = \dfrac{2}{s^3(s-1)^2}$

19. $\mathcal{L}\{e^{-t} * e^t \cos t\} = \dfrac{s-1}{(s+1)\left[(s-1)^2+1\right]}$

20. $\mathcal{L}\{e^{2t} * \sin t\} = \dfrac{1}{(s-2)(s^2+1)}$

21. $\mathcal{L}^{-1}\left\{\dfrac{1}{s+5}\,F(s)\right\} = e^{-5t} * f(t) = \displaystyle\int_0^t f(\tau)e^{-5(t-\tau)}d\tau$

22. $\mathcal{L}^{-1}\left\{\dfrac{s}{s^2+4}\,F(s)\right\} = \cos 2t * f(t) = \displaystyle\int_0^t f(\tau)\cos 2(t-\tau)\,d\tau$

23. $\mathcal{L}^{-1}\left\{\dfrac{1}{s(s+1)}\right\} = 1 * e^{-t} = \displaystyle\int_0^t e^{-(t-\tau)}d\tau = e^{-(t-\tau)}\Big|_0^t = 1 - e^{-t}$

24. $\mathcal{L}^{-1}\left\{\dfrac{1}{s(s^2+1)}\right\} = 1 * \sin t = \displaystyle\int_0^t \sin(t-\tau)\,d\tau = \cos(t-\tau)\Big|_0^t = 1 - \cos t$

25. $\mathcal{L}^{-1}\left\{\dfrac{1}{(s+1)(s-2)}\right\} = e^{-t} * e^{2t} = \displaystyle\int_0^t e^{-\tau}e^{2(t-\tau)}d\tau = \int_0^t e^{2t-3\tau}d\tau = -\dfrac{1}{3}e^{2t-3\tau}\Big|_0^t = \dfrac{1}{3}\left(e^{2t}-e^{-t}\right)$

26. $\mathcal{L}^{-1}\left\{\dfrac{1}{(s+1)^2}\right\} = e^{-t} * e^{-t} = \displaystyle\int_0^t e^{-\tau}e^{-(t-\tau)}d\tau = e^{-t}\int_0^t d\tau = te^{-t}$

27. $\mathcal{L}^{-1}\left\{\dfrac{s}{(s^2+4)^2}\right\} = \cos 2t * \dfrac{1}{2}\sin 2t = \dfrac{1}{2}\displaystyle\int_0^t \cos 2\tau \sin 2(t-\tau)\,d\tau$

$= \dfrac{1}{2}\displaystyle\int_0^t \cos 2\tau(\sin 2t \cos 2\tau - \cos 2t \sin 2\tau)\,d\tau = \dfrac{1}{2}\left[\sin 2t \int_0^t \cos^2 2\tau\,d\tau - \cos 2t \int_0^t \dfrac{1}{2}\sin 4\tau\,d\tau\right]$

$= \dfrac{1}{2}\sin 2t\left[\dfrac{1}{2}\tau + \dfrac{1}{8}\sin 4\tau\right]_0^t - \dfrac{1}{4}\cos 2t\left[-\dfrac{1}{4}\cos 4\tau\right]_0^t$

$= \dfrac{1}{2}\sin 2t\left(\dfrac{1}{2}t + \dfrac{1}{8}\sin 4t\right) + \dfrac{1}{16}\cos 2t(\cos 4t - 1)$

$= \dfrac{1}{4}t\sin 2t + \dfrac{1}{16}\sin 2t \sin 4t + \dfrac{1}{16}\cos 2t \cos 4t - \dfrac{1}{16}\cos 2t$

$= \dfrac{1}{4}t\sin 2t + \dfrac{1}{16}\left[\sin 2t(2\sin 2t \cos 2t) + \cos 2t\left(\cos^2 2t - \sin^2 2t\right) - \cos 2t\right]$

$= \dfrac{1}{4}t\sin 2t + \dfrac{1}{16}\cos 2t\left[2\sin^2 2t + \cos^2 2t - \sin^2 2t - 1\right] = \dfrac{1}{4}t\sin 2t$

28. $\mathcal{L}^{-1}\left\{\dfrac{1}{(s^2+4s+5)^2}\right\} = \mathcal{L}^{-1}\left\{\dfrac{1}{[(s+2)^2+1]^2}\right\} = e^{-2t}\sin t * e^{-2t}\sin t$

$$= \int_0^t e^{-2\tau}\sin \tau e^{-2(t-\tau)}\sin(t-\tau)\,d\tau = e^{-2t}\int_0^t \sin\tau(\sin t\cos\tau - \cos t\sin\tau)\,d\tau$$

$$= e^{-2t}\left[\sin t\int_0^t \frac{1}{2}\sin 2\tau\,d\tau - \cos t\int_0^t \frac{1}{2}(1-\cos 2\tau)\,d\tau\right]$$

$$= e^{-2t}\left[-\frac{1}{4}\sin t(\cos 2\tau)\Big|_0^t - \frac{1}{2}\cos t\left(\tau - \frac{1}{2}\sin 2\tau\right)\Big|_0^t\right]$$

$$= e^{-2t}\left[-\frac{1}{4}\sin t(\cos 2t - 1) - \frac{1}{2}\cos t\left(t - \frac{1}{2}\sin 2t\right)\right]$$

$$= \frac{1}{2}e^{-2t}\left[-\frac{1}{2}\sin t\left(\cos^2 t - \sin^2 t - 1\right) - t\cos t + \frac{1}{2}\cos t(2\sin t\cos t)\right]$$

$$= \frac{1}{2}e^{-2t}\left[\frac{1}{2}\sin t\left(-\cos^2 t + \sin^2 t + 1 + 2\cos^2 t\right) - t\cos t\right] = \frac{1}{2}e^{-2t}(\sin t - t\cos t)$$

29. Let $u = t - \tau$ so that $du = d\tau$ and

$$f*g = \int_0^t f(\tau)g(t-\tau)\,d\tau = -\int_t^0 f(t-u)g(u)\,du = g*f.$$

30. $f*(g+h) = \displaystyle\int_0^t f(\tau)[g(t-\tau)+h(t-\tau)]\,d\tau = \int_0^t f(\tau)g(t-\tau)\,d\tau + \int_0^t f(\tau)h(t-\tau)\,d\tau$

$$= \int_0^t f(\tau)[g(t-\tau)+h(t-\tau)]\,d\tau = f*g + f*h$$

31. $\mathcal{L}\{f(t)\} = \dfrac{1}{1-e^{-2as}}\left[\displaystyle\int_0^a e^{-st}dt - \int_a^{2a} e^{-st}dt\right] = \dfrac{(1-e^{-as})^2}{s(1-e^{-2as})} = \dfrac{1-e^{-as}}{s(1+e^{-as})}$

32. $\mathcal{L}\{f(t)\} = \dfrac{1}{1-e^{-2as}}\displaystyle\int_0^a e^{-st}dt = \dfrac{1}{s(1+e^{-as})}$

33. $\mathcal{L}\{f(t)\} = \dfrac{1}{1-e^{-bs}}\displaystyle\int_0^b \frac{a}{b}te^{-st}dt = \dfrac{a}{s}\left(\dfrac{1}{bs} - \dfrac{1}{e^{bs}-1}\right)$

34. $\mathcal{L}\{f(t)\} = \dfrac{1}{1-e^{-2s}}\left[\displaystyle\int_0^1 te^{-st}dt + \int_1^2 (2-t)e^{-st}dt\right] = \dfrac{1-e^{-s}}{s^2(1-e^{-2s})}$

35. $\mathcal{L}\{f(t)\} = \dfrac{1}{1-e^{-\pi s}}\displaystyle\int_0^\pi e^{-st}\sin t\,dt = \dfrac{1}{s^2+1}\cdot\dfrac{e^{\pi s/2}+e^{-\pi s/2}}{e^{\pi s/2}-e^{-\pi s/2}} = \dfrac{1}{s^2+1}\coth\dfrac{\pi s}{2}$

36. $\mathcal{L}\{f(t)\} = \dfrac{1}{1-e^{-2\pi s}}\displaystyle\int_0^\pi e^{-st}\sin t\,dt = \dfrac{1}{s^2+1}\cdot\dfrac{1}{1-e^{-\pi s}}$

37. $\mathcal{L}\{f(t)\} = \dfrac{1}{1-e^{-2\pi s}}\displaystyle\int_0^{2\pi} e^{-st}\sin t\,dt = \dfrac{1}{s^2+1}$

38. $\mathcal{L}\{f(t)\} = \dfrac{1}{1-e^{-2\pi s}}\displaystyle\int_0^{2\pi} e^{-st}\cos t\,dt = \dfrac{s}{s^2+1}$

Exercises 7.5

1. The Laplace transform of the differential equation is

$$s\,\mathcal{L}\{y\} - y(0) - \mathcal{L}\{y\} = \frac{1}{s}.$$

Solving for $\mathcal{L}\{y\}$ we obtain

$$\mathcal{L}\{y\} = -\frac{1}{s} + \frac{1}{s-1}.$$

Thus, $\qquad\qquad\qquad\qquad y = -1 + e^t.$

2. The Laplace transform of the differential equation is

$$s\,\mathcal{L}\{y\} - y(0) + 2\,\mathcal{L}\{y\} = \frac{1}{s^2}.$$

Solving for $\mathcal{L}\{y\}$ we obtain

$$\mathcal{L}\{y\} = \frac{1-s^2}{s^2(s+2)} = -\frac{1}{4}\frac{1}{s} + \frac{1}{2}\frac{1}{s^2} - \frac{3}{4}\frac{1}{s+2}.$$

Thus, $\qquad\qquad\qquad y = -\frac{1}{4} + \frac{1}{2}t - \frac{3}{4}e^{-2t}.$

3. The Laplace transform of the differential equation is

$$s\,\mathcal{L}\{y\} - y(0) + 4\,\mathcal{L}\{y\} = \frac{1}{s+4}.$$

Solving for $\mathcal{L}\{y\}$ we obtain $\mathcal{L}\{y\} = \dfrac{1}{(s+4)^2} + \dfrac{2}{s+4}.$

Thus, $\qquad\qquad\qquad y = te^{-4t} + 2e^{-4t}.$

4. The Laplace transform of the differential equation is

$$s\,\mathcal{L}\{y\} - y(0) - \mathcal{L}\{y\} = \frac{1}{s^2+1}.$$

Solving for $\mathcal{L}\{y\}$ we obtain

$$\mathcal{L}\{y\} = \frac{1}{(s^2+1)(s-1)} = -\frac{1}{2}\frac{s+1}{s^2+1} + \frac{1}{2}\frac{1}{s-1}.$$

Thus,
$$y = \frac{1}{2}e^t - \frac{1}{2}(\cos t + \sin t).$$

5. The Laplace transform of the differential equation is
$$s^2 \mathcal{L}\{y\} - sy(0) - y'(0) + 5[s\mathcal{L}\{y\} - y(0)] + 4\mathcal{L}\{y\} = 0.$$

Solving for $\mathcal{L}\{y\}$ we obtain
$$\mathcal{L}\{y\} = \frac{s+5}{s^2 + 5s + 4} = \frac{4}{3}\frac{1}{s+1} - \frac{1}{3}\frac{1}{s+4}.$$

Thus,
$$y = \frac{4}{3}e^{-t} - \frac{1}{3}e^{-4t}.$$

6. The Laplace transform of the differential equation is
$$s^2 \mathcal{L}\{y\} - sy(0) - y'(0) - 6[s\mathcal{L}\{y\} - y(0)] + 13\mathcal{L}\{y\} = 0.$$

Solving for $\mathcal{L}\{y\}$ we obtain
$$\mathcal{L}\{y\} = -\frac{3}{s^2 - 6s + 13} = -\frac{3}{2}\frac{2}{(s-3)^2 + 2^2}.$$

Thus,
$$y = -\frac{3}{2}e^{3t}\sin 2t.$$

7. The Laplace transform of the differential equation is
$$s^2 \mathcal{L}\{y\} - sy(0) - y'(0) - 6[s\mathcal{L}\{y\} - y(0)] + 9\mathcal{L}\{y\} = \frac{1}{s^2}.$$

Solving for $\mathcal{L}\{y\}$ we obtain
$$\mathcal{L}\{y\} = \frac{1+s^2}{s^2(s-3)^2} = \frac{2}{27}\frac{1}{s} + \frac{1}{9}\frac{1}{s^2} - \frac{2}{27}\frac{1}{s-3} + \frac{10}{9}\frac{1}{(s-3)^2}.$$

Thus,
$$y = \frac{2}{27} + \frac{1}{9}t - \frac{2}{27}e^{3t} + \frac{10}{9}te^{3t}.$$

8. The Laplace transform of the differential equation is
$$s^2 \mathcal{L}\{y\} - sy(0) - y'(0) - 4[s\mathcal{L}\{y\} - y(0)] + 4\mathcal{L}\{y\} = \frac{6}{s^4}.$$

Solving for $\mathcal{L}\{y\}$ we obtain
$$\mathcal{L}\{y\} = \frac{s^5 - 4s^4 + 6}{s^4(s-2)^2} = \frac{3}{4}\frac{1}{s} + \frac{9}{8}\frac{1}{s^2} + \frac{3}{4}\frac{2}{s^3} + \frac{1}{4}\frac{3!}{s^4} + \frac{1}{4}\frac{1}{s-2} - \frac{13}{8}\frac{1}{(s-2)^2}.$$

Thus,
$$y = \frac{3}{4} + \frac{9}{8}t + \frac{3}{4}t^2 + \frac{1}{4}t^3 + \frac{1}{4}e^{2t} - \frac{13}{8}te^{2t}.$$

247

9. The Laplace transform of the differential equation is

$$s^2 \mathcal{L}\{y\} - sy(0) - y'(0) - 4\left[s\mathcal{L}\{y\} - y(0)\right] + 4\mathcal{L}\{y\} = \frac{6}{(s-2)^4}.$$

Solving for $\mathcal{L}\{y\}$ we obtain $\mathcal{L}\{y\} = \dfrac{1}{20}\dfrac{5!}{(s-2)^6}$. Thus, $y = \dfrac{1}{20}t^5 e^{2t}$.

10. The Laplace transform of the differential equation is

$$s^2 \mathcal{L}\{y\} - sy(0) - y'(0) - 2\left[s\mathcal{L}\{y\} - y(0)\right] + 5\mathcal{L}\{y\} = \frac{1}{s} + \frac{1}{s^2}.$$

Solving for $\mathcal{L}\{y\}$ we obtain

$$\mathcal{L}\{y\} = \frac{4s^2 + s + 1}{s^2(s^2 - 2s + 5)} = \frac{7}{25}\frac{1}{s} + \frac{1}{5}\frac{1}{s^2} + \frac{-7s/25 + 109/25}{s^2 - 2s + 5}$$

$$= \frac{7}{25}\frac{1}{s} + \frac{1}{5}\frac{1}{s^2} - \frac{7}{25}\frac{s-1}{(s-1)^2 + 2^2} + \frac{51}{25}\frac{2}{(s-1)^2 + 2^2}.$$

Thus,

$$y = \frac{7}{25} + \frac{1}{5}t - \frac{7}{25}e^t \cos 2t + \frac{51}{25}e^t \sin 2t.$$

11. The Laplace transform of the differential equation is

$$s^2 \mathcal{L}\{y\} - sy(0) - y'(0) + \mathcal{L}\{y\} = \frac{1}{s^2 + 1}.$$

Solving for $\mathcal{L}\{y\}$ we obtain

$$\mathcal{L}\{y\} = \frac{s^3 - s^2 + s}{(s^2 + 1)^2} = \frac{s}{s^2 + 1} - \frac{1}{s^2 + 1} + \frac{1}{(s^2 + 1)^2}.$$

Thus,

$$y = \cos t - \frac{1}{2}\sin t - \frac{1}{2}t \cos t.$$

12. The Laplace transform of the differential equation is

$$s^2 \mathcal{L}\{y\} - sy(0) - y'(0) + 16\mathcal{L}\{y\} = \frac{1}{s}.$$

Solving for $\mathcal{L}\{y\}$ we obtain

$$\mathcal{L}\{y\} = \frac{s^2 + 2s + 1}{s(s^2 + 16)} = \frac{1}{16}\frac{1}{s} + \frac{15}{16}\frac{s}{s^2 + 4^2} + \frac{1}{2}\frac{4}{s^2 + 4^2}.$$

Thus,

$$y = \frac{1}{16} + \frac{15}{16}\cos 4t + \frac{1}{2}\sin 4t.$$

13. The Laplace transform of the differential equation is

$$s^2 \mathcal{L}\{y\} - sy(0) - y'(0) - \left[s\mathcal{L}\{y\} - y(0)\right] = \frac{s-1}{(s-1)^2 + 1}.$$

Solving for $\mathscr{L}\{y\}$ we obtain

$$\mathscr{L}\{y\} = \frac{1}{s(s^2 - 2s + 2)} = \frac{1}{2}\frac{1}{s} - \frac{1}{2}\frac{s-1}{(s-1)^2 + 1} + \frac{1}{2}\frac{1}{(s-1)^2 + 1}.$$

Thus,

$$y = \frac{1}{2} - \frac{1}{2}e^t \cos t + \frac{1}{2}e^t \sin t.$$

14. The Laplace transform of the differential equation is

$$s^2 \mathscr{L}\{y\} - sy(0) - y'(0) - 2\left[s\mathscr{L}\{y\} - y(0)\right] = \frac{1}{(s-1)^2 - 1}.$$

Solving for $\mathscr{L}\{y\}$ we obtain

$$\mathscr{L}\{y\} = \frac{1}{s^2(s-2)^2} = \frac{1}{4}\frac{1}{s} + \frac{1}{4}\frac{1}{s^2} - \frac{1}{4}\frac{1}{s-2} + \frac{1}{4}\frac{1}{(s-2)^2}.$$

Thus,

$$y = \frac{1}{4} + \frac{1}{4}t - \frac{1}{4}e^{2t} + \frac{1}{4}te^{2t}.$$

15. The Laplace transform of the differential equation is

$$2\left[s^3 \mathscr{L}\{y\} - s^2(0) - sy'(0) - y''(0)\right] + 3[s^2 \mathscr{L}\{y\} - sy(0) - y'(0)] - 3[s\mathscr{L}\{y\} - y(0)] - 2\mathscr{L}\{y\} = \frac{1}{s+1}.$$

Solving for $\mathscr{L}\{y\}$ we obtain

$$\mathscr{L}\{y\} = \frac{2s+3}{(s+1)(s-1)(2s+1)(s+2)} = \frac{1}{2}\frac{1}{s+1} + \frac{5}{18}\frac{1}{s-1} - \frac{8}{9}\frac{1}{s+1/2} + \frac{1}{9}\frac{1}{s+2}.$$

Thus,

$$y = \frac{1}{2}e^{-t} + \frac{5}{18}e^t - \frac{8}{9}e^{-t/2} + \frac{1}{9}e^{-2t}.$$

16. The Laplace transform of the differential equation is

$$s^3 \mathscr{L}\{y\} - s^2(0) - sy'(0) - y''(0) + 2[s^2 \mathscr{L}\{y\} - sy(0) - y'(0)] - [s\mathscr{L}\{y\} - y(0)] - 2\mathscr{L}\{y\} = \frac{3}{s^2 + 9}.$$

Solving for $\mathscr{L}\{y\}$ we obtain

$$\mathscr{L}\{y\} = \frac{s^2 + 12}{(s-1)(s+1)(s+2)(s^2 + 9)}$$

$$= \frac{13}{60}\frac{1}{s-1} - \frac{13}{20}\frac{1}{s+1} + \frac{16}{39}\frac{1}{s+2} + \frac{3}{130}\frac{s}{s^2+9} - \frac{1}{65}\frac{3}{s^2+9}.$$

Thus,

$$y = \frac{13}{60}e^t - \frac{13}{20}e^{-t} + \frac{16}{39}e^{-2t} + \frac{3}{130}\cos 3t - \frac{1}{65}\sin 3t.$$

Exercises 7.5

17. The Laplace transform of the differential equation is

$$s^4 \mathscr{L}\{y\} - s^3 y(0) - s^2 y'(0) - s y''(0) - y'''(0) - \mathscr{L}\{y\} = 0.$$

Solving for $\mathscr{L}\{y\}$ we obtain $\mathscr{L}\{y\} = \dfrac{s}{s^2 + 1}$. Thus, $y = \cos t$.

18. The Laplace transform of the differential equation is

$$s^4 \mathscr{L}\{y\} - s^3 y(0) - s^2 y'(0) - s y''(0) - y'''(0) - \mathscr{L}\{y\} = \frac{1}{s^2}.$$

Solving for $\mathscr{L}\{y\}$ we obtain

$$\mathscr{L}\{y\} = \frac{1}{s^2(s^4 - 1)} = -\frac{1}{s^2} + \frac{1}{4}\frac{1}{s-1} - \frac{1}{4}\frac{1}{s+1} + \frac{1}{2}\frac{1}{s^2+1}.$$

Thus,

$$y = -t + \frac{1}{4}e^t - \frac{1}{4}e^{-t} + \frac{1}{2}\sin t.$$

19. The Laplace transform of the differential equation is

$$s\mathscr{L}\{y\} - y(0) + \mathscr{L}\{y\} = \frac{5}{s}e^{-s}.$$

Solving for $\mathscr{L}\{y\}$ we obtain

$$\mathscr{L}\{y\} = \frac{5e^{-s}}{s(s+1)} = 5e^{-s}\left[\frac{1}{s} - \frac{1}{s+1}\right].$$

Thus,

$$y = 5\,\mathscr{U}(t-1) - 5e^{-(t-1)}\,\mathscr{U}(t-1).$$

20. The Laplace transform of the differential equation is

$$s\mathscr{L}\{y\} - y(0) + \mathscr{L}\{y\} = \frac{1}{s} - \frac{2}{s}e^{-s}.$$

Solving for $\mathscr{L}\{y\}$ we obtain

$$\mathscr{L}\{y\} = \frac{1}{s(s+1)} - \frac{2e^{-s}}{s(s+1)} = \frac{1}{s} - \frac{1}{s+1} - 2e^{-s}\left[\frac{1}{s} - \frac{1}{s+1}\right].$$

Thus,

$$y = 1 - e^{-t} - 2\left[1 - e^{-(t-1)}\right]\mathscr{U}(t-1).$$

21. The Laplace transform of the differential equation is

$$s\mathscr{L}\{y\} - y(0) + 2\mathscr{L}\{y\} = \frac{1}{s^2} - e^{-s}\frac{s+1}{s^2}.$$

Solving for $\mathscr{L}\{y\}$ we obtain

$$\mathscr{L}\{y\} = \frac{1}{s^2(s+2)} - e^{-s}\frac{s+1}{s^2(s+1)} = -\frac{1}{4}\frac{1}{s} + \frac{1}{2}\frac{1}{s^2} + \frac{1}{4}\frac{1}{s+2} - e^{-s}\left[\frac{1}{4}\frac{1}{s} + \frac{1}{2}\frac{1}{s^2} - \frac{1}{4}\frac{1}{s+2}\right].$$

Thus,

$$y = -\frac{1}{4} + \frac{1}{2}t + \frac{1}{4}e^{-2t} - \left[\frac{1}{4} + \frac{1}{2}(t-1) - \frac{1}{4}e^{-2(t-1)}\right]\mathcal{U}(t-1).$$

22. The Laplace transform of the differential equation is

$$s^2\mathcal{L}\{y\} - sy(0) - y'(0) + 4\mathcal{L}\{y\} = \frac{1}{s} - \frac{e^{-s}}{s}.$$

Solving for $\mathcal{L}\{y\}$ we obtain

$$\mathcal{L}\{y\} = \frac{1-s}{s(s^2+4)} - e^{-s}\frac{1}{s(s^2+4)} = \frac{1}{4}\frac{1}{s} - \frac{1}{4}\frac{s}{s^2+4} - \frac{1}{2}\frac{2}{s^2+4} - e^{-s}\left[\frac{1}{4}\frac{1}{s} - \frac{1}{4}\frac{s}{s^2+4}\right].$$

Thus,

$$y = \frac{1}{4} - \frac{1}{4}\cos 2t - \frac{1}{2}\sin 2t - \left[\frac{1}{4} - \frac{1}{4}\cos 2(t-1)\right]\mathcal{U}(t-1).$$

23. The Laplace transform of the differential equation is

$$s^2\mathcal{L}\{y\} - sy(0) - y'(0) + 4\mathcal{L}\{y\} = e^{-2\pi s}\frac{1}{s^2+1}.$$

Solving for $\mathcal{L}\{y\}$ we obtain

$$\mathcal{L}\{y\} = \frac{s}{s^2+4} + e^{-2\pi s}\left[\frac{1}{3}\frac{1}{s^2+1} - \frac{1}{6}\frac{2}{s^2+4}\right].$$

Thus,

$$y = \cos 2t + \left[\frac{1}{3}\sin(t-2\pi) - \frac{1}{6}\sin 2(t-2\pi)\right]\mathcal{U}(t-2\pi).$$

24. The Laplace transform of the differential equation is

$$s^2\mathcal{L}\{y\} - sy(0) - y'(0) - 5[s\mathcal{L}\{y\} - y(0)] + 6\mathcal{L}\{y\} = \frac{e^{-s}}{s}.$$

Solving for $\mathcal{L}\{y\}$ we obtain

$$\mathcal{L}\{y\} = e^{-s}\frac{1}{s(s-2)(s-3)} + \frac{1}{(s-2)(s-3)}$$

$$= e^{-s}\left[\frac{1}{6}\frac{1}{s} - \frac{1}{2}\frac{1}{s-2} + \frac{1}{3}\frac{1}{s-3}\right] - \frac{1}{s-2} + \frac{1}{s-3}.$$

Thus,

$$y = \left[\frac{1}{6} - \frac{1}{2}e^{2(t-1)} + \frac{1}{3}e^{3(t-1)}\right]\mathcal{U}(t-1) + e^{3t} - e^{2t}.$$

25. The Laplace transform of the differential equation is

$$s^2\mathcal{L}\{y\} - sy(0) - y'(0) + \mathcal{L}\{y\} = \frac{e^{-\pi s}}{s} - \frac{e^{-2\pi s}}{s}.$$

Solving for $\mathcal{L}\{y\}$ we obtain

$$\mathcal{L}\{y\} = e^{-\pi s}\left[\frac{1}{s} - \frac{s}{s^2+1}\right] - e^{-2\pi s}\left[\frac{1}{s} - \frac{s}{s^2+1}\right] + \frac{1}{s^2+1}.$$

Thus,

$$y = [1 - \cos(t-\pi)]\,\mathcal{U}(t-\pi) - [1 - \cos(t-2\pi)]\,\mathcal{U}(t-2\pi) + \sin t.$$

26. The Laplace transform of the differential equation is

$$s^2\,\mathcal{L}\{y\} - sy(0) - y'(0) + 4[s\,\mathcal{L}\{y\} - y(0)] + 3\,\mathcal{L}\{y\} = \frac{1}{s} - \frac{e^{-2s}}{s} - \frac{e^{-4s}}{s} + \frac{e^{-6s}}{s}.$$

Solving for $\mathcal{L}\{y\}$ we obtain

$$\mathcal{L}\{y\} = \frac{1}{3}\frac{1}{s} - \frac{1}{2}\frac{1}{s+1} + \frac{1}{6}\frac{1}{s+3} - e^{-2s}\left[\frac{1}{3}\frac{1}{s} - \frac{1}{2}\frac{1}{s+1} + \frac{1}{6}\frac{1}{s+3}\right]$$

$$- e^{-4s}\left[\frac{1}{3}\frac{1}{s} - \frac{1}{2}\frac{1}{s+1} + \frac{1}{6}\frac{1}{s+3}\right] + e^{-6s}\left[\frac{1}{3}\frac{1}{s} - \frac{1}{2}\frac{1}{s+1} + \frac{1}{6}\frac{1}{s+3}\right].$$

Thus,

$$y = \frac{1}{3} - \frac{1}{2}e^{-t} + \frac{1}{6}e^{-3t} - \left[\frac{1}{3} - \frac{1}{2}e^{-(t-2)} + \frac{1}{6}e^{-3(t-2)}\right]\mathcal{U}(t-2)$$

$$- \left[\frac{1}{3} - \frac{1}{2}e^{-(t-4)} + \frac{1}{6}e^{-3(t-4)}\right]\mathcal{U}(t-4) + \left[\frac{1}{3} - \frac{1}{2}e^{-(t-6)} + \frac{1}{6}e^{-3(t-6)}\right]\mathcal{U}(t-6).$$

27. Taking the Laplace transform of both sides of the differential equation and letting $c = y(0)$ we obtain

$$\mathcal{L}\{y''\} + \mathcal{L}\{2y'\} + \mathcal{L}\{y\} = 0$$

$$s^2\mathcal{L}\{y\} - sy(0) - y'(0) + 2s\,\mathcal{L}\{y\} - 2y(0) + \mathcal{L}\{y\} = 0$$

$$s^2\mathcal{L}\{y\} - cs - 2 + 2s\,\mathcal{L}\{y\} - 2c + \mathcal{L}\{y\} = 0$$

$$\left(s^2 + 2s + 1\right)\mathcal{L}\{y\} = cs + 2c + 2$$

$$\mathcal{L}\{y\} = \frac{cs}{(s+1)^2} + \frac{2c+2}{(s+1)^2}$$

$$= c\frac{s+1-1}{(s+1)^2} + \frac{2c+2}{(s+1)^2}$$

$$= \frac{c}{s+1} + \frac{c+2}{(s+1)^2}.$$

Therefore,

$$y(t) = c\mathcal{L}^{-1}\left\{\frac{1}{s+1}\right\} + (c+2)\mathcal{L}^{-1}\left\{\frac{1}{(s+1)^2}\right\} = ce^{-t} + (c+2)te^{-t}.$$

To find c we let $y(1) = 2$. Then $2 = ce^{-1} + (c+2)e^{-1} = 2(c+1)e^{-1}$ and $c = e - 1$. Thus,

$$y(t) = (e-1)e^{-t} + (e+1)te^{-t}.$$

28. Taking the Laplace transform of both sides of the differential equation and letting $c = y'(0)$ we obtain

$$\mathscr{L}\{y''\} - \mathscr{L}\{9y'\} + \mathscr{L}\{20y\} = \mathscr{L}\{1\}$$

$$s^2 \mathscr{L}\{y\} - sy(0) - y'(0) - 9s \mathscr{L}\{y\} + 9y(0) + 20 \mathscr{L}\{y\} = \frac{1}{s}$$

$$s^2 \mathscr{L}\{y\} - c - 9s \mathscr{L}\{y\} + 20 \mathscr{L}\{y\} = \frac{1}{s}$$

$$(s^2 - 9s + 20) \mathscr{L}\{y\} = \frac{1}{s} + c$$

$$\mathscr{L}\{y\} = \frac{1}{s(s^2 - 9s + 20)} + \frac{c}{s^2 - 9s + 20}$$

$$= \frac{1}{s(s-4)(s-5)} + \frac{c}{(s-4)(s-5)}$$

$$= \frac{1/20}{s} - \frac{1/4}{s-4} + \frac{1/5}{s-5} - \frac{c}{s-4} + \frac{c}{s-5}.$$

Therefore,

$$y(t) = \frac{1}{20} \mathscr{L}^{-1}\left\{\frac{1}{s}\right\} - \frac{1}{4} \mathscr{L}^{-1}\left\{\frac{1}{s-4}\right\} + \frac{1}{5} \mathscr{L}^{-1}\left\{\frac{1}{s-5}\right\} - c\mathscr{L}^{-1}\left\{\frac{1}{s-4}\right\} + c\mathscr{L}^{-1}\left\{\frac{1}{s-5}\right\}$$

$$= \frac{1}{20} - \frac{1}{4}e^{4t} + \frac{1}{5}e^{5t} - c\left(e^{4t} - e^{5t}\right).$$

To find c we compute

$$y'(t) = -e^{4t} + e^{5t} - c\left(4e^{4t} - 5e^{5t}\right)$$

and let $y'(1) = 0$. Then

$$0 = -e^4 + e^5 - c\left(4e^4 - 5e^5\right)$$

and

$$c = \frac{e^5 - e^4}{4e^4 - 5e^5} = \frac{e - 1}{4 - 5e}.$$

Thus,

$$y(t) = \frac{1}{20} - \frac{1}{4}e^{4t} + \frac{1}{5}e^{5t} - \frac{e-1}{4-5e}\left(e^{4t} - e^{5t}\right) = \frac{1}{20} + \frac{e}{4(4-5e)}e^{4t} - \frac{1}{5(4-5e)}e^{5t}.$$

29. The Laplace transform of the given equation is

$$\mathscr{L}\{f\} + \mathscr{L}\{t\} \mathscr{L}\{f\} = \mathscr{L}\{t\}.$$

253

Solving for $\mathscr{L}\{f\}$ we obtain $\mathscr{L}\{f\} = \dfrac{1}{s^2+1}$. Thus, $f(t) = \sin t$.

30. The Laplace transform of the given equation is

$$\mathscr{L}\{f\} = \mathscr{L}\{2t\} - 4\mathscr{L}\{\sin t\}\mathscr{L}\{f\}.$$

Solving for $\mathscr{L}\{f\}$ we obtain

$$\mathscr{L}\{f\} = \frac{2s^2+2}{s^2(s^2+5)} = \frac{2}{5}\frac{1}{s^2} + \frac{8}{5\sqrt{5}}\frac{\sqrt{5}}{s^2+5}.$$

Thus,

$$f(t) = \frac{2}{5}t + \frac{8}{5\sqrt{5}}\sin\sqrt{5}\,t.$$

31. The Laplace transform of the given equation is

$$\mathscr{L}\{f\} = \mathscr{L}\{te^t\} + \mathscr{L}\{t\}\mathscr{L}\{f\}.$$

Solving for $\mathscr{L}\{f\}$ we obtain

$$\mathscr{L}\{f\} = \frac{s^2}{(s-1)^3(s+1)} = \frac{1}{8}\frac{1}{s-1} + \frac{3}{4}\frac{1}{(s-1)^2} + \frac{1}{4}\frac{2}{(s-1)^3} - \frac{1}{8}\frac{1}{s+1}.$$

Thus,

$$f(t) = \frac{1}{8}e^t + \frac{3}{4}te^t + \frac{1}{4}t^2e^t - \frac{1}{8}e^{-t}$$

32. The Laplace transform of the given equation is

$$\mathscr{L}\{f\} + 2\mathscr{L}\{\cos t\}\mathscr{L}\{f\} = 4\mathscr{L}\{e^{-t}\} + \mathscr{L}\{\sin t\}.$$

Solving for $\mathscr{L}\{f\}$ we obtain

$$\mathscr{L}\{f\} = \frac{4s^2+s+5}{(s+1)^3} = \frac{4}{s+1} - \frac{7}{(s+1)^2} + 4\frac{2}{(s+1)^3}.$$

Thus,

$$f(t) = 4e^{-t} - 7te^{-t} + 4t^2e^{-t}$$

33. The Laplace transform of the given equation is

$$\mathscr{L}\{f\} + \mathscr{L}\{1\}\mathscr{L}\{f\} = \mathscr{L}\{1\}.$$

Solving for $\mathscr{L}\{f\}$ we obtain $\mathscr{L}\{f\} = \dfrac{1}{s+1}$. Thus, $f(t) = e^{-t}$.

34. The Laplace transform of the given equation is

$$\mathscr{L}\{f\} = \mathscr{L}\{\cos t\} + \mathscr{L}\{e^{-t}\}\mathscr{L}\{f\}.$$

Solving for $\mathscr{L}\{f\}$ we obtain

$$\mathscr{L}\{f\} = \frac{s}{s^2+1} + \frac{1}{s^2+1}.$$

254

Thus, $$f(t) = \cos t + \sin t.$$

35. The Laplace transform of the given equation is

$$\mathscr{L}\{f\} = \mathscr{L}\{1\} + \mathscr{L}\{t\} + \frac{8}{3}\mathscr{L}\{t^3\}\mathscr{L}\{f\}.$$

Solving for $\mathscr{L}\{f\}$ we obtain

$$\mathscr{L}\{f\} = \frac{s^2(s+1)}{s^4 - 16} = \frac{3}{8}\frac{1}{s-2} + \frac{1}{8}\frac{1}{s+2} + \frac{1}{2}\frac{s}{s^2+4} + \frac{1}{4}\frac{2}{s^2+4}.$$

Thus, $$f(t) = \frac{3}{8}e^{2t} + \frac{1}{8}e^{-2t} + \frac{1}{2}\cos 2t + \frac{1}{4}\sin 2t.$$

36. The Laplace transform of the given equation is

$$\mathscr{L}\{t\} - 2\mathscr{L}\{f\} = \mathscr{L}\{e^t - e^{-t}\}\mathscr{L}\{f\}.$$

Solving for $\mathscr{L}\{f\}$ we obtain

$$\mathscr{L}\{f\} = \frac{s^2 - 1}{2s^4} = \frac{1}{2}\frac{1}{s^2} - \frac{1}{12}\frac{3!}{s^4}.$$

Thus, $$f(t) = \frac{1}{2}t - \frac{1}{12}t^3.$$

37. The Laplace transform of the given equation is

$$s\mathscr{L}\{y\} - y(0) = \mathscr{L}\{1\} - \mathscr{L}\{\sin t\} - \mathscr{L}\{1\}\mathscr{L}\{y\}.$$

Solving for $\mathscr{L}\{f\}$ we obtain

$$\mathscr{L}\{y\} = \frac{s^3 - s^2 + s}{s(s^2+1)^2} = \frac{1}{s^2+1} + \frac{1}{2}\frac{2s}{(s^2+1)^2}.$$

Thus, $$y = \sin t - \frac{1}{2}t\sin t.$$

38. The Laplace transform of the given equation is

$$s\mathscr{L}\{y\} - y(0) + 6\mathscr{L}\{y\} + 9\mathscr{L}\{1\}\mathscr{L}\{y\} = \mathscr{L}\{1\}$$

Solving for $\mathscr{L}\{f\}$ we obtain $\mathscr{L}\{y\} = \dfrac{1}{(s+3)^2}$. Thus, $y = te^{-3t}$.

39. From equation (3) in the text the differential equation is

$$0.005\frac{di}{dt} + i + 50\int_0^t i(\tau)\,d\tau = 100[1 - \mathscr{U}(t-1)], \quad i(0) = 0.$$

The Laplace transform of this equation is

$$0.005[s\mathscr{L}\{i\} - i(0)] + \mathscr{L}\{i\} + 50\frac{1}{s}\mathscr{L}\{i\} = 100\left[\frac{1}{s} - \frac{1}{s}e^{-s}\right].$$

Solving for $\mathcal{L}\{i\}$ we obtain

$$\mathcal{L}\{i\} = \frac{20{,}000}{(s+100)^2}\,(1 - e^{-s}]).$$

Thus, $\qquad i(t) = 20{,}000te^{-100t} - 20{,}000(t-1)e^{-100(t-1)}\,\mathscr{U}(t-1).$

40. From equation (3) in the text the differential equation is

$$0.005\frac{di}{dt} + i + \frac{1}{0.02}\int_0^t i(\tau)\,d\tau = 100[t - (t-1) - \mathscr{U}(t-1)], \quad i(0) = 0$$

or

$$\frac{di}{dt} + 200i + 10{,}000\int_0^t i(\tau)\,d\tau = 20{,}000[t - (t-1)\,\mathscr{U}(t-1)], \quad i(0) = 0.$$

The Laplace transform of this equation is

$$s\,\mathcal{L}\{i\} + 200\,\mathcal{L}\{i\} + 10{,}000\,\frac{1}{s}\,\mathcal{L}\{i\} = 20{,}000\left[\frac{1}{s^2} - \frac{1}{s^2}e^{-s}\right].$$

Solving for $\mathcal{L}\{i\}$ we obtain

$$\mathcal{L}\{i\} = \frac{20{,}000}{s(s+100)^2}\,(1 - e^{-s}) = \left[\frac{2}{s} - \frac{2}{s+100} - \frac{200}{(s+100)^2}\right](1 - e^{-s}).$$

Thus,

$$i(t) = 2 - 2e^{-100t} - 200te^{-100t} - 2\,\mathscr{U}(t-1) + 2e^{-100(t-1)}\,\mathscr{U}(t-1) + 200(t-1)e^{-100(t-1)}\,\mathscr{U}(t-1).$$

41. The differential equation is

$$R\frac{dq}{dt} + \frac{1}{C}q = E_0 e^{-kt}, \quad q(0) = 0.$$

The Laplace transform of this equation is

$$R\mathcal{L}\{q\} + \frac{1}{C}\,\mathcal{L}\{q\} = E_0\,\frac{1}{s+k}\,.$$

Solving for $\mathcal{L}\{q\}$ we obtain

$$\mathcal{L}\{q\} = \frac{E_0 C}{(s+k)(RCs+1)} = \frac{E_0/R}{(s+k)(s+1/RC)}\,.$$

When $1/RC \neq k$ we have by partial fractions

$$\mathcal{L}\{q\} = \frac{E_0}{R}\left(\frac{1/(1/RC-k)}{s+k} - \frac{1/(1/RC-k)}{s+1/RC}\right) = \frac{E_0}{R}\,\frac{1}{1/RC-k}\left(\frac{1}{s+k} - \frac{1}{s+1/RC}\right).$$

Thus, $\qquad q(t) = \frac{E_0 C}{1-kRC}\left(e^{-kt} - e^{-t/RC}\right).$

When $1/RC = k$ we have

$$\mathcal{L}\{q\} = \frac{E_0}{R}\,\frac{1}{(s+k)^2}\,.$$

256

Thus, $$q(t) = \frac{E_0}{R} te^{-kt} = \frac{E_0}{R} te^{-t/RC}.$$

42. The differential equation is

$$10\frac{dq}{dt} + 10q = 30e^t - 30e^t \mathcal{U}(t - 1.5).$$

The Laplace transform of this equation is

$$s\mathcal{L}\{q\} - q_0 + \mathcal{L}\{q\} = \frac{3}{s-1} - \frac{3e^{1.5}}{s-1.5}e^{-1.5s}.$$

Solving for $\mathcal{L}\{q\}$ we obtain

$$\mathcal{L}\{q\} = \left(q_0 - \frac{3}{2}\right) \cdot \frac{1}{s+1} + \frac{3}{2} \cdot \frac{1}{s-1} - 3e^{1.5}\left(\frac{-2/5}{s+1} + \frac{2/5}{s-1.5}\right)e^{-1.55}.$$

Thus,

$$q(t) = \left(q_0 - \frac{3}{2}\right)e^{-t} + \frac{3}{2}e^t + \frac{6}{5}e^{1.5}\left(e^{-(t-1.5)} - e^{1.5(t-1.5)}\right)\mathcal{U}(t-1.5).$$

43. The differential equation is

$$2.5\frac{dq}{dt} + 12.5q = 5\,\mathcal{U}(t-3).$$

The Laplace transform of this equation is

$$s\mathcal{L}\{q\} + 5\mathcal{L}\{q\} = \frac{2}{s}e^{-3s}.$$

Solving for $\mathcal{L}\{q\}$ we obtain

$$\mathcal{L}\{q\} = \frac{2}{s(s+5)}e^{-3s} = \left(\frac{2}{5}\cdot\frac{1}{s} - \frac{2}{5}\cdot\frac{1}{s+5}\right)e^{-3s}.$$

Thus,

$$q(t) = \frac{2}{5}\mathcal{U}(t-3) - \frac{2}{5}e^{-5(t-3)}\mathcal{U}(t-3).$$

44. The differential equation is

$$50\frac{dq}{dt} + \frac{1}{0.01}q = E_0[\mathcal{U}(t-1) - \mathcal{U}(t-3)], \quad q(0) = 0$$

or

$$50\frac{dq}{dt} + 100q = E_0[\mathcal{U}(t-1) - \mathcal{U}(t-3)], \quad q(0) = 0.$$

The Laplace transform of this equation is

$$50s\,\mathcal{L}\{q\} + 100\,\mathcal{L}\{q\} = E_0\left(\frac{1}{s}e^{-s} - \frac{1}{s}e^{-3s}\right).$$

Solving for $\mathcal{L}\{q\}$ we obtain

$$\mathcal{L}\{q\} = \frac{E_0}{50}\left[\frac{e^{-s}}{s(s+2)} - \frac{e^{-3s}}{s(s+2)}\right] = \frac{E_0}{50}\left[\frac{1}{2}\left(\frac{1}{s} - \frac{1}{s+2}\right)e^{-s} - \frac{1}{2}\left(\frac{1}{s} - \frac{1}{s+2}\right)e^{-3s}\right].$$

257

Exercises 7.5

Thus,

$$q(t) = \frac{E_0}{100}\left[\left(1 - e^{-2(t-1)}\right)\mathcal{U}(t-1) - \left(1 - e^{-2(t-3)}\right)\mathcal{U}(t-3)\right].$$

45. The differential equation is

$$\frac{di}{dt} + 10i = \sin t + \cos\left(t - \frac{3\pi}{2}\right)\mathcal{U}\left(t - \frac{3\pi}{2}\right), \quad i(0) = 0.$$

The Laplace transform of this equation is

$$s\mathcal{L}\{i\} + 10\mathcal{L}\{i\} = \frac{1}{s^2 + 1} + \frac{se^{-3\pi s/2}}{s^2 + 1}.$$

Solving for $\mathcal{L}\{i\}$ we obtain

$$\mathcal{L}\{i\} = \frac{1}{(s^2 + 1)(s + 10)} + \frac{s}{(s^2 + 1)(s + 10)}e^{-3\pi s/2}$$

$$= \frac{1}{101}\left(\frac{1}{s + 10} - \frac{s}{s^2 + 1} + \frac{10}{s^2 + 1}\right) + \frac{1}{101}\left(\frac{-10}{s + 10} + \frac{10s}{s^2 + 1} + \frac{1}{s^2 + 1}\right)e^{-3\pi s/2}.$$

Thus,

$$i(t) = \frac{1}{101}\left(e^{-10t} - \cos t + 10\sin t\right)$$

$$+ \frac{1}{101}\left(-10e^{-10(t-3\pi/2)} + 10\cos\left(t - \frac{3\pi}{2}\right) + \sin\left(t - \frac{3\pi}{2}\right)\right)\mathcal{U}\left(t - \frac{3\pi}{2}\right).$$

46. The differential equation is

$$\frac{di}{dt} + \frac{R}{L}i = \frac{1}{L}E(t), \quad i(0) = 0.$$

The Laplace transform of this equation is

$$s\mathcal{L}\{i\} + \frac{R}{L}\mathcal{L}\{i\} = \frac{1}{L}\mathcal{L}\{E(t)\}.$$

From Problem 31, Exercise 7.4, we have

$$\mathcal{L}\{E(t)\} = \frac{1 - e^{-s}}{s(1 + e^{-s})}.$$

Thus,

$$\left(s + \frac{R}{L}\right)\mathcal{L}\{i\} = \frac{1}{L}\frac{1 - e^{-s}}{s(1 + e^{-s})}$$

and

$$\mathcal{L}\{i\} = \frac{1}{L} \frac{1 - e^{-s}}{s(s + R/L)(1 + e^{-s})} = \frac{1}{L} \frac{1 - e^{-s}}{s(s + R/L)} \frac{1}{1 + e^{-s}}$$

$$= \frac{1}{L} \left[\frac{L/R}{s} - \frac{L/R}{s + R/L} \right] (1 - e^{-s})(1 - e^{-s} + e^{-2s} - e^{-3s} + \cdots)$$

$$= \frac{1}{R} \left[\frac{1}{s} - \frac{1}{s + R/L} \right] (1 - 2e^{-s} + 2e^{-2s} - 2e^{-3s} + \cdots).$$

Therefore

$$i(t) = \frac{1}{R}[1 - 2\,\mathcal{U}(t - 1) + 2\,\mathcal{U}(t - 2) - 2\,\mathcal{U}(t - 3) + \cdots]$$

$$- \frac{1}{R} \Big[e^{-Rt/L} + 2e^{-R(t-1)/L}\,\mathcal{U}(t - 1) - 2e^{-R(t-2)/L}\,\mathcal{U}(t - 2)$$

$$+ 2e^{-R(t-3)/L}\,\mathcal{U}(t - 3) + \cdots \Big]$$

$$= \frac{1}{R}\left(1 - e^{-Rt/L}\right) + \frac{2}{R}\sum_{n=1}^{\infty}(-1)^n \left(1 - e^{-R(t-n)/L}\right)\mathcal{U}(t - n).$$

47. The differential equation is

$$\frac{di}{dt} + \frac{R}{L}i = \frac{1}{L}E(t), \quad i(0) = 0.$$

The Laplace transform of this equation is

$$s\mathcal{L}\{i\} + \frac{R}{L}\mathcal{L}\{i\} = \frac{1}{L}\mathcal{L}\{E(t)\}.$$

From Problem 33, Exercise 7.4, we have

$$\mathcal{L}\{E(t)\} = \frac{1}{s}\left(\frac{1}{s} - \frac{1}{e^s - 1}\right) = \frac{1}{s^2} + \frac{1}{s}\frac{1}{1 - e^s}.$$

Thus,

$$\left(s + \frac{R}{L}\right)\mathcal{L}\{i\} = \frac{1}{L}\frac{1}{s^2} + \frac{1}{L}\frac{1}{s}\frac{1}{1 - e^s}$$

and

$$\mathcal{L}\{i\} = \frac{1}{L}\frac{1}{s^2(s + R/L)} + \frac{1}{L}\frac{1}{s(s + R/L)}\frac{1}{1 - e^s}$$

$$= \frac{1}{L}\left(\frac{L/R}{s^2} - \frac{L^2/R^2}{s} + \frac{L^2/R^2}{s + R/L}\right) + \frac{1}{L}\left(\frac{L/R}{s} - \frac{L/R}{s + R/L}\right)\frac{1}{1 - e^s}$$

$$= \frac{1}{R}\left[\frac{1}{s} - \frac{L/R}{s} + \frac{L/R}{s + R/L}\right] + \frac{1}{R}\left(\frac{1}{s} - \frac{1}{s + R/L}\right)(1 + e^s + e^{2s} + e^{3s} + \cdots).$$

Thus,

$$i(t) = \frac{1}{R}\left(t - \frac{L}{R} + \frac{L}{R}e^{-Rt/L}\right) + \frac{1}{R}\sum_{n=1}^{\infty}\left(1 - e^{-R(t-n)/L}\right)\mathcal{U}(t-n).$$

For $0 \le t < 2$ we have

$$i(t) = \frac{1}{R}\left(t - \frac{L}{R} + \frac{L}{R}e^{-Rt/L}\right) + \frac{1}{R}\left(1 - e^{-R(t-1)/L}\right)\mathcal{U}(t-1)$$

$$= \begin{cases} \frac{1}{R}\left(t - \frac{L}{R} + \frac{L}{R}e^{-Rt/L}\right), & 0 \le t < 1 \\ \frac{1}{R}\left(t - \frac{L}{R} + \frac{L}{R}e^{-Rt/L}\right) + \frac{1}{R}\left(1 - e^{-R(t-1)/L}\right), & 1 \le t < 2. \end{cases}$$

48. The differential equation is

$$\frac{d^2q}{dt^2} + 20\frac{dq}{dt} + 200q = 150, \quad q(0) = q'(0) = 0.$$

The Laplace transform of this equation is

$$s^2 \mathcal{L}\{q\} + 20s\mathcal{L}\{q\} + 200\mathcal{L}\{q\} = \frac{150}{s}.$$

Solving for $\mathcal{L}\{q\}$ we obtain

$$\mathcal{L}\{q\} = \frac{150}{s(s^2 + 20s + 200)} = \frac{3}{4}\frac{1}{s} - \frac{3}{4}\frac{s+10}{(s+10)^2 + 10^2} - \frac{3}{4}\frac{10}{(s+10)^2 + 10^2}.$$

Thus,

$$q(t) = \frac{3}{4} - \frac{3}{4}e^{-10t}\cos 10t - \frac{3}{4}e^{-10t}\sin 10t$$

and

$$i(t) = q'(t) = 15e^{-10t}\sin 10t.$$

If $E(t) = 150 - 150\,\mathcal{U}(t-2)$, then

$$\mathcal{L}\{q\} = \frac{150}{s(s^2 + 20s + 200)}\left(1 - e^{-2s}\right)$$

$$q(t) = \frac{3}{4} - \frac{3}{4}e^{-10t}\cos 10t - \frac{3}{4}e^{-10t}\sin 10t - \left[\frac{3}{4} - \frac{3}{4}e^{-10(t-2)}\cos 10(t-2)\right.$$

$$\left. - \frac{3}{4}e^{-10(t-2)}\sin 10(t-2)\right]\mathcal{U}(t-2).$$

49. The differential equation is

$$\frac{d^2q}{dt^2} + 20\frac{dq}{dt} + 100q = 120\sin 10t.$$

The Laplace transform of this equation is

$$s^2 \mathcal{L}\{q\} + 20s\mathcal{L}\{q\} + 100\mathcal{L}\{q\} = \frac{120}{s^2 + 100}.$$

Solving for $\mathcal{L}\{q\}$ we obtain

$$\mathcal{L}\{q\} = \frac{1200}{(s+10)^2(s^2+100)} = \frac{3}{5}\frac{1}{s+10} + 6\frac{1}{(s+10)^2} - \frac{3}{5}\frac{s}{s^2+10^2}.$$

Thus,

$$q(t) = \frac{3}{5}e^{-10t} + 6te^{-10t} - \frac{3}{5}\cos 10t$$

and

$$i(t) = q'(t) = -60te^{-10t} + 6\sin 10t.$$

The steady-state current is $6\sin 10t$.

50. The differential equation is

$$\frac{d^2q}{dt^2} + 2\lambda\frac{dq}{dt} + \omega^2 q = \frac{E_0}{L}, \quad q(0) = q'(0) = 0.$$

The Laplace transform of this equation is

$$s^2\mathcal{L}\{q\} + 2\lambda s\mathcal{L}\{q\} + \omega^2\mathcal{L}\{q\} = \frac{E_0}{L}\frac{1}{s}$$

or

$$\left(s^2 + 2\lambda s + \omega^2\right)\mathcal{L}\{q\} = \frac{E_0}{L}\frac{1}{s}.$$

Solving for $\mathcal{L}\{q\}$ and using partial fractions we obtain

$$\mathcal{L}\{q\} = \frac{E_0}{L}\left(\frac{1/\omega^2}{s} - \frac{(1/\omega^2)s + 2\lambda/\omega^2}{s^2 + 2\lambda s + \omega^2}\right) = \frac{E_0}{L\omega^2}\left(\frac{1}{s} - \frac{s+2\lambda}{s^2+2\lambda s+\omega^2}\right).$$

For $\lambda > \omega$ we write $s^2 + 2\lambda s + \omega^2 = (s+\lambda)^2 - \left(\lambda^2 - \omega^2\right)$, so (recalling that $\omega^2 = 1/LC$,)

$$\mathcal{L}\{q\} = E_0 C\left(\frac{1}{s} - \frac{s+\lambda}{(s+\lambda)^2 - (\lambda^2-\omega^2)} - \frac{\lambda}{(s+\lambda)^2 - (\lambda^2-\omega^2)}\right).$$

Thus for $\lambda > \omega$,

$$q(t) = E_0 C\left(1 - e^{-\lambda t}\cosh\sqrt{\lambda^2-\omega^2}\,t - \frac{\lambda}{\sqrt{\lambda^2-\omega^2}}\sinh\sqrt{\lambda^2-\omega^2}\,t\right).$$

For $\lambda < \omega$ we write $s^2 + 2\lambda s + \omega^2 = (s+\lambda)^2 + \left(\omega^2 - \lambda^2\right)$, so

$$\mathcal{L}\{q\} = E_0\left(\frac{1}{s} - \frac{s+\lambda}{(s+\lambda)^2 + (\omega^2-\lambda^2)} - \frac{\lambda}{(s+\lambda)^2 + (\omega^2-\lambda^2)}\right).$$

Thus for $\lambda < \omega$,

$$q(t) = E_0 C\left(1 - e^{-\lambda t}\cos\sqrt{\omega^2-\lambda^2}\,t - \frac{\lambda}{\sqrt{\lambda^2-\omega^2}}\sin\sqrt{\omega^2-\lambda^2}\,t\right).$$

Exercises 7.5

For $\lambda = \omega$, $s^2 + 2\lambda + \omega^2 = (s + \lambda)^2$ and

$$\mathcal{L}\{q\} = \frac{E_0}{L} \frac{1}{s(s+\lambda)^2} = \frac{E_0}{L} \left(\frac{1/\lambda^2}{s} - \frac{1/\lambda^2}{s+\lambda} - \frac{1/\lambda}{(s+\lambda)^2} \right) = \frac{E_0}{L\lambda^2} \left(\frac{1}{s} - \frac{1}{s+\lambda} - \frac{\lambda}{(s+\lambda)^2} \right).$$

Thus for $\lambda = \omega$,

$$q(t) = E_0 C \left(1 - e^{-\lambda t} - \lambda t e^{-\lambda t} \right).$$

51. The differential equation is

$$\frac{d^2 q}{dt^2} + \frac{1}{LC} q = \frac{E_0}{L} e^{-kt}, \quad q(0) = q'(0) = 0.$$

The Laplace transform of this equation is

$$s^2 \mathcal{L}\{q\} + \frac{1}{LC} \mathcal{L}\{q\} = \frac{E_0}{L} \frac{1}{s+k}.$$

Solving for $\mathcal{L}\{q\}$ we obtain

$$\mathcal{L}\{q\} = \frac{E_0}{L} \frac{1}{(s+k)(s^2 + 1/LC)} = \frac{E_0}{L} \left(\frac{1/(k^2 + 1/LC)}{s+k} - \frac{s/(k^2 + 1/LC)}{s^2 + 1/LC} + \frac{k/(k^2 + 1/LC)}{s^2 + 1/LC} \right).$$

Thus,

$$q(t) = \frac{E_0}{L(k^2 + 1/LC)} \left[e^{-kt} - \cos\left(t/\sqrt{LC} \right) + k\sqrt{LC} \sin\left(t/\sqrt{LC} \right) \right].$$

52. Recall from Chapter 5 that $mx'' = -kx + f(t)$. Now $m = W/g = 32/32 = 1$ slug, and $32 = 2k$ so that $k = 16$ lb/ft. Thus, the differential equation is $x'' + 16x = f(t)$. The initial conditions are $x(0) = 0$, $x'(0) = 0$. Also, since

$$f(t) = \begin{cases} \sin t, & 0 \le t < 2\pi \\ 0, & t \ge 2\pi \end{cases}$$

and $\sin t = \sin(t - 2\pi)$ we can write

$$f(t) = \sin t - \sin(t - 2\pi) \mathcal{U}(t - 2\pi).$$

The Laplace transform of the differential equation is

$$s^2 \mathcal{L}\{x\} + 16 \mathcal{L}\{x\} = \frac{1}{s^2 + 1} - \frac{1}{s^2 + 1} e^{-2\pi s}.$$

Solving for $\mathcal{L}\{x\}$ we obtain

$$\mathcal{L}\{x\} = \frac{1}{(s^2 + 16)(s^2 + 1)} - \frac{1}{(s^2 + 16)(s^2 + 1)} e^{-2\pi s}$$

$$= \frac{-1/15}{s^2 + 16} + \frac{1/15}{s^2 + 1} - \left[\frac{-1/15}{s^2 + 16} + \frac{1/15}{s^2 + 1} \right] e^{-2\pi s}.$$

Thus,

$$x(t) = -\frac{1}{60}\sin 4t + \frac{1}{15}\sin t + \frac{1}{60}\sin 4(t-2\pi)\mathscr{U}(t-2\pi) - \frac{1}{15}\sin(t-2\pi)\mathscr{U}(t-2\pi)$$

$$= \begin{cases} -\frac{1}{60}\sin 4t + \frac{1}{15}\sin t, & 0 \le t < 2\pi \\ 0, & t \ge 2\pi. \end{cases}$$

53. Recall from Chapter 5 that $mx'' = -kx - \beta x'$. Now $m = W/g = 4/32 = \frac{1}{8}$ slug, and $4 = 2k$ so that $k = 2$ lb./ft. Thus, the differential equation is $x'' + 7x' + 16x = 0$. The initial conditions are $x(0) = -3/2$ and $x'(0) = 0$. The Laplace transform of the differential equation is

$$s^2\mathscr{L}\{x\} + \frac{3}{2}s + 7s\mathscr{L}\{x\} + \frac{21}{2} + 16\mathscr{L}\{x\} = 0.$$

Solving for $\mathscr{L}\{x\}$ we obtain

$$\mathscr{L}\{x\} = \frac{-3s/2 - 21/2}{s^2 + 7s + 16} = -\frac{3}{2}\frac{s+7/2}{(s+7/2)^2 + (\sqrt{15}/2)^2} - \frac{7\sqrt{15}}{10}\frac{\sqrt{15}/2}{(s+7/2)^2 + (\sqrt{15}/2)^2}.$$

Thus,

$$x = -\frac{3}{2}e^{-7t/2}\cos\frac{\sqrt{15}}{2}t - \frac{7\sqrt{15}}{10}e^{-7t/2}\sin\frac{\sqrt{15}}{2}t.$$

54. Recall from Chapter 5 that $mx'' = -kx + f(t)$. Now $m = W/g = 16/32 = 1/2$ slug, and $k = 4.5$, so the differential equation is

$$\frac{1}{2}x'' + 4.5x = 4\sin 3t + 2\cos 3t \quad \text{or} \quad x'' + 9x = 8\sin 3t + 4\cos 3t.$$

The initial conditions are $x(0) = x'(0) = 0$. The Laplace transform of the differential equation is

$$s^2\mathscr{L}\{x\} + 9\mathscr{L}\{x\} = \frac{24}{s^2 + 9} + \frac{4s}{s^2 + 9}.$$

Solving for $\mathscr{L}\{x\}$ we obtain

$$\mathscr{L}\{x\} = \frac{4s + 24}{(s^2 + 9)^2} = \frac{2}{3}\frac{2(3)s}{(s^2 + 9)^2} + \frac{12}{27}\frac{2(3)^3}{(s^2 + 9)^2}.$$

Thus,

$$x(t) = \frac{2}{3}t\sin 3t + \frac{4}{9}(\sin 3t - 3t\cos 3t) = \frac{2}{3}t\sin 3t + \frac{4}{9}\sin 3t - \frac{4}{3}t\cos 3t.$$

55. The differential equation is

$$EI\frac{d^4y}{dx^4} = w_0 \quad \text{or} \quad \frac{d^4y}{dx^4} = \frac{w_0}{EI}.$$

Taking the Laplace transform of both sides and using $y(0) = y'(0) = 0$ we obtain

$$s^4\mathscr{L}\{y\} - sy''(0) - y'''(0) = \frac{w_0}{EI}\frac{1}{s}.$$

Exercises 7.5

Letting $y''(0) = c_1$ and $y'''(0) = c_2$ we have

$$\mathcal{L}\{y\} = \frac{c_1}{s^3} + \frac{c_2}{s^4} + \frac{w_0}{EI}\frac{1}{s^5}$$

so that

$$y(x) = \frac{1}{2}c_1 x^2 + \frac{1}{6}c_2 x^3 + \frac{1}{24}\frac{w_0}{EI} x^4.$$

To find c_1 and c_2 we compute

$$y''(x) = c_1 + c_2 x + \frac{1}{2}\frac{w_0}{EI} x^2 \quad \text{and} \quad y'''(x) = c_2 + \frac{w_0}{EI} x.$$

Then $y''(L) = y'''(L) = 0$ yields the system

$$c_1 + c_2 L + \frac{1}{2}\frac{w_0}{EI} L^2 = 0$$

$$c_2 + \frac{w_0}{EI} L = 0.$$

Solving for c_1 and c_2 we obtain $c_1 = \frac{1}{2}w_0 L^2/EI$ and $c_2 = -w_0 L/EI$. Thus,

$$y(x) = \frac{w_0}{EI}\left(\frac{1}{4}L^2 x^2 - \frac{1}{6}Lx^3 + \frac{1}{24}x^4\right).$$

From this we find $y(\frac{L}{2}) = \dfrac{17w_0 L^4}{384EI}$ and $y_{\max} = y(L) = \dfrac{w_0 L^4}{8EI}$.

56. The differential equation is

$$EI\frac{d^4 y}{dx^4} = w_0[\mathcal{U}(x - L/3) - \mathcal{U}(x - 2L/3)].$$

Taking the Laplace transform of both sides and using $y(0) = y'(0) = 0$ we obtain

$$s^4 \mathcal{L}\{y\} - sy''(0) - y'''(0) = \frac{w_0}{EI}\frac{1}{s}\left(e^{-Ls/3} - e^{-2Ls/3}\right).$$

Letting $y''(0) = c_1$ and $y'''(0) = c_2$ we have

$$\mathcal{L}\{y\} = \frac{c_1}{s^3} + \frac{c_2}{s^4} + \frac{w_0}{EI}\frac{1}{s^5}\left(e^{-Ls/3} - e^{-2Ls/3}\right)$$

so that

$$y(x) = \frac{1}{2}c_1 x^2 + \frac{1}{6}c_2 x^3 + \frac{1}{24}\frac{w_0}{EI}\left[\left(x - \frac{L}{3}\right)^4 \mathcal{U}\left(x - \frac{L}{3}\right) - \left(x - \frac{2L}{3}\right)^4 \mathcal{U}\left(x - \frac{2L}{3}\right)\right].$$

To find c_1 and c_2 we compute

$$y''(x) = c_1 + c_2 x + \frac{1}{2}\frac{w_0}{EI}\left[\left(x - \frac{L}{3}\right)^2 \mathcal{U}\left(x - \frac{L}{3}\right) - \left(x - \frac{2L}{3}\right)^2 \mathcal{U}\left(x - \frac{2L}{3}\right)\right]$$

and

$$y'''(x) = c_2 + \frac{w_0}{EI}\left[\left(x - \frac{L}{3}\right)\mathcal{U}\left(x - \frac{L}{3}\right) - \left(x - \frac{2L}{3}\right)\mathcal{U}\left(x - \frac{2L}{3}\right)\right].$$

Then $y''(L) = y'''(L) = 0$ yields the system

$$c_1 + c_2 L + \frac{1}{2}\frac{w_0}{EI}\left[\left(\frac{2L}{3}\right)^2 - \left(\frac{L}{3}\right)^2\right] = c_1 + c_2 L + \frac{1}{6}\frac{w_0 L^2}{EI} = 0$$

$$c_2 + \frac{w_0}{EI}\left[\frac{2L}{3} - \frac{L}{3}\right] = c_2 + \frac{1}{3}\frac{w_0 L}{EI} = 0.$$

Solving for c_1 and c_2 we obtain $c_1 = \frac{1}{6}w_0 L^2/EI$ and $c_2 = -\frac{1}{3}w_0 L/EI$. Thus,

$$y(x) = \frac{w_0}{EI}\left(\frac{1}{12}L^2 x^2 - \frac{1}{18}Lx^3 + \frac{1}{24}\left[\left(x - \frac{L}{3}\right)^4 \mathscr{U}\left(x - \frac{L}{3}\right) - \left(x - \frac{2L}{3}\right)^4 \mathscr{U}\left(x - \frac{2L}{3}\right)\right]\right).$$

57. The differential equation is

$$EI\frac{d^4 y}{dx^4} = w_0[1 - \mathscr{U}(x - L/2)].$$

Taking the Laplace transform of both sides and using $y(0) = y'(0) = 0$ we obtain

$$s^4 \mathscr{L}\{y\} - sy''(0) - y'''(0) = \frac{w_0}{EI}\frac{1}{s}\left(1 - e^{-Ls/2}\right).$$

Letting $y''(0) = c_1$ and $y'''(0) = c_2$ we have

$$\mathscr{L}\{y\} = \frac{c_1}{s^3} + \frac{c_2}{s^4} + \frac{w_0}{EI}\frac{1}{s^5}\left(1 - e^{-Ls/2}\right)$$

so that

$$y(x) = \frac{1}{2}c_1 x^2 + \frac{1}{6}c_2 x^3 + \frac{1}{24}\frac{w_0}{EI}\left[x^4 - \left(x - \frac{L}{2}\right)^4 \mathscr{U}\left(x - \frac{L}{2}\right)\right].$$

To find c_1 and c_2 we compute

$$y''(x) = c_1 + c_2 x + \frac{1}{2}\frac{w_0}{EI}\left[x^2 - \left(x - \frac{L}{2}\right)^2 \mathscr{U}\left(x - \frac{L}{2}\right)\right]$$

and

$$y'''(x) = c_2 + \frac{w_0}{EI}\left[x - \left(x - \frac{L}{2}\right)\mathscr{U}\left(x - \frac{L}{2}\right)\right].$$

Then $y''(L) = y'''(L) = 0$ yields the system

$$c_1 + c_2 L + \frac{1}{2}\frac{w_0}{EI}\left[L^2 - \left(\frac{L}{2}\right)^2\right] = c_1 + c_2 L + \frac{3}{8}\frac{w_0 L^2}{EI} = 0$$

$$c_2 + \frac{w_0}{EI}\left(\frac{L}{2}\right) = c_2 + \frac{1}{2}\frac{w_0 L}{EI} = 0.$$

Solving for c_1 and c_2 we obtain $c_1 = \frac{1}{8}w_0 L^2/EI$ and $c_2 = -\frac{1}{2}w_0 L/EI$. Thus,

$$y(x) = \frac{w_0}{EI}\left(\frac{1}{16}L^2 x^2 - \frac{1}{12}Lx^3 + \frac{1}{24}x^4 - \frac{1}{12}\left(x - \frac{L}{2}\right)^4 \mathscr{U}\left(x - \frac{L}{2}\right)\right).$$

58. The differential equation is $EI\dfrac{d^4y}{dx^4} = w_0$ or $\dfrac{d^4y}{dx^4} = \dfrac{w_0}{EI}$. Taking the Laplace transform of both sides and using $y(0) = y''(0) = 0$ we obtain

$$s^4 \mathscr{L}\{y\} - s^2 y'(0) - y'''(0) = \frac{w_0}{EI}\frac{1}{s}.$$

Letting $y'(0) = c_1$ and $y'''(0) = c_2$ we have

$$\mathscr{L}\{y\} = \frac{w_0}{EI}\frac{1}{s^5} + \frac{c_1}{s^2} + \frac{c_2}{s^4}.$$

Then

$$y(x) = \frac{w_0}{24EI}t^4 + c_1 t + \frac{c_2}{6}t^3.$$

To find c_1 and c_2 we compute

$$y''(x) = \frac{w_0}{2EI}t^2 + c_2 t.$$

Then $y(L) = y''(L) = 0$ yields the system

$$c_1 L + c_2 \frac{L^3}{6} = -\frac{w_0 L^4}{24EI}$$

$$c_2 L = -\frac{w_0 L^2}{2EI}.$$

Solving for c_1 and c_2 we obtain $c_1 = w_0 L^3/24EI$ and $c_2 = -w_0 L/2EI$. Thus,

$$y(x) = \frac{w_0}{24EI}x^4 - \frac{w_0 L}{12EI}x^3 + \frac{w_0 L^3}{24EI}x.$$

59. The Laplace transform of the differential equation is

$$-\frac{d}{ds}\left[s^2 \mathscr{L}\{y\} - y'(0)\right] - s\mathscr{L}\{y\} = \frac{2}{s^3}.$$

Then

$$-s^2\left(\frac{d}{ds}\mathscr{L}\{y\}\right) - 2s\mathscr{L}\{y\} - s\mathscr{L}\{y\} = \frac{2}{s^3}$$

and

$$\frac{d}{ds}\mathscr{L}\{y\} + \frac{3}{s}\mathscr{L}\{y\} = -\frac{2}{s^5}.$$

This is a first-order linear differential equation with integrating factor $e^{\int (3/s)\,ds} = s^3$. Thus,

$$s^3 \mathscr{L}\{y\} = -\int \frac{2}{s^2}\,ds = \frac{2}{s} + c,$$

so $\mathscr{L}\{y\} = \dfrac{2}{s^4} + \dfrac{c}{s^3}$ and

$$y(t) = \frac{1}{3}t^3 + \frac{c}{2}t^2.$$

60. The Laplace transform of the differential equation is

$$-\frac{d}{ds}\left[s^2\mathcal{L}\{y\} - y'(0)\right] - 2\frac{d}{ds}[s\mathcal{L}\{y\}] + 2\mathcal{L}\{y\} = 0.$$

Then

$$-s^2\left(\frac{d}{ds}\mathcal{L}\{y\}\right) - 2s\mathcal{L}\{y\} - 2s\left(\frac{d}{ds}\mathcal{L}\{y\}\right) - 2\mathcal{L}\{y\} + 2\mathcal{L}\{y\} = 0$$

and

$$\frac{d}{ds}\mathcal{L}\{y\} + \frac{2}{s+2}\mathcal{L}\{y\} = 0.$$

This is a separable differential equation so

$$\frac{d\mathcal{L}\{y\}}{\mathcal{L}\{y\}} = -\frac{2\,ds}{s+2} \implies \ln\mathcal{L}\{y\} = -2\ln(s+2) + c \implies \mathcal{L}\{y\} = c_1 e^{-2\ln(s+2)} = c_1(s+2)^{-1}$$

and $y(t) = c_1 t e^{-2t}$.

61. (a) The Laplace transform of the differential equation is $(as^2 + bs + c)\mathcal{L}\{y\} = a$. Solving for $\mathcal{L}\{y\}$ we obtain

$$\mathcal{L}\{y\} = \frac{a}{as^2 + bs + c}.$$

Thus,

$$y_1 = \mathcal{L}^{-1}\left\{\frac{a}{as^2 + bs + c}\right\}.$$

(b) Now if $\mathcal{L}\{g(t)\} = G(s)$, the Laplace transform of equation (13) gives

$$y_2 = \mathcal{L}^{-1}\left\{\frac{G(s)}{as^2 + bs + c}\right\} = \frac{1}{a}\mathcal{L}^{-1}\left\{G(s) \cdot \frac{a}{as^2 + bs + c}\right\} = \frac{1}{a}g * y_1$$

by the convolution theorem.

62. From part (b) of Problem 61 the solution of the given initial-value problem is

$$y_2 = \int_0^t \sec\tau\, y_1(t - \tau)\, d\tau \qquad \text{where} \qquad y_1 = \mathcal{L}^{-1}\left\{\frac{1}{s^2 + 1}\right\} = \sin t.$$

Thus,

$$y_2 = \int_0^t \frac{1}{\cos\tau}(\sin t\cos\tau - \cos t\sin\tau)\, d\tau = (\sin t)\int_0^t d\tau - (\cos t)\int_0^t \frac{\sin\tau}{\cos\tau}\, d\tau$$

$$= t\sin t + \cos t \ln|\cos t|.$$

Exercises 7.6

1. The Laplace transform of the differential equation is

$$\mathscr{L}\{y\} = \frac{1}{s-3}e^{-2s}$$

so that

$$y = e^{3(t-2)}\mathcal{U}(t-2).$$

2. The Laplace transform of the differential equation is

$$\mathscr{L}\{y\} = \frac{2}{s+1} + \frac{e^{-s}}{s+1}$$

so that

$$y = 2e^{-t} + e^{-(t-1)}\mathcal{U}(t-1).$$

3. The Laplace transform of the differential equation is

$$\mathscr{L}\{y\} = \frac{1}{s^2+1}\left(1 + e^{-2\pi s}\right)$$

so that

$$y = \sin t + \sin t\,\mathcal{U}(t-2\pi).$$

4. The Laplace transform of the differential equation is

$$\mathscr{L}\{y\} = \frac{1}{4}\frac{4}{s^2+16}e^{-2\pi s}$$

so that

$$y = \frac{1}{4}\sin 4(t-2\pi)\,\mathcal{U}(t-2\pi).$$

5. The Laplace transform of the differential equation is

$$\mathscr{L}\{y\} = \frac{1}{s^2+1}\left(e^{-\pi s/2} + e^{-3\pi s/2}\right)$$

so that

$$y = \sin\left(t - \frac{\pi}{2}\right)\mathcal{U}\left(t - \frac{\pi}{2}\right) + \sin\left(t - \frac{3\pi}{2}\right)\mathcal{U}\left(t - \frac{3\pi}{2}\right) = -\cos t\,\mathcal{U}\left(t - \frac{\pi}{2}\right) + \cos t\,\mathcal{U}\left(t - \frac{\pi}{2}\right).$$

6. The Laplace transform of the differential equation is

$$\mathscr{L}\{y\} = \frac{s}{s^2+1} + \frac{1}{s^2+1}(e^{-2\pi s} + e^{-4\pi s})$$

so that

$$y = \cos t + \sin t[\mathcal{U}(t-2\pi) + \mathcal{U}(t-4\pi)].$$

7. The Laplace transform of the differential equation is

$$\mathscr{L}\{y\} = \frac{1}{s^2 + 2s}(1 + e^{-s}) = \left[\frac{1}{2}\frac{1}{s} - \frac{1}{2}\frac{1}{s+2}\right](1 + e^{-s})$$

so that

$$y = \frac{1}{2} - \frac{1}{2}e^{-2t} + \left[\frac{1}{2} - \frac{1}{2}e^{-2(t-1)}\right]\mathcal{U}(t-1).$$

8. The Laplace transform of the differential equation is

$$\mathscr{L}\{y\} = \frac{s+1}{s^2(s-2)} + \frac{1}{s(s-2)}e^{-2s} = \frac{3}{4}\frac{1}{s-2} - \frac{3}{4}\frac{1}{s} - \frac{1}{2}\frac{1}{s^2} + \left[\frac{1}{2}\frac{1}{s-2} - \frac{1}{2}\frac{1}{s}\right]e^{-2s}$$

so that

$$y = \frac{3}{4}e^{2t} - \frac{3}{4} - \frac{1}{2}t + \left[\frac{1}{2}e^{2(t-2)} - \frac{1}{2}\right]\mathcal{U}(t-2).$$

9. The Laplace transform of the differential equation is

$$\mathscr{L}\{y\} = \frac{1}{(s+2)^2 + 1}e^{-2\pi s}$$

so that

$$y = e^{-2(t-2\pi)}\sin t\,\mathcal{U}(t - 2\pi).$$

10. The Laplace transform of the differential equation is

$$\mathscr{L}\{y\} = \frac{1}{(s+1)^2}e^{-s}$$

so that

$$y = (t-1)e^{-(t-1)}\mathcal{U}(t-1).$$

11. The Laplace transform of the differential equation is

$$\mathscr{L}\{y\} = \frac{4+s}{s^2 + 4s + 13} + \frac{e^{-\pi s} + e^{-3\pi s}}{s^2 + 4s + 13}$$

$$= \frac{2}{3}\frac{3}{(s+2)^2 + 3^2} + \frac{s+2}{(s+2)^2 + 3^2} + \frac{1}{3}\frac{3}{(s+2)^2 + 3^2}\left(e^{-\pi s} + e^{-3\pi s}\right)$$

so that

$$y = \frac{2}{3}e^{-2t}\sin 3t + e^{-2t}\cos 3t + \frac{1}{3}e^{-2(t-\pi)}\sin 3(t-\pi)\mathcal{U}(t-\pi)$$

$$+ \frac{1}{3}e^{-2(t-3\pi)}\sin 3(t-3\pi)\mathcal{U}(t-3\pi).$$

12. The Laplace transform of the differential equation is

$$\mathscr{L}\{y\} = \frac{1}{(s-1)^2(s-6)} + \frac{e^{-2s} + e^{-4s}}{(s-1)(s-6)}$$

$$= -\frac{1}{25}\frac{1}{s-1} - \frac{1}{5}\frac{1}{(s-1)^2} + \frac{1}{25}\frac{1}{s-6} + \left[-\frac{1}{5}\frac{1}{s-1} + \frac{1}{5}\frac{1}{s-6}\right]\left(e^{-2s} + e^{-4s}\right)$$

so that

$$y = -\frac{1}{25}e^t - \frac{1}{5}te^t + \frac{1}{25}e^{6t} + \left[-\frac{1}{5}e^{t-2} + \frac{1}{5}e^{6(t-2)}\right]\mathcal{U}(t-2)$$

$$+ \left[-\frac{1}{5}e^{t-4} + \frac{1}{5}e^{6(t-4)}\right]\mathcal{U}(t-4).$$

13. The Laplace transform of the differential equation is

$$\mathcal{L}\{y\} = \frac{1}{2}\frac{2}{s^3}y''(0) + \frac{1}{6}\frac{3!}{s^4}y'''(0) + \frac{1}{6}\frac{P_0}{EI}\frac{3!}{s^4}e^{-Ls/2}$$

so that

$$y = \frac{1}{2}y''(0)x^2 + \frac{1}{6}y'''(0)x^3 + \frac{1}{6}\frac{P_0}{EI}\left(X - \frac{L}{2}\right)^3\mathcal{U}\left(x - \frac{L}{2}\right).$$

Using $y''(L) = 0$ and $y'''(L) = 0$ we obtain

$$y = \frac{1}{4}\frac{P_0 L}{EI}x^2 - \frac{1}{6}\frac{P_0}{EI}x^3 + \frac{1}{6}\frac{P_0}{EI}\left(x - \frac{L}{2}\right)^3\mathcal{U}\left(x - \frac{L}{2}\right)$$

$$= \begin{cases} \frac{P_0}{EI}\left(\frac{L}{4}x^2 - \frac{1}{6}x^3\right), & 0 \le x < \frac{L}{2} \\ \frac{P_0 L^2}{4EI}\left(\frac{1}{2}x - \frac{L}{12}\right), & \frac{L}{2} \le x \le L. \end{cases}$$

14. From Problem 13 we know that

$$y = \frac{1}{2}y''(0)x^2 + \frac{1}{6}y'''(0)x^3 + \frac{1}{6}\frac{P_0}{EI}\left(X - \frac{L}{2}\right)^3\mathcal{U}\left(x - \frac{L}{2}\right).$$

Using $y(L) = 0$ and $y'(L) = 0$ we obtain

$$y = \frac{1}{16}\frac{P_0 L}{EI}x^2 - \frac{1}{12}\frac{P_0}{EI}x^3 + \frac{1}{6}\frac{P_0}{EI}\left(x - \frac{L}{2}\right)^3\mathcal{U}\left(x - \frac{L}{2}\right)$$

$$= \begin{cases} \frac{P_0}{EI}\left(\frac{L}{16}x^2 - \frac{1}{12}x^3\right), & 0 \le x < \frac{L}{2} \\ \frac{P_0}{EI}\left(\frac{L}{16}x^2 - \frac{1}{12}x^3\right) + \frac{1}{6}\frac{P_0}{EI}\left(x - \frac{L}{2}\right)^3, & \frac{L}{2} \le x \le L. \end{cases}$$

15. Assume $t_0 \ge 0$ and $g(t) = \begin{cases} e^{-st}, & t \ge 0 \\ 1, & t < 0 \end{cases}$ so that

$$\mathcal{L}\{\delta(t - t_0)\} = \int_0^\infty e^{-st}\delta(t - t_0)\,dt = \int_{-\infty}^\infty g(t)\delta(t - t_0)\,dt - \int_{-\infty}^0 \delta(t - t_0)\,dt$$

$$= \int_{-\infty}^\infty g(t)\delta(t - t_0)\,dt = g(t_0) = e^{-st_0}.$$

16. If $f(t) = \begin{cases} 0, & t < 0 \\ t^2 e^{-3t}, & t > 0 \end{cases}$ then from (7),

$$\int_{-\infty}^\infty f(t)\delta(t - 4)\,dt = \int_0^\infty t^2 e^{-3t}\delta(t - 4)\,dt = 16e^{-12}.$$

17. The Laplace transform of the differential equation is

$$s^2 \mathcal{L}\{y\} - sy(0) - y'(0) + 2[s\mathcal{L}\{y\} - y(0)] + 2\mathcal{L}\{y\} = -e^{-3\pi s}$$

so that

$$\mathcal{L}\{y\} = \frac{s+1}{(s+1)^2 + 1} - \frac{e^{-3\pi s}}{(s+1)^2 + 1}$$

and

$$y = e^{-t}\cos t - e^{-(t-3\pi)}\sin(t - 3\pi)\,\mathcal{U}(t - 3\pi) = e^{-t}\cos t + e^{-(t-3\pi)}\sin t\,\mathcal{U}(t - 3\pi).$$

18. The Laplace transform of the differential equation is

$$\mathcal{L}\{y\} = \frac{1}{w}\frac{s}{s^2 + w^2}$$

so that

$$y = \frac{1}{w}\sin wt.$$

Note that $y'(0) = 1$.

19. The Laplace transform of the differential equation is

$$\mathcal{L}\{i\} = \frac{1}{L}\frac{1}{s + R/L}$$

so that

$$i(t) = \frac{1}{L}e^{-Rt/L}.$$

Note that $i(0) = 1/L \neq 0$.

20. The Laplace transform of the differential equation is

$$\mathcal{L}\{y\} = \frac{s}{s+5} = 1 - \frac{5}{s+5}$$

so that

$$y = \delta(t) - 5e^{-5t}.$$

Chapter 7 Review Exercises

1. $\mathcal{L}\{f(t)\} = \int_0^1 te^{-st}\,dt + \int_1^{\infty}(2-t)e^{-st}\,dt = \dfrac{1}{s^2} - \dfrac{2}{s^2}e^{-s}$

2. $\mathcal{L}\{f(t)\} = \int_2^4 e^{-st}\,dt = \dfrac{1}{s}\left(e^{-2s} - e^{-4s}\right)$

3. False; consider $f(t) = t^{-1/2}$.

4. False, since $f(t) = (e^t)^{10} = e^{10t}$.

5. True, since $\lim_{s\to\infty} F(s) = 1 \neq 0$. (See Theorem 7.4 in the text.)

6. False; consider $f(t) = 1$ and $g(t) = 1$.

7. $\mathcal{L}\{e^{-7t}\} = \dfrac{1}{s+7}$

8. $\mathcal{L}\{te^{-7t}\} = \dfrac{1}{(s+7)^2}$

9. $\mathcal{L}\{\sin 2t\} = \dfrac{2}{s^2+4}$

10. $\mathcal{L}\{e^{-3t}\sin 2t\} = \dfrac{2}{(s+3)^2+4}$

11. $\mathcal{L}\{t\sin 2t\} = -\dfrac{d}{ds}\left[\dfrac{2}{s^2+4}\right] = \dfrac{4s}{(s^2+4)^2}$

12. $\mathcal{L}\{\sin 2t\,\mathcal{U}(t-\pi)\} = \mathcal{L}\{\sin 2(t-\pi)\,\mathcal{U}(t-\pi)\} = \dfrac{2}{s^2+4}e^{-\pi s}$

13. $\mathcal{L}^{-1}\left\{\dfrac{20}{s^6}\right\} = \mathcal{L}^{-1}\left\{\dfrac{1}{6}\dfrac{5!}{s^6}\right\} = \dfrac{1}{6}t^5$

14. $\mathcal{L}^{-1}\left\{\dfrac{1}{3s-1}\right\} = \mathcal{L}^{-1}\left\{\dfrac{1}{3}\dfrac{1}{s-1/3}\right\} = \dfrac{1}{3}e^{t/3}$

15. $\mathcal{L}^{-1}\left\{\dfrac{1}{(s-5)^3}\right\} = \mathcal{L}^{-1}\left\{\dfrac{1}{2}\dfrac{2}{(s-5)^3}\right\} = \dfrac{1}{2}t^2e^{5t}$

16. $\mathcal{L}^{-1}\left\{\dfrac{1}{s^2-5}\right\} = \mathcal{L}^{-1}\left\{-\dfrac{1}{\sqrt{5}}\dfrac{1}{s+\sqrt{5}} + \dfrac{1}{\sqrt{5}}\dfrac{1}{s-\sqrt{5}}\right\} = -\dfrac{1}{\sqrt{5}}e^{-\sqrt{5}t} + \dfrac{1}{\sqrt{5}}e^{\sqrt{5}t}$

17. $\mathcal{L}^{-1}\left\{\dfrac{s}{s^2-10s+29}\right\} = \mathcal{L}^{-1}\left\{\dfrac{s-5}{(s-5)^2+2^2} + \dfrac{5}{2}\dfrac{2}{(s-5)^2+2^2}\right\} = e^{5t}\cos 2t + \dfrac{5}{2}e^{5t}\sin 2t$

18. $\mathcal{L}^{-1}\left\{\dfrac{1}{s^2}e^{-5s}\right\} = (t-5)\mathcal{U}(t-5)$

19. $\mathcal{L}^{-1}\left\{\dfrac{s+\pi}{s^2+\pi^2}e^{-s}\right\} = \mathcal{L}^{-1}\left\{\dfrac{s}{s^2+\pi^2}e^{-s} + \dfrac{\pi}{s^2+\pi^2}e^{-s}\right\}$

$$= \cos\pi(t-1)\mathcal{U}(t-1) + \sin\pi(t-1)\mathcal{U}(t-1)$$

20. $\mathcal{L}^{-1}\left\{\dfrac{1}{L^2s^2+n^2\pi^2}\right\} = \dfrac{1}{L^2}\dfrac{L}{n\pi}\mathcal{L}^{-1}\left\{\dfrac{n\pi/L}{s^2+(n^2\pi^2)/L^2}\right\} = \dfrac{1}{Ln\pi}\sin\dfrac{n\pi}{L}t$

21. $\mathcal{L}\left\{e^{-5t}\right\}$ exists for $s > -5$.

22. $\mathcal{L}\left\{te^{8t}f(t)\right\} = -\dfrac{d}{ds}F(s-8).$

23. $\mathcal{L}\left\{e^{a(t-k)}f(t-k)\mathcal{U}(t-k)\right\} = e^{-ks}\mathcal{L}\left\{e^{at}f(t)\right\} = e^{-ks}F(s-a)$

24. $1*1 = \displaystyle\int_0^t d\tau = t$

25. **(a)** $f(t) = t - [(t-1)+1]\mathcal{U}(t-1) + \mathcal{U}(t-1) - \mathcal{U}(t-4) = t - (t-1)\mathcal{U}(t-1) - \mathcal{U}(t-4)$

(b) $\mathcal{L}\{f(t)\} = \dfrac{1}{s^2} - \dfrac{1}{s^2}e^{-s} - \dfrac{1}{s}e^{-4s}$

(c) $\mathcal{L}\left\{e^t f(t)\right\} = \dfrac{1}{(s-1)^2} - \dfrac{1}{(s-1)^2}e^{-(s-1)} - \dfrac{1}{s-1}e^{-4(s-1)}$

26. **(a)** $f(t) = \sin t\,\mathcal{U}(t-\pi) - \sin t\,\mathcal{U}(t-3\pi) = -\sin(t-\pi)\mathcal{U}(t-\pi) + \sin(t-3\pi)\mathcal{U}(t-3\pi)$

(b) $\mathcal{L}\{f(t)\} = -\dfrac{1}{s^2+1}e^{-\pi s} + \dfrac{1}{s^2+1}e^{-3\pi s}$

(c) $\mathcal{L}\left\{e^t f(t)\right\} = -\dfrac{1}{(s-1)^2+1}e^{-\pi(s-1)} + \dfrac{1}{(s-1)^2+1}e^{-3\pi(s-1)}$

27. **(a)** $f(t) = 2 - 2\mathcal{U}(t-2) + [(t-2)+2]\mathcal{U}(t-2) = 2 + (t-2)\mathcal{U}(t-2)$

(b) $\mathcal{L}\{f(t)\} = \dfrac{2}{s} + \dfrac{1}{s^2}e^{-2s}$

(c) $\mathcal{L}\left\{e^t f(t)\right\} = \dfrac{2}{s-1} + \dfrac{1}{(s-1)^2}e^{-2(s-1)}$

28. **(a)** $f(t) = t - t\,\mathcal{U}(t-1) + (2-t)\mathcal{U}(t-1) - (2-t)\mathcal{U}(t-2)$

$$= t - 2(t-1)\mathcal{U}(t-1) + (t-2)\mathcal{U}(t-2)$$

(b) $\mathcal{L}\{f(t)\} = \dfrac{1}{s^2} - \dfrac{2}{s^2}e^{-s} + \dfrac{1}{s^2}e^{-2s}$

(c) $\mathcal{L}\{e^t f(t)\} = \dfrac{1}{(s-1)^2} - \dfrac{2}{(s-1)^2}e^{-(s-1)} + \dfrac{1}{(s-1)^2}e^{-2(s-1)}$

29. Taking the Laplace transform of the differential equation we obtain

$$\mathcal{L}\{y\} = \frac{5}{(s-1)^2} + \frac{1}{2}\frac{2}{(s-1)^3}$$

so that

$$y = 5te^t + \frac{1}{2}t^2 e^t.$$

30. Taking the Laplace transform of the differential equation we obtain

$$\mathcal{L}\{y\} = \frac{1}{(s-1)^2(s^2 - 8s + 20)}$$

$$= \frac{6}{169}\frac{1}{s-1} + \frac{1}{13}\frac{1}{(s-1)^2} - \frac{6}{169}\frac{s-4}{(s-4)^2 + 2^2} + \frac{5}{338}\frac{2}{(s-4)^2 + 2^2}$$

so that

$$y = \frac{6}{169}e^t + \frac{1}{13}te^t - \frac{6}{169}e^{4t}\cos 2t + \frac{5}{338}e^{4t}\sin 2t.$$

31. Taking the Laplace transform of the given differential equation we obtain

$$\mathcal{L}\{y\} = \frac{30}{s(s^2 - 4s + 6)}e^{-\pi s} = \left(5 \cdot \frac{1}{s} - 5 \cdot \frac{s-2}{(s-2)^2 + 2} + 5\sqrt{2} \cdot \frac{\sqrt{2}}{(s-2)^2 + 2}\right)e^{-\pi s}$$

so that

$$y = 5\,\mathcal{U}(t - \pi) - 5e^{2(t-\pi)}\cos\sqrt{2}\,(t - \pi)\,\mathcal{U}(t - \pi) + 5\sqrt{2}\,e^{2(t-\pi)}\sin\sqrt{2}\,(t - \pi)\,\mathcal{U}(t - \pi).$$

32. Taking the Laplace transform of the given differential equation we obtain

$$\mathcal{L}\{y\} = \frac{s^3 + 6s^2 + 1}{s^2(s+1)(s+5)} - \frac{1}{s^2(s+1)(s+5)}e^{-2s} - \frac{2}{s(s+1)(s+5)}e^{-2s}$$

$$= -\frac{6}{25}\cdot\frac{1}{s} + \frac{1}{5}\cdot\frac{1}{s^2} + \frac{3}{2}\cdot\frac{1}{s+1} - \frac{13}{50}\cdot\frac{1}{s+5}$$

$$- \left(-\frac{6}{25}\cdot\frac{1}{s} + \frac{1}{5}\cdot\frac{1}{s^2} + \frac{1}{4}\cdot\frac{1}{s+1} - \frac{1}{100}\cdot\frac{1}{s+5}\right)e^{-2s}$$

$$- \left(\frac{2}{5}\cdot\frac{1}{5} - \frac{1}{2}\cdot\frac{1}{s+1} + \frac{1}{10}\cdot\frac{1}{s+5}\right)e^{-2s}$$

so that

$$y = -\frac{6}{25} + \frac{1}{5}t^2 + \frac{3}{2}e^{-t} - \frac{13}{50}e^{-5t} - \frac{4}{25}\mathcal{U}(t - 2) - \frac{1}{5}(t - 2)^2\,\mathcal{U}(t - 2)$$

$$+ \frac{1}{4}e^{-(t-2)}\,\mathcal{U}(t - 2) - \frac{9}{100}e^{-5(t-2)}\,\mathcal{U}(t - 2).$$

33. Taking the Laplace transform of the differential equation we obtain

$$\mathscr{L}\{y\} = \frac{s^3+2}{s^3(s-5)} - \frac{2+2s+s^2}{s^3(s-5)}e^{-s}$$

$$= -\frac{2}{125}\frac{1}{s} - \frac{2}{25}\frac{1}{s^2} - \frac{1}{5}\frac{2}{s^3} + \frac{127}{125}\frac{1}{s-5} - \left[-\frac{37}{125}\frac{1}{s} - \frac{12}{25}\frac{1}{s^2} - \frac{1}{5}\frac{2}{s^3} + \frac{37}{125}\frac{1}{s-5} \right]e^{-s}$$

so that

$$y = -\frac{2}{125} - \frac{2}{25}t - \frac{1}{5}t^2 + \frac{127}{125}e^{5t} - \left[-\frac{37}{125} - \frac{12}{25}(t-1) - \frac{1}{5}(t-1)^2 + \frac{37}{125}e^{5(t-1)} \right]\mathscr{U}(t-1).$$

34. Taking the Laplace transform of the integral equation we obtain

$$\mathscr{L}\{f\} = \frac{s+3}{s(s+5)} = \frac{3}{5}\frac{1}{s} + \frac{2}{5}\frac{1}{s+5}$$

so that

$$f(t) = \frac{3}{5} + \frac{2}{5}e^{-5t}.$$

35. Taking the Laplace transform of the integral equation we obtain

$$\mathscr{L}\{y\} = \frac{1}{s} + \frac{1}{s^2} + \frac{1}{2}\frac{2}{s^3}$$

so that

$$y(t) = 1 + t + \frac{1}{2}t^2.$$

36. Taking the Laplace transform of the integral equation we obtain

$$(\mathscr{L}\{f\})^2 = 6 \cdot \frac{6}{s^4} \quad \text{or} \quad \mathscr{L}\{f\} = \pm 6 \cdot \frac{1}{s^2}$$

so that $f(t) = \pm 6t$.

37. The integral equation is

$$10i + 2\int_0^t i(\tau)\,d\tau = 2t^2 + 2t.$$

Taking the Laplace transform we obtain

$$\mathscr{L}\{i\} = \left(\frac{4}{s^3} + \frac{2}{s^2} \right)\frac{s}{10s+2} = \frac{s+2}{s^2(5s+2)} = -\frac{9}{s} + \frac{2}{s^2} + \frac{45}{5s+1} = -\frac{9}{s} + \frac{2}{s^2} + \frac{9}{s+1/5}.$$

Thus,

$$i(t) = -9 + 2t + 9e^{-t/5}.$$

38. The differential equation is

$$\frac{1}{2}\frac{d^2q}{dt^2} + 10\frac{dq}{dt} + 100q = 10 - 10\mathscr{U}(t-5).$$

Taking the Laplace transform we obtain

$$\mathscr{L}\{q\} = \frac{20}{2(s^2 + 20s + 200)} \left(1 - e^{-5s}\right)$$

$$= \left[\frac{1}{10}\frac{1}{s} - \frac{1}{10}\frac{s+10}{(s+10)^2 + 10^2} - \frac{1}{10}\frac{10}{(s+10)^2 + 10^2}\right]\left(1 - e^{-5s}\right)$$

so that

$$q(t) = \frac{1}{10} - \frac{1}{10}e^{-10t}\cos 10t - \frac{1}{10}e^{-10t}\sin 10t$$

$$- \left[\frac{1}{10} - \frac{1}{10}e^{-10(t-5)}\cos 10(t-5) - \frac{1}{10}e^{-10(t-5)}\sin 10(t-5)\right]\mathscr{U}(t-5).$$

39. Taking the Laplace transform of the given differential equation we obtain

$$\mathscr{L}\{y\} = \frac{2w_0}{EIL}\left(\frac{L}{48}\cdot\frac{4!}{s^5} - \frac{1}{120}\cdot\frac{5!}{s^6} + \frac{1}{120}\cdot\frac{5!}{s^6}e^{-sL/2}\right) + \frac{c_1}{2}\cdot\frac{2!}{s^3} + \frac{c_2}{6}\cdot\frac{3!}{s^4}$$

so that

$$y = \frac{2w_0}{EIL}\left[\frac{L}{48}x^4 - \frac{1}{120}x^5 + \frac{1}{120}\left(x - \frac{L}{2}\right)^5\mathscr{U}\left(x - \frac{L}{2}\right)\right] + \frac{c_1}{2}x^2 + \frac{c_2}{6}x^3$$

where $y''(0) = c_1$ and $y'''(0) = c_2$. Using $y''(L) = 0$ and $y'''(L) = 0$ we find

$$c_1 = w_0 L^2/24EI, \qquad c_2 = -w_0 L/4EI.$$

Hence

$$y = \frac{w_0}{12EIL}\left[-\frac{1}{5}x^5 + \frac{L}{2}x^4 - \frac{L^2}{2}x^3 + \frac{L^3}{4}x^2 + \frac{1}{5}\left(x - \frac{L}{2}\right)^5\mathscr{U}\left(x - \frac{L}{2}\right)\right].$$

40. Taking the Laplace transform of the given differential equation we obtain

$$\mathscr{L}\{y\} = \frac{c_1}{2}\cdot\frac{2s}{s^4 + 4} + \frac{c_2}{4}\cdot\frac{4}{s^4 + 4} + \frac{w_0}{4EI}\cdot\frac{4}{s^4 + 4}e^{-s\pi/2}$$

so that

$$y = \frac{c_1}{2}\sin x \sinh x + \frac{c_2}{4}(\sin x \cosh x - \cos x \sinh x)$$

$$+ \frac{w_0}{4EI}\left[\sin\left(x - \frac{\pi}{2}\right)\cosh\left(x - \frac{\pi}{2}\right) - \cos\left(x - \frac{\pi}{2}\right)\sinh\left(x - \frac{\pi}{2}\right)\right]\mathscr{U}\left(x - \frac{\pi}{2}\right)$$

where $y''(0) = c_1$ and $y'''(0) = c_2$. Using $y(\pi) = 0$ and $y'(\pi) = 0$ we find

$$c_1 = \frac{w_0}{EI}\frac{\sinh\frac{\pi}{2}}{\sinh\pi}, \qquad c_2 = -\frac{w_0}{EI}\frac{\cosh\frac{\pi}{2}}{\sinh\pi}.$$

Hence,

$$y = \frac{w_0}{2EI} \frac{\sinh \frac{\pi}{2}}{\sinh \pi} \sin x \sinh x - \frac{w_0}{4EI} \frac{\cosh \frac{\pi}{2}}{\sinh \pi} (\sin x \cosh x - \cos x \sinh x)$$

$$+ \frac{w_0}{4EI} \left[\sin \left(x - \frac{\pi}{2} \right) \cosh \left(x - \frac{\pi}{2} \right) - \cos \left(x - \frac{\pi}{2} \right) \sinh \left(x - \frac{\pi}{2} \right) \right] \mathcal{U} \left(x - \frac{\pi}{2} \right).$$

8 Systems of Linear Differential Equations

_____ **Exercises 8.1** _____

1. From $Dx = 2x - y$ and $Dy = x$ we obtain $y = 2x - Dx$, $Dy = 2Dx - D^2x$, and $(D^2 - 2D + 1)x = 0$. Then

$$x = c_1 e^t + c_2 t e^t \quad \text{and} \quad y = (c_1 - c_2)e^t + c_2 t e^t.$$

2. From $Dx = 4x + 7y$ and $Dy = x - 2y$ we obtain $y = \frac{1}{7}Dx - \frac{4}{7}x$, $Dy = \frac{1}{7}D^2x - \frac{4}{7}Dx$, and $(D^2 - 2D - 15)x = 0$. Then

$$x = c_1 e^{5t} + c_2 e^{-3t} \quad \text{and} \quad y = \frac{1}{7}c_1 e^{5t} - c_2 e^{-3t}.$$

3. From $Dx = -y + t$ and $Dy = x - t$ we obtain $y = t - Dx$, $Dy = 1 - D^2x$, and $(D^2 + 1)x = 1 + t$. Then

$$x = c_1 \cos t + c_2 \sin t + 1 + t$$

and

$$y = c_1 \sin t - c_2 \cos t + t - 1.$$

4. From $Dx - 4y = 1$ and $x + Dy = 2$ we obtain $y = \frac{1}{4}Dx - \frac{1}{4}$, $Dy = \frac{1}{4}D^2x$, and $(D^2 + 1)x = 2$. Then

$$x = c_1 \cos t + c_2 \sin t + 2$$

and

$$y = \frac{1}{4}c_2 \cos t - \frac{1}{4}c_1 \sin t - \frac{1}{4}c_1 \sin t - \frac{1}{4}.$$

5. From $(D^2 + 5)x - 2y = 0$ and $-2x + (D^2 + 2)y = 0$ we obtain $y = \frac{1}{2}(D^2 + 5)x$, $D^2y = \frac{1}{2}(D^4 + 5D^2)x$, and $(D^2 + 1)(D^2 + 6)x = 0$. Then

$$x = c_1 \cos t + c_2 \sin t + c_3 \cos \sqrt{6}\,t + c_4 \sin \sqrt{6}\,t$$

and

$$y = 2c_1 \cos t + 2c_2 \sin t - \frac{1}{2}c_3 \cos \sqrt{6}\,t - \frac{1}{2}c_4 \sin \sqrt{6}\,t.$$

6. From $(D + 1)x + (D - 1)y = 2$ and $3x + (D + 2)y = -1$ we obtain $x = -\frac{1}{3} - \frac{1}{3}(D + 2)y$, $Dx = -\frac{1}{3}(D^2 + 2D)y$, and $(D^2 + 5)y = -7$. Then

$$y = c_1 \cos \sqrt{5}\,t + c_2 \sin \sqrt{5}\,t - \frac{7}{5}$$

and

278

$$x = \left(-\frac{2}{3}c_1 - \frac{\sqrt{5}}{3}c_2\right)\cos\sqrt{5}\,t + \left(\frac{\sqrt{5}}{3}c_1 - \frac{2}{3}c_2\right)\sin\sqrt{5}\,t + \frac{3}{5}.$$

7. From $D^2x = 4y + e^t$ and $D^2y = 4x - e^t$ we obtain $y = \frac{1}{4}D^2x - \frac{1}{4}e^t$, $D^2y = \frac{1}{4}D^4x - \frac{1}{4}e^t$, and $(D^2 + 4)(D - 2)(D + 2)x = -3e^t$. Then

$$x = c_1\cos 2t + c_2\sin 2t + c_3e^{2t} + c_4e^{-2t} + \frac{1}{5}e^t$$

and

$$y = -c_1\cos 2t - c_2\sin 2t + c_3e^{2t} + c_4e^{-2t} - \frac{1}{5}e^t.$$

8. From $(D^2 + 5)x + Dy = 0$ and $(D + 1)x + (D - 4)y = 0$ we obtain $(D - 5)(D^2 + 4)x = 0$ and $(D - 5)(D^2 + 4)y = 0$. Then

$$x = c_1e^{5t} + c_2\cos 2t + c_3\sin 2t$$

and

$$y = c_4e^{5t} + c_5\cos 2t + c_6\sin 2t.$$

Substituting into $(D + 1)x + (D - 4)y = 0$ gives

$$(6c_1 + c_4)e^{5t} + (c_2 + 2c_3 - 4c_5 + 2c_6)\cos 2t + (-2c_2 + c_3 - 2c_5 - 4c_6)\sin 2t = 0$$

so that $c_4 = -6c_1$, $c_5 = \frac{1}{2}c_3$, $c_6 = -\frac{1}{2}c_2$, and

$$y = -6c_1e^{5t} + \frac{1}{2}c_3\cos 2t - \frac{1}{2}c_2\sin 2t.$$

9. From $Dx + D^2y = e^{3t}$ and $(D + 1)x + (D - 1)y = 4e^{3t}$ we obtain $D(D^2 + 1)x = 34e^{3t}$ and $D(D^2 + 1)y = -8e^{3t}$. Then

$$y = c_1 + c_2\sin t + c_3\cos t - \frac{4}{15}e^{3t}$$

and

$$x = c_4 + c_5\sin t + c_6\cos t + \frac{17}{15}e^{3t}.$$

Substituting into $(D + 1)x + (D - 1)y = 4e^{3t}$ gives

$$(c_4 - c_1) + (c_5 - c_6 - c_3 - c_2)\sin t + (c_6 + c_5 + c_2 - c_3)\cos t = 0$$

so that $c_4 = c_1$, $c_5 = c_3$, $c_6 = -c_2$, and

$$x = c_1 - c_2\cos t + c_3\sin t + \frac{17}{15}e^{3t}.$$

10. From $D^2x - Dy = t$ and $(D + 3)x + (D + 3)y = 2$ we obtain $D(D + 1)(D + 3)x = 1 + 3t$ and $D(D + 1)(D + 3)y = -1 - 3t$. Then

$$x = c_1 + c_2e^{-t} + c_3e^{-3t} - t + \frac{1}{2}t^2$$

and

279

$$y = c_4 + c_5 e^{-t} + c_6 e^{-3t} + t - \frac{1}{2}t^2.$$

Substituting into $(D+3)x + (D+3)y = 2$ and $D^2 x - Dy = t$ gives

$$3(c_1 + c_4) + 2(c_2 + c_5)e^{-t} = 2$$

and

$$(c_2 + c_5)e^{-t} + 3(3c_3 + c_6)e^{-3t} = 0$$

so that $c_4 = -c_1$, $c_5 = -c_2$, $c_6 = -3c_3$, and

$$y = -c_1 - c_2 e^{-t} - 3c_3 e^{-3t} + t - \frac{1}{2}t^2.$$

11. From $(D^2 - 1)x - y = 0$ and $(D-1)x + Dy = 0$ we obtain $y = (D^2 - 1)x$, $Dy = (D^3 - D)x$, and $(D-1)(D^2 + D + 1)x = 0$. Then

$$x = c_1 e^t + e^{-t/2}\left[c_2 \cos \frac{\sqrt{3}}{2}t + c_3 \sin \frac{\sqrt{3}}{2}t\right]$$

and

$$y = \left(-\frac{3}{2}c_2 - \frac{\sqrt{3}}{2}c_3\right)e^{-t/2}\cos \frac{\sqrt{3}}{2}t + \left(\frac{\sqrt{3}}{2}c_2 - \frac{3}{2}c_3\right)e^{-t/2}\sin \frac{\sqrt{3}}{2}t.$$

12. From $(2D^2 - D - 1)x - (2D+1)y = 1$ and $(D-1)x + Dy = -1$ we obtain $(2D+1)(D-1)(D+1)x = -1$ and $(2D+1)(D+1)y = -2$. Then

$$x = c_1 e^{-t/2} + c_2 e^{-t} + c_3 e^t + 1$$

and

$$y = c_4 e^{-t/2} + c_5 e^{-t} - 2.$$

Substituting into $(D-1)x + Dy = -1$ gives

$$\left(-\frac{3}{2}c_1 - \frac{1}{2}c_4\right)e^{-t/2} + (-2c_2 - c_5)e^{-t} = 0$$

so that $c_4 = -3c_1$, $c_5 = -2c_2$, and

$$y = -3c_1 e^{-t/2} - 2c_2 e^{-t} - 2.$$

13. From $(2D-5)x + Dy = e^t$ and $(D-1)x + Dy = 5e^t$ we obtain $Dy = (5-2D)x + e^t$ and $(4-D)x = 4e^t$. Then

$$x = c_1 e^{4t} + \frac{4}{3}e^t$$

and $Dy = -3c_1 e^{4t} + 5e^t$ so that

$$y = -\frac{3}{4}c_1 e^{4t} + c_2 + 5e^t.$$

14. From $Dx + Dy = e^t$ and $(-D^2 + D + 1)x + y = 0$ we obtain $y = (D^2 - D - 1)x$, $Dy = (D^3 - D^2 - D)x$, and $D^2(D - 1)x = e^t$. Then

$$x = c_1 + c_2 t + c_3 e^t + t e^t$$

and

$$y = -c_1 - c_2 - c_2 t - c_3 e^t - t e^t + e^t.$$

15. From $(D - 1)x + (D^2 + 1)y = 1$ and $(D^2 - 1)x + (D + 1)y = 2$ we obtain $D^2(D - 1)(D + 1)x = 1$ and $D^2(D - 1)(D + 1)y = 1$. Then

$$x = c_1 + c_2 t + c_3 e^t + c_4 e^{-t} - \frac{1}{2}t^2$$

and

$$y = c_5 + c_6 t + c_7 e^t + c_8 e^{-t} - \frac{1}{2}t^2.$$

Substituting into $(D - 1)x + (D^2 + 1)y = 1$ gives

$$(c_2 - c_1 - 1 + c_5) + (c_6 - c_2 - 1)t + (2c_8 - 2c_4)e^{-t} + (2c_7)e^t = 1$$

so that $c_6 = c_2 + 1$, $c_8 = c_4$, $c_7 = 0$, $c_5 = c_1 - c_2 + 2$, and

$$y = (c_1 - c_2 + 2) + (c_2 + 1)t + c_4 e^{-t} - \frac{1}{2}t^2.$$

16. From $D^2 x - 2(D^2 + D)y = \sin t$ and $x + Dy = 0$ we obtain $x = -Dy$, $D^2 x = -D^3 y$, and $D(D^2 + 2D + 2)y = -\sin t$. Then

$$y = c_1 + c_2 e^{-t} \cos t + c_3 e^{-t} \sin t + \frac{1}{5}\cos t + \frac{2}{5}\sin t$$

and

$$x = (c_2 + c_3)e^{-t} \sin t + (c_2 - c_3)e^{-t} \cos t + \frac{1}{5}\sin t - \frac{2}{5}\cos t.$$

17. From $Dx = y$, $Dy = z$. and $Dz = x$ we obtain $x = D^2 y = D^3 x$ so that $(D - 1)(D^2 + D + 1)x = 0$,

$$x = c_1 e^t + e^{-t/2}\left[c_2 \sin \frac{\sqrt{3}}{2}t + c_3 \cos \frac{\sqrt{3}}{2}t\right],$$

$$y = c_1 e^t + \left(-\frac{1}{2}c_2 - \frac{\sqrt{3}}{2}c_3\right)e^{-t/2}\sin \frac{\sqrt{3}}{2}t + \left(\frac{\sqrt{3}}{2}c_2 - \frac{1}{2}c_3\right)e^{-t/2}\cos \frac{\sqrt{3}}{2}t,$$

and

$$z = c_1 e^t + \left(-\frac{1}{2}c_2 + \frac{\sqrt{3}}{2}c_3\right)e^{-t/2}\sin \frac{\sqrt{3}}{2}t + \left(-\frac{\sqrt{3}}{2}c_2 - \frac{1}{2}c_3\right)e^{-t/2}\cos \frac{\sqrt{3}}{2}t.$$

18. From $Dx + z = e^t$, $(D - 1)x + Dy + Dz = 0$, and $x + 2y + Dz = e^t$ we obtain $z = -Dx + e^t$, $Dz = -D^2 x + e^t$, and the system $(-D^2 + D - 1)x + Dy = -e^t$ and $(-D^2 + 1)x + 2y = 0$. Then

$y = \frac{1}{2}(D^2 - 1)x$, $Dy = \frac{1}{2}D(D^2 - 1)x$, and $(D-2)(D^2 + 1)x = -2e^t$ so that

$$x = c_1 e^{2t} + c_2 \cos t + c_3 \sin t + e^t,$$

$$y = \frac{3}{2}c_1 e^{2t} - c_2 \cos t - c_3 \sin t,$$

and

$$z = -2c_1 e^{2t} - c_3 \cos t + c_2 \sin t.$$

19. From $Dx - 6y = 0$, $x - Dy + z = 0$, and $x + y - Dz = 0$ we obtain

$$\begin{vmatrix} D & -6 & 0 \\ 1 & -D & 1 \\ 1 & 1 & -D \end{vmatrix} x = \begin{vmatrix} 0 & -6 & 0 \\ 0 & -D & 1 \\ 0 & 1 & -D \end{vmatrix}$$

so that $(D+1)(D-3)(D+2)x = 0$. Then

$$x = c_1 e^{-t} + c_2 e^{3t} + c_3 e^{-2t},$$

$$y = -\frac{1}{6}c_1 e^{-t} + \frac{1}{2}c_2 e^{3t} - \frac{1}{3}c_3 e^{-2t},$$

and

$$z = -\frac{5}{6}c_1 e^{-t} + \frac{1}{2}c_2 e^{3t} - \frac{1}{3}c_3 e^{-2t}.$$

20. From $(D+1)x - z = 0$, $(D+1)y - z = 0$, and $x - y + Dz = 0$ we obtain

$$\begin{vmatrix} D+1 & 0 & -1 \\ 0 & D+1 & -1 \\ 1 & -1 & D \end{vmatrix} x = \begin{vmatrix} 0 & 0 & -1 \\ 0 & D+1 & -1 \\ 0 & -1 & D \end{vmatrix}$$

so that $D(D+1)^2 x = 0$. Then

$$x = c_1 + c_2 e^{-t} + c_3 t e^{-t},$$

$$y = c_1 + (c_2 - c_3)e^{-t} + c_3 t e^{-t},$$

and

$$z = c_1 + c_3 e^{-t}.$$

21. From $2Dx + (D-1)y = t$ and $Dx + Dy = t^2$ we obtain $(D+1)y = 2t^2 - t$. Then

$$y = c_1 e^{-t} + 2t^2 - 5t + 5$$

and $Dx = c_1 e^{-t} + t^2 - 4t + 5$ so that

$$x = -c_1 e^{-t} + c_2 + \frac{1}{3}t^3 - 2t^2 + 5t.$$

22. From $Dx - 2Dy = t^2$ and $(D+1)x - 2(D+1)y = 1$ we obtain $0 = 2t + t^2$ so that the system has no solution.

23. From $(D+5)x+y = 0$ and $4x - (D+1)y = 0$ we obtain $y = -(D+5)x$ so that $Dy = -(D^2+5D)x$. Then $4x + (D^2 + 5D)x + (D + 5)x = 0$ and $(D + 3)^2x = 0$. Thus

$$x = c_1 e^{-3t} + c_2 t e^{-3t}$$

and

$$y = -(2c_1 + c_2)e^{-3t} - 2c_2 t e^{-3t}.$$

Using $x(1) = 0$ and $y(1) = 1$ we obtain

$$c_1 e^{-3} + c_2 e^{-3} = 0$$

$$-(2c_1 + c_2)e^{-3} - 2c_2 e^{-3} = 1$$

or

$$c_1 + c_2 = 0$$

$$2c_1 + 3c_2 = -e^3.$$

Thus $c_1 = e^3$ and $c_2 = -e^3$. The solution of the initial value problem is

$$x = e^{-3t+3} - te^{-3t+3}$$

$$y = -e^{-3t+3} + 2te^{-3t+3}.$$

24. From $Dx - y = -1$ and $3x + (D-2)y = 0$ we obtain $x = -\frac{1}{3}(D-2)y$ so that $Dx = -\frac{1}{3}(D^2 - 2D)y$. Then $-\frac{1}{3}(D^2 - 2D)y = y - 1$ and $(D^2 - 2D + 3)y = 3$. Thus

$$y = e^t\left(c_1 \cos \sqrt{2}\,t + c_2 \sin \sqrt{2}\,t\right) + 1$$

and

$$x = \frac{1}{3}e^t\left[\left(c_1 - \sqrt{2}\,c_2\right)\cos \sqrt{2}\,t + \left(\sqrt{2}\,c_1 + c_2\right)\sin \sqrt{2}\,t\right] + \frac{2}{3}.$$

Using $x(0) = y(0) = 0$ we obtain

$$c_1 + 1 = 0$$

$$\frac{1}{3}\left(c_1 - \sqrt{2}\,c_2\right) + \frac{2}{3} = 0.$$

Thus $c_1 = -1$ and $c_2 = \sqrt{2}/2$. The solution of the initial value problem is

$$x = e^t\left(-\frac{2}{3}\cos \sqrt{2}\,t - \frac{\sqrt{2}}{6}\sin \sqrt{2}\,t\right) + \frac{2}{3}$$

$$y = e^t\left(-\cos \sqrt{2}\,t + \frac{\sqrt{2}}{2}\sin \sqrt{2}\,t\right) + 1.$$

25. Differentiating the equation we obtain $Dx = 2c_2e^{2t}$ and $Dy = 2c_2e^{2t}$. Thus $Dx = Dy$. Adding the equations we have $x + y = 2c_2e^{2t} = Dx$. A system is

$$Dx - Dy = 0$$

$$(D-1)x - y = 0.$$

—————— **Exercises 8.2** ——————————————————

1. Taking the Laplace transform of the system gives

$$s\,\mathcal{L}\{x\} = -\mathcal{L}\{x\} + \mathcal{L}\{y\}$$

$$s\,\mathcal{L}\{y\} - 1 = 2\,\mathcal{L}\{x\}$$

so that

$$\mathcal{L}\{x\} = \frac{1}{(s-1)(s+2)} = \frac{1}{3}\frac{1}{s-1} - \frac{1}{3}\frac{1}{s+2}$$

and

$$\mathcal{L}\{y\} = \frac{1}{s} + \frac{2}{s(s-1)(s+2)} = \frac{2}{3}\frac{1}{s-1} + \frac{1}{3}\frac{1}{s+2}.$$

Then

$$x = \frac{1}{3}e^t - \frac{1}{3}e^{-2t} \quad \text{and} \quad y = \frac{2}{3}e^t + \frac{1}{3}e^{-2t}.$$

2. Taking the Laplace transform of the system gives

$$s\,\mathcal{L}\{x\} - 1 = 2\,\mathcal{L}\{y\} + \frac{1}{s-1}$$

$$s\,\mathcal{L}\{y\} - 1 = 8\,\mathcal{L}\{x\} - \frac{1}{s^2}$$

so that

$$\mathcal{L}\{y\} = \frac{s^3 + 7s^2 - s + 1}{s(s-1)(s^2-16)} = \frac{1}{16}\frac{1}{s} - \frac{8}{15}\frac{1}{s-1} + \frac{173}{96}\frac{1}{s-4} - \frac{53}{160}\frac{1}{s+4}$$

and

$$y = \frac{1}{16} - \frac{8}{15}e^t + \frac{173}{96}e^{4t} - \frac{53}{160}e^{-4t}.$$

Then

$$x = \frac{1}{8}y' + \frac{1}{8}t = \frac{1}{8}t - \frac{1}{15}e^t + \frac{173}{192}e^{4t} + \frac{53}{320}e^{-4t}.$$

3. Taking the Laplace transform of the system gives

$$s\mathscr{L}\{x\} + 1 = \mathscr{L}\{x\} - 2\mathscr{L}\{y\}$$

$$s\mathscr{L}\{y\} - 2 = 5\mathscr{L}\{x\} - \mathscr{L}\{y\}$$

so that

$$\mathscr{L}\{x\} = \frac{-s-5}{s^2+9} = -\frac{s}{s^2+9} - \frac{5}{3}\frac{3}{s^2+9}$$

and

$$x = -\cos 3t - \frac{5}{3}\sin 3t.$$

Then

$$y = \frac{1}{2}x - \frac{1}{2}x' = 2\cos 3t - \frac{7}{3}\sin 3t.$$

4. Taking the Laplace transform of the system gives

$$(s+3)\mathscr{L}\{x\} + s\mathscr{L}\{y\} = \frac{1}{s}$$

$$(s-1)\mathscr{L}\{x\} + (s-1)\mathscr{L}\{y\} = \frac{1}{s-1}$$

so that

$$\mathscr{L}\{y\} = \frac{5s-1}{3s(s-1)^2} = -\frac{1}{3}\frac{1}{s} + \frac{1}{3}\frac{1}{s-1} + \frac{4}{3}\frac{1}{(s-1)^2}$$

and

$$\mathscr{L}\{x\} = \frac{1-2s}{3s(s-1)^2} = \frac{1}{3}\frac{1}{s} - \frac{1}{3}\frac{1}{s-1} - \frac{1}{3}\frac{1}{(s-1)^2}.$$

Then

$$x = \frac{1}{3} - \frac{1}{3}e^t - \frac{1}{3}te^t \quad\text{and}\quad y = -\frac{1}{3} + \frac{1}{3}e^t + \frac{4}{3}te^t.$$

5. Taking the Laplace transform of the system gives

$$(2s-2)\mathscr{L}\{x\} + s\mathscr{L}\{y\} = \frac{1}{s}$$

$$(s-3)\mathscr{L}\{x\} + (s-3)\mathscr{L}\{y\} = \frac{2}{s}$$

so that

$$\mathscr{L}\{x\} = \frac{-s-3}{s(s-2)(s-3)} = -\frac{1}{2}\frac{1}{s} + \frac{5}{2}\frac{1}{s-2} - \frac{2}{s-3}$$

and

$$\mathscr{L}\{y\} = \frac{3s-1}{s(s-2)(s-3)} = -\frac{1}{6}\frac{1}{s} - \frac{5}{2}\frac{1}{s-2} + \frac{8}{3}\frac{1}{s-3}.$$

285

Then

$$x = -\frac{1}{2} + \frac{5}{2}e^{2t} - 2e^{3t} \quad \text{and} \quad y = -\frac{1}{6} - \frac{5}{2}e^{2t} + \frac{8}{3}e^{3t}.$$

6. Taking the Laplace transform of the system gives

$$(s+1)\mathcal{L}\{x\} - (s-1)\mathcal{L}\{y\} = -1$$

$$s\mathcal{L}\{x\} + (s+2)\mathcal{L}\{y\} = 1$$

so that

$$\mathcal{L}\{y\} = \frac{s+1/2}{s^2+s+1} = \frac{s+1/2}{(s+1/2)^2 + (\sqrt{3}/2)^2}$$

and

$$\mathcal{L}\{x\} = \frac{-3/2}{s^2+s+1} = \frac{-3/2}{(s+1/2)^2 + (\sqrt{3}/2)^2}.$$

Then

$$y = e^{-t/2}\cos\frac{\sqrt{3}}{2}t \quad \text{and} \quad x = e^{-t/2}\sin\frac{\sqrt{3}}{2}t.$$

7. Taking the Laplace transform of the system gives

$$(s^2+1)\mathcal{L}\{x\} - \mathcal{L}\{y\} = -2$$

$$-\mathcal{L}\{x\} + (s^2+1)\mathcal{L}\{y\} = 1$$

so that

$$\mathcal{L}\{x\} = \frac{-2s^2-1}{s^4+2s^2} = -\frac{1}{2}\frac{1}{s^2} - \frac{3}{2}\frac{1}{s^2+2}$$

and

$$x = -\frac{1}{2}t - \frac{3}{2\sqrt{2}}\sin\sqrt{2}t.$$

Then

$$y = x'' + x = -\frac{1}{2}t + \frac{3}{2\sqrt{2}}\sin\sqrt{2}t.$$

8. Taking the Laplace transform of the system gives

$$(s+1)\mathcal{L}\{x\} + \mathcal{L}\{y\} = 1$$

$$4\mathcal{L}\{x\} - (s+1)\mathcal{L}\{y\} = 1$$

so that

$$\mathcal{L}\{x\} = \frac{s+2}{s^2+2s+5} = \frac{s+1}{(s+1)^2+2^2} + \frac{1}{2}\frac{2}{(s+1)^2+2^2}$$

and

286

$$\mathscr{L}\{y\} = \frac{-s+3}{s^2+2s+5} = -\frac{s+1}{(s+1)^2+2^2} + 2\frac{2}{(s+1)^2+2^2}.$$

Then

$$x = e^{-t}\cos 2t + \frac{1}{2}e^{-t}\sin 2t \quad \text{and} \quad y = -e^{-t}\cos 2t + 2e^{-t}\sin 2t.$$

9. Adding the equations and then subtracting them gives

$$\frac{d^2x}{dt^2} = \frac{1}{2}t^2 + 2t$$

$$\frac{d^2y}{dt^2} = \frac{1}{2}t^2 - 2t.$$

Taking the Laplace transform of the system gives

$$\mathscr{L}\{x\} = 8\frac{1}{s} + \frac{1}{24}\frac{4!}{s^5} + \frac{1}{3}\frac{3!}{s^4}$$

and

$$\mathscr{L}\{y\} = \frac{1}{24}\frac{4!}{s^5} - \frac{1}{3}\frac{3!}{s^4}$$

so that

$$x = 8 + \frac{1}{24}t^4 + \frac{1}{3}t^3 \quad \text{and} \quad y = \frac{1}{24}t^4 - \frac{1}{3}t^3.$$

10. Taking the Laplace transform of the system gives

$$(s-4)\,\mathscr{L}\{x\} + s^3\,\mathscr{L}\{y\} = \frac{6}{s^2+1}$$

$$(s+2)\,\mathscr{L}\{x\} - 2s^3\,\mathscr{L}\{y\} = 0$$

so that

$$\mathscr{L}\{x\} = \frac{4}{(s-2)(s^2+1)} = \frac{4}{5}\frac{1}{s-2} - \frac{4}{5}\frac{s}{s^2+1} - \frac{8}{5}\frac{1}{s^2+1}$$

and

$$\mathscr{L}\{y\} = \frac{2s+4}{s^3(s-2)(s^2+1)} = \frac{1}{s} - \frac{2}{s^2} - 2\frac{2}{s^3} + \frac{1}{5}\frac{1}{s-2} - \frac{6}{5}\frac{s}{s^2+1} + \frac{8}{5}\frac{1}{s^2+1}.$$

Then

$$x = \frac{4}{5}e^{2t} - \frac{4}{5}\cos t - \frac{8}{5}\sin t$$

and

$$y = 1 - 2t - 2t^2 + \frac{1}{5}e^{2t} - \frac{6}{5}\cos t + \frac{8}{5}\sin t.$$

11. Taking the Laplace transform of the system gives

$$s^2\,\mathscr{L}\{x\} + 3(s+1)\mathscr{L}\{y\} = 2$$

$$s^2\,\mathscr{L}\{x\} + 3\mathscr{L}\{y\} = \frac{1}{(s+1)^2}$$

287

so that

$$\mathcal{L}\{x\} = -\frac{2s+1}{s^3(s+1)} = \frac{1}{s} + \frac{1}{s^2} + \frac{1}{2}\frac{2}{s^3} - \frac{1}{s+1}.$$

Then

$$x = 1 + t + \frac{1}{2}t^2 - e^{-t}$$

and

$$y = \frac{1}{3}te^{-t} - \frac{1}{3}x'' = \frac{1}{3}te^{-t} + \frac{1}{3}e^{-t} - \frac{1}{3}.$$

12. Taking the Laplace transform of the system gives

$$(s-4)\,\mathcal{L}\{x\} + 2\mathcal{L}\{y\} = \frac{2e^{-s}}{s}$$

$$-3\,\mathcal{L}\{x\} + (s+1)\,\mathcal{L}\{y\} = \frac{1}{2} + \frac{e^{-s}}{s}$$

so that

$$\mathcal{L}\{x\} = \frac{-1/2}{(s-1)(s-2)} + e^{-s}\frac{1}{(s-1)(s-2)}$$

$$= \left[\frac{1}{2}\frac{1}{s-1} - \frac{1}{2}\frac{1}{s-2}\right] + e^{-s}\left[-\frac{1}{s-1} + \frac{1}{s-2}\right]$$

and

$$\mathcal{L}\{y\} = \frac{e^{-s}}{s} + \frac{s/4-1}{(s-1)(s-2)} + e^{-s}\frac{-s/2+2}{(s-1)(s-2)}$$

$$= \frac{3}{4}\frac{1}{s-1} - \frac{1}{2}\frac{1}{s-2} + e^{-s}\left[\frac{1}{s} - \frac{3}{2}\frac{1}{s-1} + \frac{1}{s-2}\right].$$

Then

$$x = \frac{1}{2}e^t - \frac{1}{2}e^{2t} + \left[-e^{t-1} + e^{2(t-1)}\right]\mathcal{U}(t-1)$$

and

$$y = \frac{3}{4}e^t - \frac{1}{2}e^{2t} + \left[1 - \frac{3}{2}e^{t-1} + e^{2(t-1)}\right]\mathcal{U}(t-1).$$

13. The system is

$$x_1'' = -3x_1 + 2(x_2 - x_1)$$

$$x_2'' = -2(x_2 - x_1)$$

$$x_1(0) = 0$$

$$x_1'(0) = 1$$

$$x_2(0) = 1$$

$$x_2'(0) = 0.$$

Taking the Laplace transform of the system gives

$$(s^2 + 5)\,\mathscr{L}\{x_1\} - 2\mathscr{L}\{x_2\} = 1$$

$$-2\,\mathscr{L}\{x_1\} + (s^2 + 2)\,\mathscr{L}\{x_2\} = s$$

so that

$$\mathscr{L}\{x_1\} = \frac{s^2 + 2s + 2}{s^4 + 7s^2 + 6} = \frac{2}{5}\frac{s}{s^2 + 1} + \frac{1}{5}\frac{1}{s^2 + 1} - \frac{2}{5}\frac{s}{s^2 + 6} + \frac{4}{5\sqrt{6}}\frac{\sqrt{6}}{s^2 + 6}$$

and

$$\mathscr{L}\{x_2\} = \frac{s^3 + 5s + 2}{(s^2 + 1)(s^2 + 6)} = \frac{4}{5}\frac{s}{s^2 + 1} + \frac{2}{5}\frac{1}{s^2 + 1} + \frac{1}{5}\frac{s}{s^2 + 6} - \frac{2}{5\sqrt{6}}\frac{\sqrt{6}}{s^2 + 6}.$$

Then

$$x_1 = \frac{2}{5}\cos t + \frac{1}{5}\sin t - \frac{2}{5}\cos\sqrt{6}\,t + \frac{4}{5\sqrt{6}}\sin\sqrt{6}\,t$$

and

$$x_2 = \frac{4}{5}\cos t + \frac{2}{5}\sin t + \frac{1}{5}\cos\sqrt{6}\,t - \frac{2}{5\sqrt{6}}\sin\sqrt{6}\,t.$$

14. In this system x_1 and x_2 represent displacements of masses m_1 and m_2 from their equilibrium positions. Since the net forces acting on m_1 and m_2 are

$$-k_1x_1 + k_2(x_2 - x_1) \quad \text{and} \quad -k_2(x_2 - x_1) - k_3x_2,$$

respectively, Newton's second law of motion gives

$$m_1x_1'' = -k_1x_1 + k_2(x_2 - x_1)$$

$$m_2x_2'' = -k_2(x_2 - x_1) - k_3x_2.$$

Using $k_1 = k_2 = k_3 = 1$, $m_1 = m_2 = 1$, $x_1(0) = 0$, $x_1(0) = -1$, $x_2(0) = 0$, and $x_2'(0) = 1$, and

Exercises 8.2

taking the Laplace transform of the system, we obtain

$$(2 + s^2)\mathscr{L}\{x_1\} - \mathscr{L}\{x_2\} = -1$$

$$\mathscr{L}\{x_1\} - (2 + s^2)\mathscr{L}\{x_2\} = -1$$

so that

$$\mathscr{L}\{x_1\} = -\frac{1}{s^2 + 3} \quad \text{and} \quad \mathscr{L}\{x_2\} = \frac{1}{s^2 + 3}.$$

Then

$$x_1 = -\frac{1}{\sqrt{3}}\sin\sqrt{3}\,t \quad \text{and} \quad x_2 = \frac{1}{\sqrt{3}}\sin\sqrt{3}\,t.$$

15. (a) By Kirchoff's first law we have $i_1 = i_2 + i_3$. By Kirchoff's second law, on each loop we have $E(t) = Ri_1 + L_1 i_2'$ and $E(t) = Ri_1 + L_2 i_3'$ or $L_1 i_2' + Ri_2 + Ri_3 = E(t)$ and $L_2 i_3' + Ri_2 + Ri_3 = E(t)$.

(b) Taking the Laplace transform of the system

$$0.01 i_2' + 5 i_2 + 5 i_3 = 100$$

$$0.0125 i_3' + 5 i_2 + 5 i_3 = 100$$

gives

$$(s + 500)\,\mathscr{L}\{i_2\} + 500\mathscr{L}\{i_3\} = \frac{10{,}000}{s}$$

$$400\mathscr{L}\{i_2\} + (s + 400)\,\mathscr{L}\{i_3\} = \frac{8{,}000}{s}$$

so that

$$\mathscr{L}\{i_3\} = \frac{8{,}000}{s^2 + 900s} = \frac{80}{9}\frac{1}{s} - \frac{80}{9}\frac{1}{s + 900}.$$

Then

$$i_3 = \frac{80}{9} - \frac{80}{9}e^{-900t} \quad \text{and} \quad i_2 = 20 - 0.0025 i_3' - i_3 = \frac{100}{9} - \frac{100}{9}e^{-900t}.$$

(c) $i_1 = i_2 + i_3 = 20 - 20e^{-900t}.$

16. (a) By Kirchoff's first law we have $i_1 = i_2 + i_3$. By Kirchoff's second law, on each loop we have $E(t) = Li_1' + R_1 i_2$ and $E(t) = Li_1' + R_2 i_3 + \frac{1}{C}q$ so that $q = CR_1 i_2 - CR_2 i_3$. Then $i_3 = q' = CR_1 i_2' - CR_2 i_3'$ so that the system is

$$Li_2' + Li_3' + R_1 i_2 = E(t)$$

$$-R_1 i_2' + R_2 i_3' + \frac{1}{C}i_3 = 0.$$

(b) Taking the Laplace transform of the system

$$i_2' + i_3' + 10i_2 = 120 - 120\,\mathcal{U}(t-2)$$

$$-10i_2' + 5i_3' + 5i_3 = 0$$

gives

$$(s+10)\,\mathcal{L}\{i_2\} + s\mathcal{L}\{i_3\} = \frac{120}{s}\left(1 - e^{-2s}\right)$$

$$-10s\mathcal{L}\{i_2\} + 5(s+1)\,\mathcal{L}\{i_3\} = 0$$

so that

$$\mathcal{L}\{i_2\} = \frac{120(s+1)}{(3s^2 + 11s + 10)s}\left(1 - e^{-2s}\right) = \left[\frac{48}{s + 5/3} - \frac{60}{s+2} + \frac{12}{s}\right]\left(1 - e^{-2s}\right)$$

and

$$\mathcal{L}\{i_3\} = \frac{240}{3s^2 + 11s + 10}\left(1 - e^{-2s}\right) = \left[\frac{240}{s + 5/3} - \frac{240}{s+2}\right]\left(1 - e^{-2s}\right).$$

Then

$$i_2 = 12 + 48e^{-5t/3} - 60e^{-2t} - \left[12 + 48e^{-5(t-2)/3} - 60e^{-2(t-2)}\right]\mathcal{U}(t-2)$$

and

$$i_3 = 240e^{-5t/3} - 240e^{-2t} - \left[240e^{-5(t-2)/3} - 240e^{-2(t-2)}\right]\mathcal{U}(t-2).$$

(c) $i_1 = i_2 + i_3 = 12 + 288e^{-5t/3} - 300e^{-2t} - \left[12 + 288e^{-5(t-2)/3} - 300e^{-2(t-2)}\right]\mathcal{U}(t-2).$

17. Taking the Laplace transform of the system

$$i_2' + 11i_2 + 6i_3 = 50\sin t$$

$$i_3' + 6i_2 + 6i_3 = 50\sin t$$

gives

$$(s+11)\,\mathcal{L}\{i_2\} + 6\mathcal{L}\{i_3\} = \frac{50}{s^2 + 1}$$

$$6\mathcal{L}\{i_2\} + (s+6)\,\mathcal{L}\{i_3\} = \frac{50}{s^2 + 1}$$

so that

$$\mathcal{L}\{i_2\} = \frac{50s}{(s+2)(s+15)(s^2+1)} = -\frac{20}{13}\frac{1}{s+2} + \frac{375}{1469}\frac{1}{s+15} + \frac{145}{113}\frac{s}{s^2+1} + \frac{85}{113}\frac{1}{s^2+1}.$$

Then

$$i_2 = -\frac{20}{13}e^{-2t} + \frac{375}{1469}e^{-15t} + \frac{145}{113}\cos t + \frac{85}{113}\sin t$$

and

$$i_3 = \frac{25}{3}\sin t - \frac{1}{6}i_2' - \frac{11}{6}i_2 = \frac{30}{13}e^{-2t} + \frac{250}{1469}e^{-15t} - \frac{280}{113}\cos t + \frac{810}{113}\sin t.$$

18. By Kirchoff's first law we have $i_1 = i_2 + i_3$. By Kirchoff's second law, on each loop we have $E(t) = Li_1' + Ri_2$ and $E(t) = Li_1' + \frac{1}{C}q$ so that $q = CRi_2$. Then $i_3 = q' = CRi_2'$ so that system is

$$Li' + Ri_2 = E(t)$$

$$CRi_2' + i_2 - i_1 = 0.$$

19. Taking the Laplace transform of the system

$$0.5i_1' + 50i_2 = 60$$

$$0.005i_2' + i_2 - i_1 = 0$$

gives

$$s\,\mathcal{L}\{i_1\} + 100\,\mathcal{L}\{i_2\} = \frac{120}{s}$$

$$-200\,\mathcal{L}\{i_1\} + (s + 200)\,\mathcal{L}\{i_2\} = 0$$

so that

$$\mathcal{L}\{i_2\} = \frac{24{,}000}{s(s^2 + 200s + 20{,}000)} = \frac{6}{5}\frac{1}{s} - \frac{6}{5}\frac{s + 100}{(s + 100)^2 + 100^2} - \frac{6}{5}\frac{100}{(s + 100)^2 + 100^2}.$$

Then

$$i_2 = \frac{6}{5} - \frac{6}{5}e^{-100t}\cos 100t - \frac{6}{5}e^{-100t}\sin 100t$$

and

$$i_1 = 0.005i_2' + i_2 = \frac{6}{5} - \frac{6}{5}e^{-100t}\cos 100t.$$

20. Taking the Laplace transform of the system

$$2i_1' + 50i_2 = 60$$

$$0.005i_2' + i_2 - i_1 = 0$$

gives

$$2s\mathcal{L}\{i_1\} + 50\,\mathcal{L}\{i_2\} = \frac{60}{s}$$

$$-200\mathcal{L}\{i_1\} + (s + 200)\,\mathcal{L}\{i_2\} = 0$$

so that

$$\mathcal{L}\{i_2\} = \frac{6{,}000}{s(s^2 + 200s + 5{,}000)}$$

$$= \frac{6}{5}\frac{1}{s} - \frac{6}{5}\frac{s + 100}{(s + 100)^2 - (50\sqrt{2})^2} - \frac{6\sqrt{2}}{5}\frac{50\sqrt{2}}{(s + 100)^2 - (50\sqrt{2})^2}.$$

Then

$$i_2 = \frac{6}{5} - \frac{6}{5}e^{-100t}\cosh 50\sqrt{2}\,t - \frac{6\sqrt{2}}{5}e^{-100t}\sinh 50\sqrt{2}\,t$$

and

$$i_1 = 0.005i_2' + i_2 = \frac{6}{5} - \frac{6}{5}e^{-100t}\cosh 50\sqrt{2}\,t - \frac{9\sqrt{2}}{10}e^{-100t}\sinh 50\sqrt{2}\,t.$$

21. (a) Using Kirchoff's first law we write $i_1 = i_2 + i_3$. Since $i_2 = dq/dt$ we have $i_1 - i_3 = dq/dt$. Using Kirchoff's second law and summing the voltage drops across the shorter loop gives

$$E(t) = iR_1 + \frac{1}{C}q, \tag{1}$$

so that

$$i_1 = \frac{1}{R_1}E(t) - \frac{1}{R_1 C}q.$$

Then

$$\frac{dq}{dt} = i_1 - i_3 = \frac{1}{R_1}E(t) - \frac{1}{R_1 C}q - i_3$$

and

$$R_1\frac{dq}{dt} + \frac{1}{C}q + R_1 i_3 = E(t).$$

Summing the voltage drops across the longer loop gives

$$E(t) = i_1 R_1 + L\frac{di_3}{dt} + R_2 i_3.$$

Combining this with (1) we obtain

$$i_1 R_1 + L\frac{di_3}{dt} + R_2 i_3 = i_1 R_1 + \frac{1}{C}q$$

or

$$L\frac{di_3}{dt} + R_2 i_3 - \frac{1}{C}q = 0.$$

(b) Using $L = R_1 = R_2 = C = 1$, $E(t) = 50e^{-t}\,\mathcal{U}(t-1) = 50e^{-1}e^{-(t-1)}\mathcal{U}(t-1)$, $q(0) = i_3(0) = 0$, and taking the Laplace transform of the system we obtain

$$(s+1)\mathcal{L}\{q\} + \mathcal{L}\{i_3\} = \frac{50e^{-1}}{s+1}e^{-s}$$

$$(s+1)\mathcal{L}\{i_3\} - \mathcal{L}\{q\} = 0,$$

so that

$$\mathcal{L}\{q\} = \frac{50e^{-1}e^{-s}}{(s+1)^2 + 1}$$

and

$$q(t) = 50e^{-1}e^{-(t-1)}\sin(t-1)\mathcal{U}(t-1) = 50e^{-t}\sin(t-1)\mathcal{U}(t-1).$$

22. Taking the Laplace transform of the system

$$4\theta_1'' + \theta_2'' + 8\theta_1 = 0$$

$$\theta_1'' + \theta_2'' + 2\theta_2 = 0$$

gives

$$4\left(s^2 + 2\right)\mathcal{L}\{\theta_1\} + s^2\mathcal{L}\{\theta_2\} = 3s$$

$$s^2\mathcal{L}\{\theta_1\} + \left(s^2 + 2\right)\mathcal{L}\{\theta_2\} = 0$$

so that

$$\left(3s^2 + 4\right)\left(s^2 + 4\right)\mathcal{L}\{\theta_2\} = -3s^3$$

or

$$\mathcal{L}\{\theta_2\} = \frac{1}{2}\frac{s}{s^2 + 4/3} - \frac{3}{2}\frac{s}{s^2 + 4}.$$

Then

$$\theta_2 = \frac{1}{2}\cos\frac{2}{\sqrt{3}}t - \frac{3}{2}\cos 2t \quad \text{and} \quad \theta_1'' = -\theta_2'' - 2\theta_2$$

so that

$$\theta_1 = \frac{1}{4}\cos\frac{2}{\sqrt{3}}t + \frac{3}{4}\cos 2t.$$

Exercises 8.3

1. Let $x_1 = y$, $x_2 = y'$, and $y'' = 3y' - 4y + \sin 3t$ so that

$$x_1' = x_2$$

$$x_2' = 3x_2 - 4x_1 + \sin 3t.$$

2. Let $x_1 = y$, $x_2 = y'$, and $y'' = -2y' + \frac{5}{2}y$ so that

$$x_1' = x_2$$

$$x_2' = -2x_2 + \frac{5}{2}x_1.$$

3. Let $x_1 = y$, $x_2 = y'$, $x_3 = y''$, and $y''' = 3y'' - 6y' + 10y + t^2 + 1$ so that

$$x_1' = x_2$$

$$x_2' = x_3$$

$$x_3' = 3x_3 - 6x_2 + 10x_1 + t^2 + 1.$$

4. Let $x_1 = y$, $x_2 = y'$, $x_3 = y''$, and $y''' = -\frac{1}{4}y + \frac{1}{4}e^t$ so that

$$x_1' = x_2$$

$$x_2' = x_3$$

$$x_3' = -\frac{1}{4}x_1 + \frac{1}{4}e^t.$$

5. Let $x_1 = y$, $x_2 = y'$, $x_3 = y''$, $x_4 = y'''$, and $y^{(4)} = 2y'' - 4y' - y + t$ so that

$$x_1' = x_2$$

$$x_2' = x_3$$

$$x_3' = x_4$$

$$x_4' = 2x_3 - 4x_2 - x_1 + t.$$

6. Let $x_1 = y$, $x_2 = y'$, $x_3 = y''$, $x_4 = y'''$, and $y^{(4)} = -\frac{1}{2}y''' + 4y + 10$ so that

$$x_1' = x_2$$

$$x_2' = x_3$$

$$x_3' = x_4$$

$$x_4' = -\frac{1}{2}x_4 + 4x_1 + 10.$$

7. Let $x_1 = y$, $x_2 = y'$, and $y'' = \frac{t}{t+1}y$ so that

$$x_1' = x_2$$

$$x_2' = \frac{t}{t+1}x_1.$$

8. Let $x_1 = y$, $x_2 = y'$, and $y'' = (-1/t)y' + [(4 - t^2)/t^2]y$ so that

$$x_1' = x_2$$

$$x_2' = -\frac{1}{t}x_2 + \frac{4 - t^2}{t^2}x_1.$$

9. From

$$x' + 4x - y' = 7t$$

$$x' + y' - 2y = 3t$$

we obtain

$$2x' + 4x - 2y = 10t$$

$$2y' - 4x - 2y = -4t$$

so that

$$x' = -2x + y + 5t$$

$$y' = 2x + y - 2t.$$

10. This is a degenerate system.

11. Adding equations, we obtain

$$Dx = t^2 + 5t - 2$$

$$Dy = -x + 5t - 2.$$

12. From $x'' - 2y'' = \sin t$ and $x'' + y'' = \cos t$ we obtain

$$3x'' = 2\cos t + \sin t$$

$$3y'' = \cos t - \sin t.$$

Let $x_1 = x$, $x_2 = x'$, $x_3 = y$, and $x_4 = y'$. Then

$$x_1' = x_2$$

$$x_2' = \frac{2}{3}\cos t + \frac{1}{3}\sin t$$

$$x_3' = x_4$$

$$x_4' = \frac{1}{3}\cos t - \frac{1}{3}\sin t.$$

13. Since

$$Dx - Dy = 2 - \frac{1}{2}x \quad \text{and} \quad Dx - Dy = e^t$$

the system is degenerate.

14. Let $y_1 = x_1$, $y_2 = x_1'$, $y_3 = x_2$, and $y_4 = x_2'$ so that

$$y_1' = y_2$$

$$y_2' = -\frac{k_1 + k_2}{m_1}y_1 + \frac{k_2}{m_1}y_3$$

$$y_3' = y_4$$

$$y_4' = -\frac{k_2}{m_2}(y_3 - y_1).$$

15. Let $z_1 = x$, $z_2 = x'$, $z_3 = x''$, $z_4 = y$, and $z_5 = y'$ so that

$$z_1' = z_2$$

$$z_2' = z_3$$

$$z_3' = 4z_1 - 3z_3 + 4z_5$$

$$z_4' = z_5$$

$$z_5' = 10t^2 - 4z_2 + 3z_5.$$

16. Let $z_1 = x$, $z_2 = Dx$, $z_3 = y$, and

$$2D^2x = y - 6t^2 + 4t - 10$$

$$2Dy = -y + 6t^2 + 4t + 10$$

so that

$$Dz_1 = z_2$$

$$Dz_2 = \frac{1}{2}z_3 - 3t^2 + 2t - 5$$

$$Dz_3 = -\frac{1}{2}z_3 + 6t^2 + 4t + 10.$$

17. Taking the Laplace transform of the system gives

$$\left(s + \frac{2}{25}\right)\mathcal{L}\{x_1\} - \frac{1}{50}\mathcal{L}\{x_2\} = 25$$

$$\frac{2}{25}\mathcal{L}\{x_1\} - \left(s + \frac{2}{25}\right)\mathcal{L}\{x_2\} = 0$$

so that

$$\mathcal{L}\{x_1\} = \frac{625(25s + 2)}{(25s + 1)(25s + 3)} = \frac{25}{2}\frac{1}{s + 1/25} + \frac{25}{2}\frac{1}{s + 3/25}.$$

Then

$$x_1 = \frac{25}{2}e^{-t/25} + \frac{25}{2}e^{-3t/25}$$

and

$$x_2 = 50x_1' + 4x_1 = 25e^{-t/25} - 25e^{-3t/25}.$$

18. The system is

$$x_1' = 2 \cdot 3 + \frac{1}{50}x_2 - \frac{1}{50}x_1 \cdot 4$$

$$x_2' = \frac{1}{50}x_1 \cdot 4 - \frac{1}{50}x_2 - \frac{1}{50}x_2 \cdot 3.$$

297

19. Let x_1, x_2, and x_3 be the amounts of salt in tanks A, B, and C, respectively, so that

$$x_1' = \frac{1}{100}x_2 \cdot 2 - \frac{1}{100}x_1 \cdot 6 = \frac{1}{50}x_2 - \frac{3}{50}x_1$$

$$x_2' = \frac{1}{100}x_1 \cdot 6 + \frac{1}{100}x_3 - \frac{1}{100}x_2 \cdot 2 - \frac{1}{100}x_2 \cdot 5 = \frac{3}{50}x_1 - \frac{7}{100}x_2 + \frac{1}{100}x_3$$

$$x_3' = \frac{1}{100}x_2 \cdot 5 - \frac{1}{100}x_3 - \frac{1}{100}x_3 \cdot 4 = \frac{1}{20}x_2 - \frac{1}{20}x_3.$$

20. Let

$$a_1 Dx + a_2 Dy = b_1 x + b_2 y$$

$$a_3 Dx + a_4 Dy = b_3 x + b_4 y$$

so that if

$$\begin{vmatrix} a_1 & a_2 \\ a_3 & a_4 \end{vmatrix} = a_1 a_4 - a_2 a_3 = 0,$$

then the system is degenerate.

21. Since $Dx + Dy = -x - y$ and $Dx + Dy = -\frac{1}{2}y$ we obtain $y = -2x$ and $Dx = -x$. Then $x = c_1 e^{-t}$ and $y = -2c_1 e^{-t}$.

Exercises 8.4

1. (a) $\mathbf{A} + \mathbf{B} = \begin{pmatrix} 4-2 & 5+6 \\ -6+8 & 9-10 \end{pmatrix} = \begin{pmatrix} 2 & 11 \\ 2 & -1 \end{pmatrix}$

(b) $\mathbf{B} - \mathbf{A} = \begin{pmatrix} -2-4 & 6-5 \\ 8+6 & -10-9 \end{pmatrix} = \begin{pmatrix} -6 & 1 \\ 14 & -19 \end{pmatrix}$

(c) $2\mathbf{A} + 3\mathbf{B} = \begin{pmatrix} 8 & 10 \\ -12 & 18 \end{pmatrix} + \begin{pmatrix} -6 & 18 \\ 24 & -30 \end{pmatrix} = \begin{pmatrix} 2 & 28 \\ 12 & -12 \end{pmatrix}$

2. (a) $\mathbf{A} - \mathbf{B} = \begin{pmatrix} -2-3 & 0+1 \\ 4-0 & 1-2 \\ 7+4 & 3+2 \end{pmatrix} = \begin{pmatrix} -5 & 1 \\ 4 & -1 \\ 11 & 5 \end{pmatrix}$

(b) $\mathbf{B} - \mathbf{A} = \begin{pmatrix} 3+2 & -1-0 \\ 0-4 & 2-1 \\ -4-7 & -2-3 \end{pmatrix} = \begin{pmatrix} 5 & -1 \\ -4 & 1 \\ -11 & -5 \end{pmatrix}$

(c) $2(\mathbf{A} + \mathbf{B}) = 2 \begin{pmatrix} 1 & -1 \\ 4 & 3 \\ 3 & 1 \end{pmatrix} = \begin{pmatrix} 2 & -2 \\ 8 & 6 \\ 6 & 2 \end{pmatrix}$

3. (a) $\mathbf{AB} = \begin{pmatrix} -2 - 9 & 12 - 6 \\ 5 + 12 & -30 + 8 \end{pmatrix} = \begin{pmatrix} -11 & 6 \\ 17 & -22 \end{pmatrix}$

(b) $\mathbf{BA} = \begin{pmatrix} -2 - 30 & 3 + 24 \\ 6 - 10 & -9 + 8 \end{pmatrix} = \begin{pmatrix} -32 & 27 \\ -4 & -1 \end{pmatrix}$

(c) $\mathbf{A}^2 = \begin{pmatrix} 4 + 15 & -6 - 12 \\ -10 - 20 & 15 + 16 \end{pmatrix} = \begin{pmatrix} 19 & -18 \\ -30 & 31 \end{pmatrix}$

(d) $\mathbf{B}^2 = \begin{pmatrix} 1 + 18 & -6 + 12 \\ -3 + 6 & 18 + 4 \end{pmatrix} = \begin{pmatrix} 19 & 6 \\ 3 & 22 \end{pmatrix}$

4. (a) $\mathbf{AB} = \begin{pmatrix} -4 + 4 & 6 - 12 & -3 + 8 \\ -20 + 10 & 30 - 30 & -15 + 20 \\ -32 + 12 & 48 - 36 & -24 + 24 \end{pmatrix} = \begin{pmatrix} 0 & -6 & 5 \\ -10 & 0 & 5 \\ -20 & 12 & 0 \end{pmatrix}$

(b) $\mathbf{BA} = \begin{pmatrix} -4 + 30 - 24 & -16 + 60 - 36 \\ 1 - 15 + 16 & 4 - 30 + 24 \end{pmatrix} = \begin{pmatrix} 2 & 8 \\ 2 & -2 \end{pmatrix}$

5. (a) $\mathbf{BC} = \begin{pmatrix} 9 & 24 \\ 3 & 8 \end{pmatrix}$

(b) $\mathbf{A(BC)} = \begin{pmatrix} 1 & -2 \\ -2 & 4 \end{pmatrix} \begin{pmatrix} 9 & 24 \\ 3 & 8 \end{pmatrix} = \begin{pmatrix} 3 & 8 \\ -6 & -16 \end{pmatrix}$

(c) $\mathbf{C(BA)} = \begin{pmatrix} 0 & 2 \\ 3 & 4 \end{pmatrix} \begin{pmatrix} 0 & 0 \\ 0 & 0 \end{pmatrix} = \begin{pmatrix} 0 & 0 \\ 0 & 0 \end{pmatrix}$

(d) $\mathbf{A(B + C)} = \begin{pmatrix} 1 & -2 \\ -2 & 4 \end{pmatrix} \begin{pmatrix} 6 & 5 \\ 5 & 5 \end{pmatrix} = \begin{pmatrix} -4 & -5 \\ 8 & 10 \end{pmatrix}$

6. (a) $\mathbf{AB} = (5 \quad -6 \quad 7) \begin{pmatrix} 3 \\ 4 \\ -1 \end{pmatrix} = (-16)$

(b) $\mathbf{BA} = \begin{pmatrix} 3 \\ 4 \\ -1 \end{pmatrix} (5 \quad -6 \quad 7) = \begin{pmatrix} 15 & -18 & 21 \\ 20 & -24 & 28 \\ -5 & 6 & -7 \end{pmatrix}$

299

Exercises 8.4

(c) $(\mathbf{BA})\mathbf{C} = \begin{pmatrix} 15 & -18 & 21 \\ 20 & -24 & 28 \\ -5 & 6 & -7 \end{pmatrix} \begin{pmatrix} 1 & 2 & 4 \\ 0 & 1 & -1 \\ 3 & 2 & 1 \end{pmatrix} = \begin{pmatrix} 78 & 54 & 99 \\ 104 & 72 & 132 \\ -26 & -18 & -33 \end{pmatrix}$

(d) Since $\mathbf{AB}$ is 1×1 and $\mathbf{C}$ is 3×3 the product $(\mathbf{AB})\mathbf{C}$ is not defined.

7. (a) $\mathbf{A}^T \mathbf{A} = (4 \quad 8 \quad -10) \begin{pmatrix} 4 \\ 8 \\ -10 \end{pmatrix} = (180)$

(b) $\mathbf{B}^T \mathbf{B} = \begin{pmatrix} 2 \\ 4 \\ 5 \end{pmatrix} (2 \quad 4 \quad 5) = \begin{pmatrix} 4 & 8 & 10 \\ 8 & 16 & 20 \\ 10 & 20 & 25 \end{pmatrix}$

(c) $\mathbf{A} + \mathbf{B}^T = \begin{pmatrix} 4 \\ 8 \\ -10 \end{pmatrix} + \begin{pmatrix} 2 \\ 4 \\ 5 \end{pmatrix} = \begin{pmatrix} 6 \\ 12 \\ -5 \end{pmatrix}$

8. (a) $\mathbf{A} + \mathbf{B}^T = \begin{pmatrix} 1 & 2 \\ 2 & 4 \end{pmatrix} + \begin{pmatrix} -2 & 5 \\ 3 & 7 \end{pmatrix} = \begin{pmatrix} -1 & 7 \\ 5 & 11 \end{pmatrix}$

(b) $2\mathbf{A}^T - \mathbf{B}^T = \begin{pmatrix} 2 & 4 \\ 4 & 8 \end{pmatrix} - \begin{pmatrix} -2 & 5 \\ 3 & 7 \end{pmatrix} = \begin{pmatrix} 4 & -1 \\ 1 & 1 \end{pmatrix}$

(c) $\mathbf{A}^T(\mathbf{A} - \mathbf{B}) = \begin{pmatrix} 1 & 2 \\ 2 & 4 \end{pmatrix} \begin{pmatrix} 3 & -1 \\ -3 & -3 \end{pmatrix} = \begin{pmatrix} -3 & -7 \\ -6 & -14 \end{pmatrix}$

9. (a) $(\mathbf{AB})^T = \begin{pmatrix} 7 & 10 \\ 38 & 75 \end{pmatrix}^T = \begin{pmatrix} 7 & 38 \\ 10 & 75 \end{pmatrix}$

(b) $\mathbf{B}^T \mathbf{A}^T = \begin{pmatrix} 5 & -2 \\ 10 & -5 \end{pmatrix} \begin{pmatrix} 3 & 8 \\ 4 & 1 \end{pmatrix} = \begin{pmatrix} 7 & 38 \\ 10 & 75 \end{pmatrix}$

10. (a) $\mathbf{A}^T + \mathbf{B}^T = \begin{pmatrix} 5 & -4 \\ 9 & 6 \end{pmatrix} + \begin{pmatrix} -3 & -7 \\ 11 & 2 \end{pmatrix} = \begin{pmatrix} 2 & -11 \\ 20 & 8 \end{pmatrix}$

(b) $(\mathbf{A} + \mathbf{B})^T = \begin{pmatrix} 2 & 20 \\ -11 & 8 \end{pmatrix}^T = \begin{pmatrix} 2 & -11 \\ 20 & 8 \end{pmatrix}$

11. $\begin{pmatrix} -4 \\ 8 \end{pmatrix} - \begin{pmatrix} 4 \\ 16 \end{pmatrix} + \begin{pmatrix} -6 \\ 9 \end{pmatrix} = \begin{pmatrix} -14 \\ 1 \end{pmatrix}$

12. $\begin{pmatrix} 6t \\ 3t^2 \\ -3t \end{pmatrix} + \begin{pmatrix} -t+1 \\ -t^2+t \\ 3t-3 \end{pmatrix} - \begin{pmatrix} 6t \\ 8 \\ -10t \end{pmatrix} = \begin{pmatrix} -t+1 \\ 2t^2+t-8 \\ 10t-3 \end{pmatrix}$

13. $\begin{pmatrix} -19 \\ 18 \end{pmatrix} - \begin{pmatrix} 19 \\ 20 \end{pmatrix} = \begin{pmatrix} -38 \\ -2 \end{pmatrix}$

14. $\begin{pmatrix} -9t+3 \\ 13t-5 \\ -6t+4 \end{pmatrix} + \begin{pmatrix} -t \\ 1 \\ 4 \end{pmatrix} - \begin{pmatrix} 2 \\ 8 \\ -6 \end{pmatrix} = \begin{pmatrix} -10t+1 \\ 13t-12 \\ -6t+14 \end{pmatrix}$

15. Since $\det \mathbf{A} = 0$, $\mathbf{A}$ is singular.

16. Since $\det \mathbf{A} = 3$, $\mathbf{A}$ is nonsingular.

$$\mathbf{A}^{-1} = \frac{1}{3}\begin{pmatrix} 4 & -5 \\ -1 & 2 \end{pmatrix}$$

17. Since $\det \mathbf{A} = 4$, $\mathbf{A}$ is nonsingular.

$$\mathbf{A}^{-1} = \frac{1}{4}\begin{pmatrix} -5 & -8 \\ 3 & 4 \end{pmatrix}$$

18. Since $\det \mathbf{A} = -6$, $\mathbf{A}$ is nonsingular.

$$\mathbf{A}^{-1} = -\frac{1}{6}\begin{pmatrix} 2 & -10 \\ -2 & 7 \end{pmatrix}$$

19. Since $\det \mathbf{A} = 2$, $\mathbf{A}$ is nonsingular. The cofactors are

$$\begin{array}{lll} A_{11} = 0 & A_{12} = 2 & A_{13} = -4 \\ A_{21} = -1 & A_{22} = 2 & A_{23} = -3 \\ A_{31} = 1 & A_{32} = -2 & A_{33} = 5. \end{array}$$

Then

$$\mathbf{A}^{-1} = \frac{1}{2}\begin{pmatrix} 0 & 2 & -4 \\ -1 & 2 & -3 \\ 1 & -2 & 5 \end{pmatrix}^T = \frac{1}{2}\begin{pmatrix} 0 & -1 & 1 \\ 2 & 2 & -2 \\ -4 & -3 & 5 \end{pmatrix}.$$

20. Since $\det \mathbf{A} = 27$, $\mathbf{A}$ is nonsingular. The cofactors are

$$\begin{array}{lll} A_{11} = -1 & A_{12} = 4 & A_{13} = 22 \\ A_{21} = 7 & A_{22} = -1 & A_{23} = -19 \\ A_{31} = -1 & A_{32} = 4 & A_{33} = -5. \end{array}$$

Then

$$\mathbf{A}^{-1} = \frac{1}{27}\begin{pmatrix} -1 & 4 & 22 \\ 7 & -1 & -19 \\ -1 & 4 & -5 \end{pmatrix}^T = \frac{1}{27}\begin{pmatrix} -1 & 7 & -1 \\ 4 & -1 & 4 \\ 22 & -19 & -5 \end{pmatrix}.$$

21. Since $\det \mathbf{A} = -9$, $\mathbf{A}$ is nonsingular. The cofactors are

$$
\begin{aligned}
A_{11} &= -2 & A_{12} &= -13 & A_{13} &= 8 \\
A_{21} &= -2 & A_{22} &= 5 & A_{23} &= -1 \\
A_{31} &= -1 & A_{32} &= 7 & A_{33} &= -5.
\end{aligned}
$$

Then

$$\mathbf{A}^{-1} = -\frac{1}{9}\begin{pmatrix} -2 & -13 & 8 \\ -2 & 5 & -1 \\ -1 & 7 & -5 \end{pmatrix}^T = -\frac{1}{9}\begin{pmatrix} -2 & -2 & -1 \\ -13 & 5 & 7 \\ 8 & -1 & -5 \end{pmatrix}.$$

22. Since $\det \mathbf{A} = 0$, $\mathbf{A}$ is singular.

23. Since $\det \mathbf{A}(t) = 2e^{3t} \neq 0$, $\mathbf{A}$ is nonsingular.

$$\mathbf{A}^{-1} = \frac{1}{2}e^{-3t}\begin{pmatrix} 3e^{4t} & -e^{4t} \\ -4e^{-t} & 2e^{-t} \end{pmatrix}$$

24. Since $\det \mathbf{A}(t) = 2e^{2t} \neq 0$, $\mathbf{A}$ is nonsingular.

$$\mathbf{A}^{-1} = \frac{1}{2}e^{-2t}\begin{pmatrix} e^t \sin t & 2e^t \cos t \\ -e^t \cos t & 2e^t \sin t \end{pmatrix}$$

25. $\dfrac{d\mathbf{X}}{dt} = \begin{pmatrix} -5e^{-t} \\ -2e^{-t} \\ 7e^{-t} \end{pmatrix}$

26. $\dfrac{d\mathbf{X}}{dt} = \begin{pmatrix} \cos 2t + 8\sin 2t \\ -6\cos 2t - 10\sin 2t \end{pmatrix}$

27. $\mathbf{X} = \begin{pmatrix} 2e^{2t} + 8e^{-3t} \\ -2e^{2t} + 4e^{-3t} \end{pmatrix}$ so that $\dfrac{d\mathbf{X}}{dt} = \begin{pmatrix} 4e^{2t} - 24e^{-3t} \\ -4e^{2t} - 12e^{-3t} \end{pmatrix}.$

28. $\dfrac{d\mathbf{X}}{dt} = \begin{pmatrix} 10te^{2t} + 5e^{2t} \\ 3t\cos 3t + \sin 3t \end{pmatrix}$

29. (a) $\dfrac{d\mathbf{A}}{dt} = \begin{pmatrix} 4e^{4t} & -\pi\sin \pi t \\ 2 & 6t \end{pmatrix}$

302

(b) $\int_0^2 \mathbf{A}(t)\,dt = \begin{pmatrix} \frac{1}{4}e^{4t} & \frac{1}{\pi}\sin \pi t \\ t^2 & t^3 - t \end{pmatrix} \Big|_{t=0}^{t=2} = \begin{pmatrix} \frac{1}{4}e^8 - \frac{1}{4} & 0 \\ 4 & 6 \end{pmatrix}$

(c) $\int_0^t \mathbf{A}(s)\,ds = \begin{pmatrix} \frac{1}{4}e^{4s} & \frac{1}{\pi}\sin \pi s \\ s^2 & s^3 - s \end{pmatrix} \Big|_{s=0}^{s=t} = \begin{pmatrix} \frac{1}{4}e^{4t} - \frac{1}{4} & \frac{1}{\pi}\sin \pi t \\ t^2 & t^3 - t \end{pmatrix}$

30. (a) $\dfrac{d\mathbf{A}}{dt} = \begin{pmatrix} -2t/(t^2 + 1)^2 & 3 \\ 2t & 1 \end{pmatrix}$

(b) $\dfrac{d\mathbf{B}}{dt} = \begin{pmatrix} 6 & 0 \\ -1/t^2 & 4 \end{pmatrix}$

(c) $\int_0^1 \mathbf{A}(t)\,dt = \begin{pmatrix} \tan^{-1} t & \frac{3}{2}t^2 \\ \frac{1}{3}t^3 & \frac{1}{2}t^2 \end{pmatrix} \Big|_{t=0}^{t=1} = \begin{pmatrix} \frac{\pi}{4} & \frac{3}{2} \\ \frac{1}{3} & \frac{1}{2} \end{pmatrix}$

(d) $\int_1^2 \mathbf{B}(t)\,dt = \begin{pmatrix} 3t^2 & 2t \\ \ln t & 2t^2 \end{pmatrix} \Big|_{t=1}^{t=2} = \begin{pmatrix} 9 & 2 \\ \ln 2 & 6 \end{pmatrix}$

(e) $\mathbf{A}(t)\mathbf{B}(t) = \begin{pmatrix} 6t/(t^2 + 1) + 3 & 2/(t^2 + 1) + 12t^2 \\ 6t^3 + 1 & 2t^2 + 4t^2 \end{pmatrix}$

(f) $\dfrac{d}{dt}\mathbf{A}(t)\mathbf{B}(t) = \begin{pmatrix} (6 - 6t^2)/(t^2 + 1)^2 & -4t/(t^2 + 1)^2 + 24t \\ 18t^2 & 12t \end{pmatrix}$

(g) $\int_1^t \mathbf{A}(s)\mathbf{B}(s)\,ds = \begin{pmatrix} 6s/(s^2 + 1) + 3 & 2/(s^2 + 1) + 12s^2 \\ 6s^3 + 1 & 6s^2 \end{pmatrix} \Big|_{s=1}^{s=t}$

$= \begin{pmatrix} 3t + 3\ln(t^2 + 1) - 3 - 3\ln 2 & 4t^3 + 2\tan^{-1} t - 4 - \pi/2 \\ (3/2)t^4 + t - (5/2) & 2t^3 - 2 \end{pmatrix}$

31. $\begin{pmatrix} 1 & 1 & -2 & | & 14 \\ 2 & -1 & 1 & | & 0 \\ 6 & 3 & 4 & | & 1 \end{pmatrix} \Longrightarrow \begin{pmatrix} 1 & 1 & -2 & | & 14 \\ 0 & -3 & 5 & | & -28 \\ 0 & 6 & 1 & | & 1 \end{pmatrix} \Longrightarrow \begin{pmatrix} 1 & 0 & -1/3 & | & 14/3 \\ 0 & 1 & -5/3 & | & 28/3 \\ 0 & 0 & 11 & | & -55 \end{pmatrix}$

$(-7) - 2 - 2(12)$

$\Longrightarrow \begin{pmatrix} 1 & 0 & 0 & | & 3 \\ 0 & 1 & 0 & | & 1 \\ 0 & 0 & 1 & | & -5 \end{pmatrix}$

Thus $x = 3$, $y = 1$, and $z = -5$.

32. $\begin{pmatrix} 5 & -2 & 4 & | & 10 \\ 1 & 1 & 1 & | & 9 \\ 4 & -3 & 3 & | & 1 \end{pmatrix} \Longrightarrow \begin{pmatrix} 1 & 1 & 1 & | & 9 \\ 0 & -7 & -1 & | & -35 \\ 0 & -7 & -1 & | & -35 \end{pmatrix} \Longrightarrow \begin{pmatrix} 1 & 0 & 6/7 & | & 4 \\ 0 & 1 & 1/7 & | & 5 \\ 0 & 0 & 0 & | & 0 \end{pmatrix}$

Letting $z = t$ we find $y = 5 - \frac{1}{7}t$, and $x = 4 - \frac{6}{7}t$.

33. $\begin{pmatrix} 1 & -1 & -5 & | & 7 \\ 5 & 4 & -16 & | & -10 \\ 0 & 1 & 1 & | & -5 \end{pmatrix} \Longrightarrow \begin{pmatrix} 1 & -1 & -5 & | & 7 \\ 0 & 1 & 1 & | & -5 \\ 0 & 9 & 9 & | & -45 \end{pmatrix} \Longrightarrow \begin{pmatrix} 1 & 0 & -4 & | & 2 \\ 0 & 1 & 1 & | & -5 \\ 0 & 0 & 0 & | & 0 \end{pmatrix}$

Letting $z = t$ we find $y = -5 - t$, and $x = 2 + 4t$.

34. $\begin{pmatrix} 1 & 1 & -3 & | & 6 \\ 4 & 2 & -1 & | & 7 \\ 3 & 1 & 1 & | & 4 \end{pmatrix} \Longrightarrow \begin{pmatrix} 1 & 1 & -3 & | & 6 \\ 0 & -2 & 11 & | & -17 \\ 0 & -2 & 10 & | & -14 \end{pmatrix} \Longrightarrow \begin{pmatrix} 1 & 0 & 5/2 & | & -5/2 \\ 0 & 1 & -11/2 & | & 17/2 \\ 0 & 0 & -1 & | & 3 \end{pmatrix}$

$$\Longrightarrow \begin{pmatrix} 1 & 0 & 0 & | & 5 \\ 0 & 1 & 0 & | & -8 \\ 0 & 0 & 1 & | & -3 \end{pmatrix}$$

Thus $x = 5$, $y = -8$, and $z = -3$.

35. $\begin{pmatrix} 2 & 1 & 1 & | & 4 \\ 10 & -2 & 2 & | & -1 \\ 6 & -2 & 4 & | & 8 \end{pmatrix} \Longrightarrow \begin{pmatrix} 1 & 1/2 & 1/2 & | & 2 \\ 0 & -7 & -3 & | & -21 \\ 0 & -5 & 1 & | & 4 \end{pmatrix} \Longrightarrow \begin{pmatrix} 1 & 0 & 2/7 & | & 1/2 \\ 0 & 1 & 3/7 & | & 3 \\ 0 & 0 & 22/7 & | & 11 \end{pmatrix}$

$2(-4) - 1(28) - 8$

$$\Longrightarrow \begin{pmatrix} 1 & 0 & 0 & | & -1/2 \\ 0 & 1 & 0 & | & 3/2 \\ 0 & 0 & 1 & | & 7/2 \end{pmatrix}$$

Thus $x = -1/2$, $y = 3/2$, and $z = 7/2$.

36. $\begin{pmatrix} 1 & 0 & 2 & | & 8 \\ 1 & 2 & -2 & | & 4 \\ 2 & 5 & -6 & | & 6 \end{pmatrix} \Longrightarrow \begin{pmatrix} 1 & 0 & 2 & | & 8 \\ 0 & 2 & -4 & | & -4 \\ 0 & 5 & -10 & | & -10 \end{pmatrix} \Longrightarrow \begin{pmatrix} 1 & 0 & 2 & | & 8 \\ 0 & 1 & -2 & | & -2 \\ 0 & 0 & 0 & | & 0 \end{pmatrix}$

Letting $z = t$ we find $y = -2 + 2t$, and $x = 8 - 2t$.

37.
$$\begin{pmatrix} 1 & 1 & -1 & -1 & | & -1 \\ 1 & 1 & 1 & 1 & | & 3 \\ 1 & -1 & 1 & -1 & | & 3 \\ 4 & 1 & -2 & 1 & | & 0 \end{pmatrix} \implies \begin{pmatrix} 1 & 1 & -1 & -1 & | & -1 \\ 0 & 0 & 2 & 2 & | & 4 \\ 0 & -2 & 2 & 0 & | & 4 \\ 0 & -3 & 2 & 5 & | & 4 \end{pmatrix} \implies \begin{pmatrix} 1 & 0 & 0 & -1 & | & 1 \\ 0 & 1 & -1 & 0 & | & -2 \\ 0 & 0 & 2 & 2 & | & 4 \\ 0 & 0 & -1 & 5 & | & -2 \end{pmatrix}$$

$$\implies \begin{pmatrix} 1 & 0 & 0 & -1 & | & 1 \\ 0 & 1 & 0 & 1 & | & 0 \\ 0 & 0 & 1 & 1 & | & 2 \\ 0 & 0 & 0 & 6 & | & 0 \end{pmatrix} \implies \begin{pmatrix} 1 & 0 & 0 & 0 & | & 1 \\ 0 & 1 & 0 & 0 & | & 0 \\ 0 & 0 & 1 & 0 & | & 2 \\ 0 & 0 & 0 & 1 & | & 0 \end{pmatrix}$$

Thus $x_1 = 1$, $x_2 = 0$, $x_3 = 2$, and $x_4 = 0$.

38.
$$\begin{pmatrix} 1 & 3 & 1 & | & 0 \\ 2 & 1 & 1 & | & 0 \\ 7 & 1 & 3 & | & 0 \end{pmatrix} \implies \begin{pmatrix} 1 & 3 & 1 & | & 0 \\ 0 & -5 & -1 & | & 0 \\ 0 & -20 & -4 & | & 0 \end{pmatrix} \implies \begin{pmatrix} 1 & 0 & 2/5 & | & 0 \\ 0 & 1 & 1/5 & | & 0 \\ 0 & 0 & 0 & | & 0 \end{pmatrix}$$

Letting $x_3 = t$, we find $x_2 = -\frac{1}{5}t$ and $x_1 = -\frac{2}{5}t$.

39.
$$\begin{pmatrix} 1 & 2 & 4 & | & 2 \\ 2 & 4 & 3 & | & 1 \\ 1 & 2 & -1 & | & 7 \end{pmatrix} \implies \begin{pmatrix} 1 & 2 & 4 & | & 2 \\ 0 & 0 & -5 & | & -3 \\ 0 & 0 & -5 & | & 5 \end{pmatrix} \implies \begin{pmatrix} 1 & 2 & 0 & | & -2/5 \\ 0 & 0 & 1 & | & 3/5 \\ 0 & 0 & 0 & | & 8 \end{pmatrix}$$

There is no solution.

40.
$$\begin{pmatrix} 1 & 1 & -1 & 3 & | & 1 \\ 0 & 1 & -1 & -4 & | & 0 \\ 1 & 2 & -2 & -1 & | & 6 \\ 4 & 7 & -7 & 0 & | & 9 \end{pmatrix} \implies \begin{pmatrix} 1 & 1 & -1 & 3 & | & 1 \\ 0 & 1 & -1 & -4 & | & 0 \\ 0 & 1 & -1 & -4 & | & 5 \\ 0 & 3 & -3 & -12 & | & 5 \end{pmatrix} \implies \begin{pmatrix} 1 & 0 & 0 & 7 & | & 1 \\ 0 & 1 & -1 & -4 & | & 0 \\ 0 & 0 & 0 & 0 & | & 5 \\ 0 & 0 & 0 & 0 & | & 5 \end{pmatrix}$$

There is no solution.

41. We solve

$$\det(\mathbf{A} - \lambda\mathbf{I}) = \begin{vmatrix} -1-\lambda & 2 \\ -7 & 8-\lambda \end{vmatrix} = (\lambda - 6)(\lambda - 1) = 0.$$

For $\lambda_1 = 6$ we have

$$\begin{pmatrix} -7 & 2 & | & 0 \\ -7 & 2 & | & 0 \end{pmatrix} \implies \begin{pmatrix} 1 & -2/7 & | & 0 \\ 0 & 0 & | & 0 \end{pmatrix}$$

so that $k_1 = \frac{2}{7}k_2$. If $k_2 = 7$ then

$$\mathbf{K}_1 = \begin{pmatrix} 2 \\ 7 \end{pmatrix}.$$

For $\lambda_2 = 1$ we have

$$\begin{pmatrix} -2 & 2 & | & 0 \\ -7 & 7 & | & 0 \end{pmatrix} \implies \begin{pmatrix} 1 & -1 & | & 0 \\ 0 & 0 & | & 0 \end{pmatrix}$$

so that $k_1 = k_2$. If $k_2 = 1$ then

$$\mathbf{K}_2 = \begin{pmatrix} 1 \\ 1 \end{pmatrix}.$$

42. We solve

$$\det(\mathbf{A} - \lambda\mathbf{I}) = \begin{vmatrix} 2 - \lambda & 1 \\ 2 & 1 - \lambda \end{vmatrix} = \lambda(\lambda - 3) = 0.$$

For $\lambda_1 = 0$ we have

$$\begin{pmatrix} 2 & 1 & | & 0 \\ 2 & 1 & | & 0 \end{pmatrix} \implies \begin{pmatrix} 1 & 1/2 & | & 0 \\ 0 & 0 & | & 0 \end{pmatrix}$$

so that $k_1 = -\frac{1}{2}k_2$. If $k_2 = 2$ then

$$\mathbf{K}_1 = \begin{pmatrix} -1 \\ 2 \end{pmatrix}.$$

For $\lambda_2 = 3$ we have

$$\begin{pmatrix} -1 & 1 & | & 0 \\ 2 & -2 & | & 0 \end{pmatrix} \implies \begin{pmatrix} 1 & -1 & | & 0 \\ 0 & 0 & | & 0 \end{pmatrix}$$

so that $k_1 = k_2$. If $k_2 = 1$ then

$$\mathbf{K}_2 = \begin{pmatrix} 1 \\ 1 \end{pmatrix}.$$

43. We solve

$$\det(\mathbf{A} - \lambda\mathbf{I}) = \begin{vmatrix} -8 - \lambda & -1 \\ 16 & -\lambda \end{vmatrix} = (\lambda + 4)^2 = 0.$$

For $\lambda_1 = \lambda_2 = -4$ we have

$$\begin{pmatrix} -4 & -1 & | & 0 \\ 16 & 4 & | & 0 \end{pmatrix} \implies \begin{pmatrix} 1 & 1/4 & | & 0 \\ 0 & 0 & | & 0 \end{pmatrix}$$

so that $k_1 = -\frac{1}{4}k_2$. If $k_2 = 4$ then

$$\mathbf{K}_1 = \begin{pmatrix} -1 \\ 4 \end{pmatrix}.$$

44. We solve

$$\det(\mathbf{A} - \lambda\mathbf{I}) = \begin{vmatrix} 1-\lambda & 1 \\ 1/4 & 1-\lambda \end{vmatrix} = (\lambda - 3/2)(\lambda - 1/2) = 0.$$

For $\lambda_1 = 3/2$ we have

$$\begin{pmatrix} -1/2 & 1 & | & 0 \\ 1/4 & -1/2 & | & 0 \end{pmatrix} \Longrightarrow \begin{pmatrix} 1 & -2 & | & 0 \\ 0 & 0 & | & 0 \end{pmatrix}$$

so that $k_1 = 2k_2$. If $k_2 = 1$ then

$$\mathbf{K}_1 = \begin{pmatrix} 2 \\ 1 \end{pmatrix}.$$

If $\lambda_2 = 1/2$ then

$$\begin{pmatrix} 1/2 & 1 & | & 0 \\ 1/4 & 1/2 & | & 0 \end{pmatrix} \Longrightarrow \begin{pmatrix} 1 & 2 & | & 0 \\ 0 & 0 & | & 0 \end{pmatrix}$$

so that $k_1 = -2k_2$. If $k_2 = 1$ then

$$\mathbf{K}_2 = \begin{pmatrix} -2 \\ 1 \end{pmatrix}.$$

45. We solve

$$\det(\mathbf{A} - \lambda\mathbf{I}) = \begin{vmatrix} 5-\lambda & -1 & 0 \\ 0 & -5-\lambda & 9 \\ 5 & -1 & -\lambda \end{vmatrix} = \begin{vmatrix} 4-\lambda & -1 & 0 \\ 4-\lambda & -5-\lambda & 9 \\ 4-\lambda & -1 & -\lambda \end{vmatrix} = \lambda(4-\lambda)(\lambda+4) = 0.$$

If $\lambda_1 = 0$ then

$$\begin{pmatrix} 5 & -1 & 0 & | & 0 \\ 0 & -5 & 9 & | & 0 \\ 5 & -1 & 0 & | & 0 \end{pmatrix} \Longrightarrow \begin{pmatrix} 1 & 0 & -9/25 & | & 0 \\ 0 & 1 & -9/5 & | & 0 \\ 0 & 0 & 0 & | & 0 \end{pmatrix}$$

so that $k_1 = \frac{9}{25}k_3$ and $k_2 = \frac{9}{5}k_3$. If $k_3 = 25$ then

$$\mathbf{K}_1 = \begin{pmatrix} 9 \\ 45 \\ 25 \end{pmatrix}.$$

If $\lambda_2 = 4$ then

$$\begin{pmatrix} 1 & -1 & 0 & | & 0 \\ 0 & -9 & 9 & | & 0 \\ 5 & -1 & -4 & | & 0 \end{pmatrix} \Longrightarrow \begin{pmatrix} 1 & 0 & -1 & | & 0 \\ 0 & 1 & -1 & | & 0 \\ 0 & 0 & 0 & | & 0 \end{pmatrix}$$

307

so that $k_1 = k_3$ and $k_2 = k_3$. If $k_3 = 1$ then

$$\mathbf{K}_2 = \begin{pmatrix} 1 \\ 1 \\ 1 \end{pmatrix}.$$

If $\lambda_3 = -4$ then

$$\begin{pmatrix} 9 & -1 & 0 & | & 0 \\ 0 & -1 & 9 & | & 0 \\ 5 & -1 & 4 & | & 0 \end{pmatrix} \Longrightarrow \begin{pmatrix} 1 & 0 & -1 & | & 0 \\ 0 & 1 & -9 & | & 0 \\ 0 & 0 & 0 & | & 0 \end{pmatrix}$$

so that $k_1 = k_3$ and $k_2 = 9k_3$. If $k_3 = 1$ then

$$\mathbf{K}_3 = \begin{pmatrix} 1 \\ 9 \\ 1 \end{pmatrix}.$$

46. We solve

$$\det(\mathbf{A} - \lambda\mathbf{I}) = \begin{vmatrix} 3 - \lambda & 0 & 0 \\ 0 & 2 - \lambda & 0 \\ 4 & 0 & 1 - \lambda \end{vmatrix} = (3 - \lambda)(2 - \lambda)(1 - \lambda) = 0.$$

If $\lambda_1 = 1$ then

$$\begin{pmatrix} 2 & 0 & 0 & | & 0 \\ 0 & 1 & 0 & | & 0 \\ 4 & 0 & 0 & | & 0 \end{pmatrix} \Longrightarrow \begin{pmatrix} 1 & 0 & 0 & | & 0 \\ 0 & 1 & 0 & | & 0 \\ 0 & 0 & 0 & | & 0 \end{pmatrix}$$

so that $k_1 = 0$ and $k_2 = 0$. If $k_3 = 1$ then

$$\mathbf{K}_1 = \begin{pmatrix} 0 \\ 0 \\ 1 \end{pmatrix}.$$

If $\lambda_2 = 2$ then

$$\begin{pmatrix} 1 & 0 & 0 & | & 0 \\ 0 & 0 & 0 & | & 0 \\ 4 & 0 & -1 & | & 0 \end{pmatrix} \Longrightarrow \begin{pmatrix} 1 & 0 & 0 & | & 0 \\ 0 & 0 & 1 & | & 0 \\ 0 & 0 & 0 & | & 0 \end{pmatrix}$$

so that $k_1 = 0$ and $k_3 = 0$. If $k_2 = 1$ then

$$\mathbf{K}_2 = \begin{pmatrix} 0 \\ 1 \\ 0 \end{pmatrix}.$$

If $\lambda_3 = 3$ then

$$
\begin{pmatrix} 0 & 0 & 0 & | & 0 \\ 0 & -1 & 0 & | & 0 \\ 4 & 0 & -2 & | & 0 \end{pmatrix} \implies \begin{pmatrix} 1 & 0 & -1/2 & | & 0 \\ 0 & 1 & 0 & | & 0 \\ 0 & 0 & 0 & | & 0 \end{pmatrix}
$$

so that $k_1 = \frac{1}{2}k_3$ and $k_2 = 0$. If $k_3 = 2$ then

$$
\mathbf{K}_3 = \begin{pmatrix} 1 \\ 0 \\ 2 \end{pmatrix}.
$$

47. We solve

$$
\det(\mathbf{A} - \lambda\mathbf{I}) = \begin{vmatrix} -\lambda & 4 & 0 \\ -1 & -4-\lambda & 0 \\ 0 & 0 & -2-\lambda \end{vmatrix} = -(\lambda+2)^3 = 0.
$$

For $\lambda_1 = \lambda_2 = \lambda_3 = -2$ we have

$$
\begin{pmatrix} 2 & 4 & 0 & | & 0 \\ -1 & -2 & 0 & | & 0 \\ 0 & 0 & 0 & | & 0 \end{pmatrix} \implies \begin{pmatrix} 1 & 2 & 0 & | & 0 \\ 0 & 0 & 0 & | & 0 \\ 0 & 0 & 0 & | & 0 \end{pmatrix}
$$

so that $k_1 = -2k_2$. If $k_2 = 1$ and $k_3 = 1$ then

$$
\mathbf{K}_1 = \begin{pmatrix} -2 \\ 1 \\ 0 \end{pmatrix} \quad \text{and} \quad \mathbf{K}_2 = \begin{pmatrix} 0 \\ 0 \\ 1 \end{pmatrix}.
$$

48. We solve

$$
\det(\mathbf{A} - \lambda\mathbf{I}) = \begin{vmatrix} 1-\lambda & 6 & 0 \\ 0 & 2-\lambda & 1 \\ 0 & 1 & 2-\lambda \end{vmatrix} = \begin{vmatrix} 1-\lambda & 6 & 0 \\ 0 & 3-\lambda & 3-\lambda \\ 0 & 1 & 2-\lambda \end{vmatrix} = (3-\lambda)(1-\lambda)^2 = 0.
$$

For $\lambda = 3$ we have

$$
\begin{pmatrix} -2 & 6 & 0 & | & 0 \\ 0 & 0 & 0 & | & 0 \\ 0 & 1 & -1 & | & 0 \end{pmatrix} \implies \begin{pmatrix} 1 & 0 & -3 & | & 0 \\ 0 & 1 & -1 & | & 0 \\ 0 & 0 & 0 & | & 0 \end{pmatrix}
$$

so that $k_1 = 3k_3$ and $k_2 = k_3$. If $k_3 = 1$ then

$$
\mathbf{K}_1 = \begin{pmatrix} 3 \\ 1 \\ 1 \end{pmatrix}.
$$

For $\lambda_2 = \lambda_3 = 1$ we have

$$\begin{pmatrix} 0 & 6 & 0 & | & 0 \\ 0 & 1 & 1 & | & 0 \\ 0 & 1 & 1 & | & 0 \end{pmatrix} \implies \begin{pmatrix} 0 & 1 & 0 & | & 0 \\ 0 & 0 & 1 & | & 0 \\ 0 & 0 & 0 & | & 0 \end{pmatrix}$$

so that $k_2 = 0$ and $k_3 = 0$. If $k_1 = 1$ then

$$\mathbf{K}_2 = \begin{pmatrix} 1 \\ 0 \\ 0 \end{pmatrix}.$$

49. We solve

$$\det(\mathbf{A} - \lambda\mathbf{I}) = \begin{vmatrix} -1 - \lambda & 2 \\ -5 & 1 - \lambda \end{vmatrix} = \lambda^2 + 9 = (\lambda - 3i)(\lambda + 3i) = 0.$$

For $\lambda_1 = 3i$ we have

$$\begin{pmatrix} -1 - 3i & 2 & | & 0 \\ -5 & 1 - 3i & | & 0 \end{pmatrix} \implies \begin{pmatrix} 1 & -(1/5) + (3/5)i & | & 0 \\ 0 & 0 & | & 0 \end{pmatrix}$$

so that $k_1 = \left(\frac{1}{5} - \frac{3}{5}i\right) k_2$. If $k_2 = 5$ then

$$\mathbf{K}_1 = \begin{pmatrix} 1 - 3i \\ 5 \end{pmatrix}.$$

For $\lambda_2 = -3i$ we have

$$\begin{pmatrix} -1 + 3i & 2 & | & 0 \\ -5 & 1 + 3i & | & 0 \end{pmatrix} \implies \begin{pmatrix} 1 & -\frac{1}{5} - \frac{3}{5}i & | & 0 \\ 0 & 0 & | & 0 \end{pmatrix}$$

so that $k_1 = \left(\frac{1}{5} + \frac{3}{5}i\right) k_2$. If $k_2 = 5$ then

$$\mathbf{K}_2 = \begin{pmatrix} 1 + 3i \\ 5 \end{pmatrix}.$$

50. We solve

$$\det(\mathbf{A} - \lambda\mathbf{I}) = \begin{vmatrix} 2 - \lambda & -1 & 0 \\ 5 & 2 - \lambda & 4 \\ 0 & 1 & 2 - \lambda \end{vmatrix} = -\lambda^3 + 6\lambda^2 - 13\lambda + 10 = (\lambda - 2)(-\lambda^2 + 4\lambda - 5)$$

$$= (\lambda - 2)(\lambda - (2 + i))(\lambda - (2 - i)) = 0.$$

For $\lambda_1 = 2$ we have

$$\begin{pmatrix} 0 & -1 & 0 & | & 0 \\ 5 & 0 & 4 & | & 0 \\ 0 & 1 & 0 & | & 0 \end{pmatrix} \implies \begin{pmatrix} 1 & 0 & 4/5 & | & 0 \\ 0 & 1 & 0 & | & 0 \\ 0 & 0 & 0 & | & 0 \end{pmatrix}$$

so that $k_1 = -\frac{4}{5}k_3$ and $k_2 = 0$. If $k_3 = 5$ then

$$\mathbf{K}_1 = \begin{pmatrix} -4 \\ 0 \\ 5 \end{pmatrix}.$$

For $\lambda_2 = 2 + i$ we have

$$\begin{pmatrix} -i & -1 & 0 & | & 0 \\ 5 & -i & 4 & | & 0 \\ 0 & 1 & -i & | & 0 \end{pmatrix} \implies \begin{pmatrix} 1 & -i & 0 & | & 0 \\ 0 & 1 & -i & | & 0 \\ 0 & 0 & 0 & | & 0 \end{pmatrix}$$

so that $k_1 = ik_2$ and $k_2 = ik_3$. If $k_3 = i$ then

$$\mathbf{K}_2 = \begin{pmatrix} -i \\ -1 \\ i \end{pmatrix}.$$

For $\lambda_3 = 2 - i$ we have

$$\begin{pmatrix} i & -1 & 0 & | & 0 \\ 5 & i & 4 & | & 0 \\ 0 & 1 & i & | & 0 \end{pmatrix} \implies \begin{pmatrix} 1 & i & 0 & | & 0 \\ 0 & 1 & i & | & 0 \\ 0 & 0 & 0 & | & 0 \end{pmatrix}$$

so that $k_1 = -ik_2$ and $k_2 = -ik_3$. If $k_3 = i$ then

$$\mathbf{K}_3 = \begin{pmatrix} -1 \\ 1 \\ i \end{pmatrix}.$$

51. Let

$$\mathbf{A} = \begin{pmatrix} a_{11} & a_{12} \\ a_{21} & a_{22} \end{pmatrix}.$$

Then

$$\frac{d}{dt}[\mathbf{A}(t)\mathbf{X}(t)] = \frac{d}{dt}\begin{pmatrix} a_1 & a_2 \\ a_3 & a_4 \end{pmatrix}\begin{pmatrix} x_1 \\ x_2 \end{pmatrix} = \frac{d}{dt}\begin{pmatrix} a_1 x_1 + a_2 x_2 \\ a_3 x_1 + a_4 x_2 \end{pmatrix} = \begin{pmatrix} a_1 x_1' + a_1' x_1 + a_2 x_2' + a_2' x_2 \\ a_3 x_1' + a_3' x_1 + a_4 x_2' + a_4' x_2 \end{pmatrix}$$

$$= \begin{pmatrix} a_1 & a_2 \\ a_3 & a_4 \end{pmatrix}\begin{pmatrix} x_1' \\ x_2' \end{pmatrix} + \begin{pmatrix} a_1' & a_2' \\ a_3' & a_4' \end{pmatrix}\begin{pmatrix} x_1 \\ x_2 \end{pmatrix} = \mathbf{A}(t)\mathbf{X}'(t) + \mathbf{A}'(t)\mathbf{X}(t).$$

52. Assume $\det \mathbf{A} \neq 0$ and $\mathbf{AB} = \mathbf{I}$, so that

$$\begin{pmatrix} a_{11} & a_{12} \\ a_{21} & a_{22} \end{pmatrix}\begin{pmatrix} b_{11} & b_{12} \\ b_{21} & b_{22} \end{pmatrix} = \begin{pmatrix} 1 & 0 \\ 0 & 1 \end{pmatrix}.$$

Then

$$a_{11}b_{11} + a_{12}b_{21} = 1 \qquad a_{11}b_{12} + a_{12}b_{22} = 0$$
$$\text{and}$$
$$a_{21}b_{11} + a_{21}b_{21} = 0 \qquad a_{21}b_{12} + a_{21}b_{22} = 1$$

and by Cramer's rule

$$b_{11} = \frac{a_{22}}{\det \mathbf{A}} \qquad b_{12} = \frac{-a_{12}}{\det \mathbf{A}}$$

$$b_{21} = \frac{-a_{21}}{\det \mathbf{A}} \qquad b_{22} = \frac{a_{11}}{\det \mathbf{A}}.$$

Thus

$$\mathbf{A}^{-1} = \mathbf{B} = \frac{1}{\det \mathbf{A}} \begin{pmatrix} a_{22} & -a_{12} \\ -a_{21} & a_{11} \end{pmatrix}.$$

53. Since $\mathbf{A}$ is nonsingular, $\mathbf{AB} = \mathbf{AC}$ implies $\mathbf{A}^{-1}\mathbf{AB} = \mathbf{A}^{-1}\mathbf{AC}$. Then $\mathbf{IB} = \mathbf{IC}$ and $\mathbf{B} = \mathbf{C}$.

54. Since

$$(\mathbf{AB})(\mathbf{B}^{-1}\mathbf{A}^{-1}) = \mathbf{A}(\mathbf{BB}^{-1})\mathbf{A}^{-1} = \mathbf{AIA}^{-1} = \mathbf{AA}^{-1} = \mathbf{I}$$

and

$$(\mathbf{B}^{-1}\mathbf{A}^{-1})(\mathbf{AB}) = \mathbf{B}^{-1}(\mathbf{A}^{-1}\mathbf{A})\mathbf{B} = \mathbf{B}^{-1}\mathbf{IB} = \mathbf{B}^{-1}\mathbf{B} = \mathbf{I}$$

we have

$$(\mathbf{AB})^{-1} = \mathbf{B}^{-1}\mathbf{A}^{-1}.$$

55. No; consider

$$\mathbf{A} = \begin{pmatrix} 1 & 0 \\ 0 & 0 \end{pmatrix} \quad \text{and} \quad \mathbf{B} = \begin{pmatrix} 0 & 0 \\ 1 & 0 \end{pmatrix}.$$

Exercises 8.5

1. Let $\mathbf{X} = \begin{pmatrix} x \\ y \end{pmatrix}$. Then

$$\mathbf{X}' = \begin{pmatrix} 3 & -5 \\ 4 & 8 \end{pmatrix} \mathbf{X}.$$

2. Let $\mathbf{X} = \begin{pmatrix} x \\ y \end{pmatrix}$. Then

$$\mathbf{X}' = \begin{pmatrix} 4 & -7 \\ 5 & 0 \end{pmatrix} \mathbf{X}.$$

3. Let $\mathbf{X} = \begin{pmatrix} x \\ y \\ z \end{pmatrix}$. Then

$$\mathbf{X}' = \begin{pmatrix} -3 & 4 & -9 \\ 6 & -1 & 0 \\ 10 & 4 & 3 \end{pmatrix} \mathbf{X}.$$

4. Let $\mathbf{X} = \begin{pmatrix} x \\ y \\ z \end{pmatrix}$. Then

$$\mathbf{X}' = \begin{pmatrix} 1 & -1 & 0 \\ 1 & 0 & 2 \\ -1 & 0 & 1 \end{pmatrix} \mathbf{X}.$$

5. Let $\mathbf{X} = \begin{pmatrix} x \\ y \\ z \end{pmatrix}$. Then

$$\mathbf{X}' = \begin{pmatrix} 1 & -1 & 1 \\ 2 & 1 & -1 \\ 1 & 1 & 1 \end{pmatrix} \mathbf{X} + \begin{pmatrix} 0 \\ -3t^2 \\ t^2 \end{pmatrix} + \begin{pmatrix} t \\ 0 \\ -t \end{pmatrix} + \begin{pmatrix} -1 \\ 0 \\ 2 \end{pmatrix}.$$

6. Let $\mathbf{X} = \begin{pmatrix} x \\ y \end{pmatrix}$. Then

$$\mathbf{X}' = \begin{pmatrix} -3 & 4 \\ 5 & 9 \end{pmatrix} \mathbf{X} + \begin{pmatrix} e^{-t} \sin 2t \\ 4e^{-t} \cos 2t \end{pmatrix}.$$

7. $\dfrac{dx}{dt} = 4x + 2y + e^t; \quad \dfrac{dy}{dt} = -x + 3y - e^t$

8. $\dfrac{dx}{dt} = 7x + 5y - 9z - 8e^{-2t}; \quad \dfrac{dy}{dt} = 4x + y + z + 2e^{5t}; \quad \dfrac{dz}{dt} = -2y + 3z + e^{5t} - 3e^{-2t}$

9. $\dfrac{dx}{dt} = x - y + 2z + e^{-t} - 3t; \quad \dfrac{dy}{dt} = 3x - 4y + z + 2e^{-t} + t; \quad \dfrac{dz}{dt} = -2x + 5y + 6z + 2e^{-t} - t$

10. $\dfrac{dx}{dt} = 3x - 7y + 4\sin t + (t - 4)e^{4t}; \quad \dfrac{dy}{dt} = x + y + 8\sin t + (2t + 1)e^{4t}$

11. Since

$$\mathbf{X}' = \begin{pmatrix} -5 \\ -10 \end{pmatrix} e^{-5t} \quad \text{and} \quad \begin{pmatrix} 3 & -4 \\ 4 & -7 \end{pmatrix} \mathbf{X} = \begin{pmatrix} -5 \\ -10 \end{pmatrix} e^{-5t}$$

we see that

$$\mathbf{X}' = \begin{pmatrix} 3 & -4 \\ 4 & -7 \end{pmatrix} \mathbf{X}.$$

Exercises 8.5

12. Since

$$\mathbf{X}' = \begin{pmatrix} 5\cos t - 5\sin t \\ 2\cos t - 4\sin t \end{pmatrix} e^t \quad \text{and} \quad \begin{pmatrix} -2 & 5 \\ -2 & 4 \end{pmatrix} \mathbf{X} = \begin{pmatrix} 5\cos t - 5\sin t \\ 2\cos t - 4\sin t \end{pmatrix} e^t$$

we see that

$$\mathbf{X}' = \begin{pmatrix} -2 & 5 \\ -2 & 4 \end{pmatrix} \mathbf{X}.$$

13. Since

$$\mathbf{X}' = \begin{pmatrix} 3/2 \\ -3 \end{pmatrix} e^{-3t/2} \quad \text{and} \quad \begin{pmatrix} -1 & 1/4 \\ 1 & -1 \end{pmatrix} \mathbf{X} = \begin{pmatrix} 3/2 \\ -3 \end{pmatrix} e^{-3t/2}$$

we see that

$$\mathbf{X}' = \begin{pmatrix} -1 & 1/4 \\ 1 & -1 \end{pmatrix} \mathbf{X}.$$

14. Since

$$\mathbf{X}' = \begin{pmatrix} 5 \\ -1 \end{pmatrix} e^t + \begin{pmatrix} 4 \\ -4 \end{pmatrix} te^t \quad \text{and} \quad \begin{pmatrix} 2 & 1 \\ -1 & 0 \end{pmatrix} \mathbf{X} = \begin{pmatrix} 5 \\ -1 \end{pmatrix} e^t + \begin{pmatrix} 4 \\ -4 \end{pmatrix} te^t$$

we see that

$$\mathbf{X}' = \begin{pmatrix} 2 & 1 \\ -1 & 0 \end{pmatrix} \mathbf{X}.$$

15. Since

$$\mathbf{X}' = \begin{pmatrix} 0 \\ 0 \\ 0 \end{pmatrix} \quad \text{and} \quad \begin{pmatrix} 1 & 2 & 1 \\ 6 & -1 & 0 \\ -1 & -2 & -1 \end{pmatrix} \mathbf{X} = \begin{pmatrix} 0 \\ 0 \\ 0 \end{pmatrix}$$

we see that

$$\mathbf{X}' = \begin{pmatrix} 1 & 2 & 1 \\ 6 & -1 & 0 \\ -1 & -2 & -1 \end{pmatrix} \mathbf{X}.$$

16. Since

$$\mathbf{X}' = \begin{pmatrix} \cos t \\ \frac{1}{2}\sin t - \frac{1}{2}\cos t \\ -\cos t - \sin t \end{pmatrix} \quad \text{and} \quad \begin{pmatrix} 1 & 0 & 1 \\ 1 & 1 & 0 \\ -2 & 0 & -1 \end{pmatrix} \mathbf{X} = \begin{pmatrix} \cos t \\ \frac{1}{2}\sin t - \frac{1}{2}\cos t \\ -\cos t - \sin t \end{pmatrix}$$

we see that

$$\mathbf{X}' = \begin{pmatrix} 1 & 0 & 1 \\ 1 & 1 & 0 \\ -2 & 0 & -1 \end{pmatrix} \mathbf{X}.$$

17. Yes, since $W(\mathbf{X}_1, \mathbf{X}_2) = -2e^{-8t} \neq 0$ and $\mathbf{X}_1$ and $\mathbf{X}_2$ are linearly independent on $-\infty < t < \infty$.

18. Yes, since $W(\mathbf{X}_1, \mathbf{X}_2) = 8e^{2t} \neq 0$ and $\mathbf{X}_1$ and $\mathbf{X}_2$ are linearly independent on $-\infty < t < \infty$.

19. No, since $W(\mathbf{X}_1, \mathbf{X}_2, \mathbf{X}_3) = 0$ and $\mathbf{X}_1$, $\mathbf{X}_2$, and $\mathbf{X}_3$ are linearly dependent on $-\infty < t < \infty$.

20. Yes, since $W(\mathbf{X}_1, \mathbf{X}_2, \mathbf{X}_3) = -84e^{-t} \neq 0$ and $\mathbf{X}_1$, $\mathbf{X}_2$, and $\mathbf{X}_3$ are linearly independent on $-\infty < t < \infty$.

21. Since

$$\mathbf{X}'_p = \begin{pmatrix} 2 \\ -1 \end{pmatrix} \quad \text{and} \quad \begin{pmatrix} 1 & 4 \\ 3 & 2 \end{pmatrix} \mathbf{X}_p + \begin{pmatrix} 2 \\ -4 \end{pmatrix} t + \begin{pmatrix} -7 \\ -18 \end{pmatrix} = \begin{pmatrix} 2 \\ -1 \end{pmatrix}$$

we see that

$$\mathbf{X}'_p = \begin{pmatrix} 1 & 4 \\ 3 & 2 \end{pmatrix} \mathbf{X}_p + \begin{pmatrix} 2 \\ -4 \end{pmatrix} t + \begin{pmatrix} -7 \\ -18 \end{pmatrix}.$$

22. Since

$$\mathbf{X}'_p = \begin{pmatrix} 0 \\ 0 \end{pmatrix} \quad \text{and} \quad \begin{pmatrix} 2 & 1 \\ 1 & -1 \end{pmatrix} \mathbf{X}_p + \begin{pmatrix} -5 \\ 2 \end{pmatrix} = \begin{pmatrix} 0 \\ 0 \end{pmatrix}$$

we see that

$$\mathbf{X}'_p = \begin{pmatrix} 2 & 1 \\ 1 & -1 \end{pmatrix} \mathbf{X}_p + \begin{pmatrix} -5 \\ 2 \end{pmatrix}.$$

23. Since

$$\mathbf{X}'_p = \begin{pmatrix} 2 \\ 0 \end{pmatrix} e^t + \begin{pmatrix} 1 \\ -1 \end{pmatrix} te^t \quad \text{and} \quad \begin{pmatrix} 2 & 1 \\ 3 & 4 \end{pmatrix} \mathbf{X}_p - \begin{pmatrix} 1 \\ 7 \end{pmatrix} e^t = \begin{pmatrix} 2 \\ 0 \end{pmatrix} e^t + \begin{pmatrix} 1 \\ -1 \end{pmatrix} te^t$$

we see that

$$\mathbf{X}'_p = \begin{pmatrix} 2 & 1 \\ 3 & 4 \end{pmatrix} \mathbf{X}_p - \begin{pmatrix} 1 \\ 7 \end{pmatrix} e^t.$$

24. Since

$$\mathbf{X}'_p = \begin{pmatrix} 3\cos 3t \\ 0 \\ -3\sin 3t \end{pmatrix} \quad \text{and} \quad \begin{pmatrix} 1 & 2 & 3 \\ -4 & 2 & 0 \\ -6 & 1 & 0 \end{pmatrix} \mathbf{X}_p + \begin{pmatrix} -1 \\ 4 \\ 3 \end{pmatrix} \sin 3t = \begin{pmatrix} 3\cos 3t \\ 0 \\ -3\sin 3t \end{pmatrix}$$

we see that

$$\mathbf{X}'_p = \begin{pmatrix} 1 & 2 & 3 \\ -4 & 2 & 0 \\ -6 & 1 & 0 \end{pmatrix} \mathbf{X}_p + \begin{pmatrix} -1 \\ 4 \\ 3 \end{pmatrix} \sin 3t.$$

25. Let

$$\mathbf{X}_1 = \begin{pmatrix} 6 \\ -1 \\ -5 \end{pmatrix} e^{-t}, \quad \mathbf{X}_2 = \begin{pmatrix} -3 \\ 1 \\ 1 \end{pmatrix} e^{-2t}, \quad \mathbf{X}_3 = \begin{pmatrix} 2 \\ 1 \\ 1 \end{pmatrix} e^{3t}, \quad \text{and} \quad \mathbf{A} = \begin{pmatrix} 0 & 6 & 0 \\ 1 & 0 & 1 \\ 1 & 1 & 0 \end{pmatrix}.$$

Then

$$\mathbf{X}_1' = \begin{pmatrix} -6 \\ 1 \\ 5 \end{pmatrix} e^{-t} = \mathbf{AX}_1,$$

$$\mathbf{X}_2' = \begin{pmatrix} 6 \\ -2 \\ -2 \end{pmatrix} e^{-2t} = \mathbf{AX}_2,$$

$$\mathbf{X}_3' = \begin{pmatrix} 6 \\ 3 \\ 3 \end{pmatrix} e^{3t} = \mathbf{AX}_3,$$

and $W(\mathbf{X}_1, \mathbf{X}_2, \mathbf{X}_3) = 20 \neq 0$ so that $\mathbf{X}_1$, $\mathbf{X}_2$, and $\mathbf{X}_3$ form a fundamental set for $\mathbf{X}' = \mathbf{AX}$ on $-\infty < t < \infty$.

26. Let

$$\mathbf{X}_1 = \begin{pmatrix} 1 \\ -1 - \sqrt{2} \end{pmatrix} e^{\sqrt{2}t},$$

$$\mathbf{X}_2 = \begin{pmatrix} 1 \\ -1 + \sqrt{2} \end{pmatrix} e^{-\sqrt{2}t},$$

$$\mathbf{X}_p = \begin{pmatrix} 1 \\ 0 \end{pmatrix} t^2 + \begin{pmatrix} -2 \\ 4 \end{pmatrix} t + \begin{pmatrix} 1 \\ 0 \end{pmatrix},$$

and

$$\mathbf{A} = \begin{pmatrix} -1 & -1 \\ -1 & 1 \end{pmatrix}.$$

Then

$$\mathbf{X}_1' = \begin{pmatrix} \sqrt{2} \\ -2 - \sqrt{2} \end{pmatrix} e^{\sqrt{2}t} = \mathbf{AX}_1,$$

$$\mathbf{X}_2' = \begin{pmatrix} -\sqrt{2} \\ -2 - \sqrt{2} \end{pmatrix} e^{-\sqrt{2}t} = \mathbf{AX}_2,$$

$$\mathbf{X}_p' = \begin{pmatrix} 2 \\ 0 \end{pmatrix} t + \begin{pmatrix} -2 \\ 4 \end{pmatrix} = \mathbf{AX}_p + \begin{pmatrix} 1 \\ 1 \end{pmatrix} t^2 + \begin{pmatrix} 4 \\ -6 \end{pmatrix} t + \begin{pmatrix} -1 \\ 5 \end{pmatrix},$$

and $W(\mathbf{X}_1, \mathbf{X}_2) = 2\sqrt{2} \neq 0$ so that $\mathbf{X}_p$ is a particular solution and $\mathbf{X}_1$ and $\mathbf{X}_2$ form a fundamental set on $-\infty < t < \infty$.

27. $\Phi(t) = \begin{pmatrix} e^{2t} & e^{7t} \\ -2e^{2t} & 3e^{7t} \end{pmatrix}$ and $\Phi^{-1}(t) = \dfrac{1}{5e^{9t}} \begin{pmatrix} 3e^{7t} & -e^{7t} \\ 2e^{2t} & e^{2t} \end{pmatrix}.$

28. $\Phi(t) = \begin{pmatrix} -e^{-t} & e^{5t} \\ e^{-t} & e^{5t} \end{pmatrix}$ and $\Phi^{-1}(t) = -\dfrac{1}{2e^{4t}} \begin{pmatrix} e^{5t} & -e^{5t} \\ -e^{-t} & -e^{-t} \end{pmatrix}$.

29. $\Phi(t) = \begin{pmatrix} -e^{t} & -te^{t} \\ 3e^{t} & 3te^{t} - e^{t} \end{pmatrix}$ and $\Phi^{-1}(t) = \dfrac{1}{e^{2t}} \begin{pmatrix} 3te^{t} - e^{t} & te^{t} \\ -3e^{t} & -e^{t} \end{pmatrix}$.

30. $\Phi(t) = \begin{pmatrix} 2\cos t & -2\sin t \\ 3\cos t + \sin t & -3\sin t + \cos t \end{pmatrix}$ and $\Phi^{-1}(t) = \dfrac{1}{2} \begin{pmatrix} -3\sin t + \cos t & 2\sin t \\ -3\cos t - \sin t & 2\cos t \end{pmatrix}$.

31. We have

$$\mathbf{X}(t) = c_1 \begin{pmatrix} 1 \\ -2 \end{pmatrix} e^{2t} + c_2 \begin{pmatrix} 1 \\ 3 \end{pmatrix} e^{7t}$$

so that

$$\mathbf{X}(0) = c_1 \begin{pmatrix} 1 \\ -2 \end{pmatrix} + c_2 \begin{pmatrix} 1 \\ 3 \end{pmatrix} = \begin{pmatrix} 1 \\ 0 \end{pmatrix}$$

and

$$\mathbf{X}(0) = c_1 \begin{pmatrix} 1 \\ -2 \end{pmatrix} + c_2 \begin{pmatrix} 1 \\ 3 \end{pmatrix} = \begin{pmatrix} 0 \\ 1 \end{pmatrix}$$

which give $c_1 = 3/5$, $c_2 = 2/5$, and $c_1 = -1/5$, $c_2 = 1/5$. Then

$$\mathbf{V}_1 = \frac{3}{5} \begin{pmatrix} 1 \\ -2 \end{pmatrix} e^{2t} + \frac{2}{5} \begin{pmatrix} 1 \\ 3 \end{pmatrix} e^{7t} \quad \text{and} \quad \mathbf{V}_2 = -\frac{1}{5} \begin{pmatrix} 1 \\ -2 \end{pmatrix} e^{2t} + \frac{1}{5} \begin{pmatrix} 1 \\ 3 \end{pmatrix} e^{7t},$$

so

$$\Psi(t) = \begin{pmatrix} \frac{3}{5}e^{2t} + \frac{2}{5}e^{7t} & -\frac{1}{5}e^{2t} + \frac{1}{5}e^{7t} \\ -\frac{6}{5}e^{2t} + \frac{6}{5}e^{7t} & \frac{2}{5}e^{2t} + \frac{3}{5}e^{7t} \end{pmatrix}.$$

32. We have

$$\mathbf{X}(t) = c_1 \begin{pmatrix} -1 \\ 1 \end{pmatrix} e^{-t} + c_2 \begin{pmatrix} 1 \\ 1 \end{pmatrix} e^{5t}$$

so that

$$\mathbf{X}(0) = c_1 \begin{pmatrix} -1 \\ 1 \end{pmatrix} + c_2 \begin{pmatrix} 1 \\ 1 \end{pmatrix} = \begin{pmatrix} 1 \\ 0 \end{pmatrix}$$

and

$$\mathbf{X}(0) = c_1 \begin{pmatrix} -1 \\ 1 \end{pmatrix} + c_2 \begin{pmatrix} 1 \\ 1 \end{pmatrix} = \begin{pmatrix} 0 \\ 1 \end{pmatrix}$$

which give $c_1 = -1/2$, $c_2 = 1/2$, and $c_1 = 1/2$, $c_2 = 1/2$. Then

$$\mathbf{V}_1 = -\frac{1}{2} \begin{pmatrix} -1 \\ 1 \end{pmatrix} e^{-t} + \frac{1}{2} \begin{pmatrix} 1 \\ 1 \end{pmatrix} e^{5t} \quad \text{and} \quad \mathbf{V}_2 = \frac{1}{2} \begin{pmatrix} -1 \\ 1 \end{pmatrix} e^{-t} + \frac{1}{2} \begin{pmatrix} 1 \\ 1 \end{pmatrix} e^{5t},$$

so

$$\Psi(t) = \begin{pmatrix} \frac{1}{2}e^{-t} + \frac{1}{2}e^{5t} & -\frac{1}{2}e^{-t} + \frac{1}{2}e^{5t} \\ -\frac{1}{2}e^{-t} + \frac{1}{2}e^{5t} & \frac{1}{2}e^{-t} + \frac{1}{2}e^{5t} \end{pmatrix}.$$

33. We have

$$\mathbf{X}(t) = c_1 \begin{pmatrix} -1 \\ 3 \end{pmatrix} e^t + c_2 \begin{pmatrix} -1 \\ 3 \end{pmatrix} te^t + c_2 \begin{pmatrix} 0 \\ -1 \end{pmatrix} e^t$$

so that

$$\mathbf{X}(0) = c_1 \begin{pmatrix} -1 \\ 3 \end{pmatrix} + c_2 \begin{pmatrix} -1 \\ 3 \end{pmatrix} + c_2 \begin{pmatrix} 0 \\ -1 \end{pmatrix} = \begin{pmatrix} 1 \\ 0 \end{pmatrix}$$

and

$$\mathbf{X}(0) = c_1 \begin{pmatrix} -1 \\ 3 \end{pmatrix} + c_2 \begin{pmatrix} -1 \\ 3 \end{pmatrix} + c_2 \begin{pmatrix} 0 \\ -1 \end{pmatrix} = \begin{pmatrix} 0 \\ 1 \end{pmatrix}$$

which give $c_1 = -1$, $c_2 = -3$, and $c_1 = 0$, $c_2 = -1$. Then

$$\Psi(t) = \begin{pmatrix} 3te^t + e^t & te^t \\ -9te^t & -3te^t + e^t \end{pmatrix}.$$

34. We have

$$\mathbf{X}(t) = c_1 \begin{pmatrix} 2\cos t \\ 3\cos t + \sin t \end{pmatrix} + c_2 \begin{pmatrix} -2\sin t \\ \cos t - 3\sin t \end{pmatrix}$$

so that

$$\mathbf{X}\left(\frac{\pi}{2}\right) = c_1 \begin{pmatrix} 0 \\ 1 \end{pmatrix} + c_2 \begin{pmatrix} -2 \\ -3 \end{pmatrix} = \begin{pmatrix} 1 \\ 0 \end{pmatrix}$$

and

$$\mathbf{X}\left(\frac{\pi}{2}\right) = c_1 \begin{pmatrix} 0 \\ 1 \end{pmatrix} + c_2 \begin{pmatrix} -2 \\ -3 \end{pmatrix} = \begin{pmatrix} 0 \\ 1 \end{pmatrix}$$

which give $c_1 = -3/2$, $c_2 = -1/2$, and $c_1 = 1$, $c_2 = 0$. Then

$$\Psi(t) = \begin{pmatrix} -3\cos t + \sin t & 2\cos t \\ -5\cos t & 3\cos t + \sin t \end{pmatrix}.$$

35. Since $\mathbf{X}(t_0) = \Phi(t_0)\mathbf{C} = \mathbf{X}_0$ we have $\mathbf{C} = \Phi^{-1}(t_0)\mathbf{X}_0$ and $\mathbf{X}(t) = \Phi(t)\Phi^{-1}(t_0)\mathbf{X}_0$.

36. Since the column vectors of $\Psi(t)$ solve $\mathbf{X}' = \mathbf{AX}$ we know that $\mathbf{X} = \Psi(t)\mathbf{X}_0$ solves $\mathbf{X}' = \mathbf{AX}$, and $\mathbf{X}(t_0) = \Psi(t_0)\mathbf{X}_0 = \mathbf{IX}_0 = \mathbf{X}_0$.

37. Since $\mathbf{X} = \Phi(t)\Phi^{-1}(t_0)\mathbf{X}_0$ and $\mathbf{X} = \Psi(t)\mathbf{X}_0$ we see that $\left[\Phi(t)\Phi^{-1}(t_0) - \Psi(t)\right]\mathbf{X}_0 = \mathbf{0}$. Since $\mathbf{X}_0$ is arbitrary it follows that $\Phi(t)\Phi^{-1}(t_0) - \Psi(t) = \mathbf{0}$.

1. The system is

$$\mathbf{X}' = \begin{pmatrix} 1 & 2 \\ 4 & 3 \end{pmatrix} \mathbf{X}$$

and $\det(\mathbf{A} - \lambda\mathbf{I}) = (\lambda - 5)(\lambda + 1) = 0$. For $\lambda_1 = 5$ we obtain

$$\begin{pmatrix} -4 & 2 & | & 0 \\ 4 & -2 & | & 0 \end{pmatrix} \Longrightarrow \begin{pmatrix} 1 & -1/2 & | & 0 \\ 0 & 0 & | & 0 \end{pmatrix} \quad \text{so that} \quad \mathbf{K}_1 = \begin{pmatrix} 1 \\ 2 \end{pmatrix}.$$

For $\lambda_2 = -1$ we obtain

$$\begin{pmatrix} 2 & 2 & | & 0 \\ 4 & 4 & | & 0 \end{pmatrix} \Longrightarrow \begin{pmatrix} 1 & 1 & | & 0 \\ 0 & 0 & | & 0 \end{pmatrix} \quad \text{so that} \quad \mathbf{K}_2 = \begin{pmatrix} -1 \\ 1 \end{pmatrix}.$$

Then

$$\mathbf{X} = c_1 \begin{pmatrix} 1 \\ 2 \end{pmatrix} e^{5t} + c_2 \begin{pmatrix} -1 \\ 1 \end{pmatrix} e^{-t}.$$

2. The system is

$$\mathbf{X}' = \begin{pmatrix} 0 & 2 \\ 8 & 0 \end{pmatrix} \mathbf{X}$$

and $\det(\mathbf{A} - \lambda\mathbf{I}) = (\lambda - 4)(\lambda + 4) = 0$. For $\lambda_1 = 4$ we obtain

$$\begin{pmatrix} -4 & 2 & | & 0 \\ 8 & -4 & | & 0 \end{pmatrix} \Longrightarrow \begin{pmatrix} 1 & -1/2 & | & 0 \\ 0 & 0 & | & 0 \end{pmatrix} \quad \text{so that} \quad \mathbf{K}_1 = \begin{pmatrix} 1 \\ 2 \end{pmatrix}.$$

For $\lambda_2 = -4$ we obtain

$$\begin{pmatrix} 4 & 2 & | & 0 \\ 8 & 4 & | & 0 \end{pmatrix} \Longrightarrow \begin{pmatrix} 1 & 1/2 & | & 0 \\ 0 & 0 & | & 0 \end{pmatrix} \quad \text{so that} \quad \mathbf{K}_2 = \begin{pmatrix} -1 \\ 2 \end{pmatrix}.$$

Then

$$\mathbf{X} = c_1 \begin{pmatrix} 1 \\ 2 \end{pmatrix} e^{4t} + c_2 \begin{pmatrix} -1 \\ 2 \end{pmatrix} e^{-4t}.$$

3. The system is

$$\mathbf{X}' = \begin{pmatrix} -4 & 2 \\ -5/2 & 2 \end{pmatrix} \mathbf{X}$$

and $\det(\mathbf{A} - \lambda\mathbf{I}) = (\lambda - 1)(\lambda + 3) = 0$. For $\lambda_1 = 1$ we obtain

$$\begin{pmatrix} -5 & 2 & | & 0 \\ -5/2 & 1 & | & 0 \end{pmatrix} \Longrightarrow \begin{pmatrix} -5 & 2 & | & 0 \\ 0 & 0 & | & 0 \end{pmatrix} \quad \text{so that} \quad \mathbf{K}_1 = \begin{pmatrix} 2 \\ 5 \end{pmatrix}.$$

For $\lambda_2 = -3$ we obtain

$$\begin{pmatrix} -1 & 2 & | & 0 \\ -5/2 & 5 & | & 0 \end{pmatrix} \Longrightarrow \begin{pmatrix} -1 & 2 & | & 0 \\ 0 & 0 & | & 0 \end{pmatrix} \quad \text{so that} \quad K_2 = \begin{pmatrix} 2 \\ 1 \end{pmatrix}.$$

Then

$$X = c_1 \begin{pmatrix} 2 \\ 5 \end{pmatrix} e^t + c_2 \begin{pmatrix} 2 \\ 1 \end{pmatrix} e^{-3t}.$$

4. The system is

$$X' = \begin{pmatrix} 1/2 & 9 \\ 1/2 & 2 \end{pmatrix} X$$

and $\det(A - \lambda I) = (\lambda - 7/2)(\lambda + 1) = 0$. For $\lambda_1 = 7/2$ we obtain

$$\begin{pmatrix} -3 & 9 & | & 0 \\ 1/2 & -1/2 & | & 0 \end{pmatrix} \Longrightarrow \begin{pmatrix} 1 & -3 & | & 0 \\ 0 & 0 & | & 0 \end{pmatrix} \quad \text{so that} \quad K_1 = \begin{pmatrix} 3 \\ 1 \end{pmatrix}.$$

For $\lambda_2 = -1$ we obtain

$$\begin{pmatrix} 3/2 & 9 & | & 0 \\ 1/2 & 3 & | & 0 \end{pmatrix} \Longrightarrow \begin{pmatrix} 1 & 6 & | & 0 \\ 0 & 0 & | & 0 \end{pmatrix} \quad \text{so that} \quad K_2 = \begin{pmatrix} -6 \\ 1 \end{pmatrix}.$$

Then

$$X = c_1 \begin{pmatrix} 3 \\ 1 \end{pmatrix} e^{7t/2} + c_2 \begin{pmatrix} -6 \\ 1 \end{pmatrix} e^{-t}.$$

5. The system is

$$X' = \begin{pmatrix} 10 & -5 \\ 8 & -12 \end{pmatrix} X$$

and $\det(A - \lambda I) = (\lambda - 8)(\lambda + 10) = 0$. For $\lambda_1 = 8$ we obtain

$$\begin{pmatrix} 2 & -5 & | & 0 \\ 8 & -20 & | & 0 \end{pmatrix} \Longrightarrow \begin{pmatrix} 1 & -5/2 & | & 0 \\ 0 & 0 & | & 0 \end{pmatrix} \quad \text{so that} \quad K_1 = \begin{pmatrix} 5 \\ 2 \end{pmatrix}.$$

For $\lambda_2 = -10$ we obtain

$$\begin{pmatrix} 20 & -5 & | & 0 \\ 8 & -2 & | & 0 \end{pmatrix} \Longrightarrow \begin{pmatrix} 1 & -1/4 & | & 0 \\ 0 & 0 & | & 0 \end{pmatrix} \quad \text{so that} \quad K_2 = \begin{pmatrix} 1 \\ 4 \end{pmatrix}.$$

Then

$$X = c_1 \begin{pmatrix} 5 \\ 2 \end{pmatrix} e^{8t} + c_2 \begin{pmatrix} 1 \\ 4 \end{pmatrix} e^{-10t}.$$

6. The system is

$$X' = \begin{pmatrix} -6 & 2 \\ -3 & 1 \end{pmatrix} X$$

and $\det(\mathbf{A} - \lambda\mathbf{I}) = \lambda(\lambda + 5) = 0$. For $\lambda_1 = 0$ we obtain

$$\begin{pmatrix} -6 & 2 & | & 0 \\ -3 & 1 & | & 0 \end{pmatrix} \implies \begin{pmatrix} 1 & -1/3 & | & 0 \\ 0 & 0 & | & 0 \end{pmatrix} \quad \text{so that} \quad \mathbf{K}_1 = \begin{pmatrix} 1 \\ 3 \end{pmatrix}.$$

For $\lambda_2 = -5$ we obtain

$$\begin{pmatrix} -1 & 2 & | & 0 \\ -3 & 6 & | & 0 \end{pmatrix} \implies \begin{pmatrix} 1 & -2 & | & 0 \\ 0 & 0 & | & 0 \end{pmatrix} \quad \text{so that} \quad \mathbf{K}_2 = \begin{pmatrix} 2 \\ 1 \end{pmatrix}.$$

Then

$$\mathbf{X} = c_1 \begin{pmatrix} 1 \\ 3 \end{pmatrix} + c_2 \begin{pmatrix} 2 \\ 1 \end{pmatrix} e^{-5t}.$$

7. The system is

$$\mathbf{X}' = \begin{pmatrix} 1 & 1 & -1 \\ 0 & 2 & 0 \\ 0 & 1 & -1 \end{pmatrix} \mathbf{X}$$

and $\det(\mathbf{A} - \lambda\mathbf{I}) = (\lambda - 1)(2 - \lambda)(\lambda + 1) = 0$. For $\lambda_1 = 1$, $\lambda_2 = 2$, and $\lambda_3 = -1$ we obtain

$$\mathbf{K}_1 = \begin{pmatrix} 1 \\ 0 \\ 0 \end{pmatrix}, \quad \mathbf{K}_2 = \begin{pmatrix} 2 \\ 3 \\ 1 \end{pmatrix}, \quad \text{and} \quad \mathbf{K}_3 = \begin{pmatrix} 1 \\ 0 \\ 2 \end{pmatrix},$$

so that

$$\mathbf{X} = c_1 \begin{pmatrix} 1 \\ 0 \\ 0 \end{pmatrix} e^t + c_2 \begin{pmatrix} 2 \\ 3 \\ 1 \end{pmatrix} e^{2t} + c_3 \begin{pmatrix} 1 \\ 0 \\ 2 \end{pmatrix} e^{-t}.$$

8. The system is

$$\mathbf{X}' = \begin{pmatrix} 2 & -7 & 0 \\ 5 & 10 & 4 \\ 0 & 5 & 2 \end{pmatrix} \mathbf{X}$$

and $\det(\mathbf{A} - \lambda\mathbf{I}) = (2 - \lambda)(\lambda - 5)(\lambda - 7) = 0$. For $\lambda_1 = 2$, $\lambda_2 = 5$, and $\lambda_3 = 7$ we obtain

$$\mathbf{K}_1 = \begin{pmatrix} 4 \\ 0 \\ -5 \end{pmatrix}, \quad \mathbf{K}_2 = \begin{pmatrix} -7 \\ 3 \\ 5 \end{pmatrix}, \quad \text{and} \quad \mathbf{K}_3 = \begin{pmatrix} -7 \\ 5 \\ 5 \end{pmatrix},$$

so that

$$\mathbf{X} = c_1 \begin{pmatrix} 4 \\ 0 \\ -5 \end{pmatrix} e^{2t} + c_2 \begin{pmatrix} -7 \\ 3 \\ 5 \end{pmatrix} e^{5t} + c_3 \begin{pmatrix} -7 \\ 5 \\ 5 \end{pmatrix} e^{7t}.$$

321

9. We have $\det(\mathbf{A} - \lambda\mathbf{I}) = -(\lambda + 1)(\lambda - 3)(\lambda + 2) = 0$. For $\lambda_1 = -1$, $\lambda_2 = 3$, and $\lambda_3 = -2$ we obtain

$$\mathbf{K}_1 = \begin{pmatrix} -1 \\ 0 \\ 1 \end{pmatrix}, \quad \mathbf{K}_2 = \begin{pmatrix} 1 \\ 4 \\ 3 \end{pmatrix}, \quad \text{and} \quad \mathbf{K}_3 = \begin{pmatrix} 1 \\ -1 \\ 3 \end{pmatrix},$$

so that

$$\mathbf{X} = c_1 \begin{pmatrix} -1 \\ 0 \\ 1 \end{pmatrix} e^{-t} + c_2 \begin{pmatrix} 1 \\ 4 \\ 3 \end{pmatrix} e^{3t} + c_3 \begin{pmatrix} 1 \\ -1 \\ 3 \end{pmatrix} e^{-2t}.$$

10. We have $\det(\mathbf{A} - \lambda\mathbf{I}) = -\lambda(\lambda - 1)(\lambda - 2) = 0$. For $\lambda_1 = 0$, $\lambda_2 = 1$, and $\lambda_3 = 2$ we obtain

$$\mathbf{K}_1 = \begin{pmatrix} 1 \\ 0 \\ -1 \end{pmatrix}, \quad \mathbf{K}_2 = \begin{pmatrix} 0 \\ 1 \\ 0 \end{pmatrix}, \quad \text{and} \quad \mathbf{K}_3 = \begin{pmatrix} 1 \\ 0 \\ 1 \end{pmatrix},$$

so that

$$\mathbf{X} = c_1 \begin{pmatrix} 1 \\ 0 \\ -1 \end{pmatrix} + c_2 \begin{pmatrix} 0 \\ 1 \\ 0 \end{pmatrix} e^t + c_3 \begin{pmatrix} 1 \\ 0 \\ 1 \end{pmatrix} e^{2t}.$$

11. We have $\det(\mathbf{A} - \lambda\mathbf{I}) = -(\lambda + 1)(\lambda + 1/2)(\lambda + 3/2) = 0$. For $\lambda_1 = -1$, $\lambda_2 = -1/2$, and $\lambda_3 = -3/2$ we obtain

$$\mathbf{K}_1 = \begin{pmatrix} 4 \\ 0 \\ -1 \end{pmatrix}, \quad \mathbf{K}_2 = \begin{pmatrix} -12 \\ 6 \\ 5 \end{pmatrix}, \quad \text{and} \quad \mathbf{K}_3 = \begin{pmatrix} 4 \\ 2 \\ -1 \end{pmatrix},$$

so that

$$\mathbf{X} = c_1 \begin{pmatrix} 4 \\ 0 \\ -1 \end{pmatrix} e^{-t} + c_2 \begin{pmatrix} -12 \\ 6 \\ 5 \end{pmatrix} e^{-t/2} + c_3 \begin{pmatrix} 4 \\ 2 \\ -1 \end{pmatrix} e^{-3t/2}.$$

12. We have $\det(\mathbf{A} - \lambda\mathbf{I}) = (\lambda - 3)(\lambda + 5)(6 - \lambda) = 0$. For $\lambda_1 = 3$, $\lambda_2 = -5$, and $\lambda_3 = 6$ we obtain

$$\mathbf{K}_1 = \begin{pmatrix} 1 \\ 1 \\ 0 \end{pmatrix}, \quad \mathbf{K}_2 = \begin{pmatrix} 1 \\ -1 \\ 0 \end{pmatrix}, \quad \text{and} \quad \mathbf{K}_3 = \begin{pmatrix} 2 \\ -2 \\ 11 \end{pmatrix},$$

so that

$$\mathbf{X} = c_1 \begin{pmatrix} 1 \\ 1 \\ 0 \end{pmatrix} e^{3t} + c_2 \begin{pmatrix} 1 \\ -1 \\ 0 \end{pmatrix} e^{-5t} + c_3 \begin{pmatrix} 2 \\ -2 \\ 11 \end{pmatrix} e^{6t}.$$

13. We have $\det(\mathbf{A} - \lambda\mathbf{I}) = (\lambda + 1/2)(\lambda - 1/2) = 0$. For $\lambda_1 = -1/2$ and $\lambda_2 = 1/2$ we obtain

$$\mathbf{K}_1 = \begin{pmatrix} 0 \\ 1 \end{pmatrix} \quad \text{and} \quad \mathbf{K}_2 = \begin{pmatrix} 1 \\ 1 \end{pmatrix},$$

so that

$$\mathbf{X} = c_1 \begin{pmatrix} 0 \\ 1 \end{pmatrix} e^{-t/2} + c_2 \begin{pmatrix} 1 \\ 1 \end{pmatrix} e^{t/2}.$$

If

$$\mathbf{X}(0) = \begin{pmatrix} 3 \\ 5 \end{pmatrix}$$

then $c_1 = 2$ and $c_2 = 3$.

14. We have $\det(\mathbf{A} - \lambda\mathbf{I}) = (2 - \lambda)(\lambda - 3)(\lambda + 1) = 0$. For $\lambda_1 = 2$, $\lambda_2 = 3$, and $\lambda_3 = -1$ we obtain

$$\mathbf{K}_1 = \begin{pmatrix} 5 \\ -3 \\ 2 \end{pmatrix}, \quad \mathbf{K}_2 = \begin{pmatrix} 2 \\ 0 \\ 1 \end{pmatrix}, \quad \text{and} \quad \mathbf{K}_3 = \begin{pmatrix} -2 \\ 0 \\ 1 \end{pmatrix},$$

so that

$$\mathbf{X} = c_1 \begin{pmatrix} 5 \\ -3 \\ 2 \end{pmatrix} e^{2t} + c_2 \begin{pmatrix} 2 \\ 0 \\ 1 \end{pmatrix} e^{3t} + c_3 \begin{pmatrix} -2 \\ 0 \\ 1 \end{pmatrix} e^{-t}.$$

If

$$\mathbf{X}(0) = \begin{pmatrix} 1 \\ 3 \\ 0 \end{pmatrix}$$

then $c_1 = -1$, $c_2 = 5/2$, and $c_3 = -1/2$.

In Problems 15-28 the form of the answer will vary according to the choice of eigenvector. For example, in Problem 15, if $\mathbf{K}_1$ is chosen to be $\begin{pmatrix} 1 \\ -2i \end{pmatrix}$ the solution has the form

$$\mathbf{X} = c_1 \begin{pmatrix} \cos t \\ 2\cos t + \sin t \end{pmatrix} e^{4t} + c_2 \begin{pmatrix} \sin t \\ 2\sin t - \cos t \end{pmatrix} e^{4t}.$$

15. We have $\det(\mathbf{A} - \lambda\mathbf{I}) = \lambda^2 - 8\lambda + 17 = 0$. For $\lambda_1 = 4 + i$ we obtain

$$\mathbf{K}_1 = \begin{pmatrix} 2 + i \\ 5 \end{pmatrix}$$

so that

$$\mathbf{X}_1 = \begin{pmatrix} 2 + i \\ 5 \end{pmatrix} e^{(4+i)t} = \begin{pmatrix} 2\cos t - \sin t \\ 5\cos t \end{pmatrix} e^{4t} + i \begin{pmatrix} \cos t + 2\sin t \\ 5\sin t \end{pmatrix} e^{4t}.$$

Then

$$\mathbf{X} = c_1 \begin{pmatrix} 2\cos t - \sin t \\ 5\cos t \end{pmatrix} e^{4t} + c_2 \begin{pmatrix} 2\sin t + \cos t \\ 5\sin t \end{pmatrix} e^{4t}.$$

16. We have $\det(\mathbf{A} - \lambda\mathbf{I}) = \lambda^2 + 1 = 0$. For $\lambda_1 = i$ we obtain

$$\mathbf{K}_1 = \begin{pmatrix} -1 - i \\ 2 \end{pmatrix}$$

so that

$$\mathbf{X}_1 = \begin{pmatrix} -1 - i \\ 2 \end{pmatrix} e^{it} = \begin{pmatrix} \sin t - \cos t \\ 2\cos t \end{pmatrix} + i \begin{pmatrix} -\cos t - \sin t \\ 2\sin t \end{pmatrix}.$$

Then

$$\mathbf{X} = c_1 \begin{pmatrix} \sin t - \cos t \\ 2\cos t \end{pmatrix} + c_2 \begin{pmatrix} -\cos t - \sin t \\ 2\sin t \end{pmatrix}.$$

17. We have $\det(\mathbf{A} - \lambda\mathbf{I}) = \lambda^2 - 8\lambda + 17 = 0$. For $\lambda_1 = 4 + i$ we obtain

$$\mathbf{K}_1 = \begin{pmatrix} -1 - i \\ 2 \end{pmatrix}$$

so that

$$\mathbf{X}_1 = \begin{pmatrix} -1 - i \\ 2 \end{pmatrix} e^{(4+i)t} = \begin{pmatrix} \sin t - \cos t \\ 2\cos t \end{pmatrix} e^{4t} + i \begin{pmatrix} -\sin t - \cos t \\ 2\sin t \end{pmatrix} e^{4t}.$$

Then

$$\mathbf{X} = c_1 \begin{pmatrix} \sin t - \cos t \\ 2\cos t \end{pmatrix} e^{4t} + c_2 \begin{pmatrix} -\sin t - \cos t \\ 2\sin t \end{pmatrix} e^{4t}.$$

18. We have $\det(\mathbf{A} - \lambda\mathbf{I}) = \lambda^2 - 10\lambda + 34 = 0$. For $\lambda_1 = 5 + 3i$ we obtain

$$\mathbf{K}_1 = \begin{pmatrix} 1 - 3i \\ 2 \end{pmatrix}$$

so that

$$\mathbf{X}_1 = \begin{pmatrix} 1 - 3i \\ 2 \end{pmatrix} e^{(5+3i)t} = \begin{pmatrix} \cos 3t + 3\sin 3t \\ 2\cos 3t \end{pmatrix} e^{5t} + i \begin{pmatrix} \sin 3t - 3\cos 3t \\ 2\cos 3t \end{pmatrix} e^{5t}.$$

Then

$$\mathbf{X} = c_1 \begin{pmatrix} \cos 3t + 3\sin 3t \\ 2\cos 3t \end{pmatrix} e^{5t} + c_2 \begin{pmatrix} \sin 3t - 3\cos 3t \\ 2\cos 3t \end{pmatrix} e^{5t}.$$

19. We have $\det(\mathbf{A} - \lambda\mathbf{I}) = \lambda^2 + 9 = 0$. For $\lambda_1 = 3i$ we obtain

$$\mathbf{K}_1 = \begin{pmatrix} 4 + 3i \\ 5 \end{pmatrix}$$

so that

$$X_1 = \begin{pmatrix} 4+3i \\ 5 \end{pmatrix} e^{3it} = \begin{pmatrix} 4\cos 3t - 3\sin 3t \\ 5\cos 3t \end{pmatrix} + i \begin{pmatrix} 4\sin 3t + 3\cos 3t \\ 5\sin 3t \end{pmatrix}.$$

Then

$$X = c_1 \begin{pmatrix} 4\cos 3t - 3\sin 3t \\ 5\cos 3t \end{pmatrix} + c_2 \begin{pmatrix} 4\sin 3t + 3\cos 3t \\ 5\sin 3t \end{pmatrix}.$$

20. We have $\det(\mathbf{A} - \lambda\mathbf{I}) = \lambda^2 + 2\lambda + 5 = 0$. For $\lambda_1 = -1 + 2i$ we obtain

$$K_1 = \begin{pmatrix} 2+2i \\ 1 \end{pmatrix}$$

so that

$$X_1 = \begin{pmatrix} 2+2i \\ 1 \end{pmatrix} e^{(-1+2i)t} = \begin{pmatrix} 2\cos 2t - 2\sin 2t \\ \cos 2t \end{pmatrix} e^{-t} + i \begin{pmatrix} 2\cos 2t + 2\sin 2t \\ \sin 2t \end{pmatrix} e^{-t}.$$

Then

$$X = c_1 \begin{pmatrix} 2\cos 2t - 2\sin 2t \\ \cos 2t \end{pmatrix} e^{-t} + c_2 \begin{pmatrix} 2\cos 2t + 2\sin 2t \\ \sin 2t \end{pmatrix} e^{-t}.$$

21. We have $\det(\mathbf{A} - \lambda\mathbf{I}) = -\lambda\left(\lambda^2 + 1\right) = 0$. For $\lambda_1 = 0$ we obtain

$$K_1 = \begin{pmatrix} 1 \\ 0 \\ 0 \end{pmatrix}.$$

For $\lambda_2 = i$ we obtain

$$K_2 = \begin{pmatrix} -i \\ i \\ 1 \end{pmatrix}$$

so that

$$X_2 = \begin{pmatrix} -i \\ i \\ 1 \end{pmatrix} e^{it} = \begin{pmatrix} \sin t \\ -\sin t \\ \cos t \end{pmatrix} + i \begin{pmatrix} -\cos t \\ \cos t \\ \sin t \end{pmatrix}.$$

Then

$$X = c_1 \begin{pmatrix} 1 \\ 0 \\ 0 \end{pmatrix} + c_2 \begin{pmatrix} \sin t \\ -\sin t \\ \cos t \end{pmatrix} + c_3 \begin{pmatrix} -\cos t \\ \cos t \\ \sin t \end{pmatrix}.$$

22. We have $\det(\mathbf{A} - \lambda\mathbf{I}) = (\lambda + 3)(\lambda^2 - 2\lambda + 5) = 0$. For $\lambda_1 = -3$ we obtain

$$K_1 = \begin{pmatrix} 0 \\ -2 \\ 1 \end{pmatrix}.$$

325

For $\lambda_2 = 1 + 2i$ we obtain

$$K_2 = \begin{pmatrix} -2 - i \\ -2 - 3i \\ 2 \end{pmatrix}.$$

so that

$$X_2 = \begin{pmatrix} -2\cos 2t + \sin 2t \\ -2\cos 2t + 3\sin 2t \\ 2\cos 2t \end{pmatrix} e^t + i \begin{pmatrix} -\cos 2t - 2\sin 2t \\ -3\cos 2t - 2\sin 2t \\ 2\sin 2t \end{pmatrix} e^t.$$

Then

$$X = c_1 \begin{pmatrix} 0 \\ -2 \\ 1 \end{pmatrix} e^{-3t} + c_2 \begin{pmatrix} -2\cos 2t + \sin 2t \\ -2\cos 2t + 3\sin 2t \\ 2\cos 2t \end{pmatrix} e^t + c_3 \begin{pmatrix} -\cos 2t - 2\sin 2t \\ -3\cos 2t - 2\sin 2t \\ 2\sin 2t \end{pmatrix} e^t.$$

23. We have $\det(A - \lambda I) = (1 - \lambda)(\lambda^2 - 2\lambda + 2) = 0$. For $\lambda_1 = 1$ we obtain

$$K_1 = \begin{pmatrix} 0 \\ 2 \\ 1 \end{pmatrix}.$$

For $\lambda_2 = 1 + i$ we obtain

$$K_2 = \begin{pmatrix} 1 \\ i \\ i \end{pmatrix}.$$

so that

$$X_2 = \begin{pmatrix} 1 \\ i \\ i \end{pmatrix} e^{(1+i)t} = \begin{pmatrix} \cos t \\ -\sin t \\ -\sin t \end{pmatrix} e^t + i \begin{pmatrix} \sin t \\ \cos t \\ \cos t \end{pmatrix} e^t.$$

Then

$$X = c_1 \begin{pmatrix} 0 \\ 2 \\ 1 \end{pmatrix} e^t + c_2 \begin{pmatrix} \cos t \\ -\sin t \\ -\sin t \end{pmatrix} e^t + c_3 \begin{pmatrix} \sin t \\ \cos t \\ \cos t \end{pmatrix} e^t.$$

24. We have $\det(A - \lambda I) = -(\lambda - 6)(\lambda^2 - 8\lambda + 20) = 0$. For $\lambda_1 = 6$ we obtain

$$K_1 = \begin{pmatrix} 0 \\ 1 \\ 0 \end{pmatrix}.$$

For $\lambda_2 = 4 + 2i$ we obtain

$$K_2 = \begin{pmatrix} -i \\ 0 \\ 2 \end{pmatrix}.$$

so that

$$\mathbf{X}_2 = \begin{pmatrix} -i \\ 0 \\ 2 \end{pmatrix} e^{(4+2i)t} = \begin{pmatrix} \sin 2t \\ 0 \\ 2\cos 2t \end{pmatrix} e^{4t} + i \begin{pmatrix} -\cos 2t \\ 0 \\ 2\sin 2t \end{pmatrix} e^{4t}.$$

Then

$$\mathbf{X} = c_1 \begin{pmatrix} 0 \\ 1 \\ 0 \end{pmatrix} e^{6t} + c_2 \begin{pmatrix} \sin 2t \\ 0 \\ 2\cos 2t \end{pmatrix} e^{4t} + c_3 \begin{pmatrix} -\cos 2t \\ 0 \\ 2\sin 2t \end{pmatrix} e^{4t}.$$

25. We have $\det(\mathbf{A} - \lambda\mathbf{I}) = (2 - \lambda)(\lambda^2 + 4\lambda + 13) = 0$. For $\lambda_1 = 2$ we obtain

$$\mathbf{K}_1 = \begin{pmatrix} 28 \\ -5 \\ 25 \end{pmatrix}.$$

For $\lambda_2 = -2 + 3i$ we obtain

$$\mathbf{K}_2 = \begin{pmatrix} 4 + 3i \\ -5 \\ 0 \end{pmatrix}$$

so that

$$\mathbf{X}_2 = \begin{pmatrix} 4 + 3i \\ -5 \\ 0 \end{pmatrix} e^{(-2+3i)t} = \begin{pmatrix} 4\cos 3t - 3\sin 3t \\ -5\cos 3t \\ 0 \end{pmatrix} e^{-2t} + i \begin{pmatrix} 4\sin 3t + 3\cos 3t \\ -5\sin 3t \\ 0 \end{pmatrix} e^{-2t}.$$

Then

$$\mathbf{X} = c_1 \begin{pmatrix} 28 \\ -5 \\ 25 \end{pmatrix} e^{2t} + c_2 \begin{pmatrix} 4\cos 3t - 3\sin 3t \\ -5\cos 3t \\ 0 \end{pmatrix} e^{-2t} + c_3 \begin{pmatrix} 4\sin 3t + 3\cos 3t \\ -5\sin 3t \\ 0 \end{pmatrix} e^{-2t}.$$

26. We have $\det(\mathbf{A} - \lambda\mathbf{I}) = -(\lambda + 2)(\lambda^2 + 4) = 0$. For $\lambda_1 = -2$ we obtain

$$\mathbf{K}_1 = \begin{pmatrix} 0 \\ -1 \\ 1 \end{pmatrix}.$$

For $\lambda_2 = 2i$ we obtain

$$\mathbf{K}_2 = \begin{pmatrix} -2 - 2i \\ 1 \\ 1 \end{pmatrix}$$

so that

$$\mathbf{X}_2 = \begin{pmatrix} -2 - 2i \\ 1 \\ 1 \end{pmatrix} e^{2it} = \begin{pmatrix} -2\cos 2t + 2\sin 2t \\ \cos 2t \\ \cos 2t \end{pmatrix} + i \begin{pmatrix} -2\cos 2t - 2\sin 2t \\ \sin 2t \\ \sin 2t \end{pmatrix}.$$

Then

$$\mathbf{X} = c_1 \begin{pmatrix} 0 \\ -1 \\ 1 \end{pmatrix} e^{-2t} + c_2 \begin{pmatrix} -2\cos 2t + 2\sin 2t \\ \cos 2t \\ \cos 2t \end{pmatrix} + c_3 \begin{pmatrix} -2\cos 2t - 2\sin 2t \\ \sin 2t \\ \sin 2t \end{pmatrix}.$$

27. We have $\det(\mathbf{A} - \lambda\mathbf{I}) = (1 - \lambda)(\lambda^2 + 25) = 0$. For $\lambda_1 = 1$ we obtain

$$\mathbf{K}_1 = \begin{pmatrix} 25 \\ -7 \\ 6 \end{pmatrix}.$$

For $\lambda_2 = 5i$ we obtain

$$\mathbf{K}_2 = \begin{pmatrix} 1 + 5i \\ 1 \\ 1 \end{pmatrix}$$

so that

$$\mathbf{X}_2 = \begin{pmatrix} 1 + 5i \\ 1 \\ 1 \end{pmatrix} e^{5it} = \begin{pmatrix} \cos 5t - 5\sin 5t \\ \cos 5t \\ \cos 5t \end{pmatrix} + i \begin{pmatrix} \sin 5t + 5\cos 5t \\ \sin 5t \\ \sin 5t \end{pmatrix}.$$

Then

$$\mathbf{X} = c_1 \begin{pmatrix} 25 \\ -7 \\ 6 \end{pmatrix} e^t + c_2 \begin{pmatrix} \cos 5t - 5\sin 5t \\ \cos 5t \\ \cos 5t \end{pmatrix} + c_3 \begin{pmatrix} \sin 5t + 5\cos 5t \\ \sin 5t \\ \sin 5t \end{pmatrix}.$$

If

$$\mathbf{X}(0) = \begin{pmatrix} 4 \\ 6 \\ -7 \end{pmatrix}$$

then $c_1 = c_2 = -1$ and $c_3 = 6$.

28. We have $\det(\mathbf{A} - \lambda\mathbf{I}) = \lambda^2 - 10\lambda + 29 = 0$. For $\lambda_1 = 5 + 2i$ we obtain

$$\mathbf{K}_1 = \begin{pmatrix} 1 \\ 1 - 2i \end{pmatrix}$$

so that

$$\mathbf{X}_1 = \begin{pmatrix} 1 \\ 1 - 2i \end{pmatrix} e^{(5+2i)t} = \begin{pmatrix} \cos 2t \\ \cos 2t + 2\sin 2t \end{pmatrix} e^{5t} + i \begin{pmatrix} \sin 2t \\ \sin 2t - 2\cos 2t \end{pmatrix} e^{5t}.$$

and

$$\mathbf{X} = c_1 \begin{pmatrix} \cos 2t \\ \cos 2t + 2\sin 2t \end{pmatrix} e^{5t} + c_3 \begin{pmatrix} \sin 2t \\ \sin 2t - 2\cos 2t \end{pmatrix} e^{5t}.$$

If

$$\mathbf{X}(0) = \begin{pmatrix} -2 \\ 8 \end{pmatrix}$$

328

then $c_1 = -2$ and $c_2 = 5$.

29. We have $\det(\mathbf{A} - \lambda\mathbf{I}) = \lambda^2 = 0$. For $\lambda_1 = 0$ we obtain

$$\mathbf{K} = \begin{pmatrix} 1 \\ 3 \end{pmatrix}.$$

A solution of $(\mathbf{A} - \lambda_1\mathbf{I})\mathbf{P} = \mathbf{K}$ is

$$\mathbf{P} = \begin{pmatrix} 1 \\ 2 \end{pmatrix}$$

so that

$$\mathbf{X} = c_1 \begin{pmatrix} 1 \\ 3 \end{pmatrix} + c_2 \left[\begin{pmatrix} 1 \\ 3 \end{pmatrix} t + \begin{pmatrix} 1 \\ 2 \end{pmatrix} \right].$$

30. We have $\det(\mathbf{A} - \lambda\mathbf{I}) = (\lambda + 1)^2 = 0$. For $\lambda_1 = -1$ we obtain

$$\mathbf{K} = \begin{pmatrix} 1 \\ 1 \end{pmatrix}.$$

A solution of $(\mathbf{A} - \lambda_1\mathbf{I})\mathbf{P} = \mathbf{K}$ is

$$\mathbf{P} = \begin{pmatrix} 0 \\ 1/5 \end{pmatrix}$$

so that

$$\mathbf{X} = c_1 \begin{pmatrix} 1 \\ 1 \end{pmatrix} e^{-t} + c_2 \left[\begin{pmatrix} 1 \\ 1 \end{pmatrix} te^{-t} + \begin{pmatrix} 0 \\ 1/5 \end{pmatrix} e^{-t} \right].$$

31. We have $\det(\mathbf{A} - \lambda\mathbf{I}) = (\lambda - 2)^2 = 0$. For $\lambda_1 = 2$ we obtain

$$\mathbf{K} = \begin{pmatrix} 1 \\ 1 \end{pmatrix}.$$

A solution of $(\mathbf{A} - \lambda_1\mathbf{I})\mathbf{P} = \mathbf{K}$ is

$$\mathbf{P} = \begin{pmatrix} -1/3 \\ 0 \end{pmatrix}$$

so that

$$\mathbf{X} = c_1 \begin{pmatrix} 1 \\ 1 \end{pmatrix} e^{2t} + c_2 \left[\begin{pmatrix} 1 \\ 1 \end{pmatrix} te^{2t} + \begin{pmatrix} -1/3 \\ 0 \end{pmatrix} e^{2t} \right].$$

32. We have $\det(\mathbf{A} - \lambda\mathbf{I}) = (\lambda - 6)^2 = 0$. For $\lambda_1 = 6$ we obtain

$$\mathbf{K} = \begin{pmatrix} 3 \\ 2 \end{pmatrix}.$$

A solution of $(\mathbf{A} - \lambda_1\mathbf{I})\mathbf{P} = \mathbf{K}$ is

$$\mathbf{P} = \begin{pmatrix} 1/2 \\ 0 \end{pmatrix}$$

329

so that

$$\mathbf{X} = c_1 \begin{pmatrix} 3 \\ 2 \end{pmatrix} e^{6t} + c_2 \left[\begin{pmatrix} 3 \\ 2 \end{pmatrix} t e^{6t} + \begin{pmatrix} 1/2 \\ 0 \end{pmatrix} e^{6t} \right].$$

33. We have $\det(\mathbf{A} - \lambda\mathbf{I}) = (1 - \lambda)(\lambda - 2)^2 = 0$. For $\lambda_1 = 1$ we obtain

$$\mathbf{K}_1 = \begin{pmatrix} 1 \\ 1 \\ 1 \end{pmatrix}.$$

For $\lambda_2 = 2$ we obtain

$$\mathbf{K}_2 = \begin{pmatrix} 1 \\ 0 \\ 1 \end{pmatrix} \quad \text{and} \quad \mathbf{K}_3 = \begin{pmatrix} 1 \\ 1 \\ 0 \end{pmatrix}.$$

Then

$$\mathbf{X} = c_1 \begin{pmatrix} 1 \\ 1 \\ 1 \end{pmatrix} e^t + c_2 \begin{pmatrix} 1 \\ 0 \\ 1 \end{pmatrix} e^{2t} + c_3 \begin{pmatrix} 1 \\ 1 \\ 0 \end{pmatrix} e^{2t}.$$

34. We have $\det(\mathbf{A} - \lambda\mathbf{I}) = (\lambda - 8)(\lambda + 1)^2 = 0$. For $\lambda_1 = 8$ we obtain

$$\mathbf{K}_1 = \begin{pmatrix} 2 \\ 1 \\ 2 \end{pmatrix}.$$

For $\lambda_2 = -1$ we obtain

$$\mathbf{K}_2 = \begin{pmatrix} 0 \\ -2 \\ 1 \end{pmatrix} \quad \text{and} \quad \mathbf{K}_3 = \begin{pmatrix} 1 \\ -2 \\ 0 \end{pmatrix}.$$

Then

$$\mathbf{X} = c_1 \begin{pmatrix} 2 \\ 1 \\ 2 \end{pmatrix} e^{8t} + c_2 \begin{pmatrix} 0 \\ -2 \\ 1 \end{pmatrix} e^{-t} + c_3 \begin{pmatrix} 1 \\ -2 \\ 0 \end{pmatrix} e^{-t}.$$

35. We have $\det(\mathbf{A} - \lambda\mathbf{I}) = -\lambda(5 - \lambda)^2 = 0$. For $\lambda_1 = 0$ we obtain

$$\mathbf{K}_1 = \begin{pmatrix} -4 \\ -5 \\ 2 \end{pmatrix}.$$

For $\lambda_2 = 5$ we obtain

$$\mathbf{K} = \begin{pmatrix} -2 \\ 0 \\ 1 \end{pmatrix}.$$

A solution of $(\mathbf{A} - \lambda_1\mathbf{I})\mathbf{P} = \mathbf{K}$ is

$$\mathbf{P} = \begin{pmatrix} 5/2 \\ 1/2 \\ 0 \end{pmatrix}$$

so that

$$\mathbf{X} = c_1 \begin{pmatrix} -4 \\ -5 \\ 2 \end{pmatrix} + c_2 \begin{pmatrix} -2 \\ 0 \\ 1 \end{pmatrix} e^{5t} + c_3 \left[\begin{pmatrix} -2 \\ 0 \\ 1 \end{pmatrix} te^{5t} + \begin{pmatrix} 5/2 \\ 1/2 \\ 0 \end{pmatrix} e^{5t} \right].$$

36. We have $\det(\mathbf{A} - \lambda\mathbf{I}) = (1 - \lambda)(\lambda - 2)^2 = 0$. For $\lambda_1 = 1$ we obtain

$$\mathbf{K}_1 = \begin{pmatrix} 1 \\ 0 \\ 0 \end{pmatrix}.$$

For $\lambda_2 = 2$ we obtain

$$\mathbf{K} = \begin{pmatrix} 0 \\ -1 \\ 1 \end{pmatrix}.$$

A solution of $(\mathbf{A} - \lambda_2\mathbf{I})\mathbf{P} = \mathbf{K}$ is

$$\mathbf{P} = \begin{pmatrix} 0 \\ -1 \\ 0 \end{pmatrix}$$

so that

$$\mathbf{X} = c_1 \begin{pmatrix} 1 \\ 0 \\ 0 \end{pmatrix} e^t + c_2 \begin{pmatrix} 0 \\ -1 \\ 1 \end{pmatrix} e^{2t} + c_3 \left[\begin{pmatrix} 0 \\ -1 \\ 1 \end{pmatrix} te^{2t} + \begin{pmatrix} 0 \\ -1 \\ 0 \end{pmatrix} e^{2t} \right].$$

37. We have $\det(\mathbf{A} - \lambda\mathbf{I}) = -(\lambda - 1)^3 = 0$. For $\lambda_1 = 1$ we obtain

$$\mathbf{K} = \begin{pmatrix} 0 \\ 1 \\ 1 \end{pmatrix}.$$

Solutions of $(\mathbf{A} - \lambda_1\mathbf{I})\mathbf{P} = \mathbf{K}$ and $(\mathbf{A} - \lambda_1\mathbf{I})\mathbf{Q} = \mathbf{P}$ are

$$\mathbf{P} = \begin{pmatrix} 0 \\ 1 \\ 0 \end{pmatrix} \quad \text{and} \quad \mathbf{Q} = \begin{pmatrix} 1/2 \\ 0 \\ 0 \end{pmatrix}.$$

331

so that

$$\mathbf{X} = c_1 \begin{pmatrix} 0 \\ 1 \\ 1 \end{pmatrix} + c_2 \left[\begin{pmatrix} 0 \\ 1 \\ 1 \end{pmatrix} te^t + \begin{pmatrix} 0 \\ 1 \\ 0 \end{pmatrix} e^t \right] + c_3 \left[\begin{pmatrix} 0 \\ 1 \\ 1 \end{pmatrix} \frac{t^2}{2} e^t + \begin{pmatrix} 0 \\ 1 \\ 0 \end{pmatrix} te^t + \begin{pmatrix} 1/2 \\ 0 \\ 0 \end{pmatrix} e^t \right].$$

38. We have $\det(\mathbf{A} - \lambda\mathbf{I}) = (\lambda - 4)^3 = 0$. For $\lambda_1 = 4$ we obtain

$$\mathbf{K} = \begin{pmatrix} 1 \\ 0 \\ 0 \end{pmatrix}.$$

Solutions of $(\mathbf{A} - \lambda_1\mathbf{I})\mathbf{P} = \mathbf{K}$ and $(\mathbf{A} - \lambda_1\mathbf{I})\mathbf{Q} = \mathbf{P}$ are

$$\mathbf{P} = \begin{pmatrix} 0 \\ 1 \\ 0 \end{pmatrix} \quad \text{and} \quad \mathbf{Q} = \begin{pmatrix} 0 \\ 0 \\ 1 \end{pmatrix}$$

so that

$$\mathbf{X} = c_1 \begin{pmatrix} 1 \\ 0 \\ 0 \end{pmatrix} e^{4t} + c_2 \left[\begin{pmatrix} 1 \\ 0 \\ 0 \end{pmatrix} te^{4t} + \begin{pmatrix} 0 \\ 1 \\ 0 \end{pmatrix} e^{4t} \right] + c_3 \left[\begin{pmatrix} 1 \\ 0 \\ 0 \end{pmatrix} \frac{t^2}{2} e^{4t} + \begin{pmatrix} 0 \\ 1 \\ 0 \end{pmatrix} te^{4t} + \begin{pmatrix} 0 \\ 0 \\ 1 \end{pmatrix} e^{4t} \right].$$

39. We have $\det(\mathbf{A} - \lambda\mathbf{I}) = (\lambda - 4)^2 = 0$. For $\lambda_1 = 4$ we obtain

$$\mathbf{K} = \begin{pmatrix} 2 \\ 1 \end{pmatrix}.$$

A solution of $(\mathbf{A} - \lambda_1\mathbf{I})\mathbf{P} = \mathbf{K}$ is

$$\mathbf{P} = \begin{pmatrix} 1 \\ 1 \end{pmatrix}$$

so that

$$\mathbf{X} = c_1 \begin{pmatrix} 2 \\ 1 \end{pmatrix} e^{4t} + c_2 \left[\begin{pmatrix} 2 \\ 1 \end{pmatrix} te^{4t} + \begin{pmatrix} 1 \\ 1 \end{pmatrix} e^{4t} \right].$$

If

$$\mathbf{X}(0) = \begin{pmatrix} -1 \\ 6 \end{pmatrix}$$

then $c_1 = -7$ and $c_2 = 13$.

40. We have $\det(\mathbf{A} - \lambda\mathbf{I}) = -(\lambda + 1)(\lambda - 1)^2 = 0$. For $\lambda_1 = -1$ we obtain

$$\mathbf{K}_1 = \begin{pmatrix} -1 \\ 0 \\ 1 \end{pmatrix}.$$

For $\lambda_2 = 1$ we obtain

$$\mathbf{K}_2 = \begin{pmatrix} 1 \\ 0 \\ 1 \end{pmatrix} \quad \text{and} \quad \mathbf{K}_3 = \begin{pmatrix} 0 \\ 1 \\ 0 \end{pmatrix}$$

so that

$$\mathbf{X} = c_1 \begin{pmatrix} -1 \\ 0 \\ 1 \end{pmatrix} e^{-t} + c_2 \begin{pmatrix} 1 \\ 0 \\ 1 \end{pmatrix} e^{t} + c_3 \begin{pmatrix} 0 \\ 1 \\ 0 \end{pmatrix} e^{t}.$$

If

$$\mathbf{X}(0) = \begin{pmatrix} 1 \\ 2 \\ 5 \end{pmatrix}$$

then $c_1 = 2$, $c_2 = 3$, and $c_3 = 2$.

41. We have $\det(\mathbf{A} - \lambda\mathbf{I}) = (\lambda - 5)(\lambda + 5) = 0$. For $\lambda_1 = 5$ and $\lambda_2 = -5$ we obtain

$$\mathbf{K}_1 = \begin{pmatrix} 3 \\ 1 \end{pmatrix} \quad \text{and} \quad \mathbf{K}_2 = \begin{pmatrix} -1 \\ 3 \end{pmatrix}$$

so that

$$\mathbf{\Phi}(t) = \begin{pmatrix} 3e^{5t} & -e^{-5t} \\ e^{5t} & 3e^{-5t} \end{pmatrix} \quad \text{and} \quad \mathbf{\Phi}^{-1}(t) = \frac{1}{10} \begin{pmatrix} 3e^{-5t} & e^{-5t} \\ -e^{5t} & 3e^{5t} \end{pmatrix}.$$

Then

$$\mathbf{X} = \mathbf{\Phi}(t)\mathbf{\Phi}^{-1}(0)\mathbf{X}(0) = \begin{pmatrix} \frac{6}{5}e^{5t} - \frac{1}{5}e^{-5t} \\ 4e^{5t} + 6e^{-5t} \end{pmatrix}.$$

42. We have $\det(\mathbf{A} - \lambda\mathbf{I}) = (\lambda + 3/25)(\lambda + 1/25) = 0$. For $\lambda_1 = -3/25$ and $\lambda_2 = -1/25$ we obtain

$$\mathbf{K}_1 = \begin{pmatrix} -1 \\ 2 \end{pmatrix} \quad \text{and} \quad \mathbf{K}_2 = \begin{pmatrix} 1 \\ 2 \end{pmatrix}$$

so that

$$\mathbf{\Phi}(t) = \begin{pmatrix} -e^{-3t/25} & e^{-t/25} \\ 2e^{-3t/25} & 2e^{-t/25} \end{pmatrix} \quad \text{and} \quad \mathbf{\Phi}^{-1}(t) = -\frac{1}{4}e^{4t/25} \begin{pmatrix} 2e^{-t/25} & e^{-t/25} \\ -2e^{-3t/25} & -e^{-3t/25} \end{pmatrix}.$$

Then

$$\mathbf{X} = \mathbf{\Phi}(t)\mathbf{\Phi}^{-1}(0)\mathbf{X}(0) = \begin{pmatrix} \frac{25}{2}e^{-3t/25} + \frac{25}{2}e^{-t/25} \\ -25e^{-3t/25} + 25e^{-t/25} \end{pmatrix}.$$

43. Using $\mathbf{X} = t^\lambda\mathbf{K}$ in

$$t\mathbf{X}' = \begin{pmatrix} 1 & 3 \\ -1 & 5 \end{pmatrix} \mathbf{X}$$

we obtain

$$\begin{pmatrix} 1-\lambda & 3 \\ -1 & 5-\lambda \end{pmatrix} \mathbf{K} = \begin{pmatrix} 0 \\ 0 \end{pmatrix}.$$

For nonzero solutions $\mathbf{K}$ we must have $(\lambda - 4)(\lambda - 2) = 0$. If $\lambda_1 = 2$ then

$$\mathbf{K}_1 = \begin{pmatrix} 3 \\ 1 \end{pmatrix}$$

and if $\lambda_2 = 4$ then

$$\mathbf{K}_2 = \begin{pmatrix} 1 \\ 1 \end{pmatrix}$$

so that

$$\mathbf{X} = c_1 t^2 \begin{pmatrix} 3 \\ 1 \end{pmatrix} + c_2 t^4 \begin{pmatrix} 1 \\ 1 \end{pmatrix}.$$

44. Using $\mathbf{X} = t^\lambda \mathbf{K}$ in

$$t\mathbf{X}' = \begin{pmatrix} 2 & -2 \\ 2 & 7 \end{pmatrix} \mathbf{X}$$

we obtain

$$\begin{pmatrix} 2-\lambda & -2 \\ 2 & 7-\lambda \end{pmatrix} \mathbf{K} = \begin{pmatrix} 0 \\ 0 \end{pmatrix}.$$

For nonzero solutions $\mathbf{K}$ we must have $(\lambda - 3)(\lambda - 6) = 0$. If $\lambda_1 = 3$ and $\lambda_2 = 6$ then

$$\mathbf{K}_1 = \begin{pmatrix} -2 \\ 1 \end{pmatrix} \quad \text{and} \quad \mathbf{K}_2 = \begin{pmatrix} -1 \\ 2 \end{pmatrix}$$

so that

$$\mathbf{X} = c_1 t^3 \begin{pmatrix} -2 \\ 1 \end{pmatrix} + c_2 t^6 \begin{pmatrix} -1 \\ 2 \end{pmatrix}.$$

Exercises 8.7

1. Solving

$$\begin{vmatrix} 2-\lambda & 3 \\ -1 & -2-\lambda \end{vmatrix} = \lambda^2 - 1 = (\lambda - 1)(\lambda + 1) = 0$$

we obtain eigenvalues $\lambda_1 = -1$ and $\lambda_2 = 1$. Corresponding eigenvectors are

$$\mathbf{K}_1 = \begin{pmatrix} -1 \\ 1 \end{pmatrix} \quad \text{and} \quad \mathbf{K}_2 = \begin{pmatrix} -3 \\ 1 \end{pmatrix}.$$

Thus

$$\mathbf{X}_c = c_1 \begin{pmatrix} -1 \\ 1 \end{pmatrix} e^{-t} + c_2 \begin{pmatrix} -3 \\ 1 \end{pmatrix} e^t.$$

Substituting

$$\mathbf{X}_p = \begin{pmatrix} a_1 \\ b_1 \end{pmatrix}$$

into the system yields

$$2a_1 + 3b_1 = 7$$

$$-a_1 - 2b_1 = -5,$$

from which we obtain $a_1 = -1$ and $b_1 = 3$. Then

$$\mathbf{X}(t) = c_1 \begin{pmatrix} -1 \\ 1 \end{pmatrix} e^{-t} + c_2 \begin{pmatrix} -3 \\ 1 \end{pmatrix} e^t + \begin{pmatrix} -1 \\ 3 \end{pmatrix}.$$

2. Solving

$$\begin{vmatrix} 5-\lambda & 9 \\ -1 & 11-\lambda \end{vmatrix} = \lambda^2 - 16\lambda + 64 = (\lambda - 8)^2 = 0$$

we obtain the eigenvalue $\lambda = 8$. A corresponding eigenvector is

$$\mathbf{K} = \begin{pmatrix} 3 \\ 1 \end{pmatrix}.$$

Solving $(\mathbf{A} - 8\mathbf{I})\mathbf{P} = \mathbf{K}$ we obtain

$$\mathbf{P} = \begin{pmatrix} 2 \\ 1 \end{pmatrix}.$$

Thus

$$\mathbf{X}_c = c_1 \begin{pmatrix} 3 \\ 1 \end{pmatrix} e^{8t} + c_2 \left[\begin{pmatrix} 3 \\ 1 \end{pmatrix} te^{8t} + \begin{pmatrix} 2 \\ 1 \end{pmatrix} e^{8t} \right].$$

Substituting

$$\mathbf{X}_p = \begin{pmatrix} a_1 \\ b_1 \end{pmatrix}$$

into the system yields

$$5a_1 + 9b_1 = -2$$

$$-a_1 + 11b_1 = -6,$$

from which we obtain $a_1 = 1/2$ and $b_1 = -1/2$. Then

$$\mathbf{X}(t) = c_1 \begin{pmatrix} 3 \\ 1 \end{pmatrix} e^{8t} + c_2 \left[\begin{pmatrix} 3 \\ 1 \end{pmatrix} te^{8t} + \begin{pmatrix} 2 \\ 1 \end{pmatrix} e^{8t} \right] + \begin{pmatrix} 1/2 \\ -1/2 \end{pmatrix}.$$

3. Solving

$$\begin{vmatrix} 1-\lambda & 3 \\ 3 & 1-\lambda \end{vmatrix} = \lambda^2 - 2\lambda - 8 = (\lambda - 4)(\lambda + 2) = 0$$

335

we obtain eigenvalues $\lambda_1 = -2$ and $\lambda_2 = 4$. Corresponding eigenvectors are

$$\mathbf{K}_1 = \begin{pmatrix} 1 \\ -1 \end{pmatrix} \quad \text{and} \quad \mathbf{K}_2 = \begin{pmatrix} 1 \\ 1 \end{pmatrix}.$$

Thus

$$\mathbf{X}_c = c_1 \begin{pmatrix} 1 \\ -1 \end{pmatrix} e^{-2t} + c_2 \begin{pmatrix} 1 \\ 1 \end{pmatrix} e^{4t}.$$

Substituting

$$\mathbf{X}_p = \begin{pmatrix} a_3 \\ b_3 \end{pmatrix} t^2 + \begin{pmatrix} a_2 \\ b_2 \end{pmatrix} t + \begin{pmatrix} a_1 \\ b_1 \end{pmatrix}$$

into the system yields

$$a_3 + 3b_3 = 2 \qquad a_2 + 3b_2 = 2a_3 \qquad a_1 + 3b_1 = a_2$$

$$3a_3 + b_3 = 0 \qquad 3a_2 + b_2 + 1 = 2b_3 \qquad 3a_1 + b_1 + 5 = b_2$$

from which we obtain $a_3 = -1/4$, $b_3 = 3/4$, $a_2 = 1/4$, $b_2 = -1/4$, $a_1 = -2$, and $b_1 = 3/4$. Then

$$\mathbf{X}(t) = c_1 \begin{pmatrix} 1 \\ -1 \end{pmatrix} e^{-2t} + c_2 \begin{pmatrix} 1 \\ 1 \end{pmatrix} e^{4t} + \begin{pmatrix} -1/4 \\ 3/4 \end{pmatrix} t^2 + \begin{pmatrix} 1/4 \\ -1/4 \end{pmatrix} t + \begin{pmatrix} -2 \\ 3/4 \end{pmatrix}.$$

4. Solving

$$\begin{vmatrix} 1-\lambda & -4 \\ 4 & 1-\lambda \end{vmatrix} = \lambda^2 + 2\lambda - 17 = 0$$

we obtain eigenvalues $\lambda_1 = 1 + 4i$ and $\lambda_2 = 1 - 4i$. Corresponding eigenvectors are

$$\mathbf{K}_1 = \begin{pmatrix} i \\ 1 \end{pmatrix} \quad \text{and} \quad \mathbf{K}_2 = \begin{pmatrix} -i \\ 1 \end{pmatrix}.$$

Thus

$$\mathbf{X}_c = c_1 \left[\begin{pmatrix} 0 \\ 1 \end{pmatrix} \cos 4t + \begin{pmatrix} -1 \\ 0 \end{pmatrix} \sin 4t \right] e^t + c_2 \left[\begin{pmatrix} -1 \\ 0 \end{pmatrix} \cos 4t - \begin{pmatrix} 0 \\ 1 \end{pmatrix} \sin 4t \right] e^t$$

$$= c_1 \begin{pmatrix} -\sin 4t \\ \cos 4t \end{pmatrix} e^t + c_2 \begin{pmatrix} -\cos 4t \\ -\sin 4t \end{pmatrix} e^t.$$

Substituting

$$\mathbf{X}_p = \begin{pmatrix} a_3 \\ b_3 \end{pmatrix} + \begin{pmatrix} a_2 \\ b_2 \end{pmatrix} + \begin{pmatrix} a_1 \\ b_1 \end{pmatrix} e^{6t}$$

into the system yields

$$a_3 - 4b_3 = -4 \qquad a_2 - 4b_2 = a_3 \qquad -5a_1 - 4b_1 = -9$$

$$4a_3 + b_3 = 1 \qquad 4a_2 + b_2 = b_3 \qquad 4a_1 - 5b_1 = -1$$

from which we obtain $a_3 = 0$, $b_3 = 1$, $a_2 = 4/17$, $b_2 = 1/17$, $a_1 = 1$, and $b_1 = 1$. Then

$$\mathbf{X}(t) = c_1 \begin{pmatrix} -\sin 4t \\ \cos 4t \end{pmatrix} e^t + c_2 \begin{pmatrix} -\cos 4t \\ -\sin 4t \end{pmatrix} e^t + \begin{pmatrix} 0 \\ 1 \end{pmatrix} t + \begin{pmatrix} 4/17 \\ 1/17 \end{pmatrix} + \begin{pmatrix} 1 \\ 1 \end{pmatrix} e^{6t}.$$

5. Solving

$$\begin{vmatrix} 4 - \lambda & 1/3 \\ 9 & 6 - \lambda \end{vmatrix} = \lambda^2 - 10\lambda + 21 = (\lambda - 3)(\lambda - 7) = 0$$

we obtain the eigenvalues $\lambda_1 = 3$ and $\lambda_2 = 7$. Corresponding eigenvectors are

$$\mathbf{K}_1 = \begin{pmatrix} 1 \\ -3 \end{pmatrix} \quad \text{and} \quad \mathbf{K}_2 = \begin{pmatrix} 1 \\ 9 \end{pmatrix}.$$

Thus

$$\mathbf{X}_c = c_1 \begin{pmatrix} 1 \\ -3 \end{pmatrix} e^{3t} + c_2 \begin{pmatrix} 1 \\ 9 \end{pmatrix} e^{7t}.$$

Substituting

$$\mathbf{X}_p = \begin{pmatrix} a_1 \\ b_1 \end{pmatrix} e^t$$

into the system yields

$$3a_1 + \frac{1}{3}b_1 = 3$$

$$9a_1 + 5b_1 = -10$$

from which we obtain $a_1 = 55/36$ and $b_1 = -19/4$. Then

$$\mathbf{X}(t) = c_1 \begin{pmatrix} 1 \\ -3 \end{pmatrix} e^{3t} + c_2 \begin{pmatrix} 1 \\ 9 \end{pmatrix} e^{7t} + \begin{pmatrix} 55/36 \\ -19/4 \end{pmatrix} e^t.$$

6. Solving

$$\begin{vmatrix} -1 - \lambda & 5 \\ -1 & 1 - \lambda \end{vmatrix} = \lambda^2 + 4 = 0$$

we obtain the eigenvalues $\lambda_1 = 2i$ and $\lambda_2 = -2i$. Corresponding eigenvectors are

$$\mathbf{K}_1 = \begin{pmatrix} 5 \\ 1 + 2i \end{pmatrix} \quad \text{and} \quad \mathbf{K}_2 = \begin{pmatrix} 5 \\ 1 - 2i \end{pmatrix}.$$

Thus

$$\mathbf{X}_c = c_1 \begin{pmatrix} 5 \cos 2t \\ \cos 2t - 2\sin 2t \end{pmatrix} + c_2 \begin{pmatrix} 5 \sin 2t \\ 2\cos 2t + \sin 2t \end{pmatrix}.$$

Substituting

$$\mathbf{X}_p = \begin{pmatrix} a_2 \\ b_2 \end{pmatrix} \cos t + \begin{pmatrix} a_1 \\ b_1 \end{pmatrix} \sin t$$

into the system yields

$$-a_2 + 5b_2 - a_1 = 0$$

$$-a_2 + b_2 - b_1 - 2 = 0$$

$$-a_1 + 5b_1 + a_2 + 1 = 0$$

$$-a_1 + b_1 + b_2 = 0$$

from which we obtain $a_2 = -3$, $b_2 = -2/3$, $a_1 = -1/3$, and $b_1 = 1/3$. Then

$$\mathbf{X}(t) = c_1 \begin{pmatrix} 5\cos 2t \\ \cos 2t - 2\sin 2t \end{pmatrix} + c_2 \begin{pmatrix} 5\sin 2t \\ 2\cos 2t + \sin 2t \end{pmatrix} + \begin{pmatrix} -3 \\ -2/3 \end{pmatrix} \cos t + \begin{pmatrix} -1/3 \\ 1/3 \end{pmatrix} \sin t.$$

7. Solving

$$\begin{vmatrix} 1-\lambda & 1 & 1 \\ 0 & 2-\lambda & 3 \\ 0 & 0 & 5-\lambda \end{vmatrix} = (1-\lambda)(2-\lambda)(5-\lambda) = 0$$

we obtain the eigenvalues $\lambda_1 = 1$, $\lambda_2 = 2$, and $\lambda_3 = 5$. Corresponding eigenvectors are

$$\mathbf{K}_1 = \begin{pmatrix} 1 \\ 0 \\ 0 \end{pmatrix}, \quad \mathbf{K}_2 = \begin{pmatrix} 1 \\ 1 \\ 0 \end{pmatrix} \quad \text{and} \quad \mathbf{K}_3 = \begin{pmatrix} 1 \\ 2 \\ 2 \end{pmatrix}.$$

Thus

$$\mathbf{X}_c = c_1 \begin{pmatrix} 1 \\ 0 \\ 0 \end{pmatrix} e^t + c_2 \begin{pmatrix} 1 \\ 1 \\ 0 \end{pmatrix} e^{2t} + c_3 \begin{pmatrix} 1 \\ 2 \\ 2 \end{pmatrix} e^{5t}.$$

Substituting

$$\mathbf{X}_p = \begin{pmatrix} a_1 \\ b_1 \\ c_1 \end{pmatrix} e^{4t}$$

into the system yields

$$-3a_1 + b_1 + c_1 = -1$$

$$-2b_1 + 3c_1 = 1$$

$$c_1 = -2$$

from which we obtain $c_1 = -2$, $b_1 = -7/2$, and $a_1 = -3/2$. Then

$$\mathbf{X}(t) = c_1 \begin{pmatrix} 1 \\ 0 \\ 0 \end{pmatrix} e^t + c_2 \begin{pmatrix} 1 \\ 1 \\ 0 \end{pmatrix} e^{2t} + c_3 \begin{pmatrix} 1 \\ 2 \\ 2 \end{pmatrix} e^{5t} + \begin{pmatrix} -3/2 \\ -7/2 \\ -2 \end{pmatrix} e^{4t}.$$

8. Solving

$$\begin{vmatrix} -\lambda & 0 & 5 \\ 0 & 5-\lambda & 0 \\ 5 & 0 & -\lambda \end{vmatrix} = -(\lambda - 5)^2(\lambda + 5) = 0$$

we obtain the eigenvalues $\lambda_1 = 5$, $\lambda_2 = 5$, and $\lambda_3 = -5$. Corresponding eigenvectors are

$$\mathbf{K}_1 = \begin{pmatrix} 1 \\ 0 \\ 0 \end{pmatrix}, \quad \mathbf{K}_2 = \begin{pmatrix} 1 \\ 1 \\ 1 \end{pmatrix} \quad \text{and} \quad \mathbf{K}_3 = \begin{pmatrix} 1 \\ 0 \\ -1 \end{pmatrix}.$$

Thus

$$\mathbf{X}_c = c_1 \begin{pmatrix} 1 \\ 0 \\ 1 \end{pmatrix} e^{5t} + c_2 \begin{pmatrix} 1 \\ 1 \\ 1 \end{pmatrix} e^{5t} + c_3 \begin{pmatrix} 1 \\ 0 \\ -1 \end{pmatrix} e^{-5t}.$$

Substituting

$$\mathbf{X}_p = \begin{pmatrix} a_1 \\ b_1 \\ c_1 \end{pmatrix}$$

into the system yields

$$5c_1 = -5$$

$$5b_1 = 10$$

$$5a_1 = -40$$

from which we obtain $c_1 = -1$, $b_1 = 2$, and $a_1 = -8$. Then

$$\mathbf{X}(t) = c_1 \begin{pmatrix} 1 \\ 0 \\ 1 \end{pmatrix} e^{5t} + c_2 \begin{pmatrix} 1 \\ 1 \\ 1 \end{pmatrix} e^{5t} + c_3 \begin{pmatrix} 1 \\ 0 \\ -1 \end{pmatrix} e^{-5t} + \begin{pmatrix} -8 \\ 2 \\ -1 \end{pmatrix}.$$

9. Solving

$$\begin{vmatrix} -1-\lambda & -2 \\ 3 & 4-\lambda \end{vmatrix} = \lambda^2 - 3\lambda + 2 = (\lambda - 1)(\lambda - 2) = 0$$

we obtain the eigenvalues $\lambda_1 = 1$ and $\lambda_2 = 2$. Corresponding eigenvectors are

$$\mathbf{K}_1 = \begin{pmatrix} 1 \\ -1 \end{pmatrix} \quad \text{and} \quad \mathbf{K}_2 = \begin{pmatrix} -4 \\ 6 \end{pmatrix}.$$

Thus

$$\mathbf{X}_c = c_1 \begin{pmatrix} 1 \\ -1 \end{pmatrix} e^t + c_2 \begin{pmatrix} -4 \\ 6 \end{pmatrix} e^{2t}.$$

Substituting

$$\mathbf{X}_p = \begin{pmatrix} a_1 \\ b_1 \end{pmatrix}$$

into the system yields

$$-a_1 - 2b_1 = -3$$

$$3a_1 + 4b_1 = -3$$

from which we obtain $a_1 = -9$ and $b_1 = 6$. Then

$$\mathbf{X}(t) = c_1 \begin{pmatrix} 1 \\ -1 \end{pmatrix} e^t + c_2 \begin{pmatrix} -4 \\ 6 \end{pmatrix} e^{2t} + \begin{pmatrix} -9 \\ 6 \end{pmatrix}.$$

Setting

$$\mathbf{X}(0) = \begin{pmatrix} -4 \\ 5 \end{pmatrix}$$

we obtain

$$c_1 - 4c_2 - 9 = -4$$

$$-c_1 + 6c_2 + 6 = 5.$$

Then $c_1 = 13$ and $c_2 = 2$ so

$$\mathbf{X}(t) = 13 \begin{pmatrix} 1 \\ -1 \end{pmatrix} e^t + 2 \begin{pmatrix} -4 \\ 6 \end{pmatrix} e^{2t} + \begin{pmatrix} -9 \\ 6 \end{pmatrix}.$$

10. (a) By Kirchoff's first and second (on each loop) laws, we obtain $i = i_2 + i_3$, $E = i_1 R_1 + L_1 i_2'$, and $E = i_1 R_1 + i_3 R_2 + L_2 i_3'$ so that

$$\frac{d}{dt} \begin{pmatrix} i_2 \\ i_3 \end{pmatrix} = \begin{pmatrix} -R_1/L_1 & -R_1/L_1 \\ -R_1/L_2 & -(R_1 + R_2)/L_2 \end{pmatrix} \begin{pmatrix} i_2 \\ i_3 \end{pmatrix} + \begin{pmatrix} E/L_1 \\ E/L_2 \end{pmatrix}.$$

(b) Let $\mathbf{I} = \begin{pmatrix} i_2 \\ i_3 \end{pmatrix}$ so that

$$\mathbf{I}' = \begin{pmatrix} -2 & -2 \\ -2 & -5 \end{pmatrix} \mathbf{I} + \begin{pmatrix} 60 \\ 60 \end{pmatrix}$$

and

$$\mathbf{X}_c = c_1 \begin{pmatrix} 2 \\ -1 \end{pmatrix} e^{-t} + c_2 \begin{pmatrix} 1 \\ 2 \end{pmatrix} e^{-6t}.$$

If $\mathbf{X}_p = \begin{pmatrix} a_1 \\ b_1 \end{pmatrix}$ then $\mathbf{X}_p = \begin{pmatrix} 30 \\ 0 \end{pmatrix}$ so that

$$\mathbf{X} = c_1 \begin{pmatrix} 2 \\ -1 \end{pmatrix} e^{-t} + c_2 \begin{pmatrix} 1 \\ 2 \end{pmatrix} e^{-6t} + \begin{pmatrix} 30 \\ 0 \end{pmatrix}.$$

For $\mathbf{I}(0) = \begin{pmatrix} 0 \\ 0 \end{pmatrix}$ we find $c_1 = -12$ and $c_2 = -6$.

(c) $i_1(t) = i_2(t) + i_3(t) = -12e^{-t} - 18e^{-6t} + 30$.

11. Solving

$$\begin{vmatrix} 1 - \lambda & -1 \\ -1 & 1 - \lambda \end{vmatrix} = \lambda^2 - 2\lambda = \lambda(\lambda - 2) = 0$$

we obtain the eigenvalues $\lambda_1 = 0$ and $\lambda_2 = 2$. Corresponding eigenvectors are

$$\mathbf{K}_1 = \begin{pmatrix} 1 \\ 1 \end{pmatrix} \quad \text{and} \quad \mathbf{K}_2 = \begin{pmatrix} 1 \\ -1 \end{pmatrix}.$$

Thus

$$\mathbf{X}_c = c_1 \begin{pmatrix} 1 \\ 1 \end{pmatrix} + c_2 \begin{pmatrix} 1 \\ -1 \end{pmatrix} e^{2t}.$$

Substituting

$$\mathbf{X}_p = \begin{pmatrix} a_2 \\ b_2 \end{pmatrix} t + \begin{pmatrix} a_1 \\ b_1 \end{pmatrix}$$

into the system yields

$$a_2 - b_2 = 0 \qquad\qquad a_1 - b_1 + 2 = a_2$$

$$-a_2 + b_2 = 0 \qquad\qquad -a_1 + b_1 - 5 = b_2.$$

From the first system we have $a_2 = b_2$. The second system becomes

$$a_1 - b_1 = a_2 - 2$$

$$a_1 - b_1 = -a_2 - 5.$$

If we let $b_1 = 1$, then $a_1 = a_2 - 1$ and $a_1 = -a_2 - 4$. This gives $a_2 = b_2 = -3/2$ and $a_1 = -5/2$. Thus

$$\mathbf{X}(t) = c_1 \begin{pmatrix} 1 \\ 1 \end{pmatrix} + c_2 \begin{pmatrix} 1 \\ -1 \end{pmatrix} e^{2t} + \begin{pmatrix} -3/2 \\ -3/2 \end{pmatrix} t + \begin{pmatrix} -5/2 \\ 1 \end{pmatrix}.$$

_____ Exercises 8.8 _____

1. From

$$\mathbf{X}' = \begin{pmatrix} 3 & -3 \\ 2 & -2 \end{pmatrix} \mathbf{X} + \begin{pmatrix} 4 \\ -1 \end{pmatrix}$$

we obtain

$$\mathbf{X}_c = c_1 \begin{pmatrix} 1 \\ 1 \end{pmatrix} + c_2 \begin{pmatrix} 3 \\ 2 \end{pmatrix} e^t.$$

Then

$$\mathbf{\Phi} = \begin{pmatrix} 1 & 3e^t \\ 1 & 2e^t \end{pmatrix} \quad \text{and} \quad \mathbf{\Phi}^{-1} = \begin{pmatrix} -2 & 3 \\ e^{-t} & -e^{-t} \end{pmatrix}$$

so that

$$\mathbf{U} = \int \mathbf{\Phi}^{-1} \mathbf{F} \, dt = \int \begin{pmatrix} -11 \\ 5e^{-t} \end{pmatrix} dt = \begin{pmatrix} -11t \\ -5e^{-t} \end{pmatrix}$$

and

$$\mathbf{X}_p = \mathbf{\Phi} \mathbf{U} = \begin{pmatrix} -11 \\ -11 \end{pmatrix} t + \begin{pmatrix} -15 \\ -10 \end{pmatrix}.$$

2. From

$$\mathbf{X}' = \begin{pmatrix} 2 & -1 \\ 3 & -2 \end{pmatrix} \mathbf{X} + \begin{pmatrix} 0 \\ 4 \end{pmatrix} t$$

we obtain

$$\mathbf{X}_c = c_1 \begin{pmatrix} 1 \\ 1 \end{pmatrix} e^t + c_2 \begin{pmatrix} 1 \\ 3 \end{pmatrix} e^{-t}.$$

Then

$$\mathbf{\Phi} = \begin{pmatrix} e^t & e^{-t} \\ e^t & 3e^{-t} \end{pmatrix} \quad \text{and} \quad \mathbf{\Phi}^{-1} = \begin{pmatrix} \frac{3}{2}e^{-t} & -\frac{1}{2}e^{-t} \\ -\frac{1}{2}e^t & \frac{1}{2}e^t \end{pmatrix}$$

so that

$$\mathbf{U} = \int \mathbf{\Phi}^{-1} \mathbf{F} \, dt = \int \begin{pmatrix} -2te^{-t} \\ 2te^t \end{pmatrix} dt = \begin{pmatrix} 2te^{-t} + 2e^{-t} \\ 2te^t - 2e^t \end{pmatrix}$$

and

$$\mathbf{X}_p = \mathbf{\Phi} \mathbf{U} = \begin{pmatrix} 4 \\ 8 \end{pmatrix} t + \begin{pmatrix} 0 \\ -4 \end{pmatrix}.$$

3. From

$$\mathbf{X}' = \begin{pmatrix} 3 & -5 \\ 3/4 & -1 \end{pmatrix} \mathbf{X} + \begin{pmatrix} 1 \\ -1 \end{pmatrix} e^{t/2}$$

we obtain

$$\mathbf{X}_c = c_1 \begin{pmatrix} 10 \\ 3 \end{pmatrix} e^{3t/2} + c_2 \begin{pmatrix} 2 \\ 1 \end{pmatrix} e^{t/2}.$$

Then

$$\Phi = \begin{pmatrix} 10e^{3t/2} & 2e^{t/2} \\ 3e^{3t/2} & e^{t/2} \end{pmatrix} \quad \text{and} \quad \Phi^{-1} = \begin{pmatrix} \frac{1}{4}e^{-3t/2} & -\frac{1}{2}e^{-3t/2} \\ -\frac{3}{4}e^{-t/2} & \frac{5}{2}e^{-t/2} \end{pmatrix}$$

so that

$$\mathbf{U} = \int \Phi^{-1}\mathbf{F}\, dt = \int \begin{pmatrix} \frac{3}{4}e^{-t} \\ -\frac{13}{4} \end{pmatrix} dt = \begin{pmatrix} -\frac{3}{4}e^{-t} \\ -\frac{13}{4}t \end{pmatrix}$$

and

$$\mathbf{X}_p = \Phi\mathbf{U} = \begin{pmatrix} -13/2 \\ -13/4 \end{pmatrix} te^{t/2} + \begin{pmatrix} -15/2 \\ -9/4 \end{pmatrix} e^{t/2}.$$

4. From

$$\mathbf{X}' = \begin{pmatrix} 2 & -1 \\ 4 & 2 \end{pmatrix} \mathbf{X} + \begin{pmatrix} \sin 2t \\ 2\cos 2t \end{pmatrix}$$

we obtain

$$\mathbf{X}_c = c_1 \begin{pmatrix} -\sin 2t \\ 2\cos 2t \end{pmatrix} e^{2t} + c_2 \begin{pmatrix} \cos 2t \\ 2\sin 2t \end{pmatrix} e^{2t}.$$

Then

$$\Phi = \begin{pmatrix} -e^{2t}\sin 2t & e^{2t}\cos 2t \\ 2e^{2t}\cos 2t & 2e^{2t}\sin 2t \end{pmatrix} \quad \text{and} \quad \Phi^{-1} = \begin{pmatrix} -\frac{1}{2}e^{-2t}\sin 2t & \frac{1}{4}e^{-2t}\cos 2t \\ \frac{1}{2}e^{-2t}\cos 2t & \frac{1}{4}e^{-2t}\sin 2t \end{pmatrix}$$

so that

$$\mathbf{U} = \int \Phi^{-1}\mathbf{F}\, dt = \int \begin{pmatrix} \frac{1}{2}\cos 4t \\ \frac{1}{2}\sin 4t \end{pmatrix} dt = \begin{pmatrix} \frac{1}{8}\sin 4t \\ -\frac{1}{8}\cos 4t \end{pmatrix}$$

and

$$\mathbf{X}_p = \Phi\mathbf{U} = \begin{pmatrix} -\frac{1}{8}\sin 2t\cos 4t - \frac{1}{8}\cos 2t\cos 4t \\ \frac{1}{4}\cos 2t\sin 4t - \frac{1}{4}\sin 2t\cos 4t \end{pmatrix} e^{2t}.$$

5. From

$$\mathbf{X}' = \begin{pmatrix} 0 & 2 \\ -1 & 3 \end{pmatrix} \mathbf{X} + \begin{pmatrix} 1 \\ -1 \end{pmatrix} e^{t}$$

we obtain

$$\mathbf{X}_c = c_1 \begin{pmatrix} 2 \\ 1 \end{pmatrix} e^{t} + c_2 \begin{pmatrix} 1 \\ 1 \end{pmatrix} e^{2t}.$$

Then

$$\Phi = \begin{pmatrix} 2e^{t} & e^{2t} \\ e^{t} & e^{2t} \end{pmatrix} \quad \text{and} \quad \Phi^{-1} = \begin{pmatrix} e^{-t} & -e^{-t} \\ -e^{-2t} & 2e^{-2t} \end{pmatrix}$$

so that

$$\mathbf{U} = \int \Phi^{-1}\mathbf{F}\, dt = \int \begin{pmatrix} 2 \\ -3e^{-t} \end{pmatrix} dt = \begin{pmatrix} 2t \\ 3e^{-t} \end{pmatrix}$$

and

$$\mathbf{X}_p = \Phi\mathbf{U} = \begin{pmatrix} 4 \\ 2 \end{pmatrix} te^{t} + \begin{pmatrix} 3 \\ 3 \end{pmatrix} e^{t}.$$

6. From

$$\mathbf{X}' = \begin{pmatrix} 0 & 2 \\ -1 & 3 \end{pmatrix} \mathbf{X} + \begin{pmatrix} 2 \\ e^{-3t} \end{pmatrix}$$

we obtain

$$\mathbf{X}_c = c_1 \begin{pmatrix} 2 \\ 1 \end{pmatrix} e^t + c_2 \begin{pmatrix} 1 \\ 1 \end{pmatrix} e^{2t}.$$

Then

$$\mathbf{\Phi} = \begin{pmatrix} 2e^t & e^{2t} \\ e^t & e^{2t} \end{pmatrix} \quad \text{and} \quad \mathbf{\Phi}^{-1} = \begin{pmatrix} e^{-t} & -e^{-t} \\ -e^{-2t} & 2e^{-2t} \end{pmatrix}$$

so that

$$\mathbf{U} = \int \mathbf{\Phi}^{-1} \mathbf{F} \, dt = \int \begin{pmatrix} 2e^{-t} - e^{-4t} \\ -2e^{-2t} + 2e^{-5t} \end{pmatrix} dt = \begin{pmatrix} -2e^{-t} + \frac{1}{4}e^{-4t} \\ e^{-2t} - \frac{2}{5}e^{-5t} \end{pmatrix}$$

and

$$\mathbf{X}_p = \mathbf{\Phi}\mathbf{U} = \begin{pmatrix} \frac{1}{10}e^{-3t} - 3 \\ -\frac{3}{20}e^{-3t} - 1 \end{pmatrix}.$$

7. From

$$\mathbf{X}' = \begin{pmatrix} 1 & 8 \\ 1 & -1 \end{pmatrix} \mathbf{X} + \begin{pmatrix} 12 \\ 12 \end{pmatrix} t$$

we obtain

$$\mathbf{X}_c = c_1 \begin{pmatrix} 4 \\ 1 \end{pmatrix} e^{3t} + c_2 \begin{pmatrix} -2 \\ 1 \end{pmatrix} e^{-3t}.$$

Then

$$\mathbf{\Phi} = \begin{pmatrix} 4e^{3t} & -2e^{-3t} \\ e^{3t} & e^{-3t} \end{pmatrix} \quad \text{and} \quad \mathbf{\Phi}^{-1} = \begin{pmatrix} \frac{1}{6}e^{-3t} & \frac{1}{3}e^{-3t} \\ -\frac{1}{6}e^{3t} & \frac{2}{3}e^{3t} \end{pmatrix}$$

so that

$$\mathbf{U} = \int \mathbf{\Phi}^{-1} \mathbf{F} \, dt = \int \begin{pmatrix} 6te^{-3t} \\ 6te^{3t} \end{pmatrix} dt = \begin{pmatrix} -2te^{-3t} - \frac{2}{3}e^{-3t} \\ 2te^{3t} - \frac{2}{3}e^{3t} \end{pmatrix}$$

and

$$\mathbf{X}_p = \mathbf{\Phi}\mathbf{U} = \begin{pmatrix} -12 \\ 0 \end{pmatrix} t + \begin{pmatrix} -4/3 \\ -4/3 \end{pmatrix}.$$

8. From

$$\mathbf{X}' = \begin{pmatrix} 1 & 8 \\ 1 & -1 \end{pmatrix} \mathbf{X} + \begin{pmatrix} e^{-t} \\ te^t \end{pmatrix}$$

we obtain

$$\mathbf{X}_c = c_1 \begin{pmatrix} 4 \\ 1 \end{pmatrix} e^{3t} + c_2 \begin{pmatrix} -2 \\ 1 \end{pmatrix} e^{-3t}.$$

Then

$$\Phi = \begin{pmatrix} 4e^{3t} & -2e^{3t} \\ e^{3t} & e^{-3t} \end{pmatrix} \quad \text{and} \quad \Phi^{-1} = \begin{pmatrix} \frac{1}{6}e^{-3t} & \frac{1}{3}e^{-3t} \\ -\frac{1}{6}e^{3t} & \frac{2}{3}e^{3t} \end{pmatrix}$$

so that

$$U = \int \Phi^{-1}F\, dt = \int \begin{pmatrix} \frac{1}{6}e^{-4t} + \frac{1}{3}te^{-2t} \\ -\frac{1}{6}e^{2t} + \frac{2}{3}te^{4t} \end{pmatrix} dt = \begin{pmatrix} -\frac{1}{24}e^{-4t} - \frac{1}{6}te^{-2t} - \frac{1}{12}e^{-2t} \\ -\frac{1}{12}e^{2t} + \frac{1}{6}te^{4t} - \frac{1}{24}e^{4t} \end{pmatrix}$$

and

$$X_p = \Phi U = \begin{pmatrix} -te^t - \frac{1}{4}e^t \\ -\frac{1}{8}e^{-t} - \frac{1}{8}e^t \end{pmatrix}.$$

9. From

$$X' = \begin{pmatrix} 3 & 2 \\ -2 & -1 \end{pmatrix} X + \begin{pmatrix} 2 \\ 1 \end{pmatrix} e^{-t}$$

we obtain

$$X_c = c_1 \begin{pmatrix} 1 \\ -1 \end{pmatrix} e^t + c_2 \left[\begin{pmatrix} 1 \\ -1 \end{pmatrix} te^t + \begin{pmatrix} 0 \\ 1/2 \end{pmatrix} e^t \right].$$

Then

$$\Phi = \begin{pmatrix} e^t & te^t \\ -e^t & \frac{1}{2}e^t - te^t \end{pmatrix} \quad \text{and} \quad \Phi^{-1} = \begin{pmatrix} e^{-t} - 2te^{-t} & -2te^{-t} \\ 2e^{-t} & 2e^{-t} \end{pmatrix}$$

so that

$$U = \int \Phi^{-1}F\, dt = \int \begin{pmatrix} 2e^{-2t} - 6te^{-2t} \\ 6e^{-2t} \end{pmatrix} dt = \begin{pmatrix} \frac{1}{2}e^{-2t} + 3te^{-2t} \\ -3e^{-2t} \end{pmatrix}$$

and

$$X_p = \Phi U = \begin{pmatrix} 1/2 \\ -2 \end{pmatrix} e^{-t}.$$

10. From

$$X' = \begin{pmatrix} 3 & 2 \\ -2 & -1 \end{pmatrix} X + \begin{pmatrix} 1 \\ 1 \end{pmatrix}$$

we obtain

$$X_c = c_1 \begin{pmatrix} 1 \\ -1 \end{pmatrix} e^t + c_2 \left[\begin{pmatrix} 1 \\ -1 \end{pmatrix} te^t + \begin{pmatrix} 0 \\ 1/2 \end{pmatrix} e^t \right].$$

Then

$$\Phi = \begin{pmatrix} e^t & te^t \\ -e^t & \frac{1}{2}e^t - te^t \end{pmatrix} \quad \text{and} \quad \Phi^{-1} = \begin{pmatrix} e^{-t} - 2te^{-t} & -2te^{-t} \\ 2e^{-t} & 2e^{-t} \end{pmatrix}$$

so that

$$U = \int \Phi^{-1}F\, dt = \int \begin{pmatrix} e^{-t} - 4te^{-t} \\ 2e^{-t} \end{pmatrix} dt = \begin{pmatrix} 3e^{-t} + 4te^{-t} \\ -2e^{-t} \end{pmatrix}$$

345

and

$$\mathbf{X}_p = \mathbf{\Phi U} = \begin{pmatrix} 3 \\ -5 \end{pmatrix}.$$

11. From

$$\mathbf{X}' = \begin{pmatrix} 0 & -1 \\ 1 & 0 \end{pmatrix} \mathbf{X} + \begin{pmatrix} \sec t \\ 0 \end{pmatrix}$$

we obtain

$$\mathbf{X}_c = c_1 \begin{pmatrix} \cos t \\ \sin t \end{pmatrix} + c_2 \begin{pmatrix} \sin t \\ -\cos t \end{pmatrix}.$$

Then

$$\mathbf{\Phi} = \begin{pmatrix} \cos t & \sin t \\ \sin t & -\cos t \end{pmatrix} \quad \text{and} \quad \mathbf{\Phi}^{-1} = \begin{pmatrix} \cos t & \sin t \\ \sin t & -\cos t \end{pmatrix}$$

so that

$$\mathbf{U} = \int \mathbf{\Phi}^{-1} \mathbf{F} \, dt = \int \begin{pmatrix} 1 \\ \tan t \end{pmatrix} dt = \begin{pmatrix} t \\ \ln|\sec t| \end{pmatrix}$$

and

$$\mathbf{X}_p = \mathbf{\Phi U} = \begin{pmatrix} t\cos t + \sin t \ln|\sec t| \\ t\sin t - \cos t \ln|\sec t| \end{pmatrix}.$$

12. From

$$\mathbf{X}' = \begin{pmatrix} 1 & -1 \\ 1 & 1 \end{pmatrix} \mathbf{X} + \begin{pmatrix} 3 \\ 3 \end{pmatrix} e^t$$

we obtain

$$\mathbf{X}_c = c_1 \begin{pmatrix} -\sin t \\ \cos t \end{pmatrix} e^t + c_2 \begin{pmatrix} \cos t \\ \sin t \end{pmatrix} e^t.$$

Then

$$\mathbf{\Phi} = \begin{pmatrix} -\sin t & \cos t \\ \cos t & \sin t \end{pmatrix} e^t \quad \text{and} \quad \mathbf{\Phi}^{-1} = \begin{pmatrix} -\sin t & \cos t \\ \cos t & \sin t \end{pmatrix} e^{-t}$$

so that

$$\mathbf{U} = \int \mathbf{\Phi}^{-1} \mathbf{F} \, dt = \int \begin{pmatrix} -3\sin t + 3\cos t \\ 3\cos t + 3\sin t \end{pmatrix} dt = \begin{pmatrix} 3\cos t + 3\sin t \\ 3\sin t - 3\cos t \end{pmatrix}$$

and

$$\mathbf{X}_p = \mathbf{\Phi U} = \begin{pmatrix} -3 \\ 3 \end{pmatrix} e^t.$$

13. From

$$\mathbf{X}' = \begin{pmatrix} 1 & -1 \\ 1 & 1 \end{pmatrix} \mathbf{X} + \begin{pmatrix} \cos t \\ \sin t \end{pmatrix} e^t$$

we obtain

$$\mathbf{X}_c = c_1 \begin{pmatrix} -\sin t \\ \cos t \end{pmatrix} e^t + c_2 \begin{pmatrix} \cos t \\ \sin t \end{pmatrix} e^t.$$

Then

$$\mathbf{\Phi} = \begin{pmatrix} -\sin t & \cos t \\ \cos t & \sin t \end{pmatrix} e^t \quad \text{and} \quad \mathbf{\Phi}^{-1} = \begin{pmatrix} -\sin t & \cos t \\ \cos t & \sin t \end{pmatrix} e^{-t}$$

so that

$$\mathbf{U} = \int \mathbf{\Phi}^{-1} \mathbf{F} \, dt = \int \begin{pmatrix} 0 \\ 1 \end{pmatrix} dt = \begin{pmatrix} 0 \\ t \end{pmatrix}$$

and

$$\mathbf{X}_p = \mathbf{\Phi} \mathbf{U} = \begin{pmatrix} \cos t \\ \sin t \end{pmatrix} t e^t.$$

14. From

$$\mathbf{X}' = \begin{pmatrix} 2 & -2 \\ 8 & -6 \end{pmatrix} \mathbf{X} + \begin{pmatrix} 1 \\ 3 \end{pmatrix} \frac{1}{t} e^{-2t}$$

we obtain

$$\mathbf{X}_c = c_1 \begin{pmatrix} 1 \\ 2 \end{pmatrix} e^{-2t} + c_2 \left[\begin{pmatrix} 1 \\ 2 \end{pmatrix} t e^{-2t} + \begin{pmatrix} 1/2 \\ 1/2 \end{pmatrix} e^{-2t} \right].$$

Then

$$\mathbf{\Phi} = \begin{pmatrix} 1 & 2t+1 \\ 2 & 4t+1 \end{pmatrix} e^{-2t} \quad \text{and} \quad \mathbf{\Phi}^{-1} = \begin{pmatrix} -(4t+1) & 2t+1 \\ 2 & -1 \end{pmatrix} e^{2t}$$

so that

$$\mathbf{U} = \int \mathbf{\Phi}^{-1} \mathbf{F} \, dt = \int \begin{pmatrix} 2t + 2\ln t \\ -\ln t \end{pmatrix} dt$$

and

$$\mathbf{X}_p = \mathbf{\Phi} \mathbf{U} = \begin{pmatrix} 2t + \ln t - 2t \ln t \\ 4t + 3\ln t - 4t \ln t \end{pmatrix} e^{-2t}.$$

15. From

$$\mathbf{X}' = \begin{pmatrix} 0 & 1 \\ -1 & 0 \end{pmatrix} \mathbf{X} + \begin{pmatrix} 0 \\ \sec t \tan t \end{pmatrix}$$

we obtain

$$\mathbf{X}_c = c_1 \begin{pmatrix} \cos t \\ -\sin t \end{pmatrix} + c_2 \begin{pmatrix} \sin t \\ \cos t \end{pmatrix}.$$

Then

$$\mathbf{\Phi} = \begin{pmatrix} \cos t & \sin t \\ -\sin t & \cos t \end{pmatrix} t \quad \text{and} \quad \mathbf{\Phi}^{-1} = \begin{pmatrix} \cos t & -\sin t \\ \sin t & \cos t \end{pmatrix}$$

so that

$$\mathbf{U} = \int \mathbf{\Phi}^{-1}\mathbf{F}\, dt = \int \begin{pmatrix} -\tan^2 t \\ \tan t \end{pmatrix} dt = \begin{pmatrix} t - \tan t \\ \ln|\sec t| \end{pmatrix}$$

and

$$\mathbf{X}_p = \mathbf{\Phi}\mathbf{U} = \begin{pmatrix} \cos t \\ -\sin t \end{pmatrix} t + \begin{pmatrix} -\sin t \\ \sin t \tan t \end{pmatrix} + \begin{pmatrix} \sin t \\ \cos t \end{pmatrix} \ln|\sec t|.$$

16. From

$$\mathbf{X}' = \begin{pmatrix} 0 & 1 \\ -1 & 0 \end{pmatrix} \mathbf{X} + \begin{pmatrix} 1 \\ \cot t \end{pmatrix}$$

we obtain

$$\mathbf{X}_c = c_1 \begin{pmatrix} \cos t \\ -\sin t \end{pmatrix} + c_2 \begin{pmatrix} \sin t \\ \cos t \end{pmatrix}.$$

Then

$$\mathbf{\Phi} = \begin{pmatrix} \cos t & \sin t \\ -\sin t & \cos t \end{pmatrix} \quad \text{and} \quad \mathbf{\Phi}^{-1} = \begin{pmatrix} \cos t & -\sin t \\ \sin t & \cos t \end{pmatrix}$$

so that

$$\mathbf{U} = \int \mathbf{\Phi}^{-1}\mathbf{F}\, dt = \int \begin{pmatrix} 0 \\ \csc t \end{pmatrix} dt = \begin{pmatrix} 0 \\ \ln|\csc t - \cot t| \end{pmatrix}$$

and

$$\mathbf{X}_p = \mathbf{\Phi}\mathbf{U} = \begin{pmatrix} \sin t \ln|\csc t - \cot t| \\ \cos t \ln|\csc t - \cot t| \end{pmatrix}.$$

17. From

$$\mathbf{X}' = \begin{pmatrix} 1 & 2 \\ -1/2 & 1 \end{pmatrix} \mathbf{X} + \begin{pmatrix} \csc t \\ \sec t \end{pmatrix} e^t$$

we obtain

$$\mathbf{X}_c = c_1 \begin{pmatrix} 2\sin t \\ \cos t \end{pmatrix} e^t + c_2 \begin{pmatrix} 2\cos t \\ -\sin t \end{pmatrix} e^t.$$

Then

$$\mathbf{\Phi} = \begin{pmatrix} 2\sin t & 2\cos t \\ \cos t & -\sin t \end{pmatrix} e^t \quad \text{and} \quad \mathbf{\Phi}^{-1} = \begin{pmatrix} \frac{1}{2}\sin t & \cos t \\ \frac{1}{2}\cos t & -\sin t \end{pmatrix} e^{-t}$$

so that

$$\mathbf{U} = \int \mathbf{\Phi}^{-1}\mathbf{F}\, dt = \int \begin{pmatrix} \frac{3}{2} \\ \frac{1}{2}\cos t - \tan t \end{pmatrix} dt = \begin{pmatrix} \frac{3}{2}t \\ \frac{1}{2}\ln|\sin t| - \ln|\sec t| \end{pmatrix}$$

and

$$\mathbf{X}_p = \mathbf{\Phi}\mathbf{U} = \begin{pmatrix} 3\sin t \\ \frac{3}{2}\cos t \end{pmatrix} te^t + \begin{pmatrix} \cos t \\ -\frac{1}{2}\sin t \end{pmatrix} \ln|\sin t| + \begin{pmatrix} -2\cos t \\ \sin t \end{pmatrix} \ln|\sec t|.$$

18. From

$$\mathbf{X}' = \begin{pmatrix} 1 & -2 \\ 1 & -1 \end{pmatrix} \mathbf{X} + \begin{pmatrix} \tan t \\ 1 \end{pmatrix}$$

we obtain

$$\mathbf{X}_c = c_1 \begin{pmatrix} \cos t - \sin t \\ \cos t \end{pmatrix} + c_2 \begin{pmatrix} \cos t + \sin t \\ \sin t \end{pmatrix}.$$

Then

$$\boldsymbol{\Phi} = \begin{pmatrix} \cos t - \sin t & \cos t + \sin t \\ \cos t & \sin t \end{pmatrix} \quad \text{and} \quad \boldsymbol{\Phi}^{-1} = \begin{pmatrix} -\sin t & \cos t + \sin t \\ \cos t & \sin t - \cos t \end{pmatrix}$$

so that

$$\mathbf{U} = \int \boldsymbol{\Phi}^{-1}\mathbf{F}\,dt = \int \begin{pmatrix} 2\cos t + \sin t - \sec t \\ 2\sin t - \cos t \end{pmatrix} dt = \begin{pmatrix} 2\sin t - \cos t - \ln|\sec t + \tan t| \\ -2\cos t - \sin t \end{pmatrix}$$

and

$$\mathbf{X}_p = \boldsymbol{\Phi}\mathbf{U} = \begin{pmatrix} 3\sin t \cos t - \cos^2 t - 2\sin^2 t + (\sin t - \cos t)\ln|\sec t + \tan t| \\ \sin^2 t - \cos^2 t - \cos t(\ln|\sec t + \tan t|) \end{pmatrix}.$$

19. From

$$\mathbf{X}' = \begin{pmatrix} 1 & 1 & 0 \\ 1 & 1 & 0 \\ 0 & 0 & 3 \end{pmatrix} \mathbf{X} + \begin{pmatrix} e^t \\ e^{2t} \\ te^{3t} \end{pmatrix}$$

we obtain

$$\mathbf{X}_c = c_1 \begin{pmatrix} 1 \\ -1 \\ 0 \end{pmatrix} + c_2 \begin{pmatrix} 1 \\ 1 \\ 0 \end{pmatrix} e^{2t} + c_3 \begin{pmatrix} 0 \\ 0 \\ 1 \end{pmatrix} e^{3t}.$$

Then

$$\boldsymbol{\Phi} = \begin{pmatrix} 1 & e^{2t} & 0 \\ -1 & e^{2t} & 0 \\ 0 & 0 & e^{3t} \end{pmatrix} \quad \text{and} \quad \boldsymbol{\Phi}^{-1} = \begin{pmatrix} \frac{1}{2} & -\frac{1}{2} & 0 \\ \frac{1}{2}e^{-2t} & \frac{1}{2}e^{-2t} & 0 \\ 0 & 0 & e^{-3t} \end{pmatrix}$$

so that

$$\mathbf{U} = \int \boldsymbol{\Phi}^{-1}\mathbf{F}\,dt = \int \begin{pmatrix} \frac{1}{2}e^t - \frac{1}{2}e^{2t} \\ \frac{1}{2}e^{-t} + \frac{1}{2} \\ t \end{pmatrix} dt = \begin{pmatrix} \frac{1}{2}e^t - \frac{1}{4}e^{2t} \\ -\frac{1}{2}e^{-t} + \frac{1}{2}t \\ \frac{1}{2}t^2 \end{pmatrix}$$

and

$$\mathbf{X}_p = \boldsymbol{\Phi}\mathbf{U} = \begin{pmatrix} -\frac{1}{4}e^{2t} + \frac{1}{2}te^{2t} \\ -e^t + \frac{1}{4}e^{2t} + \frac{1}{2}te^{2t} \\ \frac{1}{2}t^2 e^{3t} \end{pmatrix}.$$

20. From

$$\mathbf{X}' = \begin{pmatrix} 3 & -1 & -1 \\ 1 & 1 & -1 \\ 1 & -1 & 1 \end{pmatrix} \mathbf{X} + \begin{pmatrix} 0 \\ t \\ 2e^t \end{pmatrix}$$

we obtain

$$\mathbf{X}_c = c_1 \begin{pmatrix} 1 \\ 1 \\ 1 \end{pmatrix} e^t + c_2 \begin{pmatrix} 1 \\ 1 \\ 0 \end{pmatrix} e^{2t} + c_3 \begin{pmatrix} 1 \\ 0 \\ 1 \end{pmatrix} e^{2t}.$$

Then

$$\mathbf{\Phi} = \begin{pmatrix} e^t & e^{2t} & e^{2t} \\ e^t & e^{2t} & 0 \\ e^t & 0 & e^{2t} \end{pmatrix} \quad \text{and} \quad \mathbf{\Phi}^{-1} = \begin{pmatrix} -e^{-t} & e^{-t} & e^{-t} \\ e^{-2t} & 0 & -e^{-2t} \\ e^{-2t} & -e^{-2t} & 0 \end{pmatrix}$$

so that

$$\mathbf{U} = \int \mathbf{\Phi}^{-1}\mathbf{F}\,dt = \int \begin{pmatrix} te^{-t} + 2 \\ -2e^{-t} \\ -te^{-2t} \end{pmatrix} dt = \begin{pmatrix} -te^{-t} - e^{-t} + 2t \\ 2e^{-t} \\ \frac{1}{2}te^{-2t} + \frac{1}{4}e^{-2t} \end{pmatrix}$$

and

$$\mathbf{X}_p = \mathbf{\Phi}\mathbf{U} = \begin{pmatrix} -1/2 \\ -1 \\ -1/2 \end{pmatrix} t + \begin{pmatrix} -3/4 \\ -1 \\ -3/4 \end{pmatrix} + \begin{pmatrix} 2 \\ 2 \\ 0 \end{pmatrix} e^t + \begin{pmatrix} 2 \\ 2 \\ 2 \end{pmatrix} te^t.$$

21. From

$$\mathbf{X}' = \begin{pmatrix} 3 & -1 \\ -1 & 3 \end{pmatrix} \mathbf{X} + \begin{pmatrix} 4e^{2t} \\ 4e^{4t} \end{pmatrix}$$

we obtain

$$\mathbf{\Phi} = \begin{pmatrix} -e^{4t} & e^{2t} \\ e^{4t} & e^{2t} \end{pmatrix}, \quad \mathbf{\Phi}^{-1} = \begin{pmatrix} -\frac{1}{2}e^{-4t} & \frac{1}{2}e^{4t} \\ \frac{1}{2}e^{-2t} & \frac{1}{2}e^{2t} \end{pmatrix},$$

and

$$\mathbf{X} = \mathbf{\Phi}\mathbf{\Phi}^{-1}(0)\mathbf{X}(0) + \mathbf{\Phi}\int_0^t \mathbf{\Phi}^{-1}\mathbf{F}\,ds = \mathbf{\Phi} \cdot \begin{pmatrix} 0 \\ 1 \end{pmatrix} + \mathbf{\Phi} \cdot \begin{pmatrix} e^{-2t} + 2t - 1 \\ e^{2t} + 2t - 1 \end{pmatrix}$$

$$= \begin{pmatrix} 2 \\ 2 \end{pmatrix} te^{2t} + \begin{pmatrix} -1 \\ 1 \end{pmatrix} e^{2t} + \begin{pmatrix} -2 \\ 2 \end{pmatrix} te^{4t} + \begin{pmatrix} 2 \\ 0 \end{pmatrix} e^{4t}.$$

22. From

$$\mathbf{X}' = \begin{pmatrix} 1 & -1 \\ 1 & -1 \end{pmatrix} \mathbf{X} + \begin{pmatrix} 1/t \\ 1/t \end{pmatrix}$$

we obtain

$$\mathbf{\Phi} = \begin{pmatrix} 1 & 1+t \\ 1 & t \end{pmatrix}, \quad \mathbf{\Phi}^{-1} = \begin{pmatrix} -t & 1+t \\ 1 & -1 \end{pmatrix},$$

and

$$\mathbf{X} = \mathbf{\Phi}\mathbf{\Phi}^{-1}(1)\mathbf{X}(1) + \mathbf{\Phi}\int_1^t \mathbf{\Phi}^{-1}\mathbf{F}\,ds = \mathbf{\Phi}\cdot\begin{pmatrix} -4 \\ 3 \end{pmatrix} + \mathbf{\Phi}\cdot\begin{pmatrix} \ln t \\ 0 \end{pmatrix} = \begin{pmatrix} 3 \\ 3 \end{pmatrix}t - \begin{pmatrix} 1 \\ 4 \end{pmatrix} + \begin{pmatrix} 1 \\ 1 \end{pmatrix}\ln t.$$

23. From

$$\mathbf{X}' = \begin{pmatrix} 4 & 1 \\ 6 & 5 \end{pmatrix}\mathbf{X} + \begin{pmatrix} 50e^{7t} \\ 0 \end{pmatrix}$$

we obtain

$$\mathbf{\Psi} = \begin{pmatrix} \frac{3}{5}e^{2t} + \frac{2}{5}e^{7t} & -\frac{1}{5}e^{2t} + \frac{1}{5}e^{7t} \\ -\frac{6}{5}e^{2t} + \frac{6}{5}e^{7t} & \frac{2}{5}e^{2t} + \frac{3}{5}e^{7t} \end{pmatrix}, \quad \mathbf{\Psi}^{-1} = \begin{pmatrix} \frac{2}{5}e^{-7t} + \frac{3}{5}e^{-2t} & \frac{1}{5}e^{-7t} - \frac{1}{5}e^{-2t} \\ \frac{6}{5}e^{-7t} - \frac{6}{5}e^{-2t} & \frac{3}{5}e^{-7t} + \frac{2}{5}e^{-2t} \end{pmatrix},$$

and

$$\mathbf{X} = \mathbf{\Psi}\mathbf{X}(0) + \mathbf{\Psi}\int_0^t \mathbf{\Psi}^{-1}\mathbf{F}\,ds = \mathbf{\Psi}\cdot\begin{pmatrix} 5 \\ -5 \end{pmatrix} + \mathbf{\Psi}\cdot\begin{pmatrix} 20t + 6e^{5t} - 6 \\ 60t - 12e^{5t} + 12 \end{pmatrix}$$

$$= \begin{pmatrix} -2 \\ 4 \end{pmatrix}e^{2t} + \begin{pmatrix} 7 \\ -9 \end{pmatrix}e^{7t} + \begin{pmatrix} 20 \\ 60 \end{pmatrix}te^{7t}.$$

24. From

$$\mathbf{X}' = \begin{pmatrix} 3 & -2 \\ 5 & -3 \end{pmatrix}\mathbf{X} + \begin{pmatrix} 2 \\ 3 \end{pmatrix}$$

we obtain

$$\mathbf{\Psi} = \begin{pmatrix} \sin t - 3\cos t & 2\cos t \\ -5\cos t & \sin t + 3\cos t \end{pmatrix}, \quad \mathbf{\Psi}^{-1} = \begin{pmatrix} \sin t + 3\cos t & -2\cos t \\ 5\cos t & \sin t - 3\cos t \end{pmatrix},$$

and

$$\mathbf{X} = \mathbf{\Psi}\mathbf{X}(\pi/2) + \mathbf{\Psi}\int_{\pi/2}^t \mathbf{\Psi}^{-1}\mathbf{F}\,ds = \mathbf{\Psi}\cdot\begin{pmatrix} 0 \\ 0 \end{pmatrix} + \mathbf{\Psi}\cdot\begin{pmatrix} -2\cos t \\ \sin t - 3\cos t - 1 \end{pmatrix}$$

$$= \begin{pmatrix} 0 \\ 1 \end{pmatrix} - \begin{pmatrix} 2 \\ 3 \end{pmatrix}\cos t - \begin{pmatrix} 0 \\ 1 \end{pmatrix}\sin t.$$

25. (a) By Kirchoff's first and second (on each loop) laws, we obtain $i = i_2 + i_3$, $E = i_1R_1 + i_3R_2 + L_2i_1'$, and $E = i_1R_1 + L_1i_2' + L_2i_1'$ so that

$$\frac{d}{dt}\begin{pmatrix} i_1 \\ i_2 \end{pmatrix} = \begin{pmatrix} -(R_1 + R_2)/L_2 & R_2/L_2 \\ R_2/L_1 & -R_2/L_1 \end{pmatrix}\begin{pmatrix} i_1 \\ i_2 \end{pmatrix} + \begin{pmatrix} E/L_2 \\ 0 \end{pmatrix}.$$

(b) Let $\mathbf{I} = \begin{pmatrix} i_1 \\ i_2 \end{pmatrix}$ so that

$$\mathbf{I}' = \begin{pmatrix} -11 & 3 \\ 3 & -3 \end{pmatrix}\mathbf{I} + \begin{pmatrix} 100\sin t \\ 0 \end{pmatrix}$$

and

$$X_c = c_1 \begin{pmatrix} 1 \\ 3 \end{pmatrix} e^{-2t} + c_2 \begin{pmatrix} 3 \\ -1 \end{pmatrix} e^{-12t}.$$

Then

$$\Phi = \begin{pmatrix} e^{-2t} & 3e^{-12t} \\ 3e^{-2t} & -e^{-12t} \end{pmatrix}, \quad \Phi^{-1} = \begin{pmatrix} \frac{1}{10}e^{2t} & \frac{3}{10}e^{2t} \\ \frac{3}{10}e^{12t} & -\frac{1}{10}e^{12t} \end{pmatrix},$$

$$U = \int \Phi^{-1} F \, dt = \int \begin{pmatrix} 10e^{2t}\sin t \\ 30e^{12t}\sin t \end{pmatrix} dt = \begin{pmatrix} 2e^{2t}(2\sin t - \cos t) \\ \frac{6}{29}e^{12t}(12\sin t - \cos t) \end{pmatrix},$$

and

$$I_p = \Phi U = \begin{pmatrix} \frac{332}{29}\sin t - \frac{76}{29}\cos t \\ \frac{276}{29}\sin t - \frac{168}{29}\cos t \end{pmatrix}$$

so that

$$I = c_1 \begin{pmatrix} 1 \\ 3 \end{pmatrix} e^{-2t} + c_2 \begin{pmatrix} 3 \\ -1 \end{pmatrix} e^{-12t} + I_p.$$

If $I(0) = \begin{pmatrix} 0 \\ 0 \end{pmatrix}$ then $c_1 = 2$ and $c_2 = \frac{6}{29}$.

Exercises 8.9

1. For $A = \begin{pmatrix} 0 & 1 \\ 1 & 0 \end{pmatrix}$ we have

$$A^2 = \begin{pmatrix} 0 & 1 \\ 1 & 0 \end{pmatrix} \begin{pmatrix} 0 & 1 \\ 1 & 0 \end{pmatrix} = \begin{pmatrix} 1 & 0 \\ 0 & 1 \end{pmatrix} = I$$

$$A^3 = AA^2 = \begin{pmatrix} 0 & 1 \\ 1 & 0 \end{pmatrix} I = \begin{pmatrix} 0 & 1 \\ 1 & 0 \end{pmatrix} = A$$

$$A^4 = (A^2)^2 = I$$

$$A^5 = AA^4 = AI = A$$

and so on. In general

$$A^k = \begin{cases} A, & k = 1, 3, 5, \ldots \\ I, & k = 2, 4, 6, \ldots \end{cases}.$$

Thus

$$e^{tA} = I + \frac{A}{1!}t + \frac{A^2}{2!}t^2 + \frac{A^3}{3!}t^3 + \cdots$$

$$= I + At + \frac{1}{2!}It^2 + \frac{1}{3!}At^3 + \cdots$$

$$= I\left(1 + \frac{1}{2!}t^2 + \frac{1}{4!}t^4 + \cdots\right) + A\left(t + \frac{1}{3!}t^3 + \frac{1}{5!}t^5 + \cdots\right)$$

$$= I\cosh t + A\sinh t = \begin{pmatrix} \cosh t & \sinh t \\ \sinh t & \cosh t \end{pmatrix}$$

and

$$e^{-tA} = \begin{pmatrix} \cosh(-t) & \sinh(-t) \\ \sinh(-t) & \cosh(-t) \end{pmatrix} = \begin{pmatrix} \cosh t & -\sinh t \\ -\sinh t & \cosh t \end{pmatrix}.$$

2. For $A = \begin{pmatrix} 1 & 0 \\ 0 & 2 \end{pmatrix}$ we have

$$A^2 = \begin{pmatrix} 1 & 0 \\ 0 & 2 \end{pmatrix}\begin{pmatrix} 1 & 0 \\ 0 & 2 \end{pmatrix} = \begin{pmatrix} 1 & 0 \\ 0 & 4 \end{pmatrix},$$

$$A^3 = AA^2 = \begin{pmatrix} 1 & 0 \\ 0 & 2 \end{pmatrix}\begin{pmatrix} 1 & 0 \\ 0 & 4 \end{pmatrix} = \begin{pmatrix} 1 & 0 \\ 0 & 8 \end{pmatrix},$$

$$A^4 = AA^3 = \begin{pmatrix} 1 & 0 \\ 0 & 2 \end{pmatrix}\begin{pmatrix} 1 & 0 \\ 0 & 8 \end{pmatrix} = \begin{pmatrix} 1 & 0 \\ 0 & 16 \end{pmatrix},$$

and so on. In general

$$A^k = \begin{pmatrix} 1 & 0 \\ 0 & 2^k \end{pmatrix} \quad \text{for} \quad k = 1, 2, 3, \dots.$$

Thus,

$$e^{tA} = I + \frac{A}{1!}t + \frac{A^2}{2!}t^2 + \frac{A^3}{3!}t^3 + \cdots$$

$$= \begin{pmatrix} 1 & 0 \\ 0 & 1 \end{pmatrix} + \frac{1}{1!}\begin{pmatrix} 1 & 0 \\ 0 & 2 \end{pmatrix}t + \frac{1}{2!}\begin{pmatrix} 1 & 0 \\ 0 & 4 \end{pmatrix}t^2 + \frac{1}{3!}\begin{pmatrix} 1 & 0 \\ 0 & 8 \end{pmatrix}t^3 + \cdots$$

$$= \begin{pmatrix} 1 + t + \frac{t^2}{2!} + \frac{t^3}{3!} + \cdots & 0 \\ 0 & 1 + t + \frac{(2t)^2}{2!} + \frac{(2t)^3}{3!} + \cdots \end{pmatrix} = \begin{pmatrix} e^t & 0 \\ 0 & e^{2t} \end{pmatrix}$$

and

$$e^{-tA} = \begin{pmatrix} e^{-t} & 0 \\ 0 & e^{-2t} \end{pmatrix}.$$

353

Exercises 8.9

3. Using the result of Problem 1

$$\mathbf{X} = \begin{pmatrix} \cosh t & \sinh t \\ \sinh t & \cosh t \end{pmatrix} \begin{pmatrix} c_1 \\ c_2 \end{pmatrix} = c_1 \begin{pmatrix} \cosh t \\ \sinh t \end{pmatrix} + c_2 \begin{pmatrix} \sinh t \\ \cosh t \end{pmatrix}.$$

4. Using the result of Problem 2

$$\mathbf{X} = \begin{pmatrix} e^t & 0 \\ 0 & e^{2t} \end{pmatrix} \begin{pmatrix} c_1 \\ c_2 \end{pmatrix} = c_1 \begin{pmatrix} e^t \\ 0 \end{pmatrix} + c_2 \begin{pmatrix} 0 \\ e^t \end{pmatrix}.$$

5. To solve

$$\mathbf{X}' = \begin{pmatrix} 0 & 1 \\ 1 & 0 \end{pmatrix} \mathbf{X} + \begin{pmatrix} 1 \\ 1 \end{pmatrix}$$

we identify $t_0 = 0$, $\mathbf{F}(s) = \begin{pmatrix} 1 \\ 1 \end{pmatrix}$, and use the results of Problem 1 and equation (3) in the text.

$$\mathbf{X}(t) = e^{t\mathbf{A}}\mathbf{C} + e^{t\mathbf{A}} \int_{t_0}^{t} e^{-s\mathbf{A}}\mathbf{F}(s)\, ds$$

$$= \begin{pmatrix} \cosh t & \sinh t \\ \sinh t & \cosh t \end{pmatrix} \begin{pmatrix} c_1 \\ c_2 \end{pmatrix} + \begin{pmatrix} \cosh t & \sinh t \\ \sinh t & \cosh t \end{pmatrix} \int_0^t \begin{pmatrix} \cosh s & -\sinh s \\ -\sinh s & \cosh s \end{pmatrix} \begin{pmatrix} 1 \\ 1 \end{pmatrix} ds$$

$$= \begin{pmatrix} c_1 \cosh t + c_2 \sinh t \\ c_1 \sinh t + c_2 \cosh t \end{pmatrix} + \begin{pmatrix} \cosh t & \sinh t \\ \sinh t & \cosh t \end{pmatrix} \int_0^t \begin{pmatrix} \cosh s & -\sinh s \\ -\sinh s & \cosh s \end{pmatrix} ds$$

$$= \begin{pmatrix} c_1 \cosh t + c_2 \sinh t \\ c_1 \sinh t + c_2 \cosh t \end{pmatrix} + \begin{pmatrix} \cosh t & \sinh t \\ \sinh t & \cosh t \end{pmatrix} \begin{pmatrix} \sinh s - \cosh s \\ -\cosh s + \sinh s \end{pmatrix} \Big|_0^t$$

$$= \begin{pmatrix} c_1 \cosh t + c_2 \sinh t \\ c_1 \sinh t + c_2 \cosh t \end{pmatrix} + \begin{pmatrix} \cosh t & \sinh t \\ \sinh t & \cosh t \end{pmatrix} \begin{pmatrix} \sinh t - \cosh t \\ -\cosh t + \sinh t \end{pmatrix}$$

$$= \begin{pmatrix} c_1 \cosh t + c_2 \sinh t \\ c_1 \sinh t + c_2 \cosh t \end{pmatrix} + \begin{pmatrix} \sinh^2 t - \cosh^2 t \\ \sinh^2 t - \cosh^2 t \end{pmatrix}$$

$$= c_1 \begin{pmatrix} \cosh t \\ \sinh t \end{pmatrix} + c_2 \begin{pmatrix} \sinh t \\ \cosh t \end{pmatrix} - \begin{pmatrix} 1 \\ 1 \end{pmatrix}.$$

6. To solve

$$\mathbf{X}' = \begin{pmatrix} 0 & 1 \\ 1 & 0 \end{pmatrix} \mathbf{X} + \begin{pmatrix} \cosh t \\ \sinh t \end{pmatrix}$$

we identify $t_0 = 0$, $\mathbf{F}(s) = \begin{pmatrix} \cosh t \\ \sinh t \end{pmatrix}$, and use the results of Problem 1 and equation (3) in the text.

$$\mathbf{X}(t) = e^{t\mathbf{A}}\mathbf{C} + e^{t\mathbf{A}} \int_{t_0}^{t} e^{-s\mathbf{A}}\mathbf{F}(s)\,ds$$

$$= \begin{pmatrix} \cosh t & \sinh t \\ \sinh t & \cosh t \end{pmatrix} \begin{pmatrix} c_1 \\ c_2 \end{pmatrix} + \begin{pmatrix} \cosh t & \sinh t \\ \sinh t & \cosh t \end{pmatrix} \int_0^t \begin{pmatrix} \cosh s & -\sinh s \\ -\sinh s & \cosh s \end{pmatrix} \begin{pmatrix} \cosh s \\ \sinh s \end{pmatrix} ds$$

$$= \begin{pmatrix} c_1 \cosh t + c_2 \sinh t \\ c_1 \sinh t + c_2 \cosh t \end{pmatrix} + \begin{pmatrix} \cosh t & \sinh t \\ \sinh t & \cosh t \end{pmatrix} \int_0^t \begin{pmatrix} 1 \\ 0 \end{pmatrix} ds$$

$$= \begin{pmatrix} c_1 \cosh t + c_2 \sinh t \\ c_1 \sinh t + c_2 \cosh t \end{pmatrix} + \begin{pmatrix} \cosh t & \sinh t \\ \sinh t & \cosh t \end{pmatrix} \begin{pmatrix} s \\ 0 \end{pmatrix} \Big|_0^t$$

$$= \begin{pmatrix} c_1 \cosh t + c_2 \sinh t \\ c_1 \sinh t + c_2 \cosh t \end{pmatrix} + \begin{pmatrix} \cosh t & \sinh t \\ \sinh t & \cosh t \end{pmatrix} \begin{pmatrix} t \\ 0 \end{pmatrix}$$

$$= \begin{pmatrix} c_1 \cosh t + c_2 \sinh t \\ c_1 \sinh t + c_2 \cosh t \end{pmatrix} + \begin{pmatrix} t \cosh t \\ t \sinh t \end{pmatrix} = c_1 \begin{pmatrix} \cosh t \\ \sinh t \end{pmatrix} + c_2 \begin{pmatrix} \sinh t \\ \cosh t \end{pmatrix} + t \begin{pmatrix} \cosh t \\ \sinh t \end{pmatrix}.$$

7. To solve

$$\mathbf{X}' = \begin{pmatrix} 1 & 0 \\ 0 & 2 \end{pmatrix} \mathbf{X} + \begin{pmatrix} t \\ e^{4t} \end{pmatrix}$$

we identify $t_0 = 0$, $\mathbf{F}(s) = \begin{pmatrix} t \\ e^{4t} \end{pmatrix}$, and use the results of Problem 2 and equation (3) in the text.

$$\mathbf{X}(t) = e^{t\mathbf{A}}\mathbf{C} + e^{t\mathbf{A}} \int_{t_0}^{t} e^{-s\mathbf{A}}\mathbf{F}(s)\,ds$$

$$= \begin{pmatrix} e^t & 0 \\ 0 & e^{2t} \end{pmatrix} \begin{pmatrix} c_1 \\ c_2 \end{pmatrix} + \begin{pmatrix} e^t & 0 \\ 0 & e^{2t} \end{pmatrix} \int_0^t \begin{pmatrix} e^{-s} & 0 \\ 0 & e^{-2s} \end{pmatrix} \begin{pmatrix} s \\ e^{4s} \end{pmatrix} ds$$

$$= \begin{pmatrix} c_1 e^t \\ c_2 e^{2t} \end{pmatrix} + \begin{pmatrix} e^t & 0 \\ 0 & e^{2t} \end{pmatrix} \int_0^t \begin{pmatrix} s e^{-s} \\ e^{2s} \end{pmatrix} ds$$

$$= \begin{pmatrix} c_1 e^t \\ c_2 e^{2t} \end{pmatrix} + \begin{pmatrix} e^t & 0 \\ 0 & e^{2t} \end{pmatrix} \begin{pmatrix} -se^{-s} - e^{-s} \\ \frac{1}{2}e^{2s} \end{pmatrix} \Big|_0^t$$

$$= \begin{pmatrix} c_1 e^t \\ c_2 e^{2t} \end{pmatrix} + \begin{pmatrix} e^t & 0 \\ 0 & e^{2t} \end{pmatrix} \begin{pmatrix} -te^{-t} - e^{-t} + 1 \\ \frac{1}{2}e^{2t} - \frac{1}{2} \end{pmatrix}$$

$$= \begin{pmatrix} c_1 e^t \\ c_2 e^{2t} \end{pmatrix} + \begin{pmatrix} -t - 1 + e^t \\ \frac{1}{2}e^{4t} - \frac{1}{2}e^{2t} \end{pmatrix} = c_3 \begin{pmatrix} 1 \\ 0 \end{pmatrix} e^t + c_4 \begin{pmatrix} 0 \\ 1 \end{pmatrix} e^{2t} + \begin{pmatrix} -t - 1 \\ \frac{1}{2}e^{4t} \end{pmatrix}.$$

8. To solve

$$\mathbf{X'} = \begin{pmatrix} 1 & 0 \\ 0 & 2 \end{pmatrix} \mathbf{X} + \begin{pmatrix} 3 \\ -1 \end{pmatrix}$$

we identify $t_0 = 0$, $\mathbf{F}(s) = \begin{pmatrix} 3 \\ -1 \end{pmatrix}$, and use the results of Problem 2 and equation (3) in the text.

$$\mathbf{X}(t) = e^{t\mathbf{A}}\mathbf{C} + e^{t\mathbf{A}} \int_{t_0}^{t} e^{-s\mathbf{A}}\mathbf{F}(s)\,ds$$

$$= \begin{pmatrix} e^t & 0 \\ 0 & e^{2t} \end{pmatrix} \begin{pmatrix} c_1 \\ c_2 \end{pmatrix} + \begin{pmatrix} e^t & 0 \\ 0 & e^{2t} \end{pmatrix} \int_0^t \begin{pmatrix} e^{-s} & 0 \\ 0 & e^{-2s} \end{pmatrix} \begin{pmatrix} 3 \\ -1 \end{pmatrix} ds$$

$$= \begin{pmatrix} c_1 e^t \\ c_2 e^{2t} \end{pmatrix} + \begin{pmatrix} e^t & 0 \\ 0 & e^{2t} \end{pmatrix} \int_0^t \begin{pmatrix} 3e^{-s} \\ -e^{-2s} \end{pmatrix} ds$$

$$= \begin{pmatrix} c_1 e^t \\ c_2 e^{2t} \end{pmatrix} + \begin{pmatrix} e^t & 0 \\ 0 & e^{2t} \end{pmatrix} \begin{pmatrix} -3e^{-s} \\ \frac{1}{2}e^{-2s} \end{pmatrix} \Big|_0^t$$

$$= \begin{pmatrix} c_1 e^t \\ c_2 e^{2t} \end{pmatrix} + \begin{pmatrix} e^t & 0 \\ 0 & e^{2t} \end{pmatrix} \begin{pmatrix} -3e^{-t} - 3 \\ \frac{1}{2}e^{-2t} - \frac{1}{2} \end{pmatrix}$$

$$= \begin{pmatrix} c_1 e^t \\ c_2 e^{2t} \end{pmatrix} + \begin{pmatrix} -3 - 3e^t \\ \frac{1}{2} - \frac{1}{2}e^{2t} \end{pmatrix} = c_3 \begin{pmatrix} 1 \\ 0 \end{pmatrix} e^t + c_4 \begin{pmatrix} 0 \\ 1 \end{pmatrix} e^{2t} + \begin{pmatrix} -3 \\ \frac{1}{2} \end{pmatrix}.$$

9. Solving

$$\begin{vmatrix} 2-\lambda & 1 \\ -3 & 6-\lambda \end{vmatrix} = \lambda^2 - 8\lambda + 15 = (\lambda - 3)(\lambda - 5) = 0$$

we find eigenvalues $\lambda_1 = 3$ and $\lambda_2 = 5$. Corresponding eigenvectors are

$$\mathbf{K}_1 = \begin{pmatrix} 1 \\ 1 \end{pmatrix} \quad \text{and} \quad \mathbf{K}_2 = \begin{pmatrix} 1 \\ 3 \end{pmatrix}.$$

Then

$$\mathbf{P} = \begin{pmatrix} 1 & 1 \\ 1 & 3 \end{pmatrix}, \quad \mathbf{P}^{-1} = \begin{pmatrix} 3/2 & -1/2 \\ -1/2 & 1/2 \end{pmatrix}, \quad \text{and} \quad \mathbf{D} = \begin{pmatrix} 3 & 0 \\ 0 & 5 \end{pmatrix},$$

so

$$\mathbf{P}\mathbf{D}\mathbf{P}^{-1} = \begin{pmatrix} 2 & 1 \\ -3 & 6 \end{pmatrix}.$$

10. Solving

$$\begin{vmatrix} 2-\lambda & 1 \\ 1 & 2-\lambda \end{vmatrix} = \lambda^2 - 4\lambda + 3 = (\lambda - 1)(\lambda - 3) = 0$$

we find eigenvalues $\lambda_1 = 1$ and $\lambda_2 = 3$. Corresponding eigenvectors are

$$\mathbf{K}_1 = \begin{pmatrix} -1 \\ 1 \end{pmatrix} \quad \text{and} \quad \mathbf{K}_2 = \begin{pmatrix} 1 \\ 1 \end{pmatrix}.$$

Then

$$\mathbf{P} = \begin{pmatrix} -1 & 1 \\ 1 & 1 \end{pmatrix}, \quad \mathbf{P}^{-1} = \begin{pmatrix} -1/2 & 1/2 \\ 1/2 & 1/2 \end{pmatrix}, \quad \text{and} \quad \mathbf{D} = \begin{pmatrix} 1 & 0 \\ 0 & 3 \end{pmatrix},$$

so

$$\mathbf{PDP}^{-1} = \begin{pmatrix} 2 & 1 \\ 1 & 2 \end{pmatrix}.$$

11. From equation (2) in the text

$$e^{t\mathbf{A}} = e^{t\mathbf{PDP}^{-1}} = \mathbf{I} + t(\mathbf{PDP}^{-1}) + \frac{1}{2!}t^2(\mathbf{PDP}^{-1})^2 + \frac{1}{3!}t^3(\mathbf{PDP}^{-1})^3 + \cdots$$

$$= \mathbf{P}\left[\mathbf{I} + t\mathbf{D} + \frac{1}{2!}(t\mathbf{D})^2 + \frac{1}{3!}(t\mathbf{D})^3 + \cdots\right]\mathbf{P}^{-1} = \mathbf{P}e^{t\mathbf{D}}\mathbf{P}^{-1}.$$

12. From equation (2) in the text

$$e^{t\mathbf{D}} = \begin{pmatrix} 1 & 0 & \cdots & 0 \\ 0 & 1 & \cdots & 0 \\ \vdots & \vdots & \ddots & \vdots \\ 0 & 0 & \cdots & 1 \end{pmatrix} + \begin{pmatrix} \lambda_1 & 0 & \cdots & 0 \\ 0 & \lambda_2 & \cdots & 0 \\ \vdots & \vdots & \ddots & \vdots \\ 0 & 0 & \cdots & \lambda_n \end{pmatrix} + \frac{1}{2!}t^2 \begin{pmatrix} \lambda_1^2 & 0 & \cdots & 0 \\ 0 & \lambda_2^2 & \cdots & 0 \\ \vdots & \vdots & \ddots & \vdots \\ 0 & 0 & \cdots & \lambda_n^2 \end{pmatrix}$$

$$+ \frac{1}{3!}t^3 \begin{pmatrix} \lambda_1^3 & 0 & \cdots & 0 \\ 0 & \lambda_2^3 & \cdots & 0 \\ \vdots & \vdots & \ddots & \vdots \\ 0 & 0 & \cdots & \lambda_n^3 \end{pmatrix} + \cdots$$

$$= \begin{pmatrix} 1 + \lambda_1 t + \frac{1}{2!}(\lambda_1 t)^2 + \cdots & 0 & \cdots & 0 \\ 0 & 1 + \lambda_2 t + \frac{1}{2!}(\lambda_2 t)^2 + \cdots & \cdots & 0 \\ \vdots & \vdots & \ddots & \vdots \\ 0 & 0 & \cdots & 1 + \lambda_n t + \frac{1}{2!}(\lambda_n t)^2 + \cdots \end{pmatrix}$$

$$= \begin{pmatrix} e^{\lambda_1 t} & 0 & \cdots & 0 \\ 0 & e^{\lambda_2 t} & \cdots & 0 \\ \vdots & \vdots & \ddots & \vdots \\ 0 & 0 & \cdots & e^{\lambda_n t} \end{pmatrix}.$$

13. From Problems 9, 11, and 12, and equation (1) in the text

$$\mathbf{X} = e^{t\mathbf{A}}\mathbf{C} = \mathbf{P}e^{t\mathbf{D}}\mathbf{P}^{-1}\mathbf{C}$$

$$= \begin{pmatrix} e^{3t} & e^{5t} \\ e^{3t} & 3e^{5t} \end{pmatrix} \begin{pmatrix} e^{3t} & 0 \\ 0 & e^{5t} \end{pmatrix} \begin{pmatrix} \frac{3}{2}e^{-3t} & -\frac{1}{2}e^{-3t} \\ -\frac{1}{2}e^{-5t} & \frac{1}{2}e^{-5t} \end{pmatrix} \begin{pmatrix} c_1 \\ c_2 \end{pmatrix}$$

$$= \begin{pmatrix} \frac{3}{2}e^{3t} - \frac{1}{2}e^{5t} & -\frac{1}{2}e^{3t} + \frac{1}{2}e^{5t} \\ \frac{3}{2}e^{3t} - \frac{3}{2}e^{5t} & -\frac{1}{2}e^{3t} + \frac{3}{2}e^{5t} \end{pmatrix} \begin{pmatrix} c_1 \\ c_2 \end{pmatrix}.$$

14. From Problems 10-12 and equation (1) in the text

$$\mathbf{X} = e^{t\mathbf{A}}\mathbf{C} = \mathbf{P}e^{t\mathbf{D}}\mathbf{P}^{-1}\mathbf{C}$$

$$= \begin{pmatrix} -e^t & e^{3t} \\ e^t & e^{3t} \end{pmatrix} \begin{pmatrix} e^t & 0 \\ 0 & e^{3t} \end{pmatrix} \begin{pmatrix} -\frac{1}{2}e^{-t} & \frac{1}{2}e^{-t} \\ \frac{1}{2}e^{3t} & \frac{1}{2}e^{-3t} \end{pmatrix} \begin{pmatrix} c_1 \\ c_2 \end{pmatrix}$$

$$= \begin{pmatrix} \frac{1}{2}e^t + \frac{1}{2}e^{9t} & -\frac{1}{2}e^t + \frac{1}{2}e^{3t} \\ -\frac{1}{2}e^t + \frac{1}{2}e^{9t} & \frac{1}{2}e^t + \frac{1}{2}e^{3t} \end{pmatrix} \begin{pmatrix} c_1 \\ c_2 \end{pmatrix}.$$

Chapter 8 Review Exercises

1. True

2. $\begin{pmatrix} 1 \\ 2 \end{pmatrix} (3 \quad 4) = \begin{pmatrix} 3 & 4 \\ 6 & 8 \end{pmatrix}$ and $(3 \quad 4) \begin{pmatrix} 1 \\ 2 \end{pmatrix} = (11).$

3. $\mathbf{A}^{-1} = -\frac{1}{2} \begin{pmatrix} 4 & -2 \\ -3 & 1 \end{pmatrix} = \begin{pmatrix} -2 & 1 \\ 3/2 & -1/2 \end{pmatrix}$

4. True, since $\mathbf{AB} = \mathbf{AC}$, $\mathbf{A}^{-1}\mathbf{AB} = \mathbf{A}^{-1}\mathbf{AC}$, and $\mathbf{B} = \mathbf{C}$.

5. True, since $\mathbf{X}' = \mathbf{X}_1' + \mathbf{X}_2' = \mathbf{AX}_1 + \mathbf{AX}_2 + \mathbf{F} = \mathbf{A}(\mathbf{X}_1 + \mathbf{X}_2)\mathbf{F} = \mathbf{AX} + \mathbf{F}$.

6. True, by Theorem 8.8.

7. False; they are the zero and nonzero solutions of $\det(\mathbf{A} - \lambda\mathbf{I}) = 0$.

8. True, since if $\mathbf{AK} = \lambda\mathbf{K}$ then $\mathbf{A}(c\mathbf{K}) = c\mathbf{AK} = c(\lambda\mathbf{K}) = \lambda(c\mathbf{K})$.

9. True, by the definition of an eigenvector.

10. True, since complex roots occur in conjugate pairs.

11. False; consider $\mathbf{A} = \begin{pmatrix} 0 & 1 \\ -1 & 2 \end{pmatrix}$.

12. False;

$$\begin{pmatrix} 1 & 1 & 1 & | & 2 \\ 0 & 1 & 0 & | & 3 \\ 0 & 0 & 0 & | & 0 \end{pmatrix} \implies \begin{pmatrix} 1 & 0 & 1 & | & -1 \\ 0 & 1 & 0 & | & 3 \\ 0 & 0 & 0 & | & 0 \end{pmatrix}.$$

13. From $(D-2)x + (D-2)y = 1$ and $Dx + (2D-1)y = 3$ we obtain $(D-1)(D-2)y = -6$ and $Dx = 3 - (2D-1)y$. Then

$$y = c_1 e^{2t} + c_2 e^t - 3 \quad \text{and} \quad x = -c_2 e^t - \frac{3}{2} c_1 e^{2t} + c_3.$$

Substituting into $(D-2)x + (D-2)y = 1$ gives $c_3 = 5/2$ so that

$$x = -c_2 e^t - \frac{3}{2} c_1 e^{2t} + \frac{5}{2}.$$

14. From $(D-2)x - y = t - 2$ and $-3x + (D-4)y = -4t$ we obtain $(D-1)(D-5)x = 9 - 8t$. Then

$$x = c_1 e^t + c_2 e^{5t} - \frac{8}{5}t - \frac{3}{25}$$

and

$$y = (D-2)x - t + 2 = -c_1 e^t + 3c_2 e^{5t} + \frac{16}{25} + \frac{11}{25}t.$$

15. From $(D-2)x - y = -e^t$ and $-3x + (D-4)y = -7e^t$ we obtain $(D-1)(D-5)x = -4e^t$ so that

$$x = c_1 e^t + c_2 e^{5t} + te^t.$$

Then

$$y = (D-2)x + e^t = -c_1 e^t + 3c_2 e^{5t} - te^t + 2e^t.$$

16. From $(D+2)x + (D+1)y = \sin 2t$ and $5x + (D+3)y = \cos 2t$ we obtain $(D^2+5)y = 2\cos 2t - 7\sin 2t$. Then

$$y = c_1 \cos t + c_2 \sin t - \frac{2}{3} \cos 2t + \frac{7}{3} \sin 2t$$

and

$$x = -\frac{1}{5}(D+3)y + \frac{1}{5}\cos 2t$$

$$= \left(\frac{1}{5}c_1 - \frac{3}{5}c_2\right)\sin t + \left(-\frac{1}{5}c_2 - \frac{3}{5}c_1\right)\cos t - \frac{5}{3}\sin 2t - \frac{1}{3}\cos 2t.$$

17. Taking the Laplace transform of the system gives

$$s\mathscr{L}\{x\} + \mathscr{L}\{y\} = \frac{1}{s^2} + 1$$

$$4\mathscr{L}\{x\} + s\mathscr{L}\{y\} = 2$$

so that

$$\mathscr{L}\{x\} = \frac{s^2 - 2s + 1}{s(s-2)(s+2)} = -\frac{1}{4}\frac{1}{s} + \frac{1}{8}\frac{1}{s-2} + \frac{9}{8}\frac{1}{s+2}.$$

Then

$$x = -\frac{1}{4} + \frac{1}{8}e^{2t} + \frac{9}{8}e^{-2t} \quad \text{and} \quad y = -x' + t = \frac{9}{4}e^{-2t} - \frac{1}{4}e^{2t} + t.$$

18. Taking the Laplace transform of the system gives

$$s^2 \mathscr{L}\{x\} + s^2 \mathscr{L}\{y\} = \frac{1}{s-2}$$

$$2s\mathscr{L}\{x\} + s^2 \mathscr{L}\{y\} = -\frac{1}{s-2}$$

so that

$$\mathscr{L}\{x\} = \frac{2}{s(s-2)^2} = \frac{1}{2}\frac{1}{s} - \frac{1}{2}\frac{1}{s-2} + \frac{1}{(s-2)^2}$$

and

$$\mathscr{L}\{y\} = \frac{-s-2}{s^2(s-2)^2} = -\frac{3}{4}\frac{1}{s} - \frac{1}{2}\frac{1}{s^2} + \frac{3}{4}\frac{1}{s-2} - \frac{1}{(s-2)^2}.$$

Then

$$x = \frac{1}{2} - \frac{1}{2}e^{2t} + te^{2t} \quad \text{and} \quad y = -\frac{3}{4} - \frac{1}{2}t + \frac{3}{4}e^{2t} - te^{2t}.$$

19. (a) $\mathbf{X} = \begin{pmatrix} t^3 + 3t^2 + 5t - 2 \\ -t^3 - t + 2 \\ 4t^3 + 12t^2 + 8t + 1 \end{pmatrix}$ **(b)** $\mathbf{X}' = \begin{pmatrix} 3t^2 + 6t + 5 \\ -3t^2 - 1 \\ 12t^2 + 24t + 8 \end{pmatrix}$

20. Let $x_1 = y$, $x_2 = y'$, $x_3 = y''$, and $x_4 = y'''$ so that

$$Dx_1 = x_2$$

$$Dx_2 = x_3$$

$$Dx_3 = x_4$$

$$Dx_4 = \frac{5}{3}x_3 - 3x_1 + 2e^t - \frac{2}{3}t.$$

21. Let $x_1 = x$, $x_2 = y$, $x_3 = Dx$, and $x_4 = Dy$ so that

$$Dx_1 = x_3$$

$$Dx_2 = x_4$$

$$Dx_3 = x_4 - 2x_3 - 2x_1 - \ln t + 10t - 4$$

$$Dx_4 = -x_3 - x_1 + 5t - 2.$$

22. If

$$x = c_1 e^t + c_2 t e^t + \sin t \quad \text{and} \quad y = c_1 e^t + c_2 (t e^t + e^t) + \cos t$$

then

$$x' = c_1 e^t + c_2 (t e^t + e^t) + \cos t = y$$

and

$$y' = c_1 e^t + c_2 (t e^t + 2 e^t) - \sin t$$

$$= -(c_1 e^t + c_2 t e^t + \sin t) + 2(c_1 e^t + c_2 (t e^t + e^t) + \cos t) - 2 \cos t$$

$$= -x + 2y - 2 \cos t.$$

23. We have $\det(\mathbf{A} - \lambda \mathbf{I}) = (\lambda - 1)^2 = 0$ and $\mathbf{K} = \begin{pmatrix} 1 \\ -1 \end{pmatrix}$. A solution to $(\mathbf{A} - \lambda \mathbf{I})\mathbf{P} = \mathbf{K}$ is $\mathbf{P} = \begin{pmatrix} 0 \\ 1 \end{pmatrix}$
so that

$$\mathbf{X} = c_1 \begin{pmatrix} 1 \\ -1 \end{pmatrix} e^t + c_2 \left[\begin{pmatrix} 1 \\ -1 \end{pmatrix} t e^t + \begin{pmatrix} 0 \\ 1 \end{pmatrix} e^t \right].$$

24. We have $\det(\mathbf{A} - \lambda \mathbf{I}) = (\lambda + 6)(\lambda + 2) = 0$ so that

$$\mathbf{X} = c_1 \begin{pmatrix} 1 \\ -1 \end{pmatrix} e^{-6t} + c_2 \begin{pmatrix} 1 \\ 1 \end{pmatrix} e^{-2t}.$$

25. We have $\det(\mathbf{A} - \lambda \mathbf{I}) = \lambda^2 - 2\lambda + 5 = 0$. For $\lambda = 1 + 2i$ we obtain $\mathbf{K}_1 = \begin{pmatrix} 1 \\ i \end{pmatrix}$ and

$$\mathbf{X}_1 = \begin{pmatrix} 1 \\ i \end{pmatrix} e^{(1+2i)t} = \begin{pmatrix} \cos 2t \\ -\sin 2t \end{pmatrix} e^t + i \begin{pmatrix} \sin 2t \\ \cos 2t \end{pmatrix} e^t.$$

Then

$$\mathbf{X} = c_1 \begin{pmatrix} \cos 2t \\ -\sin 2t \end{pmatrix} e^t + c_2 \begin{pmatrix} \sin 2t \\ \cos 2t \end{pmatrix} e^t.$$

26. We have $\det(\mathbf{A} - \lambda \mathbf{I}) = \lambda^2 - 2\lambda + 2 = 0$. For $\lambda = 1 + i$ we obtain $\mathbf{K}_1 = \begin{pmatrix} 3 - i \\ 2 \end{pmatrix}$ and

$$\mathbf{X}_1 = \begin{pmatrix} 3 - i \\ 2 \end{pmatrix} e^{(1+i)t} = \begin{pmatrix} 3 \cos t + \sin t \\ 2 \cos t \end{pmatrix} e^t + i \begin{pmatrix} -\cos t + 3 \sin t \\ 2 \sin t \end{pmatrix} e^t.$$

Then

$$\mathbf{X} = c_1 \begin{pmatrix} 3 \cos t + \sin t \\ 2 \cos t \end{pmatrix} e^t + c_2 \begin{pmatrix} -\cos t + 3 \sin t \\ 2 \sin t \end{pmatrix} e^t.$$

27. We have $\det(\mathbf{A} - \lambda\mathbf{I}) = \lambda^2(3 - \lambda) = 0$ so that

$$\mathbf{X} = c_1 \begin{pmatrix} -1 \\ 1 \\ 0 \end{pmatrix} + c_2 \begin{pmatrix} -1 \\ 0 \\ 1 \end{pmatrix} + c_3 \begin{pmatrix} 1 \\ 1 \\ 1 \end{pmatrix} e^{3t}.$$

28. We have $\det(\mathbf{A} - \lambda\mathbf{I}) = -(\lambda - 2)(\lambda - 4)(\lambda + 3) = 0$ so that

$$\mathbf{X} = c_1 \begin{pmatrix} -2 \\ 3 \\ 1 \end{pmatrix} e^{2t} + c_2 \begin{pmatrix} 0 \\ 1 \\ 1 \end{pmatrix} e^{4t} + c_3 \begin{pmatrix} 7 \\ 12 \\ -16 \end{pmatrix} e^{-3t}.$$

29. We have

$$\mathbf{X}_c = c_1 \begin{pmatrix} 1 \\ 0 \end{pmatrix} e^{2t} + c_2 \begin{pmatrix} 4 \\ 1 \end{pmatrix} e^{4t}.$$

Then

$$\mathbf{\Phi} = \begin{pmatrix} e^{2t} & 4e^{4t} \\ 0 & e^{4t} \end{pmatrix}, \quad \mathbf{\Phi}^{-1} = \begin{pmatrix} e^{-2t} & -4e^{-2t} \\ 0 & e^{-4t} \end{pmatrix},$$

and

$$\mathbf{U} = \int \mathbf{\Phi}^{-1}\mathbf{F}\, dt = \int \begin{pmatrix} 2e^{-2t} - 64te^{-2t} \\ 16te^{-4t} \end{pmatrix} dt = \begin{pmatrix} 15e^{-2t} + 32te^{-2t} \\ -e^{-4t} - 4te^{-4t} \end{pmatrix},$$

so that

$$\mathbf{X}_p = \mathbf{\Phi}\mathbf{U} = \begin{pmatrix} 11 + 16t \\ -1 - 4t \end{pmatrix}.$$

30. We have

$$\mathbf{X}_c = c_1 \begin{pmatrix} 2\cos t \\ -\sin t \end{pmatrix} e^t + c_2 \begin{pmatrix} 2\sin t \\ \cos t \end{pmatrix} e^t.$$

Then

$$\mathbf{\Phi} = \begin{pmatrix} 2\cos t & 2\sin t \\ -\sin t & \cos t \end{pmatrix} e^t, \quad \mathbf{\Phi}^{-1} = \begin{pmatrix} \frac{1}{2}\cos t & -\sin t \\ \frac{1}{2}\sin t & \cos t \end{pmatrix} e^{-t},$$

and

$$\mathbf{U} = \int \mathbf{\Phi}^{-1}\mathbf{F}\, dt = \int \begin{pmatrix} \cos t - \sec t \\ \sin t \end{pmatrix} dt = \begin{pmatrix} \sin t - \ln|\sec t + \tan t| \\ -\cos t \end{pmatrix},$$

so that

$$\mathbf{X}_p = \mathbf{\Phi}\mathbf{U} = \begin{pmatrix} -2\cos t \ln|\sec t + \tan t| \\ -1 + \sin t \ln|\sec t + \tan t| \end{pmatrix}.$$

31. We have

$$\mathbf{X}_c = c_1 \begin{pmatrix} \cos t + \sin t \\ 2\cos t \end{pmatrix} + c_2 \begin{pmatrix} \sin t - \cos t \\ 2\sin t \end{pmatrix}.$$

Then

$$\mathbf{\Phi} = \begin{pmatrix} \cos t + \sin t & \sin t - \cos t \\ 2\cos t & 2\sin t \end{pmatrix}, \quad \mathbf{\Phi}^{-1} = \begin{pmatrix} \sin t & \frac{1}{2}\cos t - \frac{1}{2}\sin t \\ -\cos t & \frac{1}{2}\cos t + \frac{1}{2}\sin t \end{pmatrix},$$

and

$$\mathbf{U} = \int \mathbf{\Phi}^{-1}\mathbf{F}\,dt = \int \begin{pmatrix} \frac{1}{2}\sin t - \frac{1}{2}\cos t + \frac{1}{2}\csc t \\ -\frac{1}{2}\sin t - \frac{1}{2}\cos t + \frac{1}{2}\csc t \end{pmatrix} dt$$

$$= \begin{pmatrix} -\frac{1}{2}\cos t - \frac{1}{2}\sin t + \frac{1}{2}\ln|\csc t - \cot t| \\ \frac{1}{2}\cos t - \frac{1}{2}\sin t + \frac{1}{2}\ln|\csc t - \cot t| \end{pmatrix},$$

so that

$$\mathbf{X}_p = \mathbf{\Phi}\mathbf{U} = \begin{pmatrix} -1 \\ -1 \end{pmatrix} + \begin{pmatrix} \sin t \\ \sin t + \cos t \end{pmatrix} \ln|\csc t - \cot t|.$$

32. We have

$$\mathbf{X}_c = c_1 \begin{pmatrix} 1 \\ -1 \end{pmatrix} e^{2t} + c_2 \left[\begin{pmatrix} 1 \\ -1 \end{pmatrix} te^{2t} + \begin{pmatrix} 1 \\ 0 \end{pmatrix} e^{2t} \right].$$

Then

$$\mathbf{\Phi} = \begin{pmatrix} e^{2t} & te^{2t} + e^{2t} \\ -e^{2t} & -te^{2t} \end{pmatrix}, \quad \mathbf{\Phi}^{-1} = \begin{pmatrix} -te^{-2t} & -te^{-2t} - e^{-2t} \\ e^{-2t} & e^{-2t} \end{pmatrix},$$

and

$$\mathbf{U} = \int \mathbf{\Phi}^{-1}\mathbf{F}\,dt = \int \begin{pmatrix} t-1 \\ -1 \end{pmatrix} dt = \begin{pmatrix} \frac{1}{2}t^2 - t \\ -t \end{pmatrix},$$

so that

$$\mathbf{X}_p = \mathbf{\Phi}\mathbf{U} = \begin{pmatrix} -1/2 \\ 1/2 \end{pmatrix} t^2 e^{2t} + \begin{pmatrix} -2 \\ 1 \end{pmatrix} te^{2t}.$$

9 Numerical Methods for Ordinary Differential Equations

—————— **Exercises 9.1** ————————————————

1.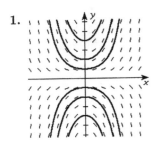

2.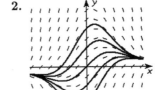

3.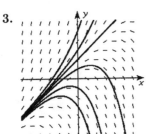

4.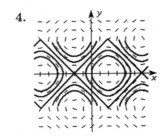

5. Setting $x + 4 = c$ we obtain $x = c - 4$, a family of vertical lines.

6. Setting $2x + y = c$ we obtain $y = -2x + c$; a family of lines with slope -2.

7. Setting $x^2 - y^2 = c$ we obtain a family of hyperbolas.

8. Setting $y - x^2 = c$ we obtain $y = x^2 + c$; a family of parabolas with veritces on the y-axis.

9. Setting $\sqrt{x^2 + y^2 + 2y + 1} = c$ we obtain $x^2 + (y + 1)^2 = c^2$; a family of circles centered at $(0, -1)$.

10. Setting $(x^2 + y^2)^{-1} = c$ we obtain $x^2 + y^2 = 1/c$; a family of circles centered at the origin.

11. Setting $y(x + y) = c$ we obtain $y^2 + xy - c = 0$ or $y = -\frac{1}{2}x \pm \frac{1}{2}\sqrt{x^2 + 4c}$; a family of hyperbolas.

12. Setting $y + e^x = c$ we obtain $y = c - e^x$; a family of exponential curves.

13. Setting $(y - 1)/(x - 2) = c$ we obtain $y = cx + 1 - 2c$; a family of lines.

14. Setting $(x - y)/(x + y) = c$ we obtain $y = (1 - c)x/(1 + c)$; a family of lines passing through the origin.

15. Setting $x = c$ we see that the isoclines form a family of vertical lines.

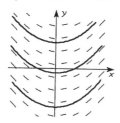

16. Setting $x + y = c$ we obtain the isoclines $y = -x + c$.

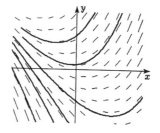

17. Setting $-x/y = c$ we obtain the isoclines $y = -x/c$.

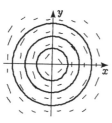

18. Setting $1/y = c$ we obtain the isoclines $y = 1/c$.

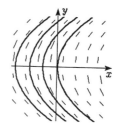

19. Setting $0.2x^2 + y = c$ we obtain the isoclines $y = c - 0.2x^2$.

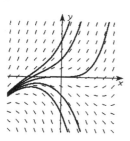

20. Setting $xe^y = c$ we obtain the isoclines $y = \ln c - \ln x$.

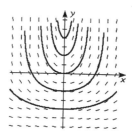

21. Setting $y - \cos \frac{\pi}{2}x = c$ we obtain the isoclines $y = \cos \frac{\pi}{2}x + c$.

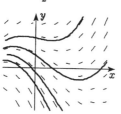

22. Setting $1 - y/x = c$ we obtain the isoclines $y = (1 - c)x$.

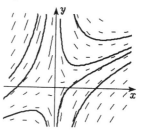

23. Solving

$$\frac{\alpha x + \beta y}{\gamma x + \delta y} = c$$

for y we obtain

$$y = \frac{c\gamma - \alpha}{\beta - c\delta} x,$$

a family of lines through the origin.

24. $y = cx$ is a solution of the differential equation if and only if

$$y' = c = \frac{\alpha x + \beta cx}{\gamma x + \delta cx}$$

if and only if

$$[\delta c^2 + (\gamma - \beta)c - \alpha]x = 0$$

if and only if

$$\delta c^2 + (\gamma - \beta)c - \alpha = 0$$

if and only if

$$c = \frac{\beta - \gamma \pm \sqrt{(\beta - \gamma)^2 + 4\alpha\delta}}{2\delta}$$

if and only if

$$(\beta - \gamma)^2 + 4\alpha\delta \geq 0.$$

25. The isoclines of $y' = 3x + 2y$ are $3x + 2y = c$ or

$$y = -\frac{3}{2}x + \frac{c}{2}.$$

If we choose $c = -3/2$ then $3x + 2y = -3/2$ is a solution of the differential equation .

26. The isoclines of $y' = 6x - 2y$ are $6x - 2y = c$ or

$$y = -3x + \frac{c}{2}.$$

If we choose $c = 3$ then $6x - 2y = 3$ is a solution of the differential equation .

27. The isoclines of $y' = 2x/y$ are $2x/y = c$ or

$$y = \frac{2}{c}x.$$

Setting $2/c = c$ we obtain $c = \pm\sqrt{2}$. Thus $y = \pm\sqrt{2}\,x$ are solutions of the differential equation .

28. The isoclines of $y' = 2y/(x + y)$ are $2y/(x + y) = c$ or

$$y = \frac{c}{2 - c}x.$$

Setting $c/(2-c) = c$ we obtain $c = 0$ or $c = 1$. Thus $y = 0$ and $y = x$ are solutions of the differential equation .

29. The isoclines of $y' = (4x + 3y)/y$ are $(4x + 3y)/y = c$ or

$$y = \frac{4}{c-3}x.$$

Setting $4/(c-3) = c$ we obtain $c^2 - 3c - 4 = (c-4)(c+1) = 0$. Thus $c = 4$ and $c = -1$ and $y = 4x$ and $y = -x$ are solutions of the differential equation .

30. The isoclines of $y' = (5x + 10y)/(-4x + 3y)$ are $(5x + 10y)/(-4x + 3y) = c$ or

$$y = \frac{4c + 5}{3c - 10}x.$$

Setting $(4c + 5)/(3c - 10) = c$ we obtain $c = 3c^2 - 14c - 5 = (3c + 1)(c - 5) = 0$. Thus $c = -1/3$ and $c = 5$ and $y = -\frac{1}{3}x$ and $y = 5x$ are solutions of the differential equation .

──────── **Exercises 9.2** ────────

All tables in this chapter were constructed in a spreadsheet program which does not support subscripts. Consequently, x_n and y_n will be indicated as $x(n)$ and $y(n)$, respectively.

1. Let $u = x + y - 1$ so that $y' = (x + y - 1)^2$ becomes

$$\frac{1}{u^2 + 1}du = dx$$

and $\tan^{-1} u = x + c$. Then $y = 1 - x + \tan(x + c)$ and $y(0) = 2$ gives $c = \pi/4$, so

$$y = 1 - x + \tan(x + \frac{\pi}{4}).$$

2.

		EULER		IMPROVED EULER	
x(n)	EXACT	h=0.1	h=0.05	h=0.1	h=0.05
0.00	2.0000	2.0000	2.0000	2.0000	2.0000
0.10	2.1230	2.1000	2.1105	2.1220	2.1228
0.20	2.3085	2.2440	2.2727	2.3049	2.3075
0.30	2.5958	2.4525	2.5142	2.5858	2.5931
0.40	3.0650	2.7596	2.8845	3.0378	3.0574
0.50	3.9082	3.2261	3.4823	3.8254	3.8840

Exercises 9.2

3.

h = 0.1	
x(n)	y(n)
1.00	5.0000
1.10	3.8000
1.20	2.9800
1.30	2.4260
1.40	2.0582
1:50	1.8207

h = 0.05	
x(n)	y(n)
1.00	5.0000
1.05	4.4000
1.10	3.8950
1.15	3.4708
1.20	3.1151
1.25	2.8179
1.30	2.5702
1.35	2.3647
1.40	2.1950
1.45	2.0557
1.50	1.9424

4.

h = 0.1	
x(n)	y(n)
0.00	2.0000
0.10	1.6000
0.20	1.3200
0.30	1.1360
0.40	1.0288
0.50	0.9830

h = 0.05	
x(n)	y(n)
0.00	2.0000
0.05	1.8000
0.10	1.6300
0.15	1.4870
0.20	1.3683
0.25	1.2715
0.30	1.1943
0.35	1.1349
0.40	1.0914
0.45	1.0623
0.50	1.0460

5.

h = 0.1	
x(n)	y(n)
0.00	0.0000
0.10	0.1000
0.20	0.2010
0.30	0.3050
0.40	0.4143
0.50	0.5315

h = 0.05	
x(n)	y(n)
0.00	0.0000
0.05	0.0500
0.10	0.1001
0.15	0.1506
0.20	0.2018
0.25	0.2538
0.30	0.3070
0.35	0.3617
0.40	0.4183
0.45	0.4770
0.50	0.5384

6.

h = 0.1		h = 0.05	
x(n)	y(n)	x(n)	y(n)
0.00	1.0000	0.00	1.0000
0.10	1.1000	0.05	1.0500
0.20	1.2220	0.10	1.1053
0.30	1.3753	0.15	1.1668
0.40	1.5735	0.20	1.2360
0.50	1.8371	0.25	1.3144
		0.30	1.4039
		0.35	1.5070
		0.40	1.6267
		0.45	1.7670
		0.50	1.9332

7.

h = 0.1		h = 0.05	
x(n)	y(n)	x(n)	y(n)
0.00	0.0000	0.00	0.0000
0.10	0.1000	0.05	0.0500
0.20	0.1905	0.10	0.0976
0.30	0.2731	0.15	0.1429
0.40	0.3492	0.20	0.1863
0.50	0.4198	0.25	0.2278
		0.30	0.2676
		0.35	0.3058
		0.40	0.3427
		0.45	0.3782
		0.50	0.4124

8.

h = 0.1		h = 0.05	
x(n)	y(n)	x(n)	y(n)
0.00	0.0000	0.00	0.0000
0.10	0.0000	0.05	0.0000
0.20	0.0100	0.10	0.0025
0.30	0.0300	0.15	0.0075
0.40	0.0601	0.20	0.0150
0.50	0.1005	0.25	0.0250
		0.30	0.0375
		0.35	0.0526
		0.40	0.0703
		0.45	0.0905
		0.50	0.1134

Exercises 9.2

9.

h = 0.1		h = 0.05	
x(n)	y(n)	x(n)	y(n)
0.00	0.5000	0.00	0.5000
0.10	0.5250	0.05	0.5125
0.20	0.5431	0.10	0.5232
0.30	0.5548	0.15	0.5322
0.40	0.5613	0.20	0.5395
0.50	0.5639	0.25	0.5452
		0.30	0.5496
		0.35	0.5527
		0.40	0.5547
		0.45	0.5559
		0.50	0.5565

10.

h = 0.1		h = 0.05	
x(n)	y(n)	x(n)	y(n)
0.00	1.0000	0.00	1.0000
0.10	1.1000	0.05	1.0500
0.20	1.2159	0.10	1.1039
0.30	1.3505	0.15	1.1619
0.40	1.5072	0.20	1.2245
0.50	1.6902	0.25	1.2921
		0.30	1.3651
		0.35	1.4440
		0.40	1.5293
		0.45	1.6217
		0.50	1.7219

11.

h = 0.1		h = 0.05	
x(n)	y(n)	x(n)	y(n)
1.00	1.0000	1.00	1.0000
1.10	1.0000	1.05	1.0000
1.20	1.0191	1.10	1.0049
1.30	1.0588	1.15	1.0147
1.40	1.1231	1.20	1.0298
1.50	1.2194	1.25	1.0506
		1.30	1.0775
		1.35	1.1115
		1.40	1.1538
		1.45	1.2057
		1.50	1.2696

12.

h = 0.1			h = 0.05	
x(n)	*y(n)*		*x(n)*	*y(n)*
1.00	0.5000		1.00	0.5000
1.10	0.5250		1.05	0.5125
1.20	0.5499		1.10	0.5250
1.30	0.5747		1.15	0.5375
1.40	0.5991		1.20	0.5499
1.50	0.6231		1.25	0.5623
			1.30	0.5746
			1.35	0.5868
			1.40	0.5989
			1.45	0.6109
			1.50	0.6228

13. (a)

h = 0.1			h = 0.05	
x	*y*		*x(n)*	*y(n)*
1.00	5.0000		1.00	5.0000
1.10	3.9900		1.05	4.4475
1.20	3.2546		1.10	3.9763
1.30	2.7236		1.15	3.5751
1.40	2.3451		1.20	3.2342
1.50	2.0801		1.25	2.9452
			1.30	2.7009
			1.35	2.4952
			1.40	2.3226
			1.45	2.1786
			1.50	2.0592

(b)

h = 0.1			h = 0.05	
x(n)	*y(n)*		*x(n)*	*y(n)*
0.00	0.0000		0.00	0.0000
0.10	0.1005		0.05	0.0501
0.20	0.2030		0.10	0.1004
0.30	0.3098		0.15	0.1512
0.40	0.4234		0.20	0.2028
0.50	0.5470		0.25	0.2554
			0.30	0.3095
			0.35	0.3652
			0.40	0.4230
			0.45	0.4832
			0.50	0.5465

(c)

h = 0.1	
x(n)	y(n)
0.00	0.0000
0.10	0.0952
0.20	0.1822
0.30	0.2622
0.40	0.3363
0.50	0.4053

h = 0.05	
x(n)	y(n)
0.00	0.0000
0.05	0.0488
0.10	0.0953
0.15	0.1397
0.20	0.1823
0.25	0.2231
0.30	0.2623
0.35	0.3001
0.40	0.3364
0.45	0.3715
0.50	0.4054

(d)

h = 0.1	
x(n)	y(n)
0.00	0.5000
0.10	0.5215
0.20	0.5362
0.30	0.5449
0.40	0.5490
0.50	0.5503

h = 0.05	
x(n)	y(n)
0.00	0.5000
0.05	0.5116
0.10	0.5214
0.15	0.5294
0.20	0.5359
0.25	0.5408
0.30	0.5444
0.35	0.5469
0.40	0.5484
0.45	0.5492
0.50	0.5495

(e)

h = 0.1	
x(n)	y(n)
1.00	1.0000
1.10	1.0095
1.20	1.0404
1.30	1.0967
1.40	1.1866
1.50	1.3260

h = 0.05	
x(n)	y(n)
1.00	1.0000
1.05	1.0024
1.10	1.0100
1.15	1.0228
1.20	1.0414
1.25	1.0663
1.30	1.0984
1.35	1.1389
1.40	1.1895
1.45	1.2526
1.50	1.3315

14. (a)

h = 0.1	
x(n)	y(n)
0.00	2.0000
0.10	1.6600
0.20	1.4172
0.30	1.2541
0.40	1.1564
0.50	1.1122

h = 0.05	
x(n)	y(n)
0.00	2.0000
0.05	1.8150
0.10	1.6571
0.15	1.5237
0.20	1.4124
0.25	1.3212
0.30	1.2482
0.35	1.1916
0.40	1.1499
0.45	1.1217
0.50	1.1056

(b)

h = 0.1	
x(n)	y(n)
0.00	1.0000
0.10	1.1110
0.20	1.2515
0.30	1.4361
0.40	1.6880
0.50	2.0488

h = 0.05	
x(n)	y(n)
0.00	1.0000
0.05	1.0526
0.10	1.1113
0.15	1.1775
0.20	1.2526
0.25	1.3388
0.30	1.4387
0.35	1.5556
0.40	1.6939
0.45	1.8598
0.50	2.0619

(c)

h = 0.1	
x(n)	y(n)
0.00	0.0000
0.10	0.0050
0.20	0.0200
0.30	0.0451
0.40	0.0805
0.50	0.1266

h = 0.05	
x(n)	y(n)
0.00	0.0000
0.05	0.0013
0.10	0.0050
0.15	0.0113
0.20	0.0200
0.25	0.0313
0.30	0.0451
0.35	0.0615
0.40	0.0805
0.45	0.1022
0.50	0.1266

(d)

h = 0.1		h = 0.05	
x(n)	y(n)	x(n)	y(n)
0.00	1.0000	0.00	1.0000
0.10	1.1079	0.05	1.0519
0.20	1.2337	0.10	1.1079
0.30	1.3806	0.15	1.1684
0.40	1.5529	0.20	1.2337
0.50	1.7557	0.25	1.3043
		0.30	1.3807
		0.35	1.4634
		0.40	1.5530
		0.45	1.6503
		0.50	1.7560

(e)

h = 0.1		h = 0.05	
x(n)	y(n)	x(n)	y(n)
1.00	0.5000	1.00	0.5000
1.10	0.5250	1.05	0.5125
1.20	0.5498	1.10	0.5250
1.30	0.5744	1.15	0.5374
1.40	0.5986	1.20	0.5498
1.50	0.6224	1.25	0.5622
		1.30	0.5744
		1.35	0.5866
		1.40	0.5987
		1.45	0.6106
		1.50	0.6224

15.

h=0.1	EULER	IMPROVED EULER
x(n)	y(n)	y(n)
1.00	1.0000	1.0000
1.10	1.2000	1.2469
1.20	1.4938	1.6668
1.30	1.9711	2.6427
1.40	2.9060	8.7988

16. Integrating $y' = f(x, y)$ we obtain

$$\int_{x_n}^{x_{n+1}} y' \, dx = \int_{x_n}^{x_{n+1}} f(x, y) \, dx$$

so that

$$y(x_{n+1} - y(x_n) \approx f(x_n, y_n)(x_{n+1} - x_n) = h f(x_n, y_n)$$

or

$$y_{n+1} = y_n + h f(x_n, y_n).$$

374

17. From $y' = f(x, y)$ and $f(x, y) \approx \frac{1}{2}[f(x_n, y_n) + f(x_{n+1}, y_{n+1})]$ we obtain

$$\int_{x_n}^{x_{n+1}} y' \, dx \approx \int_{x_n}^{x_{n+1}} \frac{1}{2}[f(x_n, y_n) + f(x_{n+1}, y_{n+1})] \, dx$$

so that

$$y(x_{n+1} - y(x_n) \approx (x_{n+1} - x_n)\frac{1}{2}[f(x_n, y_n) + f(x_{n+1}, y_{n+1})]$$

or

$$y_{n+1} = y_n + \frac{1}{2}[f(x_n, y_n) + f(x_{n+1}, y_{n+1}^*)],$$

where

$$y_{n+1}^* = y_n + hf(x_n, y_n).$$

Exercises 9.3

1. We use

$$y'' = 2 - 3y'$$

$$= 2 - 3(2x - 3y + 1)$$

$$= 9y - 6x - 1$$

so that

$$y_{n+1} = y_n + (2x_n - 3y_n + 1)h + (9y_n - 6x_n - 1)\frac{1}{2}h^2.$$

h = 0.1	
x(n)	y(n)
1.00	5.0000
1.10	3.9900
1.20	3.2546
1.30	2.7236
1.40	2.3451
1.50	2.0801

h = 0.05	
x(n)	y(n)
1.00	5.0000
1.05	4.4475
1.10	3.9763
1.15	3.5751
1.20	3.2342
1.25	2.9452
1.30	2.7009
1.35	2.4952
1.40	2.3226
1.45	2.1786
1.50	2.0592

2. We use

$$y'' = 4 - 2y'$$

$$= 4 - 2(4x - 2y)$$

$$= 4y - 8x + 4$$

so that

$$y_{n+1} = y_n + (4x_n - 2y_n + 1)h + (4y_n - 8x_n + 4)\frac{1}{2}h^2.$$

h = 0.1	
x(n)	y(n)
0.00	2.0000
0.10	1.6600
0.20	1.4172
0.30	1.2541
0.40	1.1564
0.50	1.1122

h = 0.05	
x(n)	y(n)
0.00	2.0000
0.05	1.8150
0.10	1.6571
0.15	1.5237
0.20	1.4124
0.25	1.3212
0.30	1.2482
0.35	1.1916
0.40	1.1499
0.45	1.1217
0.50	1.1056

375

3. We use

$$y'' = 2yy'$$

$$= 2y(1 + y^2)$$

$$= 2y + 2y^3$$

so that

h = 0.1	
x(n)	y(n)
0.00	0.0000
0.10	0.1000
0.20	0.2020
0.30	0.3082
0.40	0.4211
0.50	0.5438

h = 0.05	
x(n)	y(n)
0.00	0.0000
0.05	0.0500
0.10	0.1003
0.15	0.1510
0.20	0.2025
0.25	0.2551
0.30	0.3090
0.35	0.3647
0.40	0.4223
0.45	0.4825
0.50	0.5456

$$y_{n+1} = y_n + (1 + y_n^2)h + (2y_n + 2y_n^3)\frac{1}{2}h^2.$$

4. We use

$$y'' = 2x + 2yy'$$

$$= 2x + 2y(x^2 + y^2)$$

$$= 2x + 2x^2y + 2y^3$$

so that

h = 0.1	
x(n)	y(n)
0.00	1.0000
0.10	1.1100
0.20	1.2490
0.30	1.4310
0.40	1.6783
0.50	2.0300

h = 0.05	
x(n)	y(n)
0.00	1.0000
0.05	1.0525
0.10	1.1111
0.15	1.1770
0.20	1.2519
0.25	1.3378
0.30	1.4372
0.35	1.5535
0.40	1.6910
0.45	1.8557
0.50	2.0561

$$y_{n+1} = y_n + (x_n^2 + y_n^2)h + (2x_n + 2x_n^2y_n + 2y_n^3)\frac{1}{2}h^2.$$

5. We use

$$y'' = -e^{-y}y'$$

$$= -e^{-y}(e^{-y})$$

$$= -e^{-2y}$$

so that

h = 0.1	
x(n)	y(n)
0.00	0.0000
0.10	0.0950
0.20	0.1818
0.30	0.2617
0.40	0.3357
0.50	0.4046

h = 0.05	
x(n)	y(n)
0.00	0.0000
0.05	0.0488
0.10	0.0952
0.15	0.1397
0.20	0.1822
0.25	0.2230
0.30	0.2622
0.35	0.2999
0.40	0.3363
0.45	0.3714
0.50	0.4053

$$y_{n+1} = y_n + e^{-y_n}h - (e^{-2y_n})\frac{1}{2}h^2.$$

6. We use

$$y'' = 1 + 2yy'$$

$$= 1 + 2y(x + y^2)$$

$$= 1 + 2xy + 2y^3$$

so that

h = 0.1	
x(n)	y(n)
0.00	0.0000
0.10	0.0050
0.20	0.0200
0.30	0.0451
0.40	0.0804
0.50	0.1264

h = 0.05	
x(n)	y(n)
0.00	0.0000
0.05	0.0013
0.10	0.0050
0.15	0.0113
0.20	0.0200
0.25	0.0313
0.30	0.0451
0.35	0.0615
0.40	0.0805
0.45	0.1021
0.50	0.1265

$$y_{n+1} = y_n + (x_n + y_n^2)h + (1 + 2x_ny_n + 2y_n^3)\frac{1}{2}h^2.$$

7. We use

$$y'' = 2(x - y)(1 - y')$$

$$= 2(x - y)[1 - (x - y)^2]$$

$$= 2(x - y) - 2(x - y)^3$$

so that

h = 0.1	
x(n)	y(n)
0.00	0.5000
0.10	0.5213
0.20	0.5355
0.30	0.5438
0.40	0.5475
0.50	0.5482

h = 0.05	
x(n)	y(n)
0.00	0.5000
0.05	0.5116
0.10	0.5213
0.15	0.5293
0.20	0.5357
0.25	0.5406
0.30	0.5441
0.35	0.5466
0.40	0.5480
0.45	0.5487
0.50	0.5490

$$y_{n+1} = y_n + (x_n - y_n^2)h + [2(x_n - y_n) - 2(x_n - y_n^3]\frac{1}{2}h^2.$$

8. We use

$$y'' = xy' + y + \frac{y'}{2\sqrt{y}}$$

$$= x(xy + \sqrt{y}) + y + \frac{xy + \sqrt{y}}{2\sqrt{y}}$$

$$= x^2y + \frac{3}{2}x\sqrt{y} + y + \frac{1}{2}$$

so that

h = 0.1	
x(n)	y(n)
0.00	1.0000
0.10	1.1075
0.20	1.2327
0.30	1.3790
0.40	1.5504
0.50	1.7522

h = 0.05	
x(n)	y(n)
0.00	1.0000
0.05	1.0519
0.10	1.1078
0.15	1.1682
0.20	1.2334
0.25	1.3039
0.30	1.3802
0.35	1.4628
0.40	1.5524
0.45	1.6495
0.50	1.7551

$$y_{n+1} = y_n + (x_ny_n + \sqrt{y}_n)h + (x_n^2y_n + \frac{3}{2}x_n\sqrt{y}_n + y_n + \frac{1}{2})\frac{1}{2}h^2.$$

9. We use

$$y'' = 2xyy' + y^2 - \frac{xy' - y}{x^2}$$

$$= 2xy\left(xy^2 - \frac{y}{x}\right) + y^2$$

$$- \frac{1}{x}\left(xy^2 - \frac{y}{x}\right) + \frac{y}{x^2}$$

$$= 2x^2y^3 - 2y^2 + \frac{2y}{x^2}$$

so that

h = 0.1	
x(n)	y(n)
1.00	1.0000
1.10	1.0100
1.20	1.0410
1.30	1.0969
1.40	1.1857
1.50	1.3226

h = 0.05	
x(n)	y(n)
1.00	1.0000
1.05	1.0025
1.10	1.0101
1.15	1.0229
1.20	1.0415
1.25	1.0663
1.30	1.0983
1.35	1.1387
1.40	1.1891
1.45	1.2518
1.50	1.3301

$$y_{n+1} = y_n + \left(x_n y_n^2 - \frac{y_n}{x_n}\right)h + \left(2x_n^2 y_n^3 - 2y_n^2 + \frac{2y_n}{x_n^2}\right)\frac{1}{2}h^2.$$

10. We use

$$y'' = y' - 2yy'$$

$$= y - y^2 - 2y(y - y^2)$$

$$= y - 3y^2 + 2y^3$$

so that

h = 0.1	
x(n)	y(n)
1.00	0.5000
1.10	0.5250
1.20	0.5499
1.30	0.5745
1.40	0.5988
1.50	0.6226

h = 0.05	
x(n)	y(n)
1.00	0.5000
1.05	0.5125
1.10	0.5250
1.15	0.5374
1.20	0.5498
1.25	0.5622
1.30	0.5745
1.35	0.5866
1.40	0.5987
1.45	0.6107
1.50	0.6225

$$y_{n+1} = y_n + (y_n - y_n^2)h + 2(y_n - 3y_n^2 + 2y_n^3)\frac{1}{2}h^2.$$

11. We use

$$y'' = 2x + 3y^2 y'$$

$$= 2x + 3y^2(x^2 + y^3)$$

$$= 2x + 3x^2 y^2 + 3y^5$$

so that

h=0.1		EULER	IMPROVED EULER	3-TERM TAYLOR
x(n)	y(n)	y(n)	y(n)	y(n)
1.00	1.0000	1.0000	1.0000	1.0000
1.10	1.2000		1.2469	1.2400
1.20	1.4938		1.6668	1.6345
1.30	1.9711		2.6427	2.4600
1.40	2.9060		8.7988	5.6353

$$y_{n+1} = y_n + (x_n^2 + y_n^3)h + (2x_n + 3x_n^2 y_n^2 + 3y_n^5)\frac{1}{2}h^2.$$

12. Let $f(x, y) = \alpha x + \beta y$ so that $f_x = \alpha$, $f_y = \beta$, and all higher derivatives are 0. Using the Taylor series expansion for $f(x, y)$ we have

$$f(x_{n+1}, y^*_{n+1}) = f(x_n + h, y_n + hf(x_n, y_n))$$

$$= f(x_n, y_n) + f_x(x_n, y_n)h + f_y(x_n, y_n)hf(x_n, y_n)$$

$$= f(x_n, y_n) + \alpha h + \beta h f(x_n, y_n).$$

Since $f(x_n, y_n) = y'_n$ and $\alpha + \beta y'_n = y''_n$ we have

$$y_{n+1} = y_n + \frac{1}{2}h[f(x_n, y_n) + f(x_{n+1}, y^*_{n+1})]$$

$$= y_n + \frac{1}{2}h[f(x_n, y_n) + f(x_n, y_n) + \alpha h + \beta h f(x_n, y_n)]$$

$$= y_n + \frac{1}{2}h[2y'_n + h(\alpha + \beta y'_n)]$$

$$= y_n + hy'_n + \frac{1}{2}h^2 y''_n.$$

13. To solve the initial-value problem analytically we note that the differential equation is linear with integrating factor e^{-x}. Then

$$\frac{d}{dx}[e^{-x}y] = e^{-x}(x - 1)$$

and

$$y = ce^x - x.$$

From $y(1) = 5$ we find $c = 6e^{-x}$ so that

$$y = 6e^{x-1} - x.$$

For Taylor's method we use

$$y'' = 1 + y'$$

$$= 1 + x + y - 1$$

$$= x + y$$

so that

h=0.1	IMPROVED EULER	3-TERM TAYLOR	EXACT
x(n)	y(n)	y(n)	y(n)
1.00	5.0000	5.0000	5.0000
1.10	5.5300	5.5300	5.5310
1.20	6.1262	6.1262	6.1284
1.30	6.7954	6.7954	6.7992
1.40	7.5454	7.5454	7.5509
1.50	8.3847	8.3847	8.3923

$$y_{n+1} = y_n + (x_n + y_n - 1)h + (x_n + y_n)\frac{1}{2}h^2.$$

Exercises 9.4

1.

x(n)	y(n)
1.00	5.0000
1.10	3.9724
1.20	3.2284
1.30	2.6945
1.40	2.3163
1.50	2.0533

2.

x(n)	y(n)
0.00	2.0000
0.10	1.6562
0.20	1.4110
0.30	1.2465
0.40	1.1480
0.50	1.1037

3.

x(n)	y(n)
0.00	0.0000
0.10	0.1003
0.20	0.2027
0.30	0.3093
0.40	0.4228
0.50	0.5463

4.

x(n)	y(n)
0.00	1.0000
0.10	1.1115
0.20	1.2530
0.30	1.4397
0.40	1.6961
0.50	2.0670

5.

x(n)	y(n)
0.00	0.0000
0.10	0.0953
0.20	0.1823
0.30	0.2624
0.40	0.3365
0.50	0.4055

6.

x(n)	y(n)
0.00	0.0000
0.10	0.0050
0.20	0.0200
0.30	0.0451
0.40	0.0805
0.50	0.1266

7.

x(n)	y(n)
0.00	0.5000
0.10	0.5213
0.20	0.5358
0.30	0.5443
0.40	0.5482
0.50	0.5493

8.

x(n)	y(n)
0.00	1.0000
0.10	1.1079
0.20	1.2337
0.30	1.3807
0.40	1.5531
0.50	1.7561

9.

x(n)	y(n)
1.00	1.0000
1.10	1.0101
1.20	1.0417
1.30	1.0989
1.40	1.1905
1.50	1.3333

10.

x(n)	y(n)
0.00	0.5000
0.10	0.5250
0.20	0.5498
0.30	0.5744
0.40	0.5987
0.50	0.6225

11. Write the equation in the form

$$\frac{dv}{dt} = 32 - 0.025v^2 = f(t, v).$$

t(n)	v(n)
0.0	0.0000
1.0	25.2570
2.0	32.9390
3.0	34.9772
4.0	35.5503
5.0	35.7128

12. Separating variables and using partial fractions we have

$$\frac{1}{2\sqrt{32}} \left(\frac{1}{\sqrt{32} - \sqrt{0.025}\, v} + \frac{1}{\sqrt{32} + \sqrt{0.025}\, v} \right) dv = dt$$

and

$$\frac{1}{2\sqrt{32}\sqrt{0.025}} \left(\ln|\sqrt{32} + \sqrt{0.025}\, v| - \ln|\sqrt{32} - \sqrt{0.025}\, v| \right) = t + c.$$

Since $v(0) = 0$ we find $c = 0$. Solving for v we obtain

$$v(t) = \frac{16\sqrt{5}\,(e^{\sqrt{3.2}\,t} - 1)}{e^{\sqrt{3.2}\,t} + 1}$$

and $v(5) \approx 35.7678$.

13. See the table in the following problem.

14. Let $\alpha = 2.128$ and $\beta = 0.0432$. Separating variables we obtain

$$\frac{dA}{A(\alpha - \beta A)} = dt$$

$$\frac{1}{\alpha}\left(\frac{1}{A} + \frac{\beta}{\alpha - \beta A} \right) dA = dt$$

$$\frac{1}{\alpha}[\ln A - \ln(\alpha - \beta A)] = t + c$$

$$\ln \frac{A}{\alpha - \beta A} = \alpha(t + c)$$

$$\frac{A}{\alpha - \beta A} = e^{\alpha(t+c)}$$

$$A = \alpha e^{\alpha(t+c)} - \beta A e^{\alpha(t+c)}$$

$$\left[1 + \beta e^{\alpha(t+c)} \right] A = \alpha e^{\alpha(t+c)}.$$

Thus

$$A(t) = \frac{\alpha e^{\alpha(t+c)}}{1 + \beta e^{\alpha(t+c)}} = \frac{\alpha}{\beta + e^{-\alpha(t+c)}} = \frac{\alpha}{\beta + e^{-\alpha c}e^{-\alpha t}}.$$

381

From $A(0) = 0.24$ we obtain

$$0.24 = \frac{\alpha}{\beta + e^{-\alpha c}}$$

so that $e^{-\alpha c} = \alpha/0.24 - \beta \approx 8.8235$ and

$$A(t) \approx \frac{2.128}{0.0432 + 8.8235e^{-2.128t}}.$$

t (days)	1	2	3	4	5
A (observed)	2.78	13.53	36.30	47.50	49.40
A (approximated)	1.93	12.50	36.46	47.23	49.00
A (exact)	1.95	12.64	36.63	47.32	49.02

15.

x(n)	y(n)
1.00	1.0000
1.10	1.2511
1.20	1.6934
1.30	2.9425
1.40	903.0282

16. Simpson's rule on $[x_n, x_n + h]$ is

$$\int_{x_n}^{x_n+h} f(x)\,dx \approx \frac{1}{6}h\left[f(x_n) + 4f\left(x_n + \frac{1}{2}h\right) + f(x_n + h)\right].$$

For $f(x,y) = f(x)$ the Runge-Kutta method gives

$$k_1 = hf(x_n),$$

$$k_2 = hf\left(x_n + \frac{1}{2}h\right),$$

$$k_3 = hf\left(x_n + \frac{1}{2}h\right),$$

$$k_4 = hf(x_n + h),$$

and

$$y_{n+1} = y_n + \frac{1}{6}h\left[f(x_n) + 4f\left(x_n + \frac{1}{2}h\right) + f(x_n + h)\right].$$

_____ **Exercises 9.5** _____

1. For $y' - y = x - 1$ an integrating factor is $e^{-\int dx} = e^{-x}$, so that

$$\frac{d}{dx}[e^{-x}y] = (x-1)e^{-x}$$

and

$$y = e^x(-xe^{-x} + c) = -x + ce^x.$$

From $y(0) = 1$ we find $c = 1$ and $y = -x + e^x$. Comparing exact values with approximations obtained in Example 1, we find $y(0.2) \approx 1.02140276$ compared to $y_1 = 1.02140000$, $y(0.4) \approx 1.09182470$ compared to $y_2 = 1.09181796$, $y(0.6) \approx 1.22211880$ compared to $y_3 = 1.22210646$, and $y(0.8) \approx 1.42554093$ compared to $y_4 = 1.42552788$.

2. 100 **REM** ADAMS-BASHFORTH/ADAMS-MOULTON
110 **REM** METHOD TO SOLVE Y'=FNF(X,Y)
120 **REM** DEFINE FNF(X,Y) HERE
130 **REM** GET INPUTS
140 **PRINT**
150 **INPUT** "STEP SIZE=", H
160 **INPUT** "NUMBER OF STEPS (AT LEAST 4)=",N
170 **IF** N<4 **GOTO** 160
180 **INPUT** "X0 =",X
190 **INPUT** "Y0 =",Y
200 **PRINT**
210 **REM** SET UP TABLE
220 **PRINT** "X","Y"
230 **PRINT**
240 **REM** COMPUTE 3 ITERATES USING RUNGE-KUTTA
250 **DIM** Z(4)
260 Z(1)=Y
270 **FOR** I=1 **TO** 3
280 K1=H*FNF(X,Y)
290 K2=H*FNF(X+H/2,Y+K1/2)
300 K3=H*FNF(X+H/2,Y+K2/2)
310 K4=H*FNF(X+H,Y+K3)
320 Y=Y+(K1+2*K2+2*K3+K4)/6
330 Z(I+1)+Y

383

Exercises 9.5

340 X=X+H

350 **PRINT** X,Y

360 **NEXT** I

370 **REM** COMPUTE REMAINING X AND Y VALUES

380 **FOR** I=4 **TO** N

390 YP=Y+H*(55*FNF(X,Z(4))-59*FNF(X-H,Z(3))+37*FNF(X-2*H,Z(2))
    -9*FNF(X-3*H,Z(1)))/24

400 Y=Y+H*(9*FNF(X+H,YP)+19*FNF(X,Z(4))-5*FNF(X-H,Z(3))+FNF(X-2*H,Z(2)))/24

410 X=X+H

420 **PRINT** X,Y

430 Z(1)=Z(2)

440 Z(2)=Z(3)

450 Z(3)=Z(4)

460 Z(4)=Y

470 **NEXT** I

480 **END**

3.

x(n)	y(n)	
0.00	1.0000	initial condition
0.20	0.7328	Runge-Kutta
0.40	0.6461	Runge-Kutta
0.60	0.6585	Runge-Kutta
	0.7332	predictor
0.80	0.7232	corrector

4.

x(n)	y(n)	
0.00	2.0000	initial condition
0.20	1.4112	Runge-Kutta
0.40	1.1483	Runge-Kutta
0.60	1.1039	Runge-Kutta
	1.2109	predictor
0.80	1.2049	corrector

5.

x(n)	y(n)	
0.00	0.0000	initial condition
0.20	0.2027	Runge-Kutta
0.40	0.4228	Runge-Kutta
0.60	0.6841	Runge-Kutta
	1.0234	predictor
0.80	1.0297	corrector
	1.5376	predictor
1.00	1.5569	corrector

x(n)	y(n)	
0.00	0.0000	initial condition
0.10	0.1003	Runge-Kutta
0.20	0.2027	Runge-Kutta
0.30	0.3093	Runge-Kutta
	0.4227	predictor
0.40	0.4228	corrector
	0.5462	predictor
0.50	0.5463	corrector
	0.6840	predictor
0.60	0.6842	corrector
	0.8420	predictor
0.70	0.8423	corrector
	1.0292	predictor
0.80	1.0297	corrector
	1.2592	predictor
0.90	1.2603	corrector
	1.5555	predictor
1.00	1.5576	corrector

6.

x(n)	y(n)	
0.00	1.0000	initial condition
0.20	1.4414	Runge-Kutta
0.40	1.9719	Runge-Kutta
0.60	2.6028	Runge-Kutta
	3.3483	*predictor*
0.80	3.3486	corrector
	4.2276	*predictor*
1.00	4.2280	corrector

x(n)	y(n)	
0.00	1.0000	initial condition
0.10	1.2102	Runge-Kutta
0.20	1.4414	Runge-Kutta
0.30	1.6949	Runge-Kutta
	1.9719	*predictor*
0.40	1.9719	corrector
	2.2740	*predictor*
0.50	2.2740	corrector
	2.6028	*predictor*
0.60	2.6028	corrector
	2.9603	*predictor*
0.70	2.9603	corrector
	3.3486	*predictor*
0.80	3.3486	corrector
	3.7703	*predictor*
0.90	3.7703	corrector
	4.2280	*predictor*
1.00	4.2280	corrector

7.

x(n)	y(n)	
0.00	0.0000	initial condition
0.20	0.0026	Runge-Kutta
0.40	0.0201	Runge-Kutta
0.60	0.0630	Runge-Kutta
	0.1362	*predictor*
0.80	0.1360	corrector
	0.2379	*predictor*
1.00	0.2385	corrector

x(n)	y(n)	
0.00	0.0000	initial condition
0.10	0.0003	Runge-Kutta
0.20	0.0026	Runge-Kutta
0.30	0.0087	Runge-Kutta
	0.0201	*predictor*
0.40	0.0200	corrector
	0.0379	*predictor*
0.50	0.0379	corrector
	0.0630	*predictor*
0.60	0.0629	corrector
	0.0956	*predictor*
0.70	0.0956	corrector
	0.1359	*predictor*
0.80	0.1360	corrector
	0.1837	*predictor*
0.90	0.1837	corrector
	0.2384	*predictor*
1.00	0.2384	corrector

8.

x(n)	y(n)	
0.00	1.0000	initial condition
0.20	1.2337	Runge-Kutta
0.40	1.5531	Runge-Kutta
0.60	1.9961	Runge-Kutta
	2.6180	predictor
0.80	2.6214	corrector
	3.5151	predictor
1.00	3.5208	corrector

x(n)	y(n)	
0.00	1.0000	initial condition
0.10	1.1079	Runge-Kutta
0.20	1.2337	Runge-Kutta
0.30	1.3807	Runge-Kutta
	1.5530	predictor
0.40	1.5531	corrector
	1.7560	predictor
0.50	1.7561	corrector
	1.9960	predictor
0.60	1.9961	corrector
	2.2811	predictor
0.70	2.2812	corrector
	2.6211	predictor
0.80	2.6213	corrector
	3.0289	predictor
0.90	3.0291	corrector
	3.5203	predictor
1.00	3.5207	corrector

9.

x(n)	y(n)	
0.00	1.0000	initial condition
0.10	1.0052	Runge-Kutta
0.20	1.0214	Runge-Kutta
0.30	1.0499	Runge-Kutta
	1.0918	predictor
0.40	1.0918	corrector

─── Exercises 9.6 ───

1. Since the improved Euler method is a second-order Runge-Kutta method, the formula agrees with the Taylor polynomial through $k = 2$. The local truncation error is thus

$$y'''(c)\frac{h^3}{3!} \quad \text{where} \quad x_n < c < x_{n+1}.$$

2. Since the three-term Taylor formula is the Taylor polynomial through $k = 2$, the local truncation error is

$$y'''(c)\frac{h^3}{3!} \quad \text{where} \quad x_n < c < x_{n+1}.$$

3. Since the fourth-order Runge-Kutta formula agrees with the Taylor polynomial through $k = 4$, the local truncation error is

$$y^{(5)}(c)\frac{h^5}{5!} \quad \text{where} \quad x_n < c < x_{n+1}.$$

4. (a) Using the Euler method we obtain $y(0.1) \approx y_1 = 1.2$.

(b) Using $y'' = 4e^{2x}$ we see that the local truncation error is

$$y''(c)\frac{h^2}{2} = 4e^{2c}\frac{(0.1)^2}{2} = 0.02e^{2c}.$$

Since e^{2x} is an increasing function, $e^{2c} \leq e^{2(0.1)} = e^{0.2}$ for $0 \leq c \leq 0.1$. Thus an upper bound for the local truncation error is $0.02e^{0.2} = 0.0244$.

(c) Since $y(0.1) = e^{0.2} = 1.2214$, the actual error is $y(0.1) - y_1 = 0.0214$, which is less than 0.0244.

(d) Using the Euler method with $h = 0.05$ we obtain $y(0.1) \approx y_2 = 1.21$.

(e) The error in **(d)** is $1.2214 - 1.21 = 0.0114$. With global truncation error $O(h)$, when the step size is halved we expect the error for $h = 0.05$ to be one-half the error when $h = 0.1$. Comparing 0.0114 with 0.214 we see that this is the case.

5. (a) Using the improved Euler method we obtain $y(0.1) \approx y_1 = 1.22$.

(b) Using $y''' = 8e^{2x}$ we see that the local truncation error is

$$y'''(c)\frac{h^3}{6} = 8e^{2c}\frac{(0.1)^3}{6} = 0.001333e^{2c}.$$

Since e^{2x} is an increasing function, $e^{2c} \leq e^{2(0.1)} = e^{0.2}$ for $0 \leq c \leq 0.1$. Thus an upper bound for the local truncation error is $0.001333e^{0.2} = 0.001628$.

(c) Since $y(0.1) = e^{0.2} = 1.221403$, the actual error is $y(0.1) - y_1 = 0.001403$ which is less than 0.001628.

(d) Using the improved Euler method with $h = 0.05$ we obtain $y(0.1) \approx y_2 = 1.221025$.

(e) The error in **(d)** is $1.221403 - 1.221025 = 0.000378$. With global truncation error $O(h^2)$, when the step size is halved we expect the error for $h = 0.05$ to be one-fourth the error for $h = 0.1$. Comparing 0.000378 with 0.001403 we see that this is the case.

6. (a) Using the three-term Taylor method we obtain $y(0.1) \approx y_1 = 1.22$.

(b) Using $y''' = 8e^{2x}$ we see that the local truncation error is

$$y'''(c)\frac{h^3}{6} = 8e^{2c}\frac{(0.1)^3}{6} = 0.001333e^{2c}.$$

Since e^{2x} is an increasing function, $e^{2c} \leq e^{2(0.1)} = e^{0.2}$ for $0 \leq c \leq 0.1$. Thus an upper bound for the local truncation error is $0.001333e^{0.2} = 0.001628$.

(c) Since $y(0.1) = e^{0.2} = 1.221403$, the actual error is $y(0.1) - y_1 = 0.001403$ which is less than 0.001628.

(d) Using the three-term Taylor method with $h = 0.05$ we obtain $y(0.1) \approx y_2 = 1.221025$.

(e) The error in (d) is $1.221403 - 1.221025 = 0.000378$. With global truncation error $O(h^2)$, when the step size is halved we expect the error for $h = 0.05$ to be one-fourth the error for $h = 0.1$. Comparing 0.000378 with 0.001403 we see that this is the case.

7. (a) Using the fourth-order Runge-Kutta method we obtain $y(0.1) \approx y_1 = 1.2214$.

(b) Using $y^{(5)}(x) = 32e^{2x}$ we see that the local truncation error is

$$y^{(5)}(c) \frac{h^5}{120} = 32e^{2c} \frac{(0.1)^5}{120} = 0.000002667e^{2c}.$$

Since e^{2x} is an increasing function, $e^{2c} \leq e^{2(0.1)} = e^{0.2}$ for $0 \leq c \leq 0.1$. Thus an upper bound for the local truncation error is $0.000002667e^{0.2} = 0.000003257$.

(c) Since $y(0.1) = e^{0.2} = 1.221402758$, the actual error is $y(0.1) - y_1 = 0.000002758$ which is less than 0.000003257.

(d) Using the fourth-order Runge-Kutta formula with $h = 0.05$ we obtain
$y(0.1) \approx y_2 = 1.221402571$.

(e) The error in (d) is $1.221402758 - 1.221402571 = 0.000000187$. With global truncation error $O(h^4)$, when the step size is halved we expect the error for $h = 0.05$ to be one-sixteenth the error for $h = 0.1$. Comparing 0.000000187 with 0.000002758 we see that this is the case.

8. (a) Using the Euler method we obtain $y(0.1) \approx y_1 = 0.8$.

(b) Using $y'' = 5e^{-2x}$ we see that the local truncation error is

$$5e^{-2c} \frac{(0.1)^2}{2} = 0.025e^{-2c}$$

Since e^{-2x} is a decreasing function, $e^{-2c} \leq e^0 = 1$ for $0 \leq c \leq 0.1$. Thus an upper bound for the local truncation error is $0.025(1) = 0.025$.

(c) Since $y(0.1) = 0.8234$, the actual error is $y(0.1) - y_1 = 0.0234$, which is less than 0.025.

(d) Using the Euler method with $h = 0.05$ we obtain $y(0.1) \approx y_2 = 0.8125$.

(e) The error in (d) is $0.8234 - 0.8125 = 0.0109$. With global truncation error $O(h)$, when the step size is halved we expect the error for $h = 0.05$ to be one-half the error when $h = 0.1$. Comparing 0.0109 with 0.0234 we see that this is the case.

9. (a) Using the improved Euler method we obtain $y(0.1) \approx y_1 = 0.825$.

(b) Using $y''' = -10e^{-2x}$ we see that the local truncation error is

$$10e^{-2c} \frac{(0.1)^3}{6} = 0.001667e^{-2c}.$$

Since e^{-2x} is a decreasing function, $e^{-2c} \leq e^0 = 1$ for $0 \leq c \leq 0.1$. Thus an upper bound for the local truncation error is $0.001667(1) = 0.001667$.

(c) Since $y(0.1) = 0.823413$, the actual error is $y(0.1) - y_1 = 0.001587$, which is less than 0.001667.

(d) Using the improved Euler method with $h = 0.05$ we obtain $y(0.1) \approx y_2 = 0.823781$.

(e) The error in (d) is $|0.823413 - 0.8237181| = 0.000305$. With global truncation error $O(h^2)$, when the step size is halved we expect the error for $h = 0.05$ to be one-fourth the error when $h = 0.1$. Comparing 0.000305 with 0.001587 we see that this is the case.

10. **(a)** Using the three-term Taylor method we obtain $y(0.1) \approx y_1 = 0.825$.

    (b) Using $y''' = -10e^{-2x}$ we see that the local truncation error is

$$10e^{-2c} \frac{(0.1)^3}{6} = 0.001667e^{-2c}.$$

    Since e^{-2x} is a decreasing function, $e^{-2c} \leq e^0 = 1$ for $0 \leq c \leq 0.1$. Thus an upper bound for the local truncation error is $0.001667(1) = 0.001667$.

    (c) Since $y(0.1) = 0.823413$, the actual error is $y(0.1) - y_1 = 0.001587$, which is less than 0.001667.

    (d) Using the three-term Taylor method with $h = 0.05$ we obtain $y(0.1) \approx y_2 = 0.823781$.

    (e) The error in (d) is $|0.823413 - 0.8237181| = 0.000305$. With global truncation error $O(h^2)$, when the step size is halved we expect the error for $h = 0.05$ to be one-fourth the error when $h = 0.1$. Comparing 0.000305 with 0.001587 we see that this is the case.

11. **(a)** Using the fourth-order Runge-Kutta method we obtain $y(0.1) \approx y_1 = 0.823416667$.

    (b) Using $y^{(5)}(x) = -40e^{-2x}$ we see that the local truncation error is

$$40e^{-2c} \frac{(0.1)^5}{120} = 0.000003333.$$

    Since e^{-2x} is a decreasing function, $e^{-2c} \leq e^0 = 1$ for $0 \leq c \leq 0.1$. Thus an upper bound for the local truncation error is $0.000003333(1) = 0.000003333$.

    (c) Since $y(0.1) = 0.823413441$, the actual error is $|y(0.1) - y_1| = 0.000003225$, which is less than 0.000003333.

    (d) Using the fourth-order Runge-Kutta method with $h = 0.05$ we obtain $y(0.1) \approx y_2 = 0.823413627$.

    (e) The error in (d) is $|0.823413441 - 0.823413627| = 0.000000185$. With global truncation error $O(h^4)$, when the step size is halved we expect the error for $h = 0.05$ to be one-sixteenth the error when $h = 0.1$. Comparing 0.000000185 with 0.000003225 we see that this is the case.

12. **(a)** Using $y'' = 38e^{-3(x-1)}$ we see that the local truncation error is

$$y''(c) \frac{h^2}{2} = 38e^{-3(c-1)} \frac{h^2}{2} = 19h^2 e^{-3(c-1)}.$$

(b) Since $e^{-3(x-1)}$ is a decreasing function for $1 \leq x \leq 1.5$, $e^{-3(c-1)} \leq e^{-3(1-1)} = 1$ for $1 \leq c \leq 1.5$ and

$$y''(c)\frac{h^2}{2} \leq 19(0.1)^2(1) = 0.19.$$

(c) Using the Euler method with $h = 0.1$ we obtain $y(1.5) \approx 1.8207$. With $h = 0.05$ we obtain $y(1.5) \approx 1.9424$.

(d) Since $y(1.5) = 2.0532$, the error for $h = 0.1$ is $E_{0.1} = 0.2325$, while the error for $h = 0.05$ is $E_{0.05} = 0.1109$. With global truncation error $O(h)$ we expect $E_{0.1}/E_{0.05} \approx 2$. We actually have $E_{0.1}/E_{0.05} = 2.10$.

13. (a) Using $y''' = -114e^{-3(x-1)}$ we see that the local truncation error is

$$\left| y'''(c)\frac{h^3}{6} \right| = 114e^{-3(x-1)}\frac{h^3}{6} = 19h^3 e^{-3(c-1)}.$$

(b) Since $e^{-3(x-1)}$ is a decreasing function for $1 \leq x \leq 1.5$, $e^{-3(c-1)} \leq e^{-3(1-1)} = 1$ for $1 \leq c \leq 1.5$ and

$$\left| y'''(c)\frac{h^3}{6} \right| \leq 19(0.1)^3(1) = 0.019.$$

(c) Using the improved Euler method with $h = 0.1$ we obtain $y(1.5) \approx 2.080108$. With $h = 0.05$ we obtain $y(1.5) \approx 2.059166$.

(d) Since $y(1.5) = 2.053216$, the error for $h = 0.1$ is $E_{0.1} = 0.026892$, while the error for $h = 0.05$ is $E_{0.05} = 0.005950$. With global truncation error $O(h^2)$ we expect $E_{0.1}/E_{0.05} \approx 4$. We actually have $E_{0.1}/E_{0.05} = 4.52$.

14. (a) Using $y''' = -114e^{-3(x-1)}$ we see that the local truncation error is

$$\left| y'''(c)\frac{h^3}{6} \right| = 114e^{-3(x-1)}\frac{h^3}{6} = 19h^3 e^{-3(c-1)}.$$

(b) Since $e^{-3(x-1)}$ is a decreasing function for $1 \leq x \leq 1.5$, $e^{-3(c-1)} \leq e^{-3(1-1)} = 1$ for $1 \leq c \leq 1.5$ and

$$\left| y'''(c)\frac{h^3}{6} \right| \leq 19(0.1)^3(1) = 0.019.$$

(c) Using the three-term Taylor method with $h = 0.1$ we obtain $y(1.5) \approx 2.080108$. With $h = 0.05$ we obtain $y(1.5) \approx 2.059166$.

(d) Since $y(1.5) = 2.053216$, the error for $h = 0.1$ is $E_{0.1} = 0.026892$, while the error for $h = 0.05$ is $E_{0.05} = 0.005950$. With global truncation error $O(h^2)$ we expect $E_{0.1}/E_{0.05} \approx 4$. We actually have $E_{0.1}/E_{0.05} = 4.52$.

15. (a) Using $y^{(5)} = -1026e^{-3(x-1)}$ we see that the local truncation error is

$$\left| y^{(5)}(c)\frac{h^5}{120} \right| = 8.55h^5 e^{-3(c-1)}.$$

(b) Since $e^{-3(x-1)}$ is a decreasing function for $1 \le x \le 1.5$, $e^{-3(c-1)} \le e^{-3(1-1)} = 1$ for $1 \le c \le 1.5$
and

$$y^{(5)}(c)\frac{h^5}{120} \le 8.55(0.1)^5(1) = 0.0000855.$$

(c) Using the fourth-order Runge-Kutta method with $h = 0.1$ we obtain $y(1.5) \approx 2.053338827$.
With $h = 0.05$ we obtain $y(1.5) \approx 2.053222989$.

(d) Since $y(1.5) = 2.053216232$, the error for $h = 0.1$ is $E_{0.1} = 0.000122595$, while the error for
$h = 0.05$ is $E_{0.05} = 0.000006757$. With global truncation error $O(h^4)$ we expect $E_{0.1}/E_{0.05} \approx$
16. We actually have $E_{0.1}/E_{0.05} = 18.14$.

16. (a) Using $y'' = -\dfrac{1}{(x+1)^2}$ we see that the local truncation error is

$$\left| y''(c)\frac{h^2}{2} \right| = \frac{1}{(c+1)^2}\frac{h^2}{2}.$$

(b) Since $\dfrac{1}{(x+1)^2}$ is a decreasing function for $0 \le x \le 0.5$, $\dfrac{1}{(c+1)^2} \le \dfrac{1}{(0+1)^2} = 1$ for $0 \le c \le 0.5$
and

$$\left| y''(c)\frac{h^2}{2} \right| \le (1)\frac{(0.1)^2}{2} = 0.005.$$

(c) Using the Euler method with $h = 0.1$ we obtain $y(0.5) \approx 0.4198$. With $h = 0.05$ we obtain
$y(0.5) \approx 0.4124$.

(d) Since $y(0.5) = 0.4055$, the error for $h = 0.1$ is $E_{0.1} = 0.0143$, while the error for $h = 0.05$ is
$E_{0.05} = 0.0069$. With global truncation error $O(h)$ we expect $E_{0.1}/E_{0.05} \approx 2$. We actually have
$E_{0.1}/E_{0.05} = 2.06$.

17. (a) Using $y''' = \dfrac{2}{(x+1)^3}$ we see that the local truncation error is

$$y'''(c)\frac{h^3}{6} = \frac{1}{(c+1)^3}\frac{h^3}{3}.$$

(b) Since $\dfrac{1}{(x+1)^3}$ is a decreasing function for $0 \le x \le 0.5$, $\dfrac{1}{(c+1)^3} \le \dfrac{1}{(0+1)^3} = 1$ for $0 \le c \le 0.5$
and

$$y'''(c)\frac{h^3}{6} \le (1)\frac{(0.1)^3}{3} = 0.000333.$$

391

(c) Using the improved Euler method with $h = 0.1$ we obtain $y(0.5) \approx 0.405281$. With $h = 0.05$ we obtain $y(0.5) \approx 0.405419$.

(d) Since $y(0.5) = 0.405465$, the error for $h = 0.1$ is $E_{0.1} = 0.000184$, while the error for $h = 0.05$ is $E_{0.05} = 0.000046$. With global truncation error $O(h^2)$ we expect $E_{0.1}/E_{0.05} \approx 4$. We actually have $E_{0.1}/E_{0.05} = 3.98$.

18. (a) Using $y''' = \dfrac{2}{(x+1)^3}$ we see that the local truncation error is

$$y'''(c)\frac{h^3}{6} = \frac{1}{(c+1)^3}\frac{h^3}{3}.$$

(b) Since $\dfrac{1}{(x+1)^3}$ is a decreasing function for $0 \le x \le 0.5$, $\dfrac{1}{(c+1)^3} \le \dfrac{1}{(0+1)^3} = 1$ for $0 \le c \le 0.5$ and

$$y'''(c)\frac{h^3}{6} \le (1)\frac{(0.1)^3}{3} = 0.000333.$$

(c) Using the three-term Taylor method with $h = 0.1$ we obtain $y(0.5) \approx 0.404643$. With $h = 0.05$ we obtain $y(0.5) \approx 0.405270$.

(d) Since $y(0.5) = 0.405465$, the error for $h = 0.1$ is $E_{0.1} = 0.000823$, while the error for $h = 0.05$ is $E_{0.05} = 0.000195$. With global truncation error $O(h^2)$ we expect $E_{0.1}/E_{0.05} \approx 4$. We actually have $E_{0.1}/E_{0.05} = 4.22$.

19. (a) Using $y^{(5)} = \dfrac{24}{(x+1)^5}$ we see that the local truncation error is

$$y^{(5)}(c)\frac{h^5}{120} = \frac{1}{(c+1)^5}\frac{h^5}{5}.$$

(b) Since $\dfrac{1}{(x+1)^5}$ is a decreasing function for $0 \le x \le 0.5$, $\dfrac{1}{(c+1)^5} \le \dfrac{1}{(1+1)^5} = 1$ for $0 \le c \le 0.5$ and

$$y^{(5)}(c)\frac{h^5}{5} \le (1)\frac{(0.1)^5}{5} = 0.000002.$$

(c) Using the fourth-order Runge-Kutta method with $h = 0.1$ we obtain $y(0.5) \approx 0.405465168$. With $h = 0.05$ we obtain $y(0.5) \approx 0.405465111$.

(d) Since $y(0.5) = 0.405465108$, the error for $h = 0.1$ is $E_{0.1} = 0.000000060$, while the error for $h = 0.05$ is $E_{0.05} = 0.000000003$. With global truncation error $O(h^4)$ we expect $E_{0.1}/E_{0.05} \approx 16$. We actually have $E_{0.1}/E_{0.05} = 17.64$.

1. The substitution $y' = u$ leads to the iteration formulas

$$y_{n+1} = y_n + hu_n, \qquad u_{n+1} = u_n + h(4u_n - 4y_n).$$

The initial conditions are $y_0 = -2$ and $u_0 = 1$. Then

$$y_1 = y_0 + 0.1u_0 = -2 + 0.1(1) = -1.9$$

$$u_1 = u_0 + 0.1(4u_0 - 4y_0) = 1 + 0.1(4 + 8) = 2.2$$

$$y_2 = y_1 + 0.1u_1 = -1.9 + 0.1(2.2) = -1.68.$$

The general solution of the differential equation is $y = c_1 e^{2x} + c_2 x e^{2x}$. From the initial conditions we find $c_1 = -2$ and $c_2 = 5$. Thus $y = -2e^{2x} + 5xe^{2x}$ and $y(0.2) \approx 1.4918$.

2. The substitution $y' = u$ leads to the iteration formulas

$$y_{n+1} = y_n + hu_n, \qquad u_{n+1} = u_n + h\left(\frac{2}{x}u_n - \frac{2}{x^2}y_n\right).$$

The initial conditions are $y_0 = 4$ and $u_0 = 9$. Then

$$y_1 = y_0 + 0.1u_0 = 4 + 0.1(9) = 4.9$$

$$u_1 = u_0 + 0.1\left(\frac{2}{1}u_0 - \frac{2}{1}y_0\right) = 9 + 0.1[2(9) - 2(4)] = 10$$

$$y_2 = y_1 + 0.1u_1 = 4.9 + 0.1(10) = 5.9.$$

The general solution of the Cauchy-Euler differential equation is $y = c_1 x + c_2 x^2$. From the initial conditions we find $c_1 = -1$ and $c_2 = 5$. Thus $y = -x + 5x^2$ and $y(1.2) = 6$.

3. The substitution $y' = u$ leads to the system

$$y' = u, \qquad u' = 4u - 4y.$$

Using formulas (5) and (6) in the text with x corresponding to t, y corresponding to x, and u corresponding to y, we obtain

| | | | | | | | Runge-Kutta method with h=0.2 | | | |
m1	m2	m3	m4	k1	k2	k3	k4	x	y	u
								0.00	-2.0000	1.0000
0.2000	0.4400	0.5280	0.9072	2.4000	3.2800	3.5360	4.8064	0.20	-1.4928	4.4731

| | | | | | | | Runge-Kutta method with h=0.1 | | | |
m1	m2	m3	m4	k1	k2	k3	k4	x	y	u
								0.00	-2.0000	1.0000
0.1000	0.1600	0.1710	0.2452	1.2000	1.4200	1.4520	1.7124	0.10	-1.8321	2.4427
0.2443	0.3298	0.3444	0.4487	1.7099	2.0031	2.0446	2.3900	0.20	-1.4919	4.4753

393

4. The substitution $y' = u$ leads to the system

$$y' = u, \qquad u' = \frac{2}{x}u - \frac{2}{x^2}y.$$

Using formulas (5) and (6) in the text with x corresponding to t, y corresponding to x, and u corresponding to y, we obtain

Runge-Kutta method with h=0.2

m1	m2	m3	m4	k1	k2	k3	k4	x	y	u
								1.00	4.0000	9.0000
1.8000	2.0000	2.0017	2.1973	2.0000	2.0165	1.9865	1.9950	1.20	6.0001	11.0002

Runge-Kutta method with h=0.1

m1	m2	m3	m4	k1	k2	k3	k4	x	y	u
								1.00	4.0000	9.0000
0.9000	0.9500	0.9501	0.9998	1.0000	1.0023	0.9979	0.9996	1.10	4.9500	10.0000
1.0000	1.0500	1.0501	1.0998	1.0000	1.0019	0.9983	0.9997	1.20	6.0000	11.0000

5. The substitution $y' = u$ leads to the system

$$y' = u, \qquad u' = 2u - 2y + e^t \cos t.$$

Using formulas (5) and (6) in the text with y corresponding to x and u corresponding to y, we obtain

Runge-Kutta method with h=0.2

m1	m2	m3	m4	k1	k2	k3	k4	t	y	u
								0.00	1.0000	2.0000
0.4000	0.4600	0.4660	0.5320	0.6000	0.6599	0.6599	0.7170	0.20	1.4640	2.6594

Runge-Kutta method with h=0.1

m1	m2	m3	m4	k1	k2	k3	k4	t	y	u
								0.00	1.0000	2.0000
0.2000	0.2150	0.2157	0.2315	0.3000	0.3150	0.3150	0.3298	0.10	1.2155	2.3150
0.2315	0.2480	0.2487	0.2659	0.3299	0.3446	0.3444	0.3587	0.20	1.4640	2.6594

6.

Runge-Kutta method with h=0.1

m1	m2	m3	m4	k1	k2	k3	k4	t	i1	i2
								0.00	0.0000	0.0000
10.0000	0.0000	12.5000	-20.0000	0.0000	5.0000	-5.0000	22.5000	0.10	2.5000	3.7500
8.7500	-2.5000	13.4375	-28.7500	-5.0000	4.3750	-10.6250	29.6875	0.20	2.8125	5.7813
10.1563	-4.3750	17.0703	-40.0000	-8.7500	5.0781	-16.0156	40.3516	0.30	2.0703	7.4023
13.2617	-6.3672	22.9443	-55.1758	-12.7344	6.6309	-22.5488	55.3076	0.40	0.6104	9.1919
17.9712	-8.8867	31.3507	-75.9326	-17.7734	8.9856	-31.2024	75.9821	0.50	-1.5619	11.4877

7.

Runge-Kutta method with h=0.2

m1	m2	m3	m4	k1	k2	k3	k4	t	x	y
								0.00	6.0000	2.0000
2.0000	2.2800	2.3160	2.6408	1.2000	1.4000	1.4280	1.6632	0.20	8.3055	3.4199

Runge-Kutta method with h=0.1

m1	m2	m3	m4	k1	k2	k3	k4	t	x	y
								0.00	6.0000	2.0000
1.0000	1.0700	1.0745	1.1496	0.6000	0.6500	0.6535	0.7075	0.10	7.0731	2.6524
1.1494	1.2289	1.2340	1.3193	0.7073	0.7648	0.7688	0.8307	0.20	8.3055	3.4199

8.

Runge-Kutta method with h=0.2

m1	m2	m3	m4	k1	k2	k3	k4	t	x	y
								0.00	1.0000	1.0000
0.6000	0.9400	1.1060	1.7788	1.4000	2.0600	2.3940	3.7212	0.20	2.0785	3.3382

Runge-Kutta method with h=0.1

m1	m2	m3	m4	k1	k2	k3	k4	t	x	y
								0.00	1.0000	1.0000
0.3000	0.3850	0.4058	0.5219	0.7000	0.8650	0.9068	1.1343	0.10	1.4006	1.8963
0.5193	0.6582	0.6925	0.8828	1.1291	1.4024	1.4711	1.8474	0.20	2.0845	3.3502

9.

Runge-Kutta method with h=0.2

m1	m2	m3	m4	k1	k2	k3	k4	t	x	y
								0.00	-3.0000	5.0000
-1.0000	-0.9200	-0.9080	-0.8176	-0.6000	-0.7200	-0.7120	-0.8216	0.20	-3.9123	4.2857

Runge-Kutta method with h=0.1

m1	m2	m3	m4	k1	k2	k3	k4	t	x	y
								0.00	-3.0000	5.0000
-0.5000	-0.4800	-0.4785	-0.4571	-0.3000	-0.3300	-0.3290	-0.3579	0.10	-3.4790	4.6707
-0.4571	-0.4342	-0.4328	-0.4086	-0.3579	-0.3858	-0.3846	-0.4112	0.20	-3.9123	4.2857

10.

Runge-Kutta method with h=0.2

m1	m2	m3	m4	k1	k2	k3	k4	t	x	y
								0.00	0.5000	0.2000
0.6400	1.2760	1.7028	3.3558	1.3200	1.7720	2.1620	3.5794	0.20	2.1589	2.3279

Runge-Kutta method with h=0.1

m1	m2	m3	m4	k1	k2	k3	k4	t	x	y
								0.00	0.5000	0.2000
0.3200	0.4790	0.5324	0.7816	0.6600	0.7730	0.8218	1.0195	0.10	1.0207	1.0115
0.7736	1.0862	1.1929	1.6862	1.0117	1.2682	1.3692	1.7996	0.20	2.1904	2.3592

—————— **Exercises 9.8** ——————

1. We identify $P(x) = 0$, $Q(x) = 9$, $f(x) = 0$, and $h = (2-0)/4 = 0.5$. Then the finite difference equation is

$$y_{i+1} + 0.25y_i + y_{i-1} = 0.$$

The solution of the corresponding linear system gives

x	0.0	0.5	1.0	1.5	2.0
y	4.0000	-5.6774	-2.5807	6.3226	1.0000

2. We identify $P(x) = 0$, $Q(x) = -1$, $f(x) = x^2$, and $h = (1-0)/4 = 0.25$. Then the finite difference equation is

$$y_{i+1} - 2.0625y_i + y_{i-1} = 0.0625x_i^2.$$

The solution of the corresponding linear system gives

x	0.00	0.25	0.50	0.75	1.00
y	0.0000	-0.0172	-0.0316	-0.0324	0.0000

3. We identify $P(x) = 2$, $Q(x) = 1$, $f(x) = 5x$, and $h = (1-0)/5 = 0.2$. Then the finite difference equation is

$$1.2y_{i+1} - 1.96y_i + 0.8y_{i-1} = 0.04(5x_i).$$

The solution of the corresponding linear system gives

x	0.0	0.2	0.4	0.6	0.8	1.0
y	0.0000	-0.2259	-0.3356	-0.3308	-0.2167	0.0000

4. We identify $P(x) = -10$, $Q(x) = 25$, $f(x) = 1$, and $h = (1-0)/5 = 0.2$. Then the finite difference equation is

$$-y_i + 2y_{i-1} = 0.04.$$

The solution of the corresponding linear system gives

x	0.0	0.2	0.4	0.6	0.8	1.0
y	1.0000	1.9600	3.8800	7.7200	15.4000	0.0000

5. We identify $P(x) = -4$, $Q(x) = 4$, $f(x) = (1+x)e^{2x}$, and $h = (1-0)/6 = 0.1667$. Then the finite difference equation is

$$0.6667y_{i+1} - 1.8889y_i + 1.3333y_{i-1} = 0.2778(1+x_i)e^{2x_i}.$$

The solution of the corresponding linear system gives

x	0.0000	0.1667	0.3333	0.5000	0.6667	0.8333	1.0000
y	3.0000	3.3751	3.6306	3.6448	3.2355	2.1411	0.0000

6. We identify $P(x) = 5$, $Q(x) = 0$, $f(x) = 4\sqrt{x}$, and $h = (2-1)/6 = 0.1667$. Then the finite difference equation is

$$1.4167 y_{i+1} - 2y_i + 0.5833 y_{i-1} = 0.2778(4\sqrt{x_i}).$$

The solution of the corresponding linear system gives

x	1.0000	1.1667	1.3333	1.5000	1.6667	1.8333	2.0000
y	1.0000	-0.5918	-1.1626	-1.3070	-1.2704	-1.1541	-1.0000

7. We identify $P(x) = 3/x$, $Q(x) = 3/x^2$, $f(x) = 0$, and $h = (2-1)/8 = 0.125$. Then the finite difference equation is

$$\left(1 + \frac{0.1875}{x_i}\right) y_{i+1} + \left(-2 + \frac{0.0469}{x_i^2}\right) y_i + \left(1 - \frac{0.1875}{x_i}\right) y_{i-1} = 0.$$

The solution of the corresponding linear system gives

x	1.000	1.125	1.250	1.375	1.500	1.625	1.750	1.875	2.000
y	5.0000	3.8842	2.9640	2.2064	1.5826	1.0681	0.6430	0.2913	0.0000

8. We identify $P(x) = -1/x$, $Q(x) = x^{-2}$, $f(x) = \ln x/x^2$, and $h = (2-1)/8 = 0.125$. Then the finite difference equation is

$$\left(1 - \frac{0.0625}{x_i}\right) y_{i+1} + \left(-2 + \frac{0.0156}{x_i^2}\right) y_i + \left(1 + \frac{0.0625}{x_i}\right) y_{i-1} = 0.0156 \ln x_i.$$

The solution of the corresponding linear system gives

x	1.000	1.125	1.250	1.375	1.500	1.625	1.750	1.875	2.000
y	0.0000	-0.1988	-0.4168	-0.6510	-0.8992	-1.1594	-1.4304	-1.7109	-2.0000

9. We identify $P(x) = 1 - x$, $Q(x) = x$, $f(x) = x$, and $h = (1-0)/10 = 0.1$. Then the finite difference equation is

$$[1 + 0.05(1 - x_i)]y_{i+1} + [-2 + 0.01 x_i]y_i + [1 - 0.05(1 - x_i)]y_{i-1} = 0.01 x_i.$$

The solution of the corresponding linear system gives

x	0.0	0.1	0.2	0.3	0.4	0.5	0.6
y	0.0000	0.2660	0.5097	0.7357	0.9471	1.1465	1.3353

0.7	0.8	0.9	1.0
1.5149	1.6855	1.8474	2.0000

10. We identify $P(x) = x$, $Q(x) = 1$, $f(x) = x$, and $h = (1-0)/10 = 0.1$. Then the finite difference equation is

$$(1 + 0.05 x_i) y_{i+1} - 1.99 y_i + (1 - 0.05 x_i) y_{i-1} = 0.01 x_i.$$

The solution of the corresponding linear system gives

x	0.0	0.1	0.2	0.3	0.4	0.5	0.6
y	1.0000	0.8929	0.7789	0.6615	0.5440	0.4296	0.3216

	0.7	0.8	0.9	1.0
	0.2225	0.1347	0.0601	0.0000

11. We identify $P(x) = 0$, $Q(x) = -4$, $f(x) = 0$, and $h = (1 - 0)/8 = 0.125$. Then the finite difference equation is

$$y_{i+1} - 2.0625y_i + y_{i-1} = 0.$$

The solution of the corresponding linear system gives

x	0.000	0.125	0.250	0.375	0.500	0.625	0.750	0.875	1.000
y	0.0000	0.3492	0.7202	1.1363	1.6233	2.2118	2.9386	3.8490	5.0000

12. We identify $P(r) = 2/r$, $Q(r) = 0$, $f(r) = 0$, and $h = (4 - 1)/6 = 0.5$. Then the finite difference equation is

$$\left(1 + \frac{0.5}{r_i}\right) u_{i+1} - 2u_i + \left(1 - \frac{0.5}{r_i}\right) u_{i-1} = 0.$$

The solution of the corresponding linear system gives

r	1.0	1.5	2.0	2.5	3.0	3.5	4.0
u	50.0000	72.2222	83.3333	90.0000	94.4444	97.6190	100.0000

13. (a) The difference equation

$$\left(1 + \frac{h}{2}P_i\right) y_{i+1} + (-2 + h^2 Q_i)y_i + \left(1 - \frac{h}{2}P_i\right) y_{i-1} = h^2 f_i$$

is the same as the one derived on page 530 in the text. The equations are the same because the derivation was based only on the differential equation, not the boundary conditions. If we allow i to range from 0 to $n - 1$ we obtain n equations in the $n + 1$ unknowns $y_{-1}, y_0, y_1, \ldots,$ y_{n-1}. Since y_n is one of the given boundary conditions, it is not an unknown.

(b) Identifying $y_0 = y(0)$, $y_{-1} = y(0 - h)$, and $y_1 = y(0 + h)$ we have from (5) in the text

$$\frac{1}{2h}[y_1 - y_{-1}] = y'(0) = 1 \quad \text{or} \quad y_1 - y_{-1} = 2h.$$

The difference equation corresponding to $i = 0$,

$$\left(1 + \frac{h}{2}P_0\right) y_1 + (-2 + h^2 Q_0)y_0 + \left(1 - \frac{h}{2}P_0\right) y_{-1} = h^2 f_0$$

becomes, with $y_{-1} = y_1 - 2h$,

$$\left(1 + \frac{h}{2}P_0\right) y_1 + (-2 + h^2 Q_0)y_0 + \left(1 - \frac{h}{2}P_0\right) (y_1 - 2h) = h^2 f_0$$

or

$$2y_1 + (-2 + h^2 Q_0)y_0 = h^2 f_0 + 2h - P_0.$$

Alternatively, we may simply add the equation $y_1 - y_{-1} = 2h$ to the list of n difference equations obtaining $n + 1$ equations in the $n + 1$ unknowns $y_{-1}, y_0, y_1, \ldots, y_{n-1}$.

(c) Using $n = 5$ we obtain

x	0.0	0.2	0.4	0.6	0.8	1.0
y	-2.2755	-2.0755	-1.8589	-1.6126	-1.3275	-1.0000

Chapter 9 Review Exercises

1.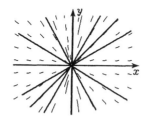

2.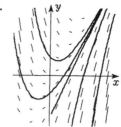

3.

h=0.1 x(n)	EULER	IMPROVED EULER	3-TERM TAYLOR	RUNGE KUTTA
1.00	2.0000	2.0000	2.0000	2.0000
1.10	2.1386	2.1549	2.1556	2.1556
1.20	2.3097	2.3439	2.3446	2.3454
1.30	2.5136	2.5672	2.5680	2.5695
1.40	2.7504	2.8246	2.8255	2.8278
1.50	3.0201	3.1157	3.1167	3.1197

h=0.05 x(n)	EULER	IMPROVED EULER	3-TERM TAYLOR	RUNGE KUTTA
1.00	2.0000	2.0000	2.0000	2.0000
1.05	2.0693	2.0735	2.0735	2.0736
1.10	2.1469	2.1554	2.1555	2.1556
1.15	2.2328	2.2459	2.2460	2.2462
1.20	2.3272	2.3450	2.3451	2.3454
1.25	2.4299	2.4527	2.4528	2.4532
1.30	2.5409	2.5689	2.5690	2.5695
1.35	2.6604	2.6937	2.6938	2.6944
1.40	2.7883	2.8269	2.8271	2.8278
1.45	2.9245	2.9686	2.9688	2.9696
1.50	3.0690	3.1187	3.1188	3.1197

4.

h=0.1 x(n)	EULER	IMPROVED EULER	3-TERM TAYLOR	RUNGE KUTTA
0.00	0.0000	0.0000	0.0000	0.0000
0.10	0.1000	0.1005	0.1000	0.1003
0.20	0.2010	0.2030	0.2025	0.2026
0.30	0.3049	0.3092	0.3087	0.3087
0.40	0.4135	0.4207	0.4202	0.4201
0.50	0.5279	0.5382	0.5377	0.5376

h=0.05 x(n)	EULER	IMPROVED EULER	3-TERM TAYLOR	RUNGE KUTTA
0.00	0.0000	0.0000	0.0000	0.0000
0.05	0.0500	0.0501	0.0500	0.0500
0.10	0.1001	0.1004	0.1003	0.1003
0.15	0.1506	0.1512	0.1511	0.1511
0.20	0.2017	0.2027	0.2027	0.2026
0.25	0.2537	0.2552	0.2551	0.2551
0.30	0.3067	0.3088	0.3088	0.3087
0.35	0.3610	0.3638	0.3638	0.3637
0.40	0.4167	0.4202	0.4202	0.4201
0.45	0.4739	0.4782	0.4782	0.4781
0.50	0.5327	0.5378	0.5377	0.5376

5.

h=0.1 x(n)	EULER	IMPROVED EULER	3-TERM TAYLOR	RUNGE KUTTA
0.50	0.5000	0.5000	0.5000	0.5000
0.60	0.6000	0.6048	0.6050	0.6049
0.70	0.7095	0.7191	0.7194	0.7194
0.80	0.8283	0.8427	0.8429	0.8431
0.90	0.9559	0.9752	0.9754	0.9757
1.00	1.0921	1.1163	1.1166	1.1169

h=0.05 x(n)	EULER	IMPROVED EULER	3-TERM TAYLOR	RUNGE KUTTA
0.50	0.5000	0.5000	0.5000	0.5000
0.55	0.5500	0.5512	0.5513	0.5512
0.60	0.6024	0.6049	0.6049	0.6049
0.65	0.6573	0.6609	0.6610	0.6610
0.70	0.7144	0.7193	0.7194	0.7194
0.75	0.7739	0.7800	0.7801	0.7801
0.80	0.8356	0.8430	0.8430	0.8431
0.85	0.8996	0.9082	0.9082	0.9083
0.90	0.9657	0.9755	0.9756	0.9757
0.95	1.0340	1.0451	1.0451	1.0452
1.00	1.1044	1.1168	1.1168	1.1169

6.

h=0.1		IMPROVED	3-TERM	RUNGE
x(n)	EULER	EULER	TAYLOR	KUTTA
1.00	1.0000	1.0000	1.0000	1.0000
1.10	1.2000	1.2380	1.2350	1.2415
1.20	1.4760	1.5910	1.5866	1.6036
1.30	1.8710	2.1524	2.1453	2.1909
1.40	2.4643	3.1458	3.1329	3.2745
1.50	3.4165	5.2510	5.2208	5.8338

h=0.05		IMPROVED	3-TERM	RUNGE
x(n)	EULER	EULER	TAYLOR	KUTTA
1.00	1.0000	1.0000	1.0000	1.0000
1.05	1.1000	1.1091	1.1088	1.1095
1.10	1.2183	1.2405	1.2401	1.2415
1.15	1.3595	1.4010	1.4004	1.4029
1.20	1.5300	1.6001	1.5994	1.6036
1.25	1.7389	1.8523	1.8515	1.8586
1.30	1.9988	2.1799	2.1789	2.1911
1.35	2.3284	2.6197	2.6182	2.6401
1.40	2.7567	3.2360	3.2340	3.2755
1.45	3.3296	4.1528	4.1497	4.2363
1.50	4.1253	5.6404	5.6350	5.8446

7. Using

$$y_{n+1} = y_n + hu_n, \qquad\qquad y_0 = 3$$

$$u_{n+1} = u_n + h(2x_n + 1)y_n, \qquad u_0 = 1$$

we obtain (when $h = 0.2$) $y_1 = y(0.2) = y_0 + hu_0 = 3 + (0.2)1 = 3.2$. When $h = 0.1$ we have

$$y_1 = y_0 + 0.1u_0 = 3 + (0.1)1 = 3.1$$

$$u_1 = u_0 + 0.1(2x_0 + 1)y_0 = 1 + 0.1(1)3 = 1.3$$

$$y_2 = y_1 + 0.1u_1 = 3.1 + 0.1(1.3) = 3.23.$$

8.

x(n)	y(n)	
0.00	2.0000	initial condition
0.10	2.4734	Runge-Kutta
0.20	3.1781	Runge-Kutta
0.30	4.3925	Runge-Kutta
	6.7689	*predictor*
0.40	7.0783	corrector

9. Using $x_0 = 1$, $y_0 = 2$, and $h = 0.1$ we have

$$x_1 = x_0 + h(x_0 + y_0) = 1 + 0.1(1 + 2) = 1.3$$

$$y_1 = y_0 + h(x_0 - y_0) = 2 + 0.1(1 - 2) = 1.9$$

and

$$x_2 = x_1 + h(x_1 + y_1) = 1.3 + 0.1(1.3 + 1.9) = 1.62$$

$$y_2 = y_1 + h(x_1 - y_1) = 1.9 + 0.1(1.3 - 1.9) = 1.84.$$

Thus, $x(0.2) \approx 1.62$ and $y(0.2) \approx 1.84$.

10. We identify $P(x) = 0$, $Q(x) = 6.55(1 + x)$, $f(x) = 1$, and $h = (1 - 0)/10 = 0.1$. Then the finite difference equation is

$$y_{i+1} + [-2 + 0.0655(1 + x_i)]y_i + y_{i-1} = 0.001$$

or

$$y_{i+1} + (0.0655x_i - 1.9345)y_i + y_{i-1} = 0.001.$$

The solution of the corresponding linear system gives

x	0.0	0.1	0.2	0.3	0.4	0.5	0.6
y	0.0000	4.1987	8.1049	11.3840	13.7038	14.7770	14.4083

0.7	0.8	0.9	1.0
12.5396	9.2847	4.9450	0.0000

Appendix

1. **(a)** $\Gamma(5) = \Gamma(4+1) = 4! = 24$

   (b) $\Gamma(7) = \Gamma(6+1) = 6! = 720$

   (c) Using Example 1 in the text,

   $$-2\sqrt{\pi} = \Gamma\left(-\frac{1}{2}\right) = \Gamma\left(-\frac{3}{2}+1\right) = -\frac{3}{2}\Gamma\left(-\frac{3}{2}\right).$$

   Thus, $\Gamma(-3/2) = 4\sqrt{\pi}/3$.

   (d) Using (c)

   $$\frac{4\sqrt{\pi}}{3} = \Gamma\left(-\frac{3}{2}\right) = \Gamma\left(-\frac{5}{2}+1\right) = -\frac{5}{2}\Gamma\left(-\frac{5}{2}\right).$$

   Thus $\Gamma(-5/2) = -8\sqrt{\pi}/15$.

2. If $t = x^5$, then $dt = 5x^4\,dx$ and $x^5\,dx = \frac{1}{5}t^{1/5}\,dt$. Now

   $$\int_0^\infty x^5 e^{-x^5}\,dx = \int_0^\infty \frac{1}{5}t^{1/5}e^{-t}\,dt = \frac{1}{5}\int_0^\infty t^{1/5}e^{-t}\,dt$$

   $$= \frac{1}{5}\Gamma\left(\frac{6}{5}\right) = \frac{1}{5}(0.92) = 0.184.$$

3. If $t = x^3$, then $dt = 3x^2\,dx$ and $x^4\,dx = \frac{1}{3}t^{2/3}\,dt$. Now

   $$\int_0^\infty x^4 e^{-x^3}\,dx = \int_0^\infty \frac{1}{3}t^{2/3}e^{-t}\,dt = \frac{1}{3}\int_0^\infty t^{2/3}e^{-t}\,dt$$

   $$= \frac{1}{3}\Gamma\left(\frac{5}{3}\right) = \frac{1}{3}(0.89) \approx 0.297.$$

4. If $t = -\ln x = \ln\frac{1}{x}$ then $dt = -\frac{1}{x}\,dx$. Also $e^t = \frac{1}{x}$, so $x = e^{-t}$ and $dx = -x\,dt = -e^{-t}\,dt$. Thus

   $$\int_0^1 x^3 \left(\ln\frac{1}{x}\right)^3 dx = \int_\infty^0 (e^{-t})^3 t^3 (-e^{-t})\,dt$$

   $$= \int_0^\infty t^3 e^{-4t}\,dt$$

   $$= \int_0^\infty \left(\frac{1}{4}u\right)^3 e^{-u} \left(\frac{1}{4}du\right) \qquad [u = 4t]$$

$$= \frac{1}{256} \int_0^\infty u^3 e^{-u} du = \frac{1}{256} \Gamma(4)$$

$$= \frac{1}{256}(3!) = \frac{3}{128}.$$

5. Since $e^{-t} \geq e^{-1}$ for $0 \leq t \leq 1$,

$$\Gamma(x) = \int_0^\infty t^{x-1} e^{-t} dt > \int_0^1 t^{x-1} e^{-t} dt \geq e^{-1} \int_0^1 t^{x-1} dt$$

$$= \frac{1}{e} \left(\frac{1}{x} t^x \right) \Big|_0^1 = \frac{1}{ex}$$

for $x > 0$. As $x \to 0^+$, we see that $\Gamma(x) \to \infty$.

6. For $x > 0$

$$\Gamma(x+1) = \int_0^\infty t^x e^{-t} dt$$

$u = t^x$	$dv = e^{-t}\, dt$
$du = xt^{x-1}\, dt$	$v = -e^{-t}$

$$= -t^x e^{-t} \Big|_0^\infty - \int_0^\infty xt^{x-1}(-e^{-t})\, dt$$

$$= x \int_0^\infty t^{x-1} e^{-t} dt = x\Gamma(x).$$

―――――― **Appendix III** ――――――

1. Expanding by the first column gives

$$\begin{vmatrix} 2 & 4 & 6 \\ -1 & 5 & 1 \\ 0 & 2 & -3 \end{vmatrix} = 2 \begin{vmatrix} 5 & 1 \\ 2 & -3 \end{vmatrix} - (-1) \begin{vmatrix} 4 & 6 \\ 2 & -3 \end{vmatrix} = 2(-15 - 2) + (-12 - 12) = -58.$$

2. Expanding by the first row gives

$$\begin{vmatrix} 1 & 4 & 2 \\ -2 & 6 & 3 \\ 9 & 8 & 4 \end{vmatrix} = 1 \begin{vmatrix} 6 & 3 \\ 8 & 4 \end{vmatrix} - 4 \begin{vmatrix} -2 & 3 \\ 9 & 4 \end{vmatrix} + 2 \begin{vmatrix} -2 & 6 \\ 9 & 8 \end{vmatrix}$$

$$= (24 - 24) - 4(-8 - 27) + 2(-16 - 54) = 0.$$

3. Expanding by the first row gives

$$\begin{vmatrix} 2 & 0 & 5 \\ 0 & 7 & 9 \\ -6 & 1 & 4 \end{vmatrix} = 2\begin{vmatrix} 7 & 9 \\ 1 & 4 \end{vmatrix} + 5\begin{vmatrix} 0 & 7 \\ -6 & 1 \end{vmatrix} = 2(28 - 9) + 5(0 + 42) = 248.$$

4. Expanding by the third row gives

$$\begin{vmatrix} 79 & 81 & 40 \\ 22 & 16 & 59 \\ 0 & 0 & 0 \end{vmatrix} = 0.$$

5. Expanding by the fourth column gives

$$\begin{vmatrix} 1 & 2 & 3 & 4 \\ 1 & 1 & 0 & 0 \\ 8 & 7 & 0 & 0 \\ 9 & 5 & 3 & 0 \end{vmatrix} = -4\begin{vmatrix} 1 & 1 & 0 \\ 8 & 0 & 0 \\ 9 & 5 & 3 \end{vmatrix} = -4(3)\begin{vmatrix} 1 & 1 \\ 8 & 7 \end{vmatrix} = -4(3)(7 - 8) = 12.$$

6. Expanding by the third row gives

$$\begin{vmatrix} 1 & 0 & 9 & 0 & 3 \\ 2 & 1 & 7 & 0 & 0 \\ 0 & 0 & 2 & 0 & 0 \\ -1 & 1 & 5 & 2 & 2 \\ 2 & 2 & 8 & 1 & 1 \end{vmatrix} = 2\begin{vmatrix} 1 & 0 & 0 & 3 \\ 2 & 1 & 0 & 0 \\ -1 & 1 & 2 & 2 \\ 2 & 2 & 1 & 1 \end{vmatrix} = 2\left(1\begin{vmatrix} 1 & 0 & 0 \\ 1 & 2 & 2 \\ 2 & 1 & 1 \end{vmatrix} - 3\begin{vmatrix} 2 & 1 & 0 \\ -1 & 1 & 2 \\ 2 & 2 & 1 \end{vmatrix} \right)$$

$$= 2(1)\begin{vmatrix} 2 & 2 \\ 1 & 1 \end{vmatrix} + 2(-3)\left(2\begin{vmatrix} 1 & 2 \\ 2 & 1 \end{vmatrix} - 1\begin{vmatrix} -1 & 2 \\ 2 & 1 \end{vmatrix} \right)$$

$$= 2(1)(2 - 2) + 2(-3)[2(1 - 4) - (-1 - 4)] = 6.$$

7. Expanding by the first column gives

$$\begin{vmatrix} e^t & e^{3t} & e^{-t} \\ e^t & 3e^{3t} & -e^{-t} \\ e^t & 9e^{3t} & e^{-t} \end{vmatrix} = e^t\begin{vmatrix} 3e^{3t} & -e^{-t} \\ 9e^{3t} & e^{-t} \end{vmatrix} - e^t\begin{vmatrix} e^{3t} & e^{-t} \\ 9e^{3t} & e^{-t} \end{vmatrix} + e^t\begin{vmatrix} e^{3t} & e^{-t} \\ 3e^{3t} & -e^{-t} \end{vmatrix}$$

$$= e^t\left(3e^{2t} + 9e^{2t} \right) - e^t\left(e^{2t} - 9e^{2t} \right) + e^t\left(-e^{2t} - 3e^{2t} \right)$$

$$= 12e^{3t} + 8e^{3t} - 4e^{3t} = 16e^{3t}.$$

8. Expanding by the first column gives

$$\begin{vmatrix} e^{2t} & \sin t & \cos t \\ 2e^{2t} & \cos t & -\sin t \\ 4e^{2t} & -\sin t & -\cos t \end{vmatrix} = e^{2t}\begin{vmatrix} \cos t & -\sin t \\ -\sin t & -\cos t \end{vmatrix} - 2e^{2t}\begin{vmatrix} \sin t & \cos t \\ -\sin t & -\cos t \end{vmatrix} + 4e^{2t}\begin{vmatrix} \sin t & \cos t \\ \cos t & -\sin t \end{vmatrix}$$

$$= e^{2t}\left(-\cos^2 t - \sin^2 t\right) - 2e^{2t}(-\sin t \cos t + \sin t \cos t) + 4e^{2t}\left(-\sin^2 t - \cos^2 t\right)$$

$$= -e^{2t} - 4e^{2t} = -5e^{2t}.$$

9. We first compute

$$\begin{vmatrix} 2 & 1 \\ 3 & 2 \end{vmatrix} = 1.$$

Then

$$x = \frac{1}{1}\begin{vmatrix} 1 & 1 \\ -2 & 2 \end{vmatrix} = 4 \quad \text{and} \quad y = \frac{1}{1}\begin{vmatrix} 2 & 1 \\ 3 & -2 \end{vmatrix} = -7.$$

10. We first compute

$$\begin{vmatrix} 5 & 4 \\ 10 & -6 \end{vmatrix} = -70.$$

Then

$$x = -\frac{1}{70}\begin{vmatrix} -1 & 4 \\ 5 & -6 \end{vmatrix} = \frac{-14}{-70} = \frac{1}{5}$$

and

$$y = -\frac{1}{70}\begin{vmatrix} 5 & -1 \\ 10 & 5 \end{vmatrix} = \frac{35}{-70} = -\frac{1}{2}.$$

11. We first compute

$$\begin{vmatrix} 1 & 2 & 1 \\ 2 & -2 & 2 \\ 1 & -4 & 3 \end{vmatrix} = -12.$$

Then

$$x = \frac{1}{-12}\begin{vmatrix} 8 & 2 & 1 \\ 7 & -2 & 2 \\ 1 & -4 & 3 \end{vmatrix} = \frac{-48}{-12} = 4,$$

$$y = \frac{1}{-12}\begin{vmatrix} 1 & 8 & 1 \\ 2 & 7 & 2 \\ 1 & 1 & 3 \end{vmatrix} = \frac{-18}{-12} = \frac{3}{2},$$

and

$$z = \frac{1}{-12}\begin{vmatrix} 1 & 2 & 8 \\ 2 & -2 & 7 \\ 1 & -4 & 1 \end{vmatrix} = \frac{-12}{-12} = 1.$$

12. We first compute

$$\begin{vmatrix} 4 & 3 & 2 \\ -1 & 0 & 2 \\ 3 & 2 & 1 \end{vmatrix} = 1.$$

Then

$$x = \begin{vmatrix} 8 & 3 & 2 \\ 12 & 0 & 2 \\ 3 & 2 & 1 \end{vmatrix} = -2, \quad y = \begin{vmatrix} 4 & 8 & 2 \\ -1 & 12 & 2 \\ 3 & 3 & 1 \end{vmatrix} = 2, \quad \text{and} \quad z = \begin{vmatrix} 4 & 3 & 8 \\ -1 & 0 & 12 \\ 3 & 2 & 3 \end{vmatrix} = 5.$$

13. (a) Expanding by the first row gives

$$\det \mathbf{A} = \begin{vmatrix} 1 & -1 & 2 \\ 2 & 1 & -1 \\ 4 & -1 & 3 \end{vmatrix} = 1 \begin{vmatrix} 1 & -1 \\ -1 & 3 \end{vmatrix} - (-1) \begin{vmatrix} 2 & -1 \\ 4 & 3 \end{vmatrix} + 2 \begin{vmatrix} 2 & 1 \\ 4 & -1 \end{vmatrix}$$

$$= (3 - 1) + (6 + 4) + 2(-2 - 4) = 0.$$

(b) Note that the third equation is the second equation plus 2 times the first equation. Letting $z = t$ and considering the first two equations, we have

$$x - y = -2t$$

$$2x + y = t.$$

Using Cramer's rule,

$$\det \mathbf{A} = \begin{vmatrix} 1 & -1 \\ 2 & 1 \end{vmatrix} = 3$$

so

$$x = \frac{1}{3} \begin{vmatrix} -2t & -1 \\ t & 1 \end{vmatrix} = -\frac{1}{3}t \quad \text{and} \quad y = \frac{1}{3} \begin{vmatrix} 1 & -2t \\ 2 & t \end{vmatrix} = \frac{5}{3}t.$$

Thus, $x = -t/3$, $y = 5t/3$, and $z = t$ is a solution of the system, for t any real number.

(c) The system represents 3 planes intersecting in a single line.

14. The system represents two lines in the plane.

If $\det \mathbf{A} \neq 0$, the system has a unique solution; that is, the lines intersect in a single point.

If $\det \mathbf{A} = 0$, the system does not have a unique solution. In this case the lines are either parallel or they are the same line.

Appendix IV

1. $z_1 + \overline{z}_2 = (2 - i) + (5 - 3i) = 7 - 4i$

2. $4z_1 + z_2 = 4(2 - i) + (5 + 3i) = 13 - i$

3. $2z_1 - 3z_2 = 2(2 - i) - 3(5 + 3i) = -11 - 11i$

4. $z_1 z_2 = (2 - i)(5 + 3i) = 10 + i - 3i^2 = 13 + i$

5. $z_1^2 = (2 - i)(2 - i) = 4 - 4i + i^2 = 3 - 4i$

6. $\overline{z}_1(i + z_2) = (2 + i)(5 + 4i) = 10 + 13i + 4i^2 = 6 + 13i$

7. $\dfrac{z_1}{z_2} = \dfrac{2 - i}{5 + 3i}\,\dfrac{5 - 3i}{5 - 3i} = \dfrac{10 - 11i + 3i^2}{25 + 9} = \dfrac{7}{34} - \dfrac{11}{34}i$

8. $\dfrac{z_2}{z_1} = \dfrac{5 + 3i}{2 - i}\,\dfrac{2 + i}{2 + i} = \dfrac{10 + 11i + 3i^2}{4 + 1} = \dfrac{7}{5} + \dfrac{11}{5}i$

9. $\dfrac{1}{z_2} = \dfrac{1}{5 + 3i}\,\dfrac{5 - 3i}{5 - 3i} = \dfrac{5 - 3i}{25 + 9} = \dfrac{5}{34} - \dfrac{3}{34}i$

10. $\dfrac{z_1}{i} = \dfrac{2 - i}{i}\,\dfrac{-i}{-i} = \dfrac{-2i + i^2}{1} = -1 - 2i$

11. The modulus is $r = \sqrt{0^2 + 1^2} = 1$ and $\theta = \pi/2$, so
$$z = e^{i\pi/2}.$$

12. The modulus is $r = \sqrt{0^2 + 4^2} = 4$ and $\theta = -\pi/2$, so
$$z = 4e^{-i\pi/2}.$$

13. We first note that $z = i^2 = -1$. Then the modulus of z is 1 and the argument is π, so
$$z = e^{i\pi}.$$

14. We first note that $z = 6i^5 = 6i$. Then the modulus of z is 6 and the argument is $\pi/2$, so
$$z = 6e^{i\pi/2}.$$

15. The modulus is $r = \sqrt{2^2 + 2^2} = 2\sqrt{2}$ and $\theta = \pi/4$, so
$$z = 2\sqrt{2}e^{i\pi/4}.$$

16. The modulus is $r = \sqrt{5 + 5} = \sqrt{10}$ and $\theta = -3\pi/4$, so
$$z = \sqrt{10}e^{-3i\pi/4}.$$

17. The modulus is $r = \sqrt{6^2 + 6^2(3)} = 12$ and $\tan\theta = 6\sqrt{3}/6 = \sqrt{3}$, where θ is in the first quadrant, so $\theta = \pi/3$ and

$$z = 12e^{i\pi/3}.$$

18. The modulus is $r = \sqrt{10^2(3) + 10^2} = 20$ and $\tan\theta = 10/(-10\sqrt{3}) = -\sqrt{3}/3$, where θ is in the second quadrant, so $\theta = 5\pi/6$ and

$$z = 20e^{5i\pi/6}.$$

19. We first note that $z = i - \sqrt{3}\,i^2 = \sqrt{3} + i$. Then the modulus of z is $r = \sqrt{1^2 + 3} = 2$ and $\tan\theta = 1/\sqrt{3}$, where θ is in the first quadrant, so $\theta = \pi/6$ and

$$z = 2e^{i\pi/6}.$$

20. The modulus is $r = \sqrt{(-7)^2 + 7^2} = 7\sqrt{2}$ and $\tan\theta = 7/(-7) = -1$, where θ is in the second quadrant, so $\theta = 3\pi/4$ and

$$z = 7\sqrt{2}e^{3i\pi/4}.$$

21. $z = 8e^{-i\pi} = 8[\cos(-\pi) + i\sin(-\pi)] = -8$

22. $z = 2e^{7i\pi/4} = 2[\cos 7\pi/4 + i\sin 7\pi/4] = 2(\sqrt{2}/2 - i\sqrt{2}/2) = \sqrt{2} - \sqrt{2}\,i$

23. We use the exponential version of the polar form.

$$[r(\cos\theta + i\sin\theta)]^n = [re^{i\theta}]^n = r^n e^{in\theta} = r^2[\cos n\theta + i\sin n\theta]$$

24. We first express $1 + i$ in polar form as

$$1 + i = \sqrt{2}\left(\cos\frac{\pi}{4} + i\sin\frac{\pi}{4}\right).$$

Then

$$(1+i)^{10} = (\sqrt{2})^{10}\left(\cos\frac{10\pi}{4} + i\sin\frac{10\pi}{4}\right) = 32\left(\cos\frac{5\pi}{2} + i\sin\frac{5\pi}{2}\right) = 32(0 + i) = 32i.$$

25. Using

$$e^{i\theta} = \cos\theta + i\sin\theta$$

and

$$e^{-i\theta} = \cos(-\theta) + i\sin(-\theta) = \cos\theta - i\sin\theta$$

we obtain

$$e^{i\theta} + e^{-i\theta} = 2\cos\theta \qquad \text{or} \qquad \cos\theta = \frac{e^{i\theta} + e^{-i\theta}}{2}$$

and

$$e^{i\theta} - e^{-i\theta} = 2i\sin\theta \qquad \text{or} \qquad \sin\theta = \frac{e^{i\theta} - e^{-i\theta}}{2i}.$$

409